GREAT EVENTS
FROM
HISTORY II

GREAT EVENTS FROM HISTORY II

Science
and
Technology
Series

Volume 2
1910-1931

Edited by

FRANK N. MAGILL

SALEM PRESS

Pasadena, California   Englewood Cliffs, New Jersey

∞ The paper used in these volumes conforms to the
American National Standard for Permanence of Paper
for Printed Library Materials, Z39.48-1984.

Library of Congress Cataloging-in-Publication Data
Great events from history II. Science and technology
series / edited by Frank N. Magill.
  p. cm.
  Includes bibliographical references and index.
  1. Science—History—20th century. 2. Technology—
History—20th century. I. Magill, Frank Northen, 1907-
  .
Q125.G825 1991
509'.04—dc20
ISBN 0-89356-637-3 (set)   91-23313
ISBN 0-89356-639-x (volume 2)   CIP

PRINTED IN THE UNITED STATES OF AMERICA

92-0372

LIST OF EVENTS IN VOLUME II

GREAT EVENTS
FROM
HISTORY II

THOMSON CONFIRMS THE POSSIBILITY OF ISOTOPES

Category of event: Physics
Time: 1910
Locale: Cavendish Laboratory, Cambridge, England

Thomson was the first to isolate isotopes of stable elements

Principal personages:

SIR JOSEPH JOHN THOMSON (1856-1940), a British physicist at the Cavendish Laboratory who was the discoverer of the electron and winner of the 1906 Nobel Prize in Physics

FRANCIS WILLIAM ASTON (1877-1945), a British physicist at the Cavendish Laboratory who developed and perfected the mass spectrograph and was the winner of the 1922 Nobel Prize in Physics

WILLIAM PROUT (1785-1850), a British biochemist who first proposed that the atomic weights of elements were whole number multiples of the weight of hydrogen

HEINRICH HERTZ (1857-1894), a German physicist who devised an instrument to measure the shape of both electrical and magnetic waves

ERNEST RUTHERFORD (1871-1937), a leading physicist at the Cavendish Laboratory who contributed fundamental knowledge toward radioactivity and the structure of the atom

Summary of Event

In the history of science, isotopes remain one of the unpredicted facets of nature. Isotopes are one or more forms of a chemical element and act similarly in chemical or physical reactions. Isotopes differ in their radioactive transformations, and they possess different atomic weights. In 1803, John Dalton proposed a new atomic theory of chemistry which claimed that chemical elements in a compound combined by weight in whole number proportions to one another. By 1815, William Prout took Dalton's hypothesis one step further and claimed that the atomic weights of elements were integral multiples of the hydrogen atom. For example, if the weight of hydrogen was 1, then the weight of carbon was 12 and oxygen was 16. Over the next decade, there were a large number of carefully controlled experiments to determine atomic weights of several elements. These results did not support Prout's hypothesis. For example, the atomic weight of chlorine was found to be 35.5. It took the discovery of isotopes in the early part of the twentieth century to justify Prout's original theory.

Sir Joseph John Thomson was appointed professor of physics at the University of Cambridge in 1884, although his career was associated with the Cavendish Laboratory, both as one of the leading scientists and as its director. Thomson's initial area of research was electrical discharges through gases, using the cathode ray discharge tube as the instrument for the exploration of matter. One area of controversy and competition between English and German scientists was whether the cathode ray discharge was composed of waves or particles. The first scientist to prove the case conclusively would gain both prestige and national honor. Thomson did not fit the public notion of a gifted scientist. His mathematical abilities were not highly refined, he possessed poor hand-eye coordination, and he was regarded as a clumsy experimenter. His genius was the ability to visualize mentally the necessary experimental parameters and hence produce intricate experiments. He also possessed the ability to create models that explained experimental results. Thomson accepted the challenge of creating the exact experiment that would prove that discharges from the cathode ray tube were composed of particles.

Beginning in 1884, when he became the director of the Cavendish Laboratory, Thomson pursued a series of experiments on electrical discharges. By the early 1890's, Thomson realized that the research of Heinrich Hertz and his student Philipp Lenard, which showed the penetration of discharges through metal foil, was, in fact, a partial validation of Thomson's theory of particles. In addition, his own research provided evidence that cathode ray discharges traveled at half the speed of light, again supporting a particle theory rather than a wave theory, where waves traveled at the speed of light. Other physicists in England also demonstrated that cathode ray discharges, acting as particles, traveled in a curved pattern in the presence of a magnetic field. Yet, none of these experiments offered a definitive proof of the particle theory.

The stalemate between the two competing theories changed with the arrival of Ernest Rutherford at Cavendish. Thomson and Rutherford began a series of X-ray experiments, and the results substantiated their theory because the radiated gases retained their conductivity after the radiation had been shut off. This condition could be explained only if either positive or negative charges were produced by radiation.

In 1899, Thomson compiled the evidence of his research and created a model of the atom with negatively charged particles on the outside. By 1904, Thomson was further able to refine the model of the atom with electrons accelerating on concentric rings surrounding the atom. This later model proposed an inner ring containing the smallest number of electrons and the outer rings containing progressively more electrons. The beginning of particle and nuclear physics can be dated from this moment, and all future work must credit Thomson for his contributions.

After the discovery of the electron, Thomson directed his research efforts toward discovering the nature of "positive electricity." As a result, without specifically looking for isotopes, Thomson became one of the first to isolate isotopes of elements. This chance event occurred as a result of the phenomenon of positive electricity, which was first identified by Wilhelm Wien. Thomson undertook the next stage by developing an instrument sensitive enough to analyze the positive electron.

One person who was pivotal to the discovery of isotopes was Francis William Aston. Aston was a gifted experimenter who possessed the capacity for infinitely refining an instrument until it produced the desired results. In addition to possessing mechanical skills, he was an expert glass blower, and he created the discharge tubes for Thomson which were necessary for atomic research. He was known for his patience while working through a series of experimental procedures many times, making minute adjustments on the instruments. Aston became interested in atomic research from reading Thomson's book *Conduction of Electricity Through Gases* (1903) and wanted to pursue research in cathode rays and X rays. Recommended by his teacher John Henry Poynting of Mason College, Aston came to Cavendish Laboratory in 1910. The collaboration between Aston and Thomson began at the moment when Thomson had turned his attention to the positive rays generated by the cathode of the discharge tube. When the electrons were stripped from an electron, the atom would become positively charged. By the use of magnetic and electric fields, it is possible to channel these positive rays in parabolic tracts. Thomson was able to identify the atoms of different elements by examining photographic plates of these tracks. Aston's first contribution at Cavendish was to improve this instrument by blowing a spherical discharge tube with a finer cathode and by making a better pump to create the vacuum. He also devised a camera for sharper photographs of the parabolic tracks. In 1910, as a result of these refinements, Thomson saw the first indication of isotopes, although he was not aware of their importance. Two years later, further improvements to this apparatus provided proof that the individual molecules of a substance have the same mass. While working on the element neon, Thomson obtained two parabolas, one with a mass of 20 and the other with a mass of 22. At first, he thought the heavier of the two isotopes was a new element but eventually came to the conclusion that he had separated the isotopes of an element.

Impact of Event

The task of identifying the large families of isotopes was left for Aston to accomplish. In 1919, Aston created the idea for a new instrument called a mass spectrograph. The idea was to treat ionized or positive atoms much in the same manner as light rays. Just as light can be dispersed into a spectrum and analyzed in terms of its constituent colors, Aston thought he could achieve similar results with atoms. By the use of magnetic fields to focus the stream of particles, he was able to create a spectrum of the atomic mass and record the result on a photographic plate. His initial test of the mass spectrograph was on the gas neon, and Aston's apparatus was able to separate the spectrum of both the heavier and lighter masses of the gas. The mass spectrograph had a distinct advantage over the parabola method of Thomson, since it was independent of the velocity of the particles. Aston found that neon had two isotopes: one with a mass of 20 and the other with a mass of 22 in a ratio of 10:1. This result reflected exactly the accepted atomic weight of neon (20.20), which was a combination of the two isotopes.

The search for isotopes became a major area of concentration in physics in the decade after 1919. A new isotope was found almost every other month. It was found that chlorine had two; bromine had isotopes of 79 and 81, which gave an atomic weight of exactly 80; krypton had six; and other elements possessed even more.

These results produced not only an entire family of nonradioactive isotopes but also finally verified the "whole number rule" of Prout's hypothesis. Nevertheless, a discrepancy remained. It appeared that the atomic weight of hydrogen was slightly greater than one. When Aston attempted to resolve this problem in 1920, he postulated that although hydrogen had a mass of 1 percent greater than a whole number, this mass was lost when atoms were "packed" to produce other elements. For example, when four atoms of hydrogen were brought together to produce one atom of helium, about 1 percent of the mass was lost. Although it required a more sophisticated model of the atom to explain the "packing fractions," the accuracy of Aston's instrument remained untarnished.

In 1927, Aston began to refine his mass spectrograph. The original instrument had an accuracy of 1 in 1,000, but Aston built an instrument with ten times that accuracy. Thus, he began a series of experiments to discover the packing fractions of a large number of elements. Some time later, the mass spectrograph was found to be sensitive enough to measure Einstein's law of mass energy conversion during a nuclear reaction. Between 1927 and 1935, Aston published the updated results. In 1935, Aston attempted to refine his instrument with ten times greater accuracy, and this instrument proved to be of critical importance to the new science of nuclear chemistry, since the accuracy of the chemical masses was essential to the success of the discipline.

The discovery of isotopes opened the way to extensive research in nuclear physics and completed those speculations begun by Prout a century earlier. Also, in the field of radioactivity—which was discovered through a separate sequence of historical events—isotopes played a central role in the development of nuclear reaction.

Bibliography

Crowther, J. G. *The Cavendish Laboratory, 1874-1974*. New York: Science History Publications, 1974. This work covers the history of Cavendish Laboratory. Various chapters cover Thomson's early years at the laboratory, his work as the director, his assistants and students, and his work on the electron. Two chapters cover his predecessor Lord Rayleigh, while subsequent chapters provide information on his successor Ernest Rutherford.

Segrè, Emilio. *From X-Rays to Quarks: Modern Physicists and Their Discoveries.* San Francisco: W. H. Freeman, 1980. Segrè was one of many physicists who participated directly in nuclear physics and wrote on the history of physics. The earlier sections of this volume cover the discoveries and theories of those who produced a coherent picture of the atom. Consequently, it is possible to appreciate the full significance of Thomson's contribution to the field of nuclear physics.

Strutt, Robert John, fourth Baron Rayleigh. *The Life of Sir J. J. Thomson, O. M., Sometime Master of Trinity College*. Cambridge, England: Cambridge University Press, 1942. This text covers Thomson's activities: the presidency of the Royal Society, the mastership of Trinity College, his views of education, and highlights of his personal life. Since Rayleigh was a friend of Thomson, he could give a firsthand account of the events that took place.

Thomson, George Paget. *J. J. Thomson and the Cavendish Laboratory in His Day*. London: Thomas Nelson, 1964. This book details the work done by Thomson and others. Describes experiments in greater detail and provides excellent drawings of the experimental equipment and photographs of the experimental results.

Thomson, J. J. *Recollections and Reflections*. London: G. Bell, 1936. While Thomson does not discuss the Nobel Prize, there is an entire chapter on "psychical research." There are several lengthy chapters on his visits to the United States. Contains extensive sections on those who influenced his life and work.

Victor W. Chen

Cross-References

Becquerel Wins the Nobel Prize for the Discovery of Natural Radioactivity (1903), p. 199; Thomson Wins the Nobel Prize for the Discovery of the Electron (1906), p. 356; Bohr Writes a Trilogy on Atomic and Molecular Structure (1912), p. 507; Rutherford Presents His Theory of the Atom (1912), p. 527; Rutherford Discovers the Proton (1914), p. 590.

EHRLICH INTRODUCES SALVARSAN AS A CURE FOR SYPHILIS

Category of event: Medicine
Time: April, 1910
Locale: The Royal Prussian Institute for Experimental Therapy, Frankfurt am Main, Germany

Ehrlich's Salvarsan was the first successful chemotherapeutic for the treatment of syphilis, ushering in a new age in medicine

Principal personages:
> PAUL EHRLICH (1854-1915), a German research physician and chemist whose research on antitrypanosomal medications paved the way for the discovery and development of Salvarsan
> WILHELM VON WALDEYER (1836-1921), a German anatomist who encouraged Ehrlich's interest in the application of chemistry to problems in biology and medicine
> FRIEDRICH VON FRERICHS (1819-1885), a German physician and professor who gave Ehrlich full autonomy to research as he wished
> SAHACHIRO HATA (1872-1938), a Japanese physician and bacteriologist who joined Ehrlich in Frankfurt in 1909 to study syphilis in animals
> FRITZ SCHAUDINN (1871-1906), a German zoologist who discovered in 1905 with Erich Hoffmann the *Treponema pallidum*, the spirochete organism of syphilis

Summary of Event

The ravages of syphilis on humankind are seldom discussed openly. A disease that struck infamous and famous, lowborn and highborn alike with indifferent finality, transmitted by direct and usually sexual contact, syphilis was both feared and reviled. Perhaps no other disease except leprosy evoked such horror in the afflicted and such loathsome revulsion by society. Many segments of society across all national boundaries were secure in their belief that syphilis was divine punishment of the wicked for their evil ways. This view held in part because it was not until 1903 that Élie Metchnikoff and Pierre-Paul-Émile Roux demonstrated the transmittal of syphilis to apes, ending the long-held belief that syphilis was exclusively a human disease. Regardless, the disease destroyed families, careers, and lives, driving its infected victims mad, destroying the brain, or destroying the cardiovascular system. It was methodical and slow, but in every case, it killed with singular precision. There was no hope of a safe and effective cure prior to Salvarsan.

Prior to 1910, conventional treatment consisted principally of mercury or, later, potassium iodide. Mercury, however, administered in large doses, led to severe ulcerations of the tongue, jaws, and palate. Swelling of the gums and loosening of the teeth resulted. Dribbling saliva and the attending fetid odor also occurred. These side effects of mercury treatment were so severe that many preferred to suffer the disease to the end rather than undergo the mercury cure. About 1906, Metchnikoff and Roux demonstrated that mercurial ointments applied very early, at the first appearance of the primary lesion, were efficacious.

Once the spirochete invaded the bloodstream and tissues, however, the infected person experienced symptoms of varying nature and degree—high fever, intense headaches, and excruciating pain. The patient's skin often erupted in pustular lesions similar in appearance to smallpox. It was the distinguishing feature of these pustular lesions that gave syphilis its other name—the Great Pox. Death brought the only relief then available.

Until 1905, no one knew the cause of syphilis. Then, the Germans Fritz Schaudinn and Erich Hoffmann discovered *Treponema pallidum*, a spirochete, the causative microorganism of syphilis. It was such a profound discovery that an inscription in dedication to Schaudinn by the German Medical Fraternity reads: *"Dem Forscher, der den Keim entdeckte, der Liebeslust und Menschensaat verdarb und tief die Menschheit schreckte, zum Dank für seine grosse Tat"* (To the scientist who discovered the germ which marred love and progeny and frightened mankind deeply, in grateful recognition of his greatest deed). Thus, discovery of the spirochete that caused syphilis made fighting the disease possible.

The "magic bullet" is compound 606, later named Salvarsan. An arsenical arsphenamine, this compound was developed from another named atoxyl, itself used in the treatment of trypanosomal infections such as sleeping sickness. The development of Salvarsan was the culmination of research begun by Paul Ehrlich in 1874 while studying the chemical affinity of biological tissues for certain dyes such as aniline. It was also a departure from his interest in tropical diseases, notably those of Africa, which were of concern because of the spread of imperialism by Western European governments, including Germany.

Ehrlich became fascinated by the reactions of dyes with biological cells and tissues while a student at the University of Strasbourg under Wilhelm von Waldeyer. It was von Waldeyer who sparked Ehrlich's interest in the chemical viewpoint of medicine. Thus, as a student, Ehrlich spent hours at his laboratory experimenting with different dyes on various tissues. In 1878, he published *Beiträge für Theorie und Praxis der histologischen Färbung* (contributions to the theory and practice of histological staining), which detailed the discriminate staining of cells and cellular components by various dyes. This study led to his discovery of mast cells.

Ehrlich joined Friedrich von Frerichs at the Charité Hospital in Berlin, where Frerichs gave Ehrlich complete autonomy in his research with no clinical duties. During this time, Ehrlich described and named important white-cell family members—eosinophils, neutrophils, basophils, and acidophils. In 1886, Ehrlich developed methylene blue as an important selective stain for ganglia cells and nerve endings.

Between 1889 and 1892, Ehrlich developed a diagnostic stain for the tubercle *bacillus*, the causative agent of tuberculosis, a microorganism discovered by Robert

Koch in 1882. In 1904, Ehrlich developed trypan-red, an effective antitrypanosomal agent of particular importance to equatorial African exploration and Western colonization. Ehrlich began studying atoxyl in 1908, the year he won jointly with Metchnikoff the Nobel Prize in Physiology or Medicine for his work on immunity. Atoxyl was effective against trypanosome infection but also imposed serious side effects upon the patient, not the least of which was a propensity to cause blindness. Atoxyl is very toxic to the optic nerve. Ehrlich correctly determined the structure of atoxyl and further established that the pentavalent arsenic atom is therapeutically poor, whereas the trivalent arsenic atom is therapeutically superior in potency. It was Ehrlich's study of atoxyl, and several hundred derivatives sought as alternatives to atoxyl in trypanosome treatment, that led to the development of derivative 606 (Salvarsan). Although the first chemotherapeutic to be effectively used against syphilis, compound 606 was discounted as an atoxyl alternative and shelved as useless for five years.

The discovery and development of compound 606 was enhanced by two critical events. First, Schaudinn and Hoffmann discovered that syphilis is a bacterially caused disease. The causative microorganism is a spirochete so frail and gossameric in substance that it is nearly impossible to detect by casual microscopic examination; Schaudinn chanced upon it one day in March, 1905. This discovery led, in turn, to August von Wassermann's development of the now famous test for syphilis—the Wassermann test. Second, a Japanese bacteriologist, Sahachiro Hata, came to Frankfurt in 1909 to study syphilis with Ehrlich. Hata had studied syphilis in rabbits in Japan. Hata's assignment was to test every atoxyl derivative ever developed under Ehrlich for its efficacy in syphilis treatment. After hundreds of tests and clinical trials, Ehrlich and Hata announced Salvarsan as an antisyphilitic chemotherapeutic at the April, 1910, Congress of Internal Medicine in Wiesbaden, Germany.

The announcement was electrifying. The remedy was immediately and widely sought, but it was not without its problems. A few deaths resulted from its use, and it was not safe for treatment of the gravely ill. Some of the difficulties inherent in Salvarsan were overcome by the development of neosalvarsan in 1912 and sodium salvarsan in 1913. Although Ehrlich achieved much, he fell short of his own assigned goal, a chemotherapeutic that would cure in one injection.

Impact of Event

Salvarsan was not without its problems. Medically, administration of Salvarsan was difficult, in part because of difficulties with its solubility. It did not, as Ehrlich wished, cure with a single dose. Physicians sometimes did not strictly comply with the recommended administration regimens. Nevertheless, the demand for Salvarsan was overwhelming. The Höchst Chemical Company geared up for production of the drug after the Georg Speyer Haus, of which Ehrlich was director, produced about sixty-five thousand doses for distribution free of charge in 1911.

Socially, the advent of Salvarsan was seen by some as a challenge to divine justice against the wicked. Between 1910 and the outbreak of World War I in 1914, Ehrlich waged an endless battle against verbal and unfounded attacks on himself and Salvarsan. He handled the scientific and medical attacks with expert authority. He was less able and less prepared to fend off the personal attacks launched against him. Two events vindicated Salvarsan and Ehrlich. The Reichstag, the German legislature, in March, 1914, investigated the charges leveled against Salvarsan and found it as effective as Ehrlich maintained. In May of 1914, a libel suit brought by the Frankfurt Hospital found the principal detractor guilty of libel and of bribing prostitutes to falsify statements concerning the hospital's treatment of patients with Salvarsan. With Ehrlich's death in August, 1915, his chemotherapy research ended and the significant success by others in the field came to a virtual standstill until 1932.

The significance of the development of Salvarsan as an antisyphilitic chemotherapeutic agent cannot be overstated. Syphilis at that time was as frightening and horrifying as leprosy and was a sentence of slow, torturous death. Salvarsan was such a significant development that Ehrlich was recommended for a 1912 and 1913 Nobel Prize for his work in chemotherapy. Ehrlich's research and belief in specific chemical interactions between cells and chemical substances were pivotal to chemotherapy. After Ehrlich's death, disorganized studies bore no success. The science of chemotherapy appeared to have lost its direction. It was several decades before any further significant advances in "wonder drugs" occurred, namely, the discovery of prontosil in 1932 and its first clinical use in 1935. On the heels of prontosil—a sulfa drug—came other sulfa drugs. The sulfa drugs would remain supreme in the fight against bacterial infection until the antibiotics, the first being penicillin, were discovered in 1928; however, they were not clinically recognized until World War II. With the discovery of streptomycin in 1943 and Aureomycin, a tetracycline, in 1944, the assault against bacteria was finally on a sound basis. Medicine possessed an arsenal with which to combat the pathogenic microbes that for centuries before visited misery and death upon humankind.

Bibliography

Bender, George A. "Ehrlich: Chemotherapy Is Launched." In *Great Moments in Medicine: A History of Medicine in Pictures.* Detroit: Northwood Institute Press, 1965. Contains nontechnical, clear prose that succinctly describes Ehrlich's studies leading to his work in chemotherapy. Provides brief biographical data on Ehrlich and notes the contributions of other researchers whose assistance or influence helped Ehrlich.

Galdston, Iago. "Microbes and Dyes," "Paul Ehrlich," and "The Saga of Salvarsan." In *Behind the Sulfa Drugs: A Short History of Chemotherapy.* New York: D. Appleton-Century, 1943. These chapters are connected because Ehrlich's interest in dyes and their reaction with cells formed the basis of his later work on immunity and chemotherapy. Although dated, the work provides a view of the field as it then existed and closer to the subject events. Good preliminary reading for a wide audience.

Klainer, Albert S., and Irving Geis. *Agents of Bacterial Disease.* New York: Harper

& Row, 1973. Intended for the better-versed reader of biological sciences material. The first three chapters discuss bacterial structure, morphology, and pathogenesis. Chapters 4 through 15 discuss the various types of bacteria and their pathogenic properties and distinctions. The last chapter discusses chemotherapeutic agents. Numerous illustrations.

Marquardt, Martha. *Paul Ehrlich*. London: William Heinemann Medical Books, 1949. Provides both a human and a scientific framework of Ehrlich, written by his secretary. Marquardt describes the historical scientific era in which Ehrlich's work rested and gives insights to his interactions with other notable researchers of his day. An excellent source on Ehrlich.

Reinfeld, Fred. "The Miracle Drugs," "How Miracle Drugs Began," and "Synthetic Drugs Made by Man." In *Miracle Drugs and the New Age of Medicine*. New York: Sterling, 1957. Provides excellent introductory reading in simple terms and with many pictures and illustrations. Introduces the reader to the history of disease and drug treatment and the development of drugs such as antibiotics.

Rodman, Morton J. *Understanding Medications: The How and Whys of Drug Therapy*. Oradell, N.J.: Medical Economics, 1981. Provides a discussion of the range of afflictions to which chemotherapy is applied. Much of the jargon is in the drug names, many of which are commonly known. Offers interactions and contraindications; geared for the better-versed reader of biological and popular medical science.

Taylor, F. Sherwood. "The Rise of Chemotherapy." In *The Conquest of Bacteria*. New York: Philosophical Library, 1942. Looks at Ehrlich's development of chemotherapy, beginning with his studies on trypanosomes. Continues with an examination of his interests in hookworm, malaria, amoebic dysentery, and leprosy. Complements the Galdston work (cited above).

Eric R. Taylor

Cross-References

Behring Discovers the Diphtheria Antitoxin (1890), p. 6; Domagk Discovers That a Sulfonamide Can Save Lives (1932), p. 968; Waksman Discovers the Antibiotic Streptomycin (1943), p. 1224; Duggar Discovers Aureomycin, the First of the Tetracyclines (1945), p. 1255.

BOAS PUBLISHES *THE MIND OF PRIMITIVE MAN*

Category of event: Anthropology
Time: 1911
Locale: New York

Boas published his views on human variation, laying the conceptual foundations of modern cultural anthropology

> *Principal personage:*
> FRANZ BOAS (1858-1942), an American anthropologist, student of the native cultures of the Pacific Northwest, museum curator, professor, and chief catalyst of anthropology as an academic discipline and as a profession in the United States

Summary of Event

In the contemporary world, the use of the word "culture" to indicate customs, beliefs, and material factors that characterize the life of particular social groups is so widespread that it is difficult to imagine that it has a short history: It was first developed by Franz Boas at the beginning of the century, it was presented in his book *The Mind of Primitive Man* (1911), and it was popularized through the influence of the anthropological tradition he and his students built.

When Sir Edward Burnett Tylor—a wealthy Englishman and amateur scholar—published the book *Primitive Culture*, in 1871, he was the first to define anthropology as the study of human culture, and culture as the knowledge and traditions acquired by humans as members of society. He used the culture concept as a synonym for "civilization," understood as the common human heritage that becomes increasingly complex and refined as human beings advance on the ladder of progress from "primitive" to more advanced stages. Tylor, in line with the prevalent ideology of his time, was a confirmed evolutionist, a believer in the existence of great qualitative differences between primitive and civilized societies.

The approach of the classic social evolutionists, as Tylor and some of his contemporaries came to be known, gave valuable results insofar as it led to the collection, classification, and comparison of much information on societies that had not been studied. The problem with their theory was that it provided an ideal scientific framework for the racial taxonomies that had been developing since the eighteenth century but which had become particularly influential. In restrospect, the definition of particular racial groups as "inferior" seemed a self-serving, even naïve attempt at justifying not only European colonialism but also the more specifically exploitative institution of slavery. Yet, by perfectly dovetailing with evolutionist theory, it led to the constitution of a very convincing historical model at the time of its formulation.

Fighting such a model, with all of its undemocratic implications, became Boas' life mission; the publication of *The Mind of Primitive Man*, in 1911, marked the first step in a process of popular dissemination of his ideas that was to have a long-range impact on Western intellectual life. The title of the book is not very representative of its content; that of the German edition, *Kultur und Rasse* (culture and race), published in 1914, is more apt but fails to give a complete picture of the range of subjects treated in this classic. Boas does not discuss only preliterate mentality or the concepts of race and culture; he also discusses the relationship between race, culture and language, the concept of heredity, the importance of adopting a historicist and holistic method in anthropological studies, and the correlation between psychology and culture. Boas' ideas, developed over several decades of research and reflection, laid the conceptual foundations of modern cultural anthropology.

These ideas evolved from an experience Boas had in 1883. Born and educated in Germany, he developed an interest in the natural sciences and, after obtaining a doctorate in physics, set out to do some geographical research on Baffin Island, in the Arctic. Here, he had his first encounter with the "primitive" Eskimo; this experience led him toward a career in anthropology. What struck him about the Eskimo was the complexity and beauty of their customs; one often finds expressions of genuine empathy for their culture in his diary, with frequent questions about the supposed superiority of Western "civilized" people.

The need to understand any culture on its own terms was further confirmed through field research Boas conducted with the Kwakiutl and other Native American groups inhabiting the Pacific Northwest coast. By 1887, when he decided to leave his native Germany for the United States, many of his distinctive views of culture had matured, and he was prepared to disseminate them. In 1899, he accepted a professorship in anthropology at Columbia University and began to attract a large number of gifted students who became instrumental in imbuing American anthropology with his ideas.

The most controversial view expressed in his book was concerning race, which ran completely against the grain of the racial determinism implicit in social evolutionary theory. (It later became the specific cause of the violent Nazi ostracism of Boas' work.) Yet, the argument Boas presented is not easy to dismiss. After reviewing the evidence derived from his analysis of hereditary processes, from general studies of physical anthropology, and particularly from his statistical approach to the description of bodily types, Boas presented clear conclusions. Racial purity simply does not exist and, because of human plasticity, it is impossible to prove a strict connection between races and the genotypical or phenotypical characteristics of individuals; in particular, there is no provable correlation between race and intelligence or personality.

One of the immediate consequences of Boas' racial indeterminism was the conviction that since genetic endowment cannot explain cultural differentiations, these can only be understood as a result of the historical development of cultural traits within a particular culture. By so arguing, Boas introduced a fundamental shift in the meaning given to the word "culture" by evolutionist anthropologists. Rather than labeling civilization in a general way, "culture" for Boas came to mean the specific heritage of a particular social group, which must be understood only within its own historical context. As a consequence, he emphasized holism and historicism in the study of cultures; also, he propounded the concept of "cultural relativism," a concept still central in contemporary anthropology.

Boas argued that, when studying languages, one should adopt a holistic approach, so that the characteristics of a language are explored for their intrinsic relevance rather than through an artificial comparison with Western linguistic categories. Furthermore, Boas pointed out that language is an expression of culture, and its study can provide insights. At the same time, culture is itself a system of symbolic significance, and cultural understanding can shed light on the cognitive processes that become expressed in a particular linguistic system.

Finally, in presenting his views on the correlation between culture and personality, Boas insisted that humankind shares psychic unity. Thus, where the evolutionists proclaimed the existence of a qualitative difference between the way of thinking of primitive man and that of civilized Western society, Boas believed that differences are only produced by the specific needs and objectives of cultures. There are no mental notions that primitive people cannot possibly attain as primitives; if members of a certain culture do not seem to pursue some mental operations, then they are not necessary or desirable within that culture. If the necessity should arise, the mental operations would also appear.

Impact of Event

The Mind of Primitive Man is a slight book; even the revised edition, published in 1938, is not long. Yet, its general impact has been remarkable. The book became a popular target of people committed to theses of racial superiority; its German edition was one of the titles selected for the Nazi book-burning of May 10, 1933. Also, over the years the book has intermittently attracted the scorn of anthropologists who selected the book as an example of Boas' theoretical vagueness, or of the inadequacy of his methodological arguments, or of the inherent contradiction of some of his approaches to the study of culture.

Many of Boas' disciples built on his ideas in ways that took them away from his original positions. For example, one of Boas' early students, Edward Sapir, proposed that certain basic aspects of culture—such as language—fundamentally affect the way the world is perceived, so that in the long run culture itself is determined by them. Other students, including Ruth Benedict and Margaret Mead, combined Boas' ideas on the correlations between culture and personality with the basic Freudian tenets on personality development and defined specific cultures on the basis of the type of "temperament" characterizing them. While it is generally accepted that Boas was the founder of American anthropology, it is also evident that his influence did not lead to a tradition of research that was theoretically homogeneous. This was not the result of the incompleteness of his theory, but rather the desire of many of Boas' students to find answers for questions he had specifically chosen to leave unanswered.

Boas did not devote much discussion to theory-building. Yet his books, such as

The Mind of Primitive Man, do offer clear theoretical statements. Boas believed that to make anthropology into a science, it was more important to insist on stringent adherence to a particular research method rather than to a particular theory. He also believed that good theory could only be built once an adequate amount of empirical data was collected; therefore, he constantly gave priority to research over analysis. Finally, and most important, many of the conceptual innovations Boas presented in his book are now so taken for granted that their originality is not fully appreciated.

It is now generally accepted that culture is learned, adaptive behavior, quite independent from all other variables such as physical traits, heredity, or geography. Since there is no predetermined process whereby cultural similarities or differences may be interpreted, the enfolding of developmental stages is rarely contested. Furthermore, by pointing to the plural reality of cultures and to the necessity of documenting cultural diversity from the inside, through direct participation, and with an eye to the internal organization and historical development of cultural patterns, Boas established the fundamental research procedures of a discipline that has acquired increasing relevance in the contemporary world.

Whenever the cultural characteristics of particular national or ethnic groups are discussed, whenever race as a determinant of cultural traits is discounted, and whenever the importance of relativism in cross-cultural understanding is mentioned, quintessential Boasian concepts are utilized. They have transformed society's view of human diversity in a fundamental way.

Bibliography

Boas, Franz. *Race, Language, and Culture*. New York: Macmillan, 1940. This is the selection of scientific papers Boas collected for publication two years before his death. It provides an excellent overview of the great range of his interests and of the way his anthropological ideas developed over time.

Bohannan, Paul, and Mark Glazer, eds. *High Points in Anthropology*. New York: Alfred A. Knopf, 1973. An excellent collection of anthropological readings. It offers a sample of the ideas of most of the recognized masters in the discipline, including Tylor and Boas. The chronological arrangement of the articles and the informative introductions produce a history of anthropology through its classic works.

Goldschmidt, Walter, ed. *The Anthropology of Franz Boas*. Menasha, Wis.: American Anthropological Association, 1959. An excellent collection of papers assessing Boas' legacy on the hundredth anniversary of his birth. Of particular interest are the articles by Leslie Spier, Margaret Mead, and Marian Smith.

Herskovits, Melville J. *Franz Boas: The Science of Man in the Making*. New York: Charles Scribner's Sons, 1953. The standard intellectual biography of Boas by one of his students who maintained a close affiliation with Boas' original conceptual approach.

Kroeber, A. L., et al. *Franz Boas, 1858-1942*. Menasha, Wis.: American Anthropological Association, 1943. A collection of articles written on the occasion of

Boas' death by his students and associates. It contains the definitive bibliography of Boas' published writings.

Lesser, Alexander. "Franz Boas." In *Totems and Teachers*, edited by Sydel Silverman. New York: Columbia University Press, 1981. A passionate account, written by one of his students, of the role played by Boas in the establishment of anthropology as an academic discipline in the United States. Special attention is given to Boas' activities as a "citizen scientist," fighting for peace, democracy, and racial equality.

Stocking, George W., Jr. *Race, Culture, and Evolution: Essays in the History of Anthropology.* New York: Free Press, 1968. A very influential series of essays by the foremost historian of American anthropology. Presents the controversial view that most of Boas' students—even those who apparently moved the farthest from his original ideas—expanded only on themes that were implicit in Boas' writings.

E. L. Cerroni-Long

Cross-References

Johannsen Coins the Terms "Gene," "Genotype," and "Phenotype" (1909), p. 433; Mead Publishes *Coming of Age in Samoa* (1928), p. 869; Benedict Publishes *Patterns of Culture* (1934), p. 997.

STURTEVANT PRODUCES
THE FIRST CHROMOSOME MAP

Category of event: Biology
Time: Fall, 1911
Locale: Columbia University, New York

Sturtevant statistically analyzed crossing-over of six sex-linked traits of the fruit fly, Drosophila, *to produce the first map of relative gene locations on chromosomes*

> *Principal personages:*
> GREGOR JOHANN MENDEL (1822-1884), an Austrian monk and science teacher, whose experiments with garden peas revealed the basic laws of heredity; he is usually referred to as the father of genetics
> THOMAS HUNT MORGAN (1866-1945), an American geneticist whose work with the fruit fly, *Drosophila melanogaster,* led to new understanding of the functions of chromosomes; awarded the 1933 Nobel Prize in Physiology or Medicine
> ALFRED HENRY STURTEVANT (1891-1970), an American geneticist who, as a student working under Thomas Hunt Morgan, mapped six sex-linked genes on the X chromosome of *Drosophila*

Summary of Event

The beginning of the twentieth century was a period of considerable research in genetics. Charles Darwin and Alfred Russel Wallace had not been able to account for the variation between members of a species in their joint paper on evolution in 1859 and in their later work. Also, in 1900, Gregor Johann Mendel's work on transmission of traits was rediscovered. It was not known if Mendel's research could be used to help explain the variation that allowed evolution to occur.

Mendel had little idea of the physical location of the genes. By pure luck, he picked seven traits of garden peas whose genes were on separate pairs of chromosomes. This led to his law of independent assortment, which stated that genes for different traits will assort randomly in sperm or egg formation. Carl Correns reported an apparent exception to his law in 1900 in the plant *Matthiola*. He found that the trait of petal color tended to be linked to the trait for seed, leaf, and stem texture. Plants with colored flowers had a hoary texture and plants with white flowers had smooth seeds. While this exception seemed to disprove Mendel's rule of independent assortment, the linked traits were actually caused by the genes for the two traits being on the same pair of chromosomes. Linked traits did not invalidate Mendel; they were merely an exception to his rule.

In 1910, Thomas Hunt Morgan reported the phenomenon of crossing-over of linked traits using *Drosophila*, the fruit fly. He realized that linked traits became unlinked. He had found that eye color and wing size were linked so that red-eyed flies had rudimentary wings and white-eyed flies had long wings. On occasion, however, he would get a fly with white eyes and rudimentary wings. Somehow, the linked traits had become unlinked. Morgan did his initial work with sex-linked traits. These traits are carried on the X chromosome. In *Drosophila* (and humans, for that matter), all eggs and male-producing sperm contain an X chromosome. This is a typical chromosome containing many genes. Females, thus, carry two X chromosomes in their body cells. Male-producing sperm carry a Y chromosome which carries few, if any, genes. Therefore all male flies have an X and a Y chromosome in their body cells.

Alfred Henry Sturtevant first became interested in inheritance while breeding horses at his father's ranch. While attending Columbia University, he had the opportunity to work in Morgan's "fly room." He then became interested in the process of crossing-over of sex-linked traits. He realized that the exchange between the X chromosomes most likely occurred during the synapsis (period in egg formation when two paired chromosomes lie next to each other) of meiosis (the process of sex cell formation). With sex-linked traits, crossing-over is significant only in egg formation. In sperm formation, the Y chromosome has few genes to cross over with its X partner. This somewhat simplifies the study of crossing-over since one does not have to account for crossing-over in sex cell formation of the male parent.

Morgan reasoned that the relative distance between the genes could be determined by the frequency of crossing-over between them. Sturtevant proceeded to develop this concept and apply it to a real situation. An analogy using a rope to represent a chromosome and beads on the rope to represent genes explains this process. Imagine bringing two such ropes together and letting them intertwine. This is similar to what happens to the two X chromosomes in synapsis of meiosis. Assume bead A is at one end, bead B is 1 meter away, and bead C is at the other end 5 meters away. Imagine that a child cuts equal portions of the ropes and ties them to the opposite rope. Assume that the child does not care where the cut occurs, and cuts at purely random lengths. It is more likely that beads A and C will be separated by his cut than beads A and B because of the larger distance between them. Using this reasoning, Sturtevant determined the distance between six sex-linked genes in *Drosophila*.

Sturtevant chose six sex-linked traits to study: First, trait A was body color. The dominant gene produced black bodies; the recessive condition gave yellow bodies. Second, trait B was eye color. The recessive condition gave white-eyed flies. The third trait, C, was closely related to trait B. If the dominant gene for trait B was present, then the dominant gene for trait C gave red eyes and the recessive gene gave eosin (pink) eyes. Flies having only recessive genes for trait B had white eyes, regardless of the gene for trait C. Trait D, the fourth trait, was also related to eye color. The dominant gene gave normal red eyes, the recessive condition gave vermillion eyes. The fifth and sixth traits were E and F for wing shape and size, respectively. If a dominant gene for both E and F was present, then the fly had normal wings. A fly with a dominant gene for E but no dominant gene for F had rudimentary wings; a fly with no dominant for E but a dominant for F had miniature wings. Finally, a fly having no dominants for either trait had both rudimentary and miniature wings.

If capital letters are used to represent the dominant genes for the six sex-linked traits and lowercase letters for the recessive genes, it follows that an X chromosome should contain either genes A, B, C, D, E, F or a, b, c, d, e, f. Crossing-over of chromosome fragments resulted in flies with other combinations on the X chromosome, such as A, B, C, d, e, f.

Using data collected from crosses in Morgan's "fly room," Sturtevant determined percentages of crossing-over between the various traits. For example, he found that crossing over occurred between traits A and B 193 times out of 16,287 trials, or 1.2 percent. Crossing-over between traits A and F occurred 260 times out of 693 trials, or 37.6 percent. Thus, Sturtevant proved that the genes for traits A and B are much closer than the ones for A and F. Likewise, he established crossing-over frequencies between all the six traits.

In order to describe his "map" of a chromosome, Sturtevant needed a unit of relative distance. He let one unit represent the distance between genes which cross over once in every one hundred times. Trait A was placed at one end of the chromosome map. Traits B and C were so close to each other that they never separated. He placed them ten units from trait A. Traits D and E were quite close to each other but could be separated. Trait D was 30.7 units from trait A. Trait E was 33.7 units from trait A. Trait F was at the other end of the chromosome and was 57.6 units from trait A. Therefore, a map showing relative distances between genes on chromosomes had been statistically derived.

Sturtevant also described double crossing-over in a 1914 publication. Sometimes chromosomes that have already crossed over with one another break at some other point and cross over again. If the genes A, B, and C are linked on a chromosome and a, b, and c on its partner chromosome, crossing-over might produce a chromosome with genes A, b, and c. Double crossing-over might then result in a chromosome with genes A, b, and C. This complicated the interpretation of the data, but was eventually clarified by Sturtevant.

Impact of Event

Thomas Hunt Morgan was initially skeptical of the existence of genes because his experimental results often seemed to be contrary to Mendel's laws. Sturtevant's work helped convince Morgan that genes exist on chromosomes, and Mendel's laws were valid. The apparent exceptions were now explainable by linkage and crossing-over and Mendel's laws became firmly established among geneticists.

Sturtevant's work spurred Morgan and his colleagues to pursue chromosome mapping of *Drosophila*. In 1915, Morgan's group published a map showing the relative location of fifty genes including genes on the nonsex-related chromosomes (autosomes). In the 1930's, interest in mapping led to maps derived by indirect physical observation of the genes of the giant chromosomes in the salivary glands of *Drosophila*. When properly stained and fixed on a slide, they showed cross patterns which could be correlated to specific genes. The physical maps did not correlate precisely to Sturtevant's statistically derived ones, although the linear order of the genes was identical. It became apparent that some portions of chromosomes are easier to break than others.

Extensive maps of the four pairs of chromosomes of *Drosophila* have been made since Sturtevant's first map, and similar interest has developed in mapping human chromosomes. Since humans have a relatively large number of chromosomes compared to *Drosophila* and studies on human inheritance are strictly limited by ethical and legal considerations, traditional crossing-over studies have been difficult. Only about one hundred of the estimated 100,000 human genes have been mapped, but new technology is making this mapping more feasible.

Human cells can be grown in tissue cultures with mouse cells, and hybrid mouse-human cells will form with as few as one human chromosome. This allows the genes on this isolated chromosome to be physically examined and mapped. Another method of mapping genes makes use of a deoxyribonucleic acid (DNA) probe. DNA is the building material of genes and is composed of chemical building blocks known as nucleotides. The nucleotide sequence of certain genes is known and can be detected on special photographs of a chromosome. Thus, one can place a particular gene at a certain place on a chromosome by studying nucleotide patterns.

The United States has a goal of having all the human genes mapped. This will require a tremendous need for researchers, new technology, and computer facilities. Some wonder if this knowledge will be of much value, while others believe it is a step toward the time when scientists can isolate particular genes easily and determine their roles. In turn, this could lead to the ability to replace defective or unwanted genes as desired. In 1911, Sturtevant mapped six sex-linked genes on the *Drosophila*. It is hoped that a large part of the human genetic component will be mapped by the one hundredth anniversary of his work.

Bibliography

Edey, Maitland, and Donald C. Johanson. *Blueprints: Solving the Mystery of Evolution*. Boston: Little, Brown, 1989. This book gives an interesting and understandable account of the advances in evolutionary theory from Linnaeus to the present. It has particularly good sections on genetics. Makes use of analogies to explain difficult genetic concepts.

Jaschik, Scott. "Many Scientists Charge Genome Mapping Project Threatens Other Research." *The Chronicle of Higher Education* 36 (July 18, 1990): 1, 24-25. This article for college teachers reviews the controversy over a $3 billion project of the United States government to map all the human genes. Shows the constant struggle over research funding as well as pros and cons of the project.

Mader, Sylvia S. *Biology*. 2d ed. Dubuque, Iowa: Wm. C. Brown, 1990. This is a popular biology text for beginning college students. It is clearly written and well illustrated. Devotes seven chapters to genetics, ranging from classic Mendelian heredity to the latest molecular genetics. Good preview for someone considering taking a genetics course.

Morgan, Thomas Hunt. *Evolution and Genetics*. Princeton, N.J.: Princeton University Press, 1925. This volume was based on a series of five lectures given by Morgan. Although dated, it provides useful information on advances in genetics up to the 1920's. The chapter on Mendel and his laws is quite interesting. The book is written at a level easily understandable to a high school biology student.

Sturtevant, A. H. *A History of Genetics*. New York: Harper & Row, 1965. A history of genetics written a few years before Sturtevant's death. Requires some knowledge of genetics to follow and might be of the most value to the professional biologist. Mentions Sturtevant's work with Morgan.

_____. "The Linear Arrangement of Six Sex-Linked Factors in *Drosophila*, as Shown by Their Mode of Association." *Journal of Experimental Zoology* 14 (1913): 43-59. This is the classic paper describing Sturtevant's first mapping of genes on chromosomes. Although written in a precise and scholarly manner, it is surprisingly easy to understand. While some of the numerical data may be technical, the sections on the mapping procedures and double crossing-over are quite fascinating.

James H. Anderson

Cross-References

De Vries and Associates Discover Mendel's Ignored Studies of Inheritance (1900), p. 61; McClung Plays a Role in the Discovery of the Sex Chromosome (1902), p. 148; Sutton States That Chromosomes Are Paired and Could Be Carriers of Hereditary Traits (1902), p. 153; Bateson and Punnett Observe Gene Linkage (1906), p. 314; Morgan Develops the Gene-Chromosome Theory (1908), p. 407; Johannsen Coins the Terms "Gene," "Genotype," and "Phenotype" (1909), p. 433; A Human Growth Hormone Gene Transferred to a Mouse Creates Giant Mice (1981), p. 2154.

BINGHAM DISCOVERS AN INCA CITY
IN THE PERUVIAN JUNGLE

Category of event: Archaeology
Time: July 24, 1911
Locale: Machu Picchu, Peru

Bingham discovered Machu Picchu, a previously unknown Inca city in the Andean jungle, extending the known range of Inca settlement and firing the public's imagination

Principal personages:
> HIRAM BINGHAM (1875-1956), a Yale professor who discovered Machu Picchu and other important prehistoric archaeological sites in Peru
> MELCHOR ARTEAGA, a Quechua Indian farmer who guided Bingham to Machu Picchu
> SERGEANT CARRASCO, a Peruvian military policeman who accompanied Bingham's expedition
> RICHARTE and ALVAREZ, two Quechua Indian farmers who lived on the site of Machu Picchu

Summary of Event

The great Inca Empire conquered by Francisco Pizarro and the Spaniards was centered in the Andean highlands of Peru, but the edges of the empire extended as far north as southern Colombia and as far south as central Chile, from the Pacific Ocean to the edges of the Brazilian jungle. While the jungle was largely peripheral to the empire, it held an intriguing role in the history of the Inca. First, legend held that Manco Capac, the first Inca ruler, had been born at Tampu Tocco (also known as "Tambo-Toqo") in the jungles of the eastern slope of the Andes. Further, history told of Vitcos and Vilcabamba, the jungle towns where the post-conquest Inca who rebelled against the Spaniards fled in 1539 and where they held out until 1572. These fabled places fired Hiram Bingham's imagination early in his career; his greatest triumph was accomplished during his attempts to locate these places.

Bingham was born in Hawaii, the son of a missionary and the third generation of his family there. He received his Ph.D. in history from Harvard University, but he had virtually no archaeological training when he began his series of South American explorations. Initially, he was lured to South America in 1907 by a historical interest in retracing the route of Simón Bolívar, the nineteenth century revolutionary hero of South America; it was during this trip that he became interested in further explorations. He returned the following year and visited his first archaeological ruins.

From the beginning, Bingham was more of an explorer in the nineteenth century mold than a scientist of the twentieth century type. He spent most of his efforts organizing teams and leading expeditions, leaving others to perform the detailed collection, analysis, and interpretation. In fact, his published works on Peru are almost all popular, rather than technical.

By 1911, Bingham had become interested in finding Vilcabamba, the last capital of the Incas, the jungle capital. His expedition consisted initially of Professor Harry Foote (a naturalist) and Doctor William Erving (a surgeon), although they would be joined later by Sergeant Carrasco, a military policeman assigned to them as an escort by the Peruvian president. In early July, this group set off, heading down the lush valley of the Urubamba River as it rushed from the high Andes into the jungle below, a drop of more than 3,000 meters in a distance of somewhat less than 100 kilometers. The deep, winding gorge flanked by dense, tropical vegetation made direct observation and search for ruins difficult; Bingham relied primarily on informants for information on where there were ruins worthy of his attention.

By the evening of July 23, the party had reached an open plain called Mandor Pampa, where, while pitching camp, they encountered a local Indian named Melchor Arteaga. Arteaga told of ruins on the tops of twin mountains nearby, Huayna Picchu and Machu Picchu. He praised those on Huayna Picchu highly but noted that those on Machu Picchu also were at least worth visiting. Bingham decided to visit these sites the following day.

The next morning broke with a dreary, cold drizzle that was to last all day, and only Bingham retained his interest in pressing on to the ruins Arteaga mentioned. In fact, Foote and Erving decided to stay in camp, and Arteaga had to be bribed with triple wages to guide Bingham to the ruins. Finally, Bingham, Arteaga, and Carrasco set out on a several-hour journey that forced them to scale cliffs, cross primitive bridges over the cascading Urubamba, and carve their way through dense jungle vegetation. Ultimately, they found their way to the farm of Richarte and Alvarez, two Quechuan Indian farmers who were using ancient Incan terraced slopes for their plantings. After a rest, the party forged on a short distance to the site of Machu Picchu.

There, they were greeted by abundant evidence of human activity. Nearly one hundred ancient agricultural terraces crawled up the slope toward the top of the lower of the two peaks, Machu Picchu, but such terraces were fairly common and not sufficient in themselves to impress Bingham. Yet, above the terraces, near the top of the mountain, were dozens of stone buildings, some large and others more modest. The true impact of these buildings would be clear a year later, after a return expedition cleared the vegetation to reveal their magnitude; however, Bingham immediately recognized their tremendous importance, even as overgrown as they were. Investigations the following year at the larger peak (Huayna Picchu) revealed a small but significant group of ruins at its top, but Bingham was far more impressed with Machu Picchu.

As he roamed over the ruins of Machu Picchu that first day, and even more so as the subsequent expedition cleared the vegetation and minutely recorded the findings, Bingham was convinced that he had located an ancient city of great importance. At the top of a steep stone stairway was a cluster of buildings of various styles. Some were temples, many of which had strangely carved rocks within, presumably shrines or representations of deities. One was a tower built of huge, carefully dressed stones (now usually interpreted as an observatory), whose circular shape was most atypical of Incan architecture. Palaces, also made of these large, dressed stones, were in areas adjacent to the temples and observatory. In another area from these elite buildings were modest gabled houses with distinctive Incan trapezoidal doorways, minus their thatched roofs but otherwise largely intact. These buildings were substantial habitations to protect their occupants against the cool night air. There also were other gabled buildings, much like the houses but with walls on only three sides, resembling historic buildings where the Inca made *chicha*, a local corn beer. Complex water systems channeled artificial streams through the settlement and produced ornamental streams and fountains. Plazas were marked by open spaces between clusters of buildings. Interspersed through the site were various types of architecture, some familiar and some exotic, some impressive and some ordinary, but all documenting the complexity and importance of the site.

Many of the larger, more impressive structures were built of stones more than 2 meters in each dimension, fitted together with angled and irregular joints, but cut so accurately that the stones fitted together perfectly and the blade of a pocket knife could not be inserted between them. This trait, so distinctive of the Inca, as well as the trapezoidal doorways, proved that the site was indeed part of the Inca Empire, a fact confirmed by the artifacts later found there.

The following year, Bingham and a somewhat larger, better-funded team returned to Machu Picchu and conducted full-scale fieldwork. They cleared the area of vegetation, mapped everything carefully, and conducted excavations to collect artifacts. They also bribed local Indians to disclose the locations of burial caves below the main site, and they investigated the surrounding area to locate Inca roads and bridges that linked the region to the rest of the empire.

It had become obvious to Bingham—as it soon would to the archaeological world in general—that Machu Picchu was a site of major importance. Its significance lay not so much in its size as in its location and its well-preserved religion and elite architecture. While many of Bingham's specific interpretations of the site were disputed by others and have not stood the test of time, his basic insight that Machu Picchu was an extraordinary discovery has proven correct.

Impact of Event

Bingham was convinced that he had discovered the last capital of the Incas, the site that he had set out to find. In some of his writings, he toyed with the possibility that it was the same place where the first Inca had been born; he became quite convinced of this by the time of some of his later writings. At the time when he was writing, there had been few other Inca sites found in the jungle; Machu Picchu remains to this day the largest and most opulent of the sites on the eastern slopes of the Andes. Further, Bingham interpreted some of the architecture at the site as part of major defensive works, something to be expected at the last Inca capital. Other archaeologists, however, have not agreed with this interpretation. Although it is clear that the site's topography would have aided defenders in the event of attack, there is no clear evidence of defensive works on the scale that Bingham believed.

Bingham's conclusion received a fatal blow from the dating of the site. Refinements in the dating of Inca artifacts and architecture on the basis of style or form and the introduction of the radiocarbon dating technique have conclusively documented that Machu Picchu existed neither early enough to have been the birthplace of the first Inca nor late enough to have been the final refuge. The Inca Empire was in existence only a brief time, from 1430 to shortly after the coming of the Spaniards in the sixteenth century; Machu Picchu was occupied in the late fifteenth and early sixteenth centuries. Clearly, it was an important site, but neither the first nor the last.

Bingham consistently called Machu Picchu a "lost city," and it is often termed a city in modern descriptions. Nevertheless, it is small by most conceptions of cities, probably never housing more than a thousand people. It is widely held that a small force of workers and maintenance population lived there year-round, while nobles or other elite came there seasonally for recreation. Another likely function of the settlement was to consolidate the Inca's tenuous hold in the jungle, giving the empire easier access to the feathers and other resources of that zone.

Bingham's discovery, though he apparently misinterpreted its significance, pointed out to archaeologists the importance of the eastern side of the Andes to the Inca, a point not previously recognized. Studies since Bingham's discovery have examined the role of trade between the highlands and the jungle, the political system that permitted the integration of such far-flung and diverse parts of the Inca Empire, and the possible impact of jungle cultures on the culture of the Incas and their highland predecessors. It is fair to say that none of these ideas would have been scrutinized so thoroughly if Machu Picchu had never been found.

Probably the most profound effect of Bingham's work is beyond archaeology. His discovery of Machu Picchu was destined to have a profound effect on the public. Bingham's expedition was like something out of a Jules Verne novel, with archaeological treasures and primitive splendor being discovered in the jungle. Bingham was willing to write for the public and had an engaging style, and his association with the National Geographic Society assured that his story would appear in the premier popular outlet of its day. In an era of literacy, readily available books, and photography, he brought his story before the public with a vividness that sparked the imagination in a way that would not be equaled until the discovery of Tutankhamen's tomb in Egypt some ten years later.

Bibliography

Bingham, Alfred M. *Portrait of an Explorer: Hiram Bingham, Discoverer of Machu Picchu*. Ames: Iowa State University Press, 1989. A fond but thorough memoir documenting Hiram Bingham's life, written by his son. The book covers Bingham's life, with the discovery of Machu Picchu figuring prominently. Illustrated with photographs from the expedition and the family archives.

Bingham, Hiram. *Inca Land*. Boston: Houghton Mifflin, 1922. This book primarily chronicles the Machu Picchu expedition for the nontechnical reader. Much of Bingham's account of the discovery of Machu Picchu in this book appears verbatim in his later works. As with all Bingham's works on Machu Picchu, the interpretation differs from that accepted today. Contains a few illustrations.

_____. *Lost City of the Incas: The Story of Machu Picchu and Its Builders*. New York: Duell, Sloan and Pearce, 1948. This book for the popular reader attempts to put Bingham's work into perspective, in the light of research by other scholars. It maintains much of the firsthand quality of his other works and provides a description of the events surrounding the discovery and examination of Machu Picchu. Several entries are taken intact from his earlier books. This book has been through several editions and reprintings and is also available in Spanish. Illustrated, with a bibliography.

_____. *Machu Picchu: A Citadel of the Incas*. New Haven, Conn.: Yale University Press, 1930. This book for the nontechnical reader focuses on the 1912 expedition that examined Machu Picchu in detail. Includes several illustrations.

Brundage, Burr Cartwright. *Empire of the Inca*. Norman: University of Oklahoma, 1963. A readable account of the history of the Inca, written for the specialist but accessible to the popular reader. The author treats both legendary and documentary history.

Hemming, John. "Machu Picchu." In *Monuments of the Incas*. Text by John Hemming. Illustrated by Edward Ranney. Boston: Little, Brown, 1982. Stunning photographs are accompanied by a brief text discussing Machu Picchu, particularly its architecture.

_____. *Machu Picchu*. New York: Newsweek, 1981. This coffee-table book traces the history and prehistory of Peru with an emphasis on Machu Picchu. It has many excellent color illustrations.

Kendall, Ann. *Everyday Life of the Incas*. New York: G. P. Putnam's Sons, 1973. A brief, well-illustrated account of the life-style of the ancient Inca.

Lumbreras, Luis G. *The Peoples and Cultures of Ancient Peru*. Translated by Betty J. Meggers. Washington, D.C.: Smithsonian Institution Press, 1974. The basic summary of ancient cultures in Peru and adjacent areas. This work is authoritative but appropriate only for the reader who wishes a more technical treatment. The focus is on the overall pattern of Peruvian prehistory, not on Machu Picchu itself.

Russell J. Barber

Cross-References

Evans Discovers the Minoan Civilization on Crete (1900), p. 67; Carter Discovers the Tomb of Tutankhamen (1922), p. 730; A Corroded Mechanism Is Recognized as an Ancient Astronomical Computer (1959), p. 1587.

LEAVITT'S STUDY OF VARIABLE STARS
UNLOCKS GALACTIC DISTANCES

Category of event: Astronomy
Time: 1912
Locale: Harvard College Observatory, Cambridge, Massachusetts

Leavitt discovered that the pulsating period of a Cepheid variable star is directly proportional to the star's brightness

> *Principal personages:*
> HENRIETTA SWAN LEAVITT (1868-1921), an American astronomer and head of the Department of Photographic Stellar Photometry at Harvard College Observatory
> HARLOW SHAPLEY (1885-1972), an American astronomer at Mount Wilson Observatory in California who later directed the Harvard College Observatory
> EDWIN POWELL HUBBLE (1889-1953), an American astronomer at Mount Wilson Observatory who measured intergalactic distances and who discovered that the universe is expanding
> EJNAR HERTZSPRUNG (1873-1967), a Danish astronomer who, with Henry Russell, classified stars based upon their colors, temperatures, and luminosities
> HENRY NORRIS RUSSELL (1877-1957), an American astronomer who, with Ejnar Hertzsprung, classified stars based upon their colors, temperatures, and luminosities

Summary of Event

The modern cosmological view of the universe is an expanding sphere of approximately one trillion galaxies. Each galaxy consists of one hundred billion to one trillion stars. Each star, including the sun, is an immense thermonuclear furnace composed mostly of the elements hydrogen and helium. The remaining one hundred-plus elements (for example, carbon, oxygen, iron) are synthesized by fusion reactions in stars and by massive star explosions (supernovas). The sun is one of approximately four hundred billion stars in the Milky Way galaxy.

By 1900, astronomers had firmly established that Earth, other planets, asteroids, and comets revolved about the sun and that the sun was only one of billions of stars in the Milky Way galaxy. Nevertheless, there were many unresolved problems. Some astronomers believed that the sun was located at the center of the Milky Way, a throwback to pre-Copernican views of Earth being the center of the universe. Other astronomers correctly theorized that the sun was an average star not located at the galactic center. Yet, evidence was lacking. The existence of other galaxies had not been clearly demonstrated, and there were no completely reliable methods for measuring the enormous distances between stars.

In 1902, Henrietta Swan Leavitt became a permanent observatory staff member at Harvard College Observatory. She studied variable stars, stars that change their luminosity (brightness) in a fairly predictable pattern over time. During her tenure at Harvard, Leavitt observed and photographed nearly 2,500 variable stars.

Variable stars can be of three principal types: eclipsing binaries, novas, and Cepheid variables. Eclipsing binaries are double-star systems where two stars orbit a common center of gravity. Periodically, one star will eclipse, or pass before, its companion star relative to the line of sight. The combined light emission from the double-star system will be reduced. Many double-star systems exist, including the dog star Sirius in the constellation Canis Major and Mizar-Alcor in the handle of the Big Dipper (Ursa Major). Novas are unstable stars which occasionally erupt and release envelopes of matter into space, temporarily increasing in brightness during the process. Cepheid variables and their similar RR Lyrae stars are older main sequence stars that have exhausted their hydrogen fuel and have switched to helium fusion for energy generation. Cepheids are unstable, periodically increasing, then decreasing their energy and light output. They become brighter, then dim, repeating the cycle every few days or weeks depending upon the star. Each Cepheid variable star has a predictable, repeatable cycle of brightening and dimming. They are named after Delta Cephei, the first such variable star discovered in the constellation Cepheus in 1768. Polaris, the North Star, is also a Cepheid.

At the time, the principal means of determining stellar distances was a trigonometric method known as parallax. A star's parallax is the line-by-sight angle subtended by the star as Earth orbits the sun. Using a right triangle formed by the observed star, the sun, and Earth as the triangle's vertices, the star's distance is calculated based upon simple trigonometric equations involving the earth-sun distance (about 150 million kilometers) and the subtended angle traced by the star in our sky. If the subtended angle is large, then the star is close. If the angle is small, the star is far. Related trigonometric methods rely upon the sun's motion relative to background stars and the motion of star clusters in the Milky Way galaxy. Trigonometric parallax methods are limited to relatively close stars. Using parallax, the very close stars Alpha Centauri and Barnard's star are 4.27 and 5.97 light-years distant, respectively. Sirius is 8.64 light-years distant. Since a light-year is the distance light travels in one year, approximately ten trillion kilometers, parallax is an extremely accurate means of measuring stellar distances. During the twentieth century, more than ten thousand stellar distances have been obtained using this method. Yet, if one considers the immensity of the universe having a radius of perhaps twenty billion light-years, parallax fails at relatively short astronomical distances (for example, fifty thousand light-years).

While studying variable stars, Leavitt measured their luminosities over time. She was equipped with photographs of the Large and Small Magellanic Clouds collected from Harvard's Peruvian observatory. Magellanic Clouds are very small galaxies visible in the Southern Hemisphere. The Small Magellanic Cloud contained seventeen Cepheid variables having very predictable periods ranging from 1.25 days to

127 days. She carefully measured the brightening and dimming of the seventeen Cepheids during their respective periods. She collected photographs of other Cepheids in the Magellanic Clouds and made additional period-luminosity studies.

While Leavitt was studying Cepheids, Ejnar Hertzsprung of the Leiden University in The Netherlands and Henry Norris Russell of the Mount Wilson Observatory in Pasadena, California, independently discovered a relationship between a star's luminosity and its spectral class (that is, color and temperature). Together, their experimental results produced the Hertzsprung-Russell diagram of stellar luminosities, the astronomical equivalent of chemistry's periodic table. According to their classification scheme, most stars lie along the "main sequence," which ranges from extremely bright blue stars ten thousand times brighter than the sun to very dim red stars one hundred times dimmer than the sun. Additional star classes outside the main sequence include red giants, supergiants, and white dwarfs. Cepheid variables are placed toward the cooler, red star end of the main sequence.

Thinking along the same lines as Hertzsprung and Russell, Leavitt carefully measured the luminosities and cyclic periods of changing luminosity for each of many Cepheid variables from the Magellanic Clouds. From her careful measurements, she graphically plotted Cepheid luminosity against Cepheid period. She discovered that a Cepheid's apparent luminosity is directly proportional to the length of its period, or the time it takes to complete one cycle of brightening and dimming. A faint Cepheid variable has a very short cyclic period during which it fluctuates in brightness, usually ranging from one to four days. A more luminous Cepheid has a longer cyclic period, usually twenty to thirty days or more.

Harlow Shapley, an astronomer at the Mount Wilson Observatory, combined Leavitt's Cepheid period-apparent luminosity relationship to parallax data for Cepheid distances. He measured the distances of moving star clusters containing Cepheids, then related the Cepheid distances to Cepheid period-luminosity data. From these experiments, Shapley constructed a Cepheid period-absolute luminosity curve. With this curve, one can plot a Cepheid variable having a specific measured period and obtain its absolute luminosity. Knowing the Cepheid's apparent and absolute luminosities, one can instantly calculate its distance and, therefore, the distances of all the stars in the star cluster containing that particular Cepheid variable.

Consequently, the distances to Cepheid variables in the Milky Way and other galaxies were determined quickly. Shapley used Cepheid distances to demonstrate that the center of the Milky Way is directed toward the constellation Sagittarius and that the sun is located approximately thirty thousand light-years from the galactic center. Edwin Powell Hubble, also of Mount Wilson Observatory, applied the technique to measure the distances to Cepheids located in distant galaxies, thereby obtaining estimates of the distances between our galaxy and others.

Impact of Event

Leavitt's discovery of the Cepheid variable period-luminosity relationship, reported in the 1912 *Harvard College Observatory Circular*, No. 173, was an important achievement in twentieth century astronomy. Her period-luminosity relationship established Cepheid variables as standard reference points for measuring distances between stars and galaxies.

Immediate applications of her work appeared in the studies of Shapley and Hubble. Shapley derived a period-absolute luminosity curve for Cepheids from Leavitt's results and from distance measurements for star clusters containing Cepheids. Each Cepheid's period gives away its absolute luminosity, which gives away its distance. With this approach, any star cluster containing Cepheid variables can be measured to obtain its approximate distance from Earth. The rationale is quite simple: If a distant group of stars contains a Cepheid variable, determination of the Cepheid's distance will give astronomers an estimate of the distance to all the stars in the cluster, relatively speaking. The stars of the cluster may be very far apart from one another, but relative to Earth, they all are approximately the same distance, the distance measured for their Cepheid variable.

Shapley used the approach to measure the distances to RR Lyrae stars, Cepheid-like pulsating stars first discovered in the constellation Lyra. RR Lyrae stars are distributed throughout the Milky Way galaxy and within globular clusters, masses of perhaps a million stars each that surround the Milky Way in a halo. Shapley noted that there are far more globular clusters in the direction of the constellation Sagittarius than there are surrounding Earth's area of space. If the sun were the center of the Milky Way galaxy, then globular clusters would be spaced roughly equally in all directions. But they are not. From this observation, Shapley concluded that the sun is located out in one of the Milky Way's spiral arms, in fact, the arm seen as the starry haze called the Milky Way. The center of the Milky Way lies hidden and distant, in the direction of the constellation Sagittarius. From RR Lyrae stars located within each globular cluster surrounding our galaxy, Shapley mapped the distance to each globular cluster and thereby produced an approximate distance map for the entire Milky Way galaxy. He demonstrated that the Milky Way is a flattened spiral disk with a thickened center. He also measured the approximate diameter of the Milky Way and estimated that the sun is about fifty thousand light-years (later corrected to thirty thousand light-years) from the galactic center.

Hubble used the work of Leavitt and Shapley to measure the distances to other galaxies, most notably Messier 31, the great nebula in the constellation Andromeda, the largest galaxy near Earth. Hubble measured the distances to RR Lyrae stars located within the Andromeda galactic disk and obtained an approximate intergalactic distance of 750,000 light-years, later recalibrated to one million light-years. This is one of the closest galaxies to Earth out of possibly one trillion. Hubble applied this technique to the measurement of distances to other galaxies. This work contributed to his later studies of galactic redshift velocities, which led to his monumental astronomical discovery that the universe is expanding.

Bibliography

Bartusiak, Marcia. *Thursday's Universe*. New York: Times Books, 1986. This wonderful book is a history of the major astronomical achievements of the twentieth century. While it is thorough in scope, it is written for a general audience. Chapter 4, "Wrapped in an Enigma," discusses the work of Leavitt and Shapley.

Ferris, Timothy. *Galaxies*. Reprint. New York: Harrison House, 1987. This very popular astronomy book is a clearly written, beautifully illustrated discussion of astronomy and cosmology. The book is very simple to read and includes many photographs of galaxies and star clusters. Excellent introduction to the subject.

Hoyle, Fred. *Astronomy*. Garden City, N.Y.: Doubleday, 1962. This introduction to astronomy, written by one of the giants of twentieth century astronomy, is a detailed history of the subject. The book also provides abundant astronomical data and clearly describes practical methods in astronomy. It is extensively illustrated and referenced.

Kippenhahn, Rudolf. *Light from the Depths of Time*. Translated by Storm Dunlop. New York: Springer-Verlag, 1987. This book contains an outstanding introduction to astronomy and cosmology for the average reader. Kippenhahn simplifies many complex astronomical concepts in a very entertaining fashion, such as how the universe would look to a two-dimensional being. Chapter 4, "Plumbing the Depths of the Milky Way," discusses the contributions of Leavitt and Shapley.

Rolfs, Claus E., and William S. Rodney. *Cauldrons in the Cosmos: Nuclear Astrophysics*. Chicago: University of Chicago Press, 1988. This detailed, graduate-level astrophysics textbook is a comprehensive summary of stars and the processes that occur inside stars. The mathematics is advanced; however, it is well written and illustrated. Chapter 1, "Astronomy-Observing the Universe," is a very informative and simple introduction to the subject.

Struve, Otto, and Velta Zebergs. *Astronomy of the Twentieth Century*. New York: Macmillan, 1962. This excellent book is a thorough survey of twentieth century astronomy. It covers both astronomical history and techniques in a very clear format for the general reader. It uses outstanding photographs, illustrations, and examples to present astronomical concepts. Graphs and simple algebraic equations make this book a strong teaching tool.

Thiel, Rudolf. *And There Was Light: The Discovery of the Universe*. Translated by Richard Winston and Clara Winston. New York: Alfred A. Knopf, 1957. Thiel's book is an interesting description of astronomical history from ancient times to 1957. It is clearly written and is well illustrated for the layperson. Book 5, "Rejuvenation," provides strong coverage of modern astronomy, including the work of Leavitt, Shapley, and others.

Tully, R. Brent, and J. Richard Fisher. *Nearby Galaxies Atlas*. Cambridge, England: Cambridge University Press, 1987. The Tully-Fisher atlas of galaxies is the most thorough survey of local galaxies. Excellent maps and illustrations chart the locations of hundreds of galaxies in the northern and southern hemispheric skies. Galaxy types and Hubble redshift velocities are provided.

Zeilik, Michael, and Elske V. P. Smith. *Introductory Astronomy and Astrophysics*. 2d ed. Philadelphia: Saunders College Publishing, 1987. This information-packed textbook is aimed at serious undergraduate-level astronomy and astrophysics students. The discussions of concepts are excellent, although one can get lost in the mathematics. The tables, diagrams, and illustrations are outstanding.

Zim, Herbert S., and Robert H. Baker. *Stars.* Illustrated by James Gordon Irving. New York: Simon & Schuster, 1951. This classic astronomy handbook is an outstanding introduction and guide for astronomers of all ages, even elementary students. The illustrations are excellent, and the constellation information is invaluable for night sky observing.

David Wason Hollar, Jr.

Cross-References

Hertzsprung Notes the Relationship Between Color and Luminosity of Stars (1905), p. 265; Russell Announces His Theory of Stellar Evolution (1913), p. 585; Shapley Proves the Sun Is Distant from the Center of Our Galaxy (1918), p. 655; Eddington Formulates the Mass-Luminosity Law for Stars (1924), p. 785; Hubble Demonstrates That Other Galaxies Are Independent Systems (1924), p. 790; Hubble Confirms the Expanding Universe (1929), p. 878.

SLIPHER OBTAINS THE SPECTRUM
OF A DISTANT GALAXY

Category of event: Astronomy
Time: 1912
Locale: Lowell Observatory, Flagstaff, Arizona

Slipher obtained the spectra of the Andromeda nebula and showed that it had a large radial velocity, suggesting that it, and other spiral nebulas, belonged to different galaxies

Principal personages:

VESTO MELVIN SLIPHER (1875-1969), an American astronomer who became the director of the Lowell Observatory, perfected spectroscopic techniques, and used them to study planetary atmospheres and rotations

PERCIVAL LOWELL (1855-1916), an American astronomer who founded Lowell Observatory and suggested spectroscopic problems to Slipher

HEBER DOUST CURTIS (1872-1942), an American astronomer who was an early and ardent supporter of the "island universe" idea and who engaged in a debate with his leading opponent, Harlow Shapley

HARLOW SHAPLEY (1885-1972), an American astronomer who worked on Cepheid variables, globular clusters, and galaxies and opposed the "island universe" idea

ADRIAAN VAN MAANEN (1884-1946), a Dutch-American astronomer whose systematic error in measurement caused a delay in the acceptance of the "island universe" idea

EDWIN POWELL HUBBLE (1889-1953), an American astronomer who was the founder of modern extragalactic astronomy; his work confirmed the "island universe" idea and provided observational evidence for the expansion of the universe

Summary of Event

Stars were not very satisfactory study subjects for early astronomers. In contrast to the planets, they did not appear to show motion relative to one another and appeared as mere points of light when viewed through a telescope. The snowy band known as the Milky Way was an exception. Ancient peoples had seen it as a reflection of their own worlds, but in the mid-eighteenth century, investigators assumed that its nebulous glow was produced by faint, distant stars. A different kind of "nebulous glow" was noted by Immanuel Kant, who suggested that these so-called nebulous stars were actually other universes outside the Milky Way. Pierre-Simon Laplace suggested that some kind of nebulous material might have been the formative material for Earth's solar system, but it was William Herschel, one of the first astronomers to concentrate on stellar astronomy, who found that many of the nebulous clouds could actually be resolved into individual stars. Herschel concluded that if sufficiently powerful telescopes were available, all the nebulous clouds would prove to be star systems. Later, however, he recognized that this hypothesis would not explain all the phenomena, reversed himself, and suggested what became known as the "nebular hypothesis." He proposed that the unresolvable nebulas were the "parents" of the stars; first came nebulous matter, then nebulas, and finally stars. After enjoying a brief period of acceptance, the hypothesis fell into disrepute after William Parsons, third Earl of Rosse, reported to the British Association for the Advancement of Science in 1844 that he had constructed a reflecting telescope that could resolve the apparently formless nebular material into discrete stars. He discovered that certain nebulas had spiral structures and was able to distinguish individual stars in several of these "spirals" that Herschel's less powerful instrument could not. Yet, even with Parson's telescope, all the nebulas could not be resolved into stars.

Advances in photographic techniques and the development of spectroscopy (analysis of light spectra) at the end of the nineteenth century made possible a more detailed examination of Parsons' spiral nebulas. Some astronomers were convinced that they were a part of our galaxy (relatively small, nearby objects) and others thought they represented different universes (large and very distant).

Although the idea of "island universes"—other worlds similar to our galaxy—had been proposed earlier on philosophical, not observational, grounds, and Kant in the eighteenth century had suggested that the spiral nebulas might represent such "island universes," the question was not completely resolved until 1935. Vesto Melvin Slipher's observations in 1912 with improved spectrographic tools (an instrument used to disperse and photograph light) provided data vital to determining whether the spirals were part of the Milky Way galaxy or part of distant, hitherto unknown worlds.

Slipher responded to a request by Percival Lowell to join the staff of the Lowell Observatory in Flagstaff, Arizona. His skill at perfecting spectroscopic equipment, his meticulous care in obtaining observations, and his cautious interpretations made it possible for him to make many important fundamental discoveries.

Using spectrographic techniques, Slipher measured the rotational periods of Mars, Venus, Jupiter, Saturn, and Uranus; identified bands in the spectra of Jupiter and Saturn as caused by ammonia and methane; and found evidence that interstellar space contained both dust and gas. Yet, he made his most profound contribution when he turned his attention to the elusive spiral nebulas. Slipher's part in early twentieth century astronomical controversy over the location of the spirals was indirect. Using an improved camera, he investigated not only the spectra of the spirals but also their velocities. Beginning with his work on the Andromeda nebula, he determined that the spirals had exceptionally large radial velocities. He found that "the great Andromeda spiral had the . . . exceptional velocity of −300 kilometers" per second, the greatest radial velocity ever observed.

Radial velocities, those measured only along the line of sight, can be either approaching or receding. For an object moving toward a wave source, the wave frequency appears to increase and to become shorter, but moving away from the source, the waves appear less frequent and the wavelength longer. This phenomenon, called the Doppler shift (shift in wavelength of light or sound caused by the relative motion of the source and receiver), can be illustrated by sound waves. When a truck approaches with its horn blasting, its pitch is higher than when the truck is at rest. Just as the truck passes, its pitch is unshifted. Then as it moves away, its horn produces a lower pitch. The same phenomenon occurs with the light waves Slipher measured with his spectrograph. The Doppler shift (produced by the radial velocity) was measured by the change in the wavelength of lines in a spectrum. The emission, or absorption, lines are shifted to the blue end (short wavelengths) of the spectrum for an approaching object, and to the red (long wavelengths) for one that is receding.

After his initial work on the Andromeda nebula, Slipher observed other spirals. When he published his results in 1914, he had obtained Doppler shifts for fourteen, all showing large radial velocities. Although he was given a standing ovation when he announced his discovery at the 1914 meeting of the American Astronomical Society and won gold medals of the Paris Academy, the Royal Astronomical Society, and the Astronomical Society of the Pacific, the interpretation of his findings became part of the "island universe" controversy. Some astronomers, such as Ejnar Hertzsprung, were convinced that since the spirals had such remarkably large radial velocities, they could not be a part of the Milky Way galaxy. Slipher, in a lecture to the American Philosophical Society in April, 1917, recognized that his observations supported the hypothesis that spiral nebulas are very distant stellar systems.

Other astronomers would not be convinced until the actual distances of the spirals could be computed. Heber Doust Curtis, one of the first to suggest a much greater distance for the spirals, immediately accepted the implications of Slipher's data. He had already reached the conclusion that the Andromeda nebula was 500,000 light-years away, and Slipher's data provided support. Curtis publicly debated the point with Harlow Shapley, who (relying on measurements by Adriaan van Maanen) insisted that the spiral nebulas were nearby nebulous objects.

After 1925, van Maanen's measurements were less influential, for Slipher's work on the direction of rotation of the spirals directly contradicted van Maanen's conclusions. Edwin Powell Hubble's demonstration from the behavior of Cepheids (pulsating variable stars) in spirals indicated that they must be remote. Nevertheless, since van Maanen's measurements seemed to represent observational facts, they were difficult to abandon even with contradictory data. Van Maanen's results eventually were ignored, not so much because they were proved wrong, but because new evidence seemed to prove incontrovertibly that the spirals were galaxies. Hubble's 1935 paper in the *Astrophysical Journal* finally brought the controversy over the distance of the spirals to closure.

Impact of Event

Slipher's meticulous spectroscopic measurements demonstrating the immense radial velocities of the spiral nebulas proved to be one of the most significant discoveries in modern astronomy. By finally succeeding at the very difficult task of obtaining the faint Andromeda nebula's spectrum, he provided evidence that this nebula was much farther away than assumed previously. After perfecting his technique, he confirmed his results on Andromeda by measuring Doppler shifts in other spirals. Although the implications of extremely large radial velocities for the spirals were that they could not be contained with the Milky Way, the "island universe" dispute between major protagonists Curtis and Shapley retarded the acceptance of the significance of his discovery.

Although Slipher's work on radial velocity was consistent with an extragalactic position for Andromeda and the other spirals, his findings did not prove the island-universe theory, since they did not provide the distance to the spirals. Slipher also confirmed that the spirals rotated. This discovery meant that through determining proper motions (apparent angular rates of motion of a star) within the spirals, the distance to them might be obtained and the dispute settled conclusively. Agreeing on the procedure in principle, van Maanen's systematic error led to a mistaken interpretation, indicating that the spirals (showing considerable proper motion) could not be at any great distance, seemingly disproving the "island universe" idea.

In 1924, Hubble discovered Cepheid variables and derived a distance of 490,000 light-years for this galaxy. This distance is far beyond the farthest globular clusters of the outer limits of our galaxy. (This estimate has now been revised to 2.2 million light-years.) Although his distance determinations might have settled the problem in 1925, doubts still lingered, because Hubble's conclusions were based on the controversial period luminosity law and because van Maanen's contradictory results were exceptionally consistent. The problem was not resolved until 1935, when a new set of measurements indicated that van Maanen was incorrect.

The most all-encompassing result from Slipher's work on the spirals was the preparation that he made for investigations of the motions of galaxies and for cosmological theories based on an expanding universe. By 1928, Slipher's measurement of the radial velocities of more than forty galaxies indicated that most galaxies apparently were moving away from the Milky Way. At about the same time, Hubble had noted that more distant galaxies had greater radial velocities. In fact, there seemed to be a direct relationship between radial velocity and distance. This relationship, known as Hubble's law (with a number connecting distance and velocity called Hubble's constant), indicates that the universe is expanding. This conclusion is based on Slipher's measurements, which showed that almost all spiral nebulas are moving away from the Milky Way (as well as from one another) with large velocities. These observations suggested not only that the spirals were galaxies like the Milky Way but also that the entire universe was expanding.

Bibliography

Berendzen, Richard, Richard Hart, and Daniel Seeley. *Man Discovers the Galaxies*. New York: Science History Publications, 1976. An excellent source that is both readable and scholarly. The volume focuses on pivotal events in the history of galactic astronomy, provides biographical information on the key players, and includes archival source materials. Includes a useful bibliography.

Macpherson, Hector. *Modern Cosmologies: A Historical Sketch of Researches and Theories Concerning the Structure of the Universe.* London: Oxford University Press, 1929. This useful little book consists of eight lectures delivered at the Royal Technical College, Glasgow, during the winter of 1928-1929. One lecture is on island universe ideas.

Munitz, M. K., ed. *Theories of the Universe: From Babylonian Myth to Modern Science.* New York: Free Press, 1957. This series of essays designed for the general reader discusses the perennial cosmological question and includes sections on concepts of island and expanding universes. Includes a selected bibliography.

North, J. D. *The Measure of the Universe: A History of Modern Cosmology.* Oxford, England: Clarendon Press, 1965. The book focuses on the development of cosmology in the first half of the twentieth century and includes a section on the expanding universe. The first part consists of a straightforward historical and theoretical narrative; the second part includes a discussion of the conceptual problems introduced in the first section. Although it is a useful source, it is less accessible to the general reader than the other books cited. Includes an appendix and a selected bibliography.

Slipher, Vesto M. "The Radial Velocity of the Andromeda Nebula." *Lowell Observatory Bulletin* 2 (1913): 56-57. Slipher's original paper giving his figures is essential for research on the topic.

Struve, Otto, and Velta Zebergs. *Astronomy in the Twentieth Century.* New York: Macmillan, 1962. The book does not claim to present a comprehensive account of all astronomical research during the twentieth century. Yet, it provides specific examples to describe some of the most significant advances and working techniques of twentieth century astronomers. Includes a glossary and a valuable appendix.

Marilyn Bailey Ogilvie

Cross-References

Leavitt's Study of Variable Stars Unlocks Galactic Distances (1912), p. 496; Shapley Proves the Sun Is Distant from the Center of Our Galaxy (1918), p. 655; Hubble Demonstrates That Other Galaxies Are Independent Systems (1924), p. 790; Oort Proves the Spiral Structure of the Milky Way (1927), p. 830; Hubble Confirms the Expanding Universe (1929), p. 878.

BOHR WRITES A TRILOGY ON
ATOMIC AND MOLECULAR STRUCTURE

Category of event: Physics
Time: 1912-1913
Locale: Copenhagen, Denmark

Bohr applied the quantum theory to Rutherford's nuclear model of the atom, providing a theoretical explanation for a variety of atomic phenomena and a program for further research

Principal personages:
> NIELS BOHR (1885-1962), a Danish physicist, head of an influential physics institute and winner of the 1922 Nobel Prize in Physics for his work on the structure of the atom
> ERNEST RUTHERFORD (1871-1937), the founder of nuclear physics and developer of the nuclear model of the atom which Bohr quantized
> SIR JOSEPH JOHN THOMSON (1856-1940), one of the foremost atomic model-builders of the early twentieth century and discoverer of the electron
> CHARLES GALTON DARWIN (1887-1962), the grandson of the evolutionist Charles Darwin, who wrote a paper whose errors drew Bohr into the questions of atomic structure

Summary of Event

Physics in the first decade of the twentieth century was not dominated by the quantum, introduced by Max Planck in 1900, or by relativity, introduced in 1905 by Albert Einstein. It was dominated by the electron, discovered in 1897 by Sir Joseph John Thomson. Theoreticians and experimentalists were busy developing an electromagnetic view of the world in which a wide variety of physical phenomena were explained in terms of electrons, their motions, and their interactions with the "ether." The successes of the electromagnetic view of the world were such that its proponents believed that eventually it could explain everything.

A number of atomic models were developed during this period, but there was little concern for working out the details. The atomic model developed by Thomson was widely accepted. It consisted of a set of coplanar rings of electrons moving within a uniformly positively charged sphere. The electrons in Thomson's model made up much of the mass of the atom. Unlike other atomic models, Thomson's model had the advantage of mechanical stability: Electrons slightly displaced in the plane of their orbit would not tear the atom apart.

It was in this intellectual atmosphere that Niels Bohr completed his doctoral dissertation in 1911 on the electron theory of metals. Bohr spent the first part of the academic year 1911-1912 in Cambridge with Thomson. He then went to Manchester in the spring of 1912 to work with Ernest Rutherford, who had recently proposed a model of the atom in which a positively charged nucleus much smaller than the size of the atom was surrounded by electrons. (Contrary to Thomson's model, in Rutherford's model, much of the mass of the atom is located in the nucleus.)

Bohr began a normal course of laboratory exercises. Yet, by the end of May, 1912, Bohr was still working primarily on the electron theory of metals and not on the central problems of radioactivity and Rutherford's nuclear model.

Bohr read a paper by Charles Galton Darwin, also working with Rutherford at Manchester, concerning the absorption by matter of "alpha particles" (helium atoms with both electrons removed). Bohr noticed an error in Darwin's study and began compiling his own ideas. He developed an analogy between the passage of alpha particles through matter and his own work on the electron theory of metals. The problem of the mechanical stability of Rutherford's model appeared when Bohr tried to calculate the effect of a passing charged particle on the electron's orbit. The question of stability was so important because of the way Bohr solved it: by fiat. Since classical mechanics could not provide a condition of stability for Rutherford's model, Bohr turned to Planck's quantum theory. Bohr assumed that for stable orbits of electrons, there exists a definite ratio between the kinetic energy of the electrons in an orbit and their frequency of rotation. The value of this ratio is Planck's constant. Bohr called these stable orbits "stationary states."

Bohr submitted these ideas to Rutherford in a memorandum, but it was not discovered until after Bohr's death in 1962. This was only a beginning: Many aspects essential to Bohr's completed theory had yet to appear. The material in this memorandum reappeared in the second and third parts of Bohr's trilogy of papers.

Bohr knew he was on the right track when he was able to fit the large number of "radioelements" (elements chemically similar to known elements but with vastly different radioactive properties) into the periodic table. He suggested that radioactive properties could be relegated to the nucleus while chemical properties were the result of the number of electrons in an atom. The radioelements could then be explained as elements that had a heavier nucleus than usual. This would give the radioelements different radioactive properties, but would keep their same chemical properties. Bohr also demonstrated that atomic number—and not atomic weight—governed the chemical properties of the elements. Bohr's theory also gave a straightforward explanation of the well-known periodicity of chemical elements.

Bohr grappled in late 1912 with John W. Nicholson's earlier atomic theory, which included Planck's quantum, and an explanation of the spectra of atoms. In the late nineteenth century, astronomers noticed lines, or gaps, in the spectrum of light from the sun. Further investigation showed that each element had its own unique set of lines. Johann Jakob Balmer developed a formula that accounted for known frequencies, but this equation had no physical significance. Nicholson's theory accounted for experimental results quite well. Bohr was briefly troubled by the inconsistencies between his theory and Nicholson's, but by early 1913, he had resolved the inconsistencies.

Up to this time, Bohr had considered atoms only in their lowest energy state. In Nicholson's theory, electrons in the atom could have energies greater than the lowest energy possible. Bohr saw a use for Nicholson's idea of using the higher energy levels and incorporated them into his theory. Adapting Nicholson's theories gave Bohr his most distinct break with classical physics. It was widely believed that the mechanical frequency of the electron as it orbited the nucleus was equal to the frequency of the spectral line that atoms would emit. Instead, Bohr equated the differences in the frequencies of two stationary states of the atom with the frequency of the emitted spectral line. Electrons jumping from one stationary state to another emitted radiation with a frequency independent of the electron's mechanical frequency.

A letter to a colleague in February, 1913, indicated that Bohr had completed work on the topics that were eventually to compose the second and third published parts of the trilogy: the periodicity of the elements, the volume of the atoms, the conditions of atomic combination, energies of X rays, dispersion, and radioactivity.

During February and March, Bohr included a discussion of the spectra of atoms. Bohr had, in fact, ruled out consideration of the optical spectrum. What led him to include spectra was his realization that his theory could explain Balmer's formula, which was expressed as a difference of two quantities. Bohr associated that difference with the difference in frequency of two stationary states.

Bohr managed to solve the problem of spectra in a manner which was convincing to him, but he had yet to provide a mathematical derivation of his results. In the early part of the first paper of the trilogy, Bohr provided three such derivations; however, they were incompatible because Bohr compiled his results on spectra with great speed. The draft of the first part of the trilogy that Bohr sent to Rutherford in early March was modified only slightly and appeared in July, 1913. The second and third parts of the trilogy, published in September and November of 1913, presented solutions to the problems contained in the Rutherford memorandum.

Impact of Event

Immediate reactions to Bohr's trilogy were mixed. There were still many physicists who did not consider Planck's quantum to have any physical significance. Those, like Nicholson, who were willing to consider the quantum, questioned portions of Bohr's approach. In particular, in the second and third parts of the trilogy, Bohr extended his theory to atoms with more than one electron. Although Bohr tried to present quantitative support for the result, he often had to rely on qualitative arguments to achieve the correct results. Even the first part did not escape criticism for its incompatible derivations of Balmer's formula and its tradition-breaking assumptions about atoms.

Acceptance increased, however, as Bohr's theory accounted for details of spectra that had eluded explanation by other models. An early victory was Bohr's attribution of a set of spectral lines called the "Pickering series" to ionized helium instead of to hydrogen. Spectroscopists examined helium and found the lines. The agreement between Bohr's prediction and the experimental results was numerically very close.

What became known as the "Correspondence Principle" appeared in the first part of the trilogy. It became a principal tool in the early development of quantum theory. The Correspondence Principle asserted that the results of quantum mechanics do not conflict with those of classical mechanics in the realm where classical mechanics is valid. In practice, the Correspondence Principle was used as a tool in order to justify using the results of classical mechanics in the calculation of quantum mechanical properties. Using this principle, Bohr's original theory was extended to other areas. The long-term impact of Bohr's trilogy on physics and physicists can be gauged from the comment of a fellow physicist: "There is hardly any other paper in the literature of physics from which grew so many new theories and discoveries."

Bohr's groundbreaking trilogy of 1913, although flawed, made way for quantum mechanics. Bohr's trilogy was generally considered to be conceptually confusing in places but able to make remarkably accurate predictions for single electron atoms. Bohr's predictions began to break down when applied to atoms with more than one electron, and some problems associated with spectral lines resisted solution. Also, although his ideas on atomic structure in the second and third papers were highly suggestive, many of the details were incorrect. He returned to atomic structure around 1920 and presented a consistent theory.

Bohr not only continued to contribute to many aspects of physics but also played a major role in educating the new generation of physicists who went on to develop quantum mechanics. Although well known to physicists, Bohr never became as well known to the public as Einstein. His trilogy represents only the first stage of a scientific career that spanned more than fifty years.

Bibliography

Bohr, Niels. *On the Constitution of Atoms and Molecules*. New York: W. A. Benjamin, 1963. Reprints Bohr's trilogy of papers. Includes a fifty-four-page introduction written by the physicist Leon Rosenfeld. Moderately technical, but an essential source for information about Bohr and the science of his day.

————————. "Reminiscences of the Founder of Nuclear Science and Some Developments Based on His Work." In *Rutherford at Manchester*, edited by J. B. Birks. London: Heywood, 1962. Presented at a meeting of the Physical Society of London. Gives Bohr's nontechnical version of how he developed his theory.

French, A. P., and P. J. Kennedy, eds. *Niels Bohr: A Centenary Volume*. Cambridge, Mass.: Harvard University Press, 1985. Discusses Bohr's early years in the second section of the book. Aims to interest the general public, professional physicists, and teachers of science.

Heilbron, John L., and Thomas Kuhn. "The Genesis of the Bohr Atom." *Historical Studies in the Physical Sciences* 1 (1969): 211-290. Attempts a plausible and comprehensive treatment of Bohr's route to the quantized atom. Critically synthesizes suggestions in the existing literature and elaborates some previously neglected strands in Bohr's scientific development. Moderately technical.

Moore, Ruth. *Niels Bohr: The Man, His Science, and the World They Changed*. New York: Alfred A. Knopf, 1966. While some of the interpretations of events in this book have been questioned by historians, it remains one of the most popular works on Bohr and his science.

Rozental, Stefan, ed. *Niels Bohr: His Life and Work as Seen by His Friends and Colleagues*. New York: John Wiley & Sons, 1967. Succeeds in its attempt to describe the scientific work of Niels Bohr so that it can be followed by the general public. Contains little directly related to Bohr's trilogy, yet it is useful because it conveys the depth of respect Bohr received from his fellow physicists.

Robert Sensenbaugh

Cross-References

Thomson Wins the Nobel Prize for the Discovery of the Electron (1906), p. 356; Thomson Confirms the Possibility of Isotopes (1910), p. 471; Rutherford Presents His Theory of the Atom (1912), p. 527.

ABEL DEVELOPS THE FIRST ARTIFICIAL KIDNEY

Category of event: Medicine
Time: 1912-1914
Locale: The Johns Hopkins University, Baltimore, Maryland

*Abel developed the technique that removed metabolic end-products and poisons
from the blood and allowed for the development of the artificial kidney*

Principal personages:

JOHN JACOB ABEL (1857-1938), an American pharmacologist and biochemist who is known as the "father of American pharmacology"
WILLEM JOHAN KOLFF (1911-   ), a Dutch-American clinician who
pioneered not only the artificial kidney but also the artificial heart
ALEXIS CARREL (1873-1944), a French surgeon and biologist whose development of microsurgical techniques has made possible modern
transplantation surgery

Summary of Event

The origins of the artificial kidney are found in the biochemical researches of
John Jacob Abel, the first professor of pharmacology at The Johns Hopkins University School of Medicine, and the clinical investigations of Willem Johan Kolff, a
Dutch physician. Abel, praised as the "father of American pharmacology," is the
prototype of the first generation of professional American scientists. To pursue a
career in physiological chemistry, Abel went to Europe where he worked in the
laboratories of several notable biochemists. Under their tutelage, he learned both the
theory and laboratory technique necessary to conduct independent biochemical research. He received his medical degree in Strasbourg in 1888. Soon after he returned to the United States in 1891, Victor Vaughn, his former chemistry professor
at Michigan, offered him a full-time instructorship in materia medica at the University of Michigan. When Abel moved to Johns Hopkins in 1893, he had not only
begun to earn a reputation for excellent research but also had incorporated German
pedagogical models into Michigan's medical education. His courses at Michigan and
The Johns Hopkins University in pharmacology were the first such courses offered
in the United States.

Around 1912, Abel began to investigate the metabolic by-products carried in the
blood. He noted that this work was difficult for it was nearly impossible to detect, let
alone study, the trace amounts of the many substances found therein. The theoretical
foundation in physical chemistry needed to solve this problem was readily available,
but no suitable technique or apparatus that could remove these substances from blood
had been devised. Abel recognized that a semipermeable membrane and a slightly
saline solution removed, by dialysis, these substances from the blood. Constructing
a dialysis machine occupied him and his colleagues, Leonard Rowntree and Benja-

min B. Turner for almost two years. Finally, their efforts were successful. Venous blood, to which hirudin, obtained from leeches, had been added to prevent clotting, flowed through a celloidin tube that had been wound loosely around a drum. The drum, immersed in a saline and dextrose solution, rotated slowly. As blood flowed through the immersed tubing, osmotic pressure removed urea and other substances, but not the plasma or cells, from the blood. The membranes allowed oxygen to pass from the solution into the blood; therefore, purified, oxygenated blood flowed back into the arteries. The first tests were performed on rabbits and dogs. The isolated substances were studied, and Abel discovered that not only was urea passed out but also free amino acids. Abel termed this process "vividiffusion." Although he experimented on rabbits and dogs only, Abel quickly realized the clinical implications of his discovery. He wrote that "in the hope of providing a substitute in such emergencies, which might tide over a dangerous crisis, as well as for the important information which it might be expected to provide, concerning the substances normally present in the blood, . . . a method has been devised by which the blood of a living animal may be submitted to dialysis outside the body, and again returned to the natural circulation." The removal of large quantities of urea and other poisonous substances occurred in a relatively short time, therefore indicating that vividiffusion could serve as an artificial kidney during cases of renal failure. Abel's physiological research necessitated removing, studying, and replacing without hemolysis (breaking of red blood cells) large amounts of blood from living animals. He noted that this process, which he termed "plasmaphaeresis," could create blood banks for the storage of blood.

In 1914, Abel published these two discoveries in a series of three articles in the *Journal of Pharmacology and Applied Therapeutics* and demonstrated the techniques in London and Groningen. Although he had suggested clinical applications for them, his interest remained primarily biochemical. Abel turned to other pharmacological pursuits, such as the crystallization of insulin, and never returned to the research possibilities which inhered in vividiffusion.

Georg Haas, a German biochemist working at Giessen, independently became interested in dialysis and in 1915 began to experiment on "blood washing." After reviewing Abel's 1914 paper, Haas substituted collodium for Abel's celloidin, and commercially prepared heparin for Abel's homemade hirudin. He used this machine on a patient and found his results promising, but noted that many technical details had to be resolved before the procedure could be applied generally in cases of renal failure.

In 1937, Kolff was a young physician at Groningen. In his account of the manufacture of the artificial kidney, he recounted his pain at seeing patients die from renal failure and added that the emotion stimulated him to search for some cure or relief. After hearing physicians discuss the possibility of dialysis on human patients, he decided to build such a machine. Kolff knew that cellophane was an excellent dialyzing membrane and that heparin was a good anticoagulant but admitted that Abel's and Haas's machines had insufficient capacity to be clinically useful. There was no theoretical barrier to constructing such a machine, which he did, but he never used it clinically. During World War II, aided by the director of the local enamel factory, Kolff constructed an artificial kidney that received its first clinical trial on March 17, 1943. Between March, 1943, and July 21, 1944, Kolff used his secretly constructed dialysis machines on fifteen patients—of which only one survived—and published his results in *Acta Medica Scandinavica*. He had collected enough data and had refined the technique, however, that by war's end, he was confident that renal dialysis was a viable therapeutic measure. He brought machines to Amsterdam and The Hague and encouraged other physicians to employ them. He continued to study hemodialysis and improve his machines. This work was successful, and in 1947 he brought improved machines to London and the United States. By the time he reached Boston, however, he had donated all of his machines. Empty-handed, therefore, he explained the technique to John P. Merrill, a physician at the Harvard Medical School, who soon became the leading American developer of renal dialysis and transplantation surgery.

Nils Alwall, of the Medical Clinic of Lund, Sweden, also developed an artificial kidney during World War II. He had no knowledge of Kolff's machine. His design differed in that it was smaller and had fewer moving parts. Also, G. Murray of Canada independently developed a dialyzer, but as these were used after 1945, Kolff's claim remains unchallenged. Kolff later emigrated to the United States, where he became an expert not only in artificial kidneys but also in artificial hearts and contributed to the development of the Jarvik-7 artificial heart, which was implanted in 1982.

Impact of Event

Abel's work not only divulged the existence of previously unknown substances in the blood and inspired the development of the artificial kidney but also spurred interest in the possibility of organ transplantation, created new questions in immunology, and raised ethical issues about the allocation of scarce resources. The development of kidney transplantations depended upon Kolff's artificial kidney. In 1902, Alexis Carrel, a French surgeon, developed the microsurgical techniques that made transplantation surgery possible. Five years later at the Rockefeller Institute, Carrel and Charles Guthrie transplanted a dog's kidney from its normal position to the neck. The kidney functioned normally, which demonstrated that renal function depended upon circulation only and not upon the nervous connections to the organ. Along with Charles Lindbergh, Carrel in the 1930's developed perfusion techniques for whole organs, not merely cells or tissues. This information is used now in cardiovascular surgery. In 1936, they developed a version of an artificial heart.

After World War II, surgeons attempted to transplant kidneys from one animal to another, but after a few days, the recipient began to reject the kidney and die. Despite these several discouraging failures, researchers in Europe and America transplanted kidneys in several patients to devise methods to combat the physiological and clinical difficulties encountered in such operations. These surgeons used artificial kidneys to sustain patients who were waiting for a transplant or to maintain them until the transplanted kidney began to function. In 1954, John P. Merrill of Boston's Peter Bent Brigham Hospital—to whom Kolff had demonstrated an artificial kidney—successfully transplanted kidneys in identical twins. The discovery in 1962 of immunosuppressant drugs made transplantation surgery more feasible and widened the range of possible donors.

After the widespread acceptance of kidney transplants, the artificial kidney became a stopgap measure only until a permanent solution—that is, a donated kidney—appeared. The machinery was cumbersome and significantly altered the patient's quality of life. The problem, however, is that the demand for organs is greater than its supply. Hospital administrators, physicians, and medical ethicists grapple with the difficult moral dilemma of how to allocate the scarce resources among individuals who need them so desperately.

There is a mutual stimulation and exchange between immunologists and transplant surgeons. Modern transplantation became possible only after Peter Medawar's discovery in the 1940's of the mechanics of immune rejection. Thomas Starzl, who worked at the University of Colorado in the 1960's, could not have begun his extensive series of transplantations without the presence of several immunosuppressant drugs. The surgeons' clinical application of these drugs, in turn, provides information that immunologists apply to such diverse fields as the struggle against AIDS (acquired immune deficiency syndrome).

Bibliography

Abel, John J., L. G. Rowntree, and B. B. Turner. "On the Removal of Diffusable Substances from the Circulating Blood of Living Animals by Dialysis." *Journal of Pharmacology and Applied Therapeutics* 5 (1914): 275-316. This is the article in which Abel announced his discovery. Although this article is difficult to locate, it is worth the effort to read it as an example of one of the clearest examples of scientific writing. Abel's clarity and elegance of experimental technique is mirrored in his prose.

Harvey, A. McGehee, Gert Brieger, Susan L. Abrams, and Victor McKusick. *A Model of Its Kind*. Vol. 1, *A Centennial History of Medicine at Johns Hopkins*. Baltimore: The Johns Hopkins University Press, 1989. A general history of The Johns Hopkins University School of Medicine that places Abel in his institutional context. Volume 2, a pictorial companion to Volume 1, contains illustrations of Abel's vividiffusion apparatus.

Kolff, Willem J. *Artificial Organs*. New York: John Wiley & Sons, 1976. An account of the medical and technical issues in the development and use of artificial kidneys and hearts. Contains no historical information.

_____. "First Clinical Experience with the Artificial Kidney." *Annals of Internal Medicine* 62 (1965): 608-619. Kolff provides an account of how he overcame various difficulties to develop the artificial kidney.

Parascandola, John. "John J. Abel and the Early Development of Pharmacology at

The Johns Hopkins University." *Bulletin of the History of Medicine* 56 (1982): 512-527. An examination of Abel's role in the separation of pharmacology from pharmacy and the establishment of professional pharmacology in the United States in the first two decades of the twentieth century.

Wilson, Leonard. "The Development of Organ Transplantation at Minnesota." In *Medical Revolution in Minnesota: A History of the University of Minnesota Medical School*. St. Paul, Minn.: Midewiwin Press, 1989. Surgeons at the University of Minnesota Medical School pioneered heart transplantation surgery. Wilson provides the background to such surgery, notably the development of kidney transplantations.

Thomas P. Gariepy

Cross-References

Landsteiner Discovers Human Blood Groups (1900), p. 56; Carrel Develops a Technique for Rejoining Severed Blood Vessels (1902), p. 134; Crile Performs the First Direct Blood Transfusion (1905), p. 275; De Vries Implants the First Jarvik-7 Artificial Heart (1982), p. 2195.

X-RAY CRYSTALLOGRAPHY IS
DEVELOPED BY THE BRAGGS

Categories of event: Physics, chemistry, and earth science
Time: 1912-1915
Locale: Cavendish Laboratory, Cambridge, England

The Braggs founded the science of X-ray crystallography, verified the very short wavelength nature of X radiation, developed spectrometers for measuring X-ray wavelengths, and deduced crystal structures of many substances

Principal personages:

SIR LAWRENCE BRAGG (1890-1971), the son of William Henry Bragg and cowinner of the 1915 Nobel Prize in Physics for the analysis of crystal structures by means of X rays; credited as the originator of the Bragg equation

SIR WILLIAM HENRY BRAGG (1862-1942), an English mathematician and physicist who became a renowned authority on particle radiation and X rays

MAX VON LAUE (1879-1960), a German physicist who was awarded the 1914 Nobel Prize in Physics for his discovery of the diffraction of X rays by crystals

WILHELM CONRAD RÖNTGEN (1845-1923), the German physicist who discovered X rays in 1895 and received the 1901 Nobel Prize in Physics for this discovery

RENÉ-JUST HAÜY (1743-1822), the French mathematician and mineralogist who argued on the basis of geometry that crystal faces are derived from the repetitive stacking of tiny cubes

AUGUSTE BRAVAIS (1811-1863), a French physicist who showed that all three-dimensional structures that arise from regularly spaced points can be reduced to fourteen three-dimensional arrangements

Summary of Event

The development of X-ray crystallography helped to answer two major questions of science: What are X rays? and What are crystals? It gave birth to a new technology for the identification and classification of crystalline substances. Shortly after the discovery of X rays by Wilhelm Conrad Röntgen, X rays were put to a variety of uses, particularly in medicine. Yet, the true nature of X rays eluded researchers. Some proclaimed X rays as a form of energy that traveled in waves. The wave theory that portrayed radiation as a series of sinusoidal waves already had proved very useful in deducing the nature of light. It was recognized that any radiation in wave form could persist as a ray only as long as the waves moved "in phase." That meant that the peaks and troughs of each wave had to oscillate together in harmony with those of adjacent waves as they moved through space. If adjacent waves did not oscillate in harmony, peaks and troughs collided, interfered with one another, immediately canceled one another's existence, and destroyed any ray.

Diffraction occurred when a light ray encountered a well-polished surface that had been etched precisely with a series of closely, evenly spaced lines, usually several thousand lines per centimeter. A surface so prepared was called a grating. After the light struck the grating, some waves left the surface "in phase" and continued onward as reflected light. Because of the fine etches, some adjacent waves had to follow slightly different path distances and thus, upon reflection, emerged "out of phase" and were terminated immediately. The selective reflection of only those waves that emerged in-phase was termed "diffraction." If one knew the spacing between the etch lines and the angle of reflection of the light, then it was possible to calculate the wavelength of the diffracted light. The phenomenon of diffraction was used to measure the wavelengths that corresponded to the various colors within visible light. Nevertheless, attempts to diffract X rays from gratings failed. This led others to proclaim that X rays were not wave forms but instead were composed of tiny "corpuscles" of high-energy matter that were able to penetrate opaque materials.

From studies of large, natural crystals, chemists and geologists had established the elements of symmetry through which one could classify, describe, and distinguish various crystal shapes. René-Just Haüy, about a century before, demonstrated that diverse shapes of crystals could be produced by repetitive stacking of tiny solid cubes. Auguste Bravais later showed, through mathematics, that all crystal forms could be built from a repetitive stacking of merely a few (fourteen) three-dimensional arrangements of points (lattice points) into "space lattices," but no one had ever proved that actual matter was arranged in space lattices. Indeed, at the times of Haüy and Bravais, the model of the atom had not been derived and, hence, even the nature of the substance contended to be present at the points that defined a space lattice was conjectural. They did not know if the tiny building blocks modeled by space lattices actually were solid matter throughout, like Haüy's cubes, or if they were the basic building blocks of crystals (mostly empty space with the only solid matter located at the lattice points described by Bravais). With the disclosure of the atomic model of Danish physicist Niels Bohr in 1913, the deduction of the nature of the building blocks of crystals had special implications. If crystal structure could be shown to consist of atoms at lattice points, then the Bohr model was supported and science then could abandon the theory of totally solid matter.

In 1912, Max von Laue first used X rays to study crystalline matter. German physicist Wilhelm Wien had estimated, based on the new quantum theory, that X rays could have wavelengths between 10^{-10} and 10^{-9} centimeters. Laue recognized that failed attempts to achieve diffraction of X rays might have resulted because no manmade grating had lines spaced finely enough to cause diffraction of such short wavelengths. Based on his knowledge of the contemporary theory about atoms and crystals, Laue recognized that the interatomic distances in crystals should be small enough to allow the crystal to function like a diffraction grating for a spectrum of appropriately short wavelengths. When Laue and coworkers Walter Friedrich and Paul Knipping passed a beam of X rays through a crystal of copper sulfate to a film, the film revealed darkening at selected spots that could be caused only by diffraction and in a pattern exemplary of the symmetry expected from space lattices. The experiment confirmed in one stroke that crystals were not solid and that their matter consisted of atoms occupying lattice sites with substantial space in between them. Further, the atomic arrangements of crystals could serve as diffraction gratings. Laue received the 1914 Nobel Prize in Physics for discovery of the diffraction of X rays in crystals, but the conclusion that X rays actually were being diffracted was accepted as a near certainty rather than proved. Sir William Henry Bragg contributed the final proof by passing one of the diffracted beams through a gas and achieved ionization of the gas in accordance with that expected from true X rays. He also used the spectrometer he built for this purpose to detect and measure specific wavelengths of X rays and to note which orientations of crystals produced the strongest reflections. While he noted that X rays, like visible light, occupy a definite part of the electromagnetic spectrum and demonstrated that different elements give off characteristic spectra of specific wavelengths, the deduction of specific spectra for each element in the periodic table was developed in detail by Henry Moseley in 1913 and 1914 and by Charles Glover Barkla from 1906 through 1916. The majority of Bragg's work, which led to the 1915 Nobel Prize in Physics, shared with his son, Lawrence, focused on actually using X rays to deduce crystal structures.

Laue documented the general nature of crystal structures, but he was unable to deduce specific details. This resulted from the fact that he transmitted his X-ray beam through the crystal, and his resulting photographic spot images could be interpreted in detail for only the simplest of crystals and then only through very cumbersome mathematics. Sir Lawrence Bragg circumvented the complexities of the interpretation by "reflecting" beams from crystals. He postulated that if the lattice models of Bravais applied to actual crystals, then a crystal structure could be thought of simply as constructed of atoms arranged in a pattern consisting of a few sets of regularly spaced parallel, flat planes. Lawrence Bragg knew from Laue's work that X rays, like visible light, behaved in accordance with wave theory. He reasoned that when X rays entered a crystal, some adjacent waves must be reflected from the regularly spaced atoms lying along the surface plane and some would travel farther to be reflected from atoms in underlying parallel planes. In order to achieve diffraction, the adjacent waves—even though they traversed two different but parallel paths—would have to leave the surface plane in-phase. The distance between the planes and the angle of incidence of the X-ray beam determined the extra distance (path difference) that a beam reflected from a lower plane would have to traverse in comparison to a beam reflected from an upper plane. In order for both reflected X-ray beams to emerge from the crystal in-phase, this path difference had to equal exactly one incident X-ray wavelength or a whole number (integral) multiple of that wavelength. If not, then waves and troughs of adjacent beams would interfere when they rejoined above the upper plane, and no reflected beam composed of out-of-phase waves could persist. The "Bragg equation," developed by Lawrence Bragg in 1912, is the mathematical expression that states that diffraction occurs only where the path difference equals an integral number of the X-ray wavelength. The theory proved valid in experiment, and diffraction from planes became the basis through which Lawrence Bragg and his father deduced the detailed structures of many crystals. Based on these results, they built three-dimensional scale models out of wire and spheres that allowed the nature of crystal structures to be visualized clearly even by nonscientists. Their compiled results were published in a book, *X-Rays and Crystal Structure* (1915), which brought them the 1915 Nobel Prize in Physics. Because of World War I, they were unable to travel to receive it. The 1915 Nobel lecture, delivered by Lawrence, was not given until 1922.

Impact of Event

The Braggs founded an entirely new discipline, X-ray crystallography, that continues to grow in scope and application. Of particular importance was the early discovery that atoms, rather than molecules, determine the nature of crystals. X-ray spectrometers of the type developed by the Braggs were used by other scientists to gain insights into the nature of the atom, particularly the innermost electron shells. The tool allowed timely validation of some of Bohr's major concepts about the atom.

X-ray diffraction became a cornerstone of the science of mineralogy. The Braggs, chemists such as Linus Pauling, and a number of mineralogists used the tool and did the pioneering work in deducing the structures of all major mineral groups. Huge reference indexes of X-ray "powder patterns" were compiled by organizations such as the American Society for Testing Materials (ASTM), and X-ray diffraction became the primary definitive method for identification of crystalline materials, including about two thousand naturally occurring minerals and many times that number of man-made inorganic and organic compounds. Mineralogists who relied primarily on optical methods prior to the Bragg's work were able to go beyond physical properties and laborious reflected-light microscopy to identify and characterize opaque minerals. Clay mineral species, because of their occurrence in small particles, defied discovery and identification under the polarizing microscope. The contribution by the Braggs permitted development of the discipline of clay mineralogy through which many properties of soils and sedimentary rocks could be explained on the basis of the clay minerals contained within them.

Metallurgy progressed from a technology to a science as metallurgists became able, for the first time, to deduce the structural order of various alloys at the atomic level. Diffracted X rays were applied in the field of biology, particularly at the Cavendish Laboratory under the direction of Lawrence Bragg. The tool proved essential for deducing the structures of hemoglobin, proteins, viruses, and eventually the double-helix structure of DNA (deoxyribonucleic acid).

Bibliography

Bragg, William H. *X-Rays and Crystal Structure*. Vol. 7 in *Physical Sciences*, edited by W. L. Bragg and G. Porter. Amsterdam: Elsevier, 1970. This volume is a compilation of papers given from 1909 through 1915. The one cited here by William Henry Bragg was given in 1914. It is a very readable, nontechnical report that shows clearly the progress at the time the Braggs were doing the work that would lead to their Nobel Prize.

Bragg, W. L. *Atomic Structure of Minerals*. Ithaca, N.Y.: Cornell University Press, 1937. This book was written when Lawrence Bragg was a visiting professor at Cornell University in 1934. It is a reference book on minerals arranged according to chemical groups. It is well illustrated and has many citations that show the extensive contributions to mineralogy from the Braggs and scientists such as Linus Pauling, W. H. Taylor, and R. W. Wyckoff.

Crowther, J. G. *The Cavendish Laboratory, 1874-1974*. New York: Science History Publications, 1974. Lawrence Bragg accepted the directorship of the National Physical Laboratory in 1937 when it was vacated because of the unexpected death of Ernest Rutherford; he remained at Cavendish until 1953. Provides a wealth of information about the Braggs' use of X-ray diffraction and about the subsequent use by other researchers.

Nobelstiftelsen. *Physics*. Vol. 1. New York: Elsevier, 1964. The compilations in this volume are all in English, and these lectures delivered by Nobel laureates are more readable than their works in technical journals. The presentation speech to Röntgen and the lectures by von Laue, Lawrence Bragg, and Barkla in this volume are particularly pertinent to the topic of X-ray diffraction. Although the Braggs shared the Nobel Prize in 1915, only Lawrence Bragg provided a Nobel lecture.

Zoltai, Tibor, and James H. Stout. *Mineralogy: Concepts and Principles*. Minneapolis: Burgess, 1984. This textbook, intended for undergraduate students of mineralogy, provides a resource for the reader wishing rigorous technical explanations of the X-ray study of crystals. It contains all necessary background in crystallography and crystal chemistry in chapters 2 through 8. Chapter 10 shows derivation of the Bragg equation and provides a very solid and very thorough introduction to X-ray crystallography.

Edward B. Nuhfer

Cross-References

Röntgen Wins the Nobel Prize for the Discovery of X Rays (1901), p. 118; Barkla Discovers the Characteristic X Rays of the Elements (1906), p. 309; Geiger and Rutherford Develop the Geiger Counter (1908), p. 412; Bohr Writes a Trilogy on Atomic and Molecular Structure (1912), p. 507; Watson and Crick Develop the Double-Helix Model for DNA (1951), p. 1406.

WEGENER PROPOSES THE
THEORY OF CONTINENTAL DRIFT

Category of event: Earth science
Time: January, 1912
Locale: Frankfurt, Germany

Wegener proposed that all lands were once part of the supercontinent of Pangaea, which then fragmented and whose pieces drifted apart to form present-day continents

Principal personages:
ALFRED LOTHAR WEGENER (1880-1930), a German meteorologist and earth scientist who proposed the theory of continental drift
FRANK BURSLEY TAYLOR (1860-1938), an American student of geology and astronomy who independently formulated the concept of continental drift
ALEXANDER LOGIE DU TOIT (1878-1948), a South African geologist who provided strong support for Wegener's theory
ARTHUR HOLMES (1890-1965), a British geologist who formulated concepts to explain the mechanism of continental drift
HARRY HAMMOND HESS (1906-1969), an American geologist who formulated the concept of seafloor spreading

Summary of Event

The concept of continental drift was developed, at least in part, to explain the striking parallelism between the Atlantic coasts, which seem as though they could fit together as pieces of a giant jigsaw puzzle. In particular, the fit between the eastern coast of South America and the western coast of Africa is very striking. The idea that continents were once joined together as part of a single landmass predates Wegener's treatise. As early as 1620, Sir Francis Bacon had discussed the possibility that the Western Hemisphere had once been joined to Africa and Europe. In 1668, P. Placet expressed similar ideas. Antonio Snider-Pellegrini in his book *La Création et ses mystères dévoilés* (1859; creation and its mysteries revealed) recognized the similarities between American and European fossil plants of the Carboniferous period (about 300 million years ago) and proposed that all continents were once part of a single landmass. By the end of the nineteenth century, Austrian geologist Eduard Suess had noticed the close correspondence between geological formations in the lands of the Southern Hemisphere and had fitted them together into a single landmass he termed "Gondwanaland." In 1908, Frank Bursley Taylor of the United States, and in 1910, Alfred Lothar Wegener of Germany independently suggested mechanisms that could account for large, lateral displacements of the earth's crust and, therefore, how continents could be driven apart. Wegener's work became the center of the debate that has lasted until the present.

The concept of continental drift was best expressed by Wegener in his book *Die Entstehung der Kontinente und Ozeane* (1912; *The Origin of Continents and Oceans*, 1924). He based the theory not only on the shape of the continents but also on geologic evidence found around the world. Wegener specifically cited similarities in fossil fauna and flora (extinct animals and plants) found in Brazil and Africa. A series of maps were developed to show three stages in the drift process, and the original supercontinent was named "Pangaea" (a word meaning "all lands"). Wegener believed that the continents, composed of light-density granitic rocks, were independently propelled and plowed through the denser basalts of the ocean floor driven by forces related to the rotation of the earth. He provided evidence based on detailed correlations of geological features and fossils indicating a common historical record on both sides of the Atlantic. He also proposed that the supercontinent of Pangaea existed before the beginning of the Mesozoic era (about 200 million years ago). The split of Pangaea was visualized as beginning during the Jurassic period (about 190 million years ago) with the southern continents moving westward and toward the equator. South America and Africa began to drift apart during the Cretaceous period (70 million years ago). The opening of the north Atlantic was accomplished during the Pleistocene epoch (approximately 2.5 million years ago). Greenland and Norway started to separate as recently as 1.5 million years ago. The Indian peninsula drifted northward, colliding with the Asian continent and giving rise to the folded mountains of the Himalayas. Similarly, the European Alps and the Atlas Mountains of North Africa were explained as a westward extension of the Himalayan Chain. Wegener also suggested that as the drifting continents met the resistance of the ocean floor, their leading edges were compressed and folded into mountains. In this way, he also explained the Western Cordillera of the Americas and the mountains of New Zealand and New Guinea. The tapering ends of Greenland and South America and the island arcs of the Antilles and East Asia were visualized as stragglers trailing behind the moving continents. Periods of glaciation found in the southern part of South America, Africa, Australia, peninsular India, and Madagascar provided further evidence of drift.

Detailed studies by the South African geologist Alexander Logie Du Toit provided strong support to Wegener's concepts. Du Toit postulated two continental masses rather than the single entity of Pangaea. He visualized the northern supercontinent of Laurasia and its southern counterpart Gondwanaland separated by a seaway called Tethys. Du Toit was also the first to propose that the continental masses of the Southern Hemisphere had moved relative to the position of the South Pole. His ideas were published in *Our Wandering Continents* (1937), a book he dedicated to Wegener. Both Wegener and Du Toit utilized four main lines of evidence to support continental drift: the geometric shape of the continents, matching rock types and geologic structures, fossil evidence, and paleoclimatological evidence (evidence based on ancient patterns of climate). It was the latter that led to the early conclusion that the geographic poles had shifted relative to the position of the continents through time. This "polar wandering" could best be explained by continental masses drifting over the fixed poles.

Continental drift was debated among earth scientists of the Southern Hemisphere and the leaders of geophysical thought of the Northern and Western Hemispheres. The eminent geophysicist Sir Harold Jeffreys of the University of Cambridge voiced opposition to the drift concept based on the concept that the earth's crust and underlying mantle were too rigid to permit such large motions. Although Wegener and Du Toit had provided compelling evidence in favor of the drift theory, one monumental problem remained: What forces could be strong enough to rupture, fragment, and cause the continents to drift? It was precisely this question that resulted in the decrease in popularity of continental drift until its rebirth in the 1960's as the new seafloor spreading and plate tectonics. Wegener had visualized the continents as being raised above the seafloor on a spinning, spheroidal earth and argued that the continents had been propelled toward the equator. Drift was explained as the result of gravitational attraction between the continents and the equatorial bulge, resulting in the movement away from the poles toward the equator. A westward drift was explained as resulting from the differential attraction of the Moon and the Sun on the continents, causing them to lag behind the rotation of the earth. Although the forces proposed by Wegener (and also by Taylor) are known to exist, they are minuscule and no one has considered them seriously as the mechanism capable of rupturing and moving continents. It was Du Toit who first proposed the idea that continents could slide over the mantle under the action of gravity (a concept presently used by some workers in defense of plate tectonics), but Arthur Holmes of the University of Edinburgh was the originator of the now popular concept of thermal convection in the earth's mantle as the main cause of drift. Holmes's model, published in 1931, is very similar to those presently used in the widely accepted theory of plate tectonics. Holmes was also the first to introduce the idea that the continents themselves do not play an active role in the drift, but act as passive members being carried along by a moving mantle in sort of a conveyor-belt motion.

Although appealing, Wegener's theory of continental drift remained controversial and was not widely accepted until Harry Hammond Hess and Robert Sinclair Dietz introduced the theory of seafloor spreading in the early 1960's.

Impact of Event

Wegener's theory of continental drift, first introduced during the second decade of the twentieth century, remains one of the most fascinating, inspiring, and controversial topics in the field of earth science. The drift theory polarized the scientific community and became the center of a heated debate until its rebirth during the second half of the century, when the concepts of seafloor spreading and plate tectonics were developed. Most earth scientists in the United States and around the globe subscribe to the theory of plate tectonics, a modern version of Wegener's continental drift.

Although continental drift was supported by a variety of geological evidence, a poor understanding of the nature of the oceanic crust prevented the development of a complete theory of earth dynamics until the 1960's. It was then that the topography of the ocean floor was mapped and magnetic and seismic characteristics established. In plate tectonics, the crust and uppermost upper mantle constitute what is now known as the lithosphere. The lithosphere lies above a soft, plastic (or ductile) zone in the mantle known as the asthenosphere. Thermal convection within the asthenosphere provides the mechanism for splitting the rigid lithosphere into distinct plates and propelling them into motion. The lithospheric plates are bounded by ocean ridges, ocean trenches, and major faults. At the ocean ridges, plates move apart where the convecting mantle rises and spreads laterally. It is at these divergent boundaries that a new ocean floor is generated. The moving plates converge at the site of oceanic trenches, where the basaltic (oceanic) lithosphere descends into the mantle under the lighter-density, granitic (continental) lithosphere. In those regions where two lithospheric plates move past each other, large transform fault boundaries are generated.

Plate tectonics provides an appealing explanation for zones of earthquakes, active volcanism, and mountain building. These events take place along plate boundaries, where they either diverge, collide, or move relative to each other. The theory has gained wide acceptance among earth scientists worldwide. Its concepts are deeply rooted on Wegener's original ideas of continental drift. The new theory provides answers to many of the critical questions of global tectonics. Yet, as commonly occurs in science, new questions and problems continue to arise. Just as in Wegener's time, notable and respected workers have voiced opposition to the new theory. Among these are V. V. Belousov of the Soviet Union and Arthur Augustus Meyerhoff of the United States. These workers provide well-founded and thought-provoking arguments against the new theory but fail to provide a theory of global tectonics as well integrated as plate tectonics.

Continental drift and its modification into the concepts of seafloor spreading and plate tectonics remains as one of the most significant theories in earth science. Although not devoid of problems, it is the most complete theory of global tectonics in existence. It is definitely a tribute to Wegener's vision, his dedication, and the courage of his convictions.

Bibliography

Du Toit, Alexander Logie. *Our Wandering Continents*. New York: Hafner, 1937. Du Toit provides strong support to Wegener's ideas on continental drift and advances important concepts that have gained acceptance in the theory of plate tectonics.

Taylor, Frank Bursley. "Bearing of the Tertiary Mountain Belt on the Origin of the Earth's Plan." *Geological Society of America* 21 (1910): 179-226. This article constitutes a classic reference, since it outlines the concept of continental drift developed by Taylor independently, but time-concurrent with Wegener's treatise.

Wegener, Alfred Lothar. *The Origin of Continents and Oceans*. Translated by J. G. A. Skerl. New York: E. P. Dutton, 1924. This is the original treatise on continental drift, a monumental and revolutionary contribution to the field of earth science, and a key reference that enhances the understanding of global tectonics.

Wilson, J. Tuzo. "A Revolution in Earth Science." *Geotimes* 13 (December, 1968): 10-16. In this excellent article, Wilson summarizes the importance of continental drift, seafloor spreading, and plate tectonics. The theory's impact on Charles Darwin's contribution to biology and major and revolutionary advances in other sciences are compared also.

Wyllie, Peter J. *The Dynamic Earth: Textbook in Geosciences*. New York: John Wiley & Sons, 1971. This outstanding reference contains separate chapters on continental drift, seafloor spreading, and plate tectonics. It also provides a comprehensive discussion of the evolution of geologic thought and an understanding of the earth's tectonic framework.

Robert G. Font

Cross-References

Lehmann Discovers the Earth's Inner Core (1936), p. 1065; Hess Concludes the Debate on Continental Drift (1960), p. 1650.

RUTHERFORD PRESENTS HIS THEORY OF THE ATOM

Category of event: Physics
Time: March 7, 1912
Locale: Manchester, England

Rutherford discovered the nucleus of the atom from experiments with radioactive elements and in the process deduced the true nature of the atom

> *Principal personages:*
> ERNEST RUTHERFORD (1871-1937), an English physicist who discovered that the atom consists of a dense nucleus surrounded by "orbiting" electrons; winner of the 1908 Nobel Prize in Chemistry
> SIR JOSEPH JOHN THOMSON (1856-1940), an English physicist who discovered the electron and won the 1906 Nobel Prize in Physics
> HANS GEIGER (1882-1945), a German physicist who was Rutherford's laboratory assistant and who became a leading figure in the study of radioactive elements
> ERNEST MARSDEN, a student of Rutherford who acted as his primary assistant in the investigation that led to the discovery of the atomic nucleus
> NIELS BOHR (1885-1962), a Danish physicist who developed the modern science of quantum mechanics and a more refined view of the atom; winner of the 1922 Nobel Prize in Physics

Summary of Event

By 1909, Ernest Rutherford had been engaged in a decade-long study of the nature of radioactive particles. He had suspected that they were actually pieces of atoms themselves. This belief was radical in 1909, if not altogether heretical. Not everyone was convinced that the atom existed at all, much less that it was composed of pieces even smaller. The models of the atom that existed by the beginning of the twentieth century were little more than ideology. There was very little hard science to support any of the theories.

Important studies were being conducted, and the study of newly discovered radioactivity was providing some of the best opportunities to look into the nature of the infinitesimally small atom, but it was elusive, at best. In 1909, the atom could not be revealed directly, so if there were to be any discovery concerning its nature, it would be indirect. If any theory on the atom were to be accepted, it would have to be convincing, clever, clear, and backed up by experimental confirmation.

Up until the beginning of the twentieth century, nearly all atomic theory had come straight from philosophers. The early Greeks conjectured that one could divide matter no smaller than tiny particles they called *atomos*, meaning indivisible. In English, *atomos* became "atom." Atomic theory was made more or less respectable by

Robert Boyle in the seventeenth century, but it was still philosophy without hard scientific evidence.

On April 29, 1897, atomic science was transformed from philosophy to hard science. That evening, Sir Joseph John Thomson announced he had discovered tiny subatomic particles, which he called corpuscles, which were much smaller than the atom. (They were later renamed electrons.) At once, the confirmation was made not only that atoms existed but also that they were probably made up of even smaller particles.

In 1907, Rutherford accepted a position at Manchester, England. His experiments concerning the particles that appeared to emanate from the radioactive atom had been narrowed to a series of experiments that he hoped would finally identify them and their nature. Assisting him were Hans Geiger and an undergraduate student named Ernest Marsden.

Enough data from Thomson's work had filtered in so that Rutherford and his assistants knew that the electron was a piece of the atom and that it was both considerably lighter and smaller than the whole atom. They also knew its charge was negative, so that whatever was left of the atom had to be much heavier and have a net positive charge. On the other hand, the particles that were emitted by the radioactive material Rutherford was examining were much heavier than the electrons, but still smaller than a whole atom. The question that perplexed Rutherford was whether, like the electron, these were also a part of the atom.

Thomson had invented his own theoretical model of the atom from what he knew of the nature of the electron. According to Thomson's theory, the atom was made up of a positively charged fluidized interior of great volume, compared with the tiny negatively charged electron enclosed in the fluid. Thomson described the aggregate as similar to "plum pudding."

The experimental apparatus that Rutherford had set up was quite simple, compared with the multimillion-dollar devices used by physicists a century later. It consisted of a glass tube that held an alpha particle emitter at one end. At the other end was a target of gold foil and beyond that a fluorescent screen that acted as the detector.

The theory behind Rutherford's experiment was that the alpha particle would race down the tube from its source and strike the atoms in the gold foil. If the atom were made up of Thomson's "plum pudding," then as the massive alpha particle struck the electrons, it would not be deflected at all or only slightly. The alpha particle strikes on the fluorescent screen would, therefore, appear dead center or deflected only slightly to one or the other side of the center. By measuring where the tiny blips of light struck off dead center, Rutherford could calculate the angle of deflection from the target and indirectly determine the mass of whatever the alpha particle had struck on its way down the tube.

Rutherford unknowingly predated the identical technique used decades later in the invention and development of particle accelerators, giant atom smashers that would use pieces of atoms to probe into the interior of others. Rutherford was using a natural accelerator to accomplish essentially the same thing: the radioactive atom. He reasoned that the deflections of the more massive alpha particles striking tiny electrons would be minimal, but that if, by the most bizarre of circumstances, should one encounter a series of electrons on its way through the atom, the deflection might register as much as 45 degrees.

The experiments began in 1910 with Geiger assisting Marsden, counting the almost invisible flashes of light on the fluorescent screen through a magnifying lens in a completely blackened laboratory. They immediately found an astonishing effect. One out of about eight thousand alpha particles was deflected at an angle, varying from greater than 45 to 180 degrees.

Rutherford withdrew to ponder the meaning of the results. It was obvious to him that plum pudding could never account for such wild diversions, even in the few deflections he had observed. He considered that perhaps the nucleus held a charge vastly greater than any hypothesized and that the alpha particle was being whipped around the interior of the atom like a comet tossed back into the deep solar system by the sun. The only other plausible explanation was that the core of the atom was extremely dense and extremely small when compared with the total size of the atom itself; he could deduce the size from the relatively low number of deflections and the density by the degree of deflections.

Thomson was the most famous physicist of his day, and his theory of a fluidized nucleus had received relatively widespread acceptance. As Rutherford pondered what looked more and more like the final picture of the atomic structure, he began to doubt Thomson's theory. Rutherford had worked with Thomson in the Cavendish laboratories at the University of Cambridge prior to his position at Manchester. He did not want to criticize his mentor. Despite his clamorous exterior, Rutherford was quietly insecure about his mathematical prowess and ability to extrapolate from his findings in a public debate against Thomson. Fate decided the outcome, as Rutherford was able to critique the work of another, less famous colleague, J. A. Crowther, who had performed an experiment that Crowther said had confirmed Thomson's fluidized nucleus. On March 7, 1912, Rutherford presented his theory at the Manchester Literary and Philosophical Society, attacking the work of Crowther. In the process, he also criticized the fluidized nucleus theory.

Rutherford said that the atom was composed of a tiny, pinpoint nucleus that occupied only a minuscule portion of the total volume of the atom, but, at the same time, contained nearly all of its mass. The electrons, he said, orbited like tiny, flyweight particles at huge distances from the densely packed core.

It was an elegant but fundamentally flawed notion. Rutherford had the correct idea of the nucleus. It is minuscule. At the same time, electrons do exist at a great distance, but they do not "orbit" in the classical sense; they "exist" in a quantum state that a student of Rutherford, Niels Bohr, would clarify. In the process, Bohr would change the face of physics. Rutherford's discovery would be the last major finding of classical physics. By 1913, Rutherford's vision would be supplanted by Bohr's quantum view.

Impact of Event

From the time of classical Greece, man had viewed matter as made up of tiny, indivisible particles. The notion was nothing more than an ideological guess. It held through the millennia not because of its inherent accuracy but because of the lack of technology to prove otherwise. This idea became so firmly implanted that it became a kind of theology of reason without implicit cause.

When Rutherford's ingenious device proved this notion wrong, demonstrating that matter was made up of tiny particles that were divisible again and again, it was met with immediate disbelief. At least Thomson's atom had substance, but, according to Rutherford, atoms were made up mostly of space, with microscopic particles occupying a central core that contained the composite mass. Even smaller particles that buzzed around the core at vast distances, embedded in the empty space, were specks of tiny particles called electrons.

The response of the day was quiet skepticism. Rutherford had won the 1908 Nobel Prize in Chemistry four years before his announcement to the Manchester Literary and Philosophical Society. The honor of the Nobel Prize was not enough to convince the largely disjointed community of theoretical physicists. It was somewhat outrageous to most that Rutherford would attempt to convince the world through his atomic model that matter was basically a cloud of energy and that mass itself was an illusion.

Albert Einstein would soon quantify the relationship between matter and energy, ($E = mc^2$) and Bohr would redefine the atom in new and innovative terms. Bohr described everything equal in size or smaller than the atom in terms of quantum mechanics, demonstrating that the laws of the larger universe simply did not apply inside the electron cloud.

Rutherford was a pioneer of transition. He took the aspect of discovery as deeply inside the atom as one could within the framework of Newtonian physics. A new science had to be developed to go even deeper. Quantum mechanics joined with Einstein's work on relativity and would reorder physics and redefine the nature of all matter and energy.

Bibliography

Asimov, Isaac. *Understanding Physics*. Vol. 3. New York: Walker, 1966. This book was written for the general public. The book succeeds brilliantly in not only describing physics so that it is easy to understand but also including history so that it is vital and interesting. Principally, it discusses the electron, proton, and neutron.

Cline, Barbara Lovett. *The Questioners*. New York: Thomas Y. Crowell, 1965. This book is written as a biography of the lives of the quantum physicists. It begins with Rutherford and a delightful, detailed discussion of what went on behind the scenes of the Rutherford team. Describes the work of the other physicists of the day, from Bohr to Einstein, and how their efforts blended into quantum physics. An exciting book for a wide audience.

Crease, Robert P., and Charles C. Mann. *The Second Creation*. New York: Macmillan, 1986. In this book, Crease and Mann follow the making of twentieth century physics from its nineteenth century roots to the enigmatic mysteries of the late 1980's. Examines characters and personalities as well as the issues of physics. Rutherford's work is discussed in detail, from his fundamental discoveries to the full implications of his collaboration with Bohr after 1912. Highly readable.

Hawking, Stephen W. *A Brief History of Time*. New York: Bantam Books, 1988. In this readable work, one of the most prominent physicists of our time examines the universe from his view of creation to the late 1980's. Hawking examines the whole cosmos, from the atom and its innermost parts to the far-flung reaches of space. Written for the general reader; illustrated.

Pagels, Heinz R. *The Cosmic Code*. New York: Simon & Schuster, 1982. This book describes quantum physics as "the language of nature." Pagels, a physicist, embarks on a literary quest to explain some of the most profoundly difficult topics in quantum physics in a nontechnical manner for the lay reader. Offers a concise view of the evolution of atomic theory, from the work of Rutherford to the most complex grand unified theories. Illustrated.

Dennis Chamberland

Cross-References

Becquerel Wins the Nobel Prize for the Discovery of Natural Radioactivity (1903), p. 199; Einstein States His Theory of Special Relativity: $E = mc^2$ (1905), p. 297; Thomson Wins the Nobel Prize for the Discovery of the Electron (1906), p. 356; Bohr Writes a Trilogy on Atomic and Molecular Structure (1912), p. 507; Rutherford Discovers the Proton (1914), p. 590; Einstein Completes His Theory of General Relativity (1915), p. 625; Lawrence Develops the Cyclotron (1931), p. 953; Chadwick Discovers the Neutron (1932), p. 973; Cockcroft and Walton Split the Atom with a Particle Accelerator (1932), p. 978; The Liquid Bubble Chamber Is Developed (1953), p. 1470.

HESS DISCOVERS COSMIC RAYS
THROUGH HIGH-ALTITUDE IONIZATIONS

Categories of event: Physics and astronomy
Time: August 7 and 12, 1912
Locale: Aussig, Austria

Hess pioneered dangerous high-altitude balloon experiments, which revealed that air ionization increases with height, indicating the existence of cosmic rays originating outside Earth and its solar system

Principal personages:

VICTOR FRANZ HESS (1883-1964), an Austrian experimental physicist who was a cowinner of the 1936 Nobel Prize in Physics

FRANZ EXNER (1849-1926), an Austrian physicist who headed the group working on atmospheric electricity

ROBERT ANDREWS MILLIKAN (1868-1953), an American physicist, winner of the 1923 Nobel Prize in Physics, who termed the excess ionization discovered by Hess "cosmic rays"

CARL DAVID ANDERSON (1905-   ), an American physicist who discovered the positron and was a cowinner with Hess of the 1936 Nobel Prize in Physics

Summary of Event

Shortly before and after the turn of the twentieth century, a series of discoveries of surprising radiations marked a new direction in physics. Wilhelm Conrad Röntgen created X rays within an evacuated tube in his laboratory, then Antoine-Henri Becquerel discovered radioactive rays emitted from elements in the earth; this discovery led the Curies (Marie and Pierre) to discover radium. Victor Franz Hess undertook a search for the sources of radioactivity, and this led him, instead, to discover a new and more puzzling set of radiations—cosmic rays—which had their origins outside Earth and beyond the sun.

In 1910, Hess had earned his Ph.D. at the University of Graz. Hess committed himself to understanding a set of strange atmospheric charging effects. As assistant at the Institute of Radium Research of the Vienna Academy of Science, he joined a group under Franz Exner and Ergon von Schweidler working on atmospheric electricity. Hess performed his experiments during ten courageous balloon flights that ultimately proved the extraterrestrial origin of cosmic rays.

The beginning of the twentieth century presented scientists with a puzzling fact. A tightly sealed electroscope slowly developed an electric charge even when all sources of electrical leakage were carefully eliminated. Scientists wondered if the strange charging was merely a nuisance or if it pointed to some new science awaiting discovery. The charging diminished slightly with thick shielding over the electroscope. If the charging were real, a very penetrating radiation might produce it by colliding with the trapped air inside the sealed electroscope and releasing electrons. The charging was as strong over the oceans as over the land; therefore, radioactivity from rocks could not be the source of the penetrating rays. Since the land and oceans were not the source, perhaps the rays came from the skies. Measurements were made on the Eiffel Tower and in primitive balloon flights with little change in the charging. If the sky was the source, then the source was quite high. In 1910, Hess undertook the problem and decided upon a strategy to attain greater heights. The electroscope was the basic instrument used to study the strange charging. Electrons were removed carefully from the air before sealing a small amount in the electroscope. Initially, the sealed air was an excellent insulator, but, in time, conduction appeared, pointing to the presence of free electron charges in the electroscope and the charging effect. Hess designed special electroscopes with the aid of the Vienna Academy of Science and went to the Austrian Aeroclub. Hess had calculated that heights greater than one and one-half that of the Eiffel Tower were needed to begin to show a real dependence of charging upon altitude and that much greater altitudes were necessary to distinguish a different sky source from ground radiation. He requested the Aeroclub to provide high-altitude balloon flights. The electroscopes were designed for very low temperatures and pressures high above. The Aeroclub agreed. Hess gathered daring companions, and in 1911, he began his series of dangerous balloon experiments.

Hess began his next-to-last flight with two companions on August 7, 1912, from the vicinity of Aussig, Austria. Hess monitored his three electroscopes, one companion navigated, and the other checked altitude and temperature. After rising for two and one-half hours, the balloon drifted between 4,000 and 5,000 meters for one hour more, covering 200 kilometers to Pieskew, Germany, near Berlin. At the highest altitude, Hess's electroscopes were four times faster than at ground level. He believed the radiations responsible for the charging effects were coming from outside Earth.

Hess's next ascent was to determine if the extraterrestrial rays originated in the sun. He scheduled the balloon flight for August 12 to coincide with a solar eclipse. He took the balloon to 3,000 meters and found no reduction in the intensity of the rays as the sun disappeared from view. This eliminated the sun as a major source of the cosmic rays. The August 12 flight marked the end of the historic set of the ten flights, half of which were carried out at night. Hess summarized his conclusions in a paper published that November, "The results of my observations are best explained by the assumption that a radiation of very great penetrating power enters our atmosphere from above."

The radiation found by Hess decreased with distance near the earth but began its increase at about 150 meters. At an altitude of about 5 kilometers, the radiation, causing the electroscope discharge, was several times stronger than at the earth's surface. The radiation was the same both day and night and was unaffected by the solar eclipse. There was less air at higher altitudes to block the rays. The rays were cosmic.

Confirmation by other scientists came slowly. W. Kohlhorster found that the unknown rays were twelve times as intense at 10 kilometers altitude in a balloon as on the earth's surface. Nevertheless, general acceptance was still slow. Many scientists could not envision rays coming from outer space. In 1913, Hess founded the meteorological station at Hoch Obir to continue his radiation studies, where he worked until World War I intervened. After the war, Hess traveled to the United States and set up the research laboratory of the U.S. Radium Corporation in New York. Also, he served as a consultant to the Bureau of Mines and established contacts. Two years after his 1923 return to Austria, Hess acquired his own laboratory at Graz University. In 1925, Robert Andrews Millikan acknowledged full acceptance of Hess's pioneering efforts by labeling the unknown radiation as "cosmic rays."

Hess enlisted international aid from the Rockefeller Foundation, the Vienna Academy of Science, and the Prussian Academy of Science, as well as the Emergency Society for German Sciences, to begin the now-famous Hafelekar Spitze Observatory for cosmic ray research near Innsbruck. He found a small daily variation in cosmic ray intensity pointing to a small fractional contribution to the overall cosmic ray intensity of the sun. His accumulated data indicated the origin of cosmic rays to be beyond our galaxy.

Impact of Event

With the recognition that cosmic rays were real, physicists became aware that they had an extraordinary tool for investigating not only outer space but also the innermost parts of matter. Evidence accumulated that the cosmic rays possess extraordinary energy and small particles require large energies for their production. Carl David Anderson was one of the first to put these extreme energies to use to produce a new particle that existed only in the dreams of theorists.

Physicists often measure radiation energy in units of volts. This unit measures the energy of an electron or a proton, which has the same value of charge as the electron. For example, visible light requires a particle energy of several volts to generate the light, while at 50,000 volts, the particle could generate penetrating X rays.

Anderson knew that cosmic rays possess extraordinary energies, although he did not know the full extent of these energies. He enlisted the rays in tracking down the positron, the positively charged twin of the tiny electron. He photographed a vapor-filled vessel located in a large magnetic field, while exposing the contents to Hess's ever-present cosmic rays. His discovery of the positron came in a cloud chamber picture of the collision debris left when the antiparticle was hit by a 500-million-volt cosmic ray. No other instrument at his time could generate such energies.

The vital connection between Hess's work and the discovery of the positron was made clear to the public by Anderson. He praised Hess's work on cosmic rays and stated: "All of our knowledge of interstellar space must for some time continue to proceed from further exploration of the cosmic ray."

A wide range of new experimental techniques point to supernovas, which occur about every hundred years in our galaxy by the explosion of a massive star at the end of its life. Supernovas throw off energetic particles, mainly protons, which are the core or nucleus of hydrogen, the lightest atom, and alpha particles, which are the nucleus of the next lightest atom, helium. There is also a small component of many heavier atomic nuclei. All these particles are born with very high energies and can acquire more energy in their long journey within galaxies. Gamma rays, which are very energetic X rays, are formed also by the cosmic rays when they encounter magnetic fields in space, near or far from the supernova. The cosmic rays generated by supernovas have almost unimaginable energies and pervade the galaxy throughout its life, raining down on any planets within.

Other cosmic rays may originate in the neutron star, which is often born in the remains of the supernova explosion if the neutron star has a companion star from which it can draw matter. Whatever the exact source, the cosmic rays, particles and gammas, are space relics that can tell scientists much about the unknowns astronomers encountered in their journeys if they can be deciphered with newer equipment. Thus, the discoveries and puzzles prompted by cosmic rays continue to the late twentieth century.

Bibliography

Auger, Pierre. *What Are Cosmic Rays?* Translated by Maurice M. Shapiro. Rev. ed. Chicago: University of Chicago Press, 1945. This is a translation from the French of the popular book by a well-known authority. It presents fascinating investigations of cosmic rays. The physics is clear and simple. Hess's contributions are discussed in chapter 1.

Hess, Victor F. *The Electrical Conductivity of the Atmosphere and Its Causes*. Translated by L. W. Codd. New York: D. Van Nostrand, 1928; *Cosmic Radiation and its Biological Effects*. 2d ed. New York: Fordham University Press, 1949. Translations of Hess's two technical works are available for those who have a good science background or for those who have a historical interest in cosmic rays.

Hillas, A. M. *Cosmic Rays*. New York: Pergamon Press, 1972. For those with a technical background. Chapter 1 presents a review without mathematics. The pioneering efforts of Hess are presented, and, most interesting, an excerpt of his 1912 paper that reviews his balloon results is given, in translation, in the second half of the book. Also included are original papers by other colleagues.

Pasachoff, J. M. *Contemporary Astronomy*. Philadelphia: W. B. Saunders, 1977. An undergraduate text in astronomy that requires basic knowledge of mathematics or physics. It includes a general review of the universe, the stars, and the solar system. Chapter 8 has a section on cosmic rays, their nature, and their probable origins in supernovas.

Rossi, Bruno. *Cosmic Rays*. New York: McGraw-Hill, 1964. A very readable and authoritative book by a well-known physicist who worked with cosmic rays. Chapter 1 gives fascinating details on Hess's measurements and ballooning experiments.

Details of cosmic rays can be understood easily. Although dated, this is a good book for an introductory study of cosmic rays.

Peter J. Walsh

Cross-References

Millikan Names Cosmic Rays and Investigates Their Absorption (1920), p. 694; Anderson Discovers the Positron (1932), p. 983.

EDISON INTRODUCES THE KINETOPHONE
TO SHOW THE FIRST TALKING PICTURES

Category of event: Applied science
Time: 1913
Locale: West Orange, New Jersey

Edison developed a system of talking pictures using a phonograph linked to a film projector

Principal personages:

THOMAS ALVA EDISON (1847-1931), the inventor of the electric light, the phonograph, and the motion picture camera, who established the world's first industrial research laboratories

WILLIAM KENNEDY LAURIE DICKSON (1860-1937), a mechanic and inventor who assisted Edison in the development of the technology of motion pictures, film projection, and talking pictures

MILLER REESE HUTCHISON (1876-1944), an independent inventor who produced the Klaxon, or car horn, before joining Edison's laboratory to work on motion pictures

LEE DE FOREST (1873-1961), an American inventor who produced one of the first vacuum tubes and played an important role in the development of radio

GEORGE EASTMAN (1854-1932), an American inventor and industrialist who pioneered the development of inexpensive and simple photography for the general public

Summary of Event

Thomas Alva Edison began experimenting on a device that would show moving pictures because he wanted a visual image to accompany the music reproduced by his phonograph. He said that moving pictures would do for the eye what the phonograph had done for the ear. He thought that both sound and visual images could be stored on a phonograph cylinder and then reproduced at any time by the user. He selected William Kennedy Laurie Dickson from his staff to work on the project at his new laboratory in West Orange, New Jersey. Dickson was an accomplished experimenter with a strong interest in photography. Dickson started work in 1887. He fixed small photographs onto a phonograph cylinder and viewed them through a microscope as they rotated. He found that sequential images of a moving object gave the impression of movement when passed rapidly through the viewer's line of sight. Edison and Dickson had examined several devices that exploited the phenomenon of persistence of vision—when the eye retains the image a short time after it has disappeared. It was well known that a sequence of images could be manipulated to give the visual illusion of movement. Edison and Dickson were confident that a series of small photographs could achieve this effect. This was the conceptual beginning of motion pictures.

By 1888, Dickson had built a device which could reproduce both sight and sound. This "moving view" apparatus contained a phonograph cylinder and a drum covered with a series of small photographs. Both were centered on a common axle. When the axle was turned, the viewer watched the moving pictures through a microscope and listened to the accompanying sound track through earphones connected to a reproducing diaphragm on the cylinder. This device was the first attempt to show talking pictures. Further experiments proved that this approach was not feasible because the sound and the vision elements could not be synchronized. The phonograph cylinder had to revolve with a continuous motion to ensure good reproduction of the sound track, while the photograph drum needed an intermittent motion: The image had to be moved into the line of sight, fixed there for a fraction of a second so that the eye could record it, and then rapidly moved out of the line of sight. Despite months of experiments, the problem proved insurmountable, forcing Edison to drop the idea of combining sight and sound in one device.

Once released from the demands of talking pictures, Dickson experimented on the best method of manipulating sequential photographs to give the impression of movement. His research produced the important innovation of the perforated filmstrip that replaced the photographs on a revolving drum. Dickson was aware of the use of thin celluloid strips as photographic film. He ordered a strip of film from George Eastman of Rochester, New York, who had used film strips in his cameras. Dickson exposed the images one after another on the continuous tape of film. The edges of the film strip were cut with holes to fit the teeth of the ratchet that moved the strip rapidly past the lens. The film camera, patented by Edison in 1891, was a light-proof box containing a lens, shutter, electric motor, and a length of perforated filmstrip made of celluloid.

Edison also patented a device for viewing the filmstrip—the kinetoscope. This was a large box containing the strip of positive images which were moved past an illuminated eyepiece at the top of the machine. An electric motor moved the filmstrip to the eyepiece, where a slotted disc exposed the images to the viewer at a rate of about forty frames a second. The kinetoscope was designed as an arcade machine. It closely resembled the coin slot phonograph, which had become popular in penny arcades and public places. By 1893, the first kinetoscopes were placed next to phonographs in arcades. Two years later, Edison took the next step of putting a phonograph in the bottom part of the kinetoscope housing. Named the kinetophone, this machine was a second attempt to show talking pictures. The viewer looked through the eyepiece to see the images while listening to the sound track on ear tubes connnected to the phonograph. The problems of synchronizing sight and sound again proved too difficult to overcome. The kinetophone was a commercial failure and very few were manufactured. Yet, this machine set an important precedent of a self-contained sight and sound system.

Edison was confident that he could perfect this technology and capture a mass audience. After introducing a commercial film projector, Edison resumed experiments on the kinetophone in 1899. The machine now consisted of a film projector linked to a special long-playing phonograph. The film strips of the kinetoscopes had run for less than a minute, enough to keep the customer's attention in an arcade but insufficient to satisfy an audience in a film theater. As audiences became more accustomed to the novelty of moving pictures, they wanted to see films that told a story. The average playing time of an Edison phonograph cylinder at this time was about two minutes; it was not enough to accommodate the longer films being made at the turn of the century.

The best format for a long-playing phonograph was the disc rather than the cylinder. Invented by Emile Berliner, the disc-playing talking machine had become a serious competitor to Edison's phonograph. The playing time of a disc record could easily be extended to around seven minutes, and oversized discs offered much longer playing times. Edison found it difficult to desert the format he had invented and concentrated instead on increasing the size of the cylinder. The kinetophone was developed around oversized cylinders of about 11 centimeters in diameter and 19 centimeters in length. Playing time was about six minutes. Once the playing time had been increased, there still remained the task of amplifying the volume of the playback to ensure that the sound track could be heard from every seat in the theater. Increased volume could be achieved by putting more pressure on the reproducing needle as it made its way along the groove, but this caused wear on the wax cylinder that ultimately eradicated the sound. An inventor, Daniel Higham of Massachusetts, was hired by Edison to work on the kinetophone in 1908. Higham designed an oversized reproducer assembly which contained a special valve that enhanced the movement of the diaphragm as it picked up the sound vibrations made by the reproducing needle. The result was a much louder playback.

Edison made his close associate, Miller Reese Hutchison, the director of the kinetophone program. Hutchison developed methods of sound recording with numerous horns in order to achieve a more balanced sound track. By 1910, Hutchison had a working kinetophone to show to the press. The entertainment consisted of an announcer making a variety of sounds and a dancer performing with musical accompaniment. Although this demonstration was a success, thousands of additional experiments were undertaken to perfect the synchronization of sight and sound. Hutchison tried a variety of controlling devices to coordinate the film projector at the rear of the auditorium with the phonograph behind the screen. After rejecting a system of electrical controls, Hutchison finally decided on a simple mechanical system. A clutch mechanism was used to adjust the speed of the revolving cylinder of the phonograph to keep it in time with the film. The film projectionist worked the clutch with a cord that ran on pulleys. In 1913, the kinetophone was formally introduced with Edison's claim that he had perfected talking pictures.

Impact of Event

The kinetophone had a profound effect on motion picture audiences. When it was first publicly demonstrated in New York City, the newspapers reported that gasps of astonishment could be heard when sound came from the screen. The kinetophone was so popular that it was soon on the road, thrilling audiences all over America. It became the leading profit maker for the Edison enterprise in 1913, exceeding income from silent pictures, phonographs, and records.

The first talking pictures garnered national publicity, bringing more fame to Edison and more profits to his film exhibitors. It also gave encouragement to other inventors who were working on talking pictures, including Lee de Forest, the inventor of an early vacuum tube called the audion. Where Edison's approach had stayed within the realm of existing knowledge of acoustics and mechanics, de Forest's experiments were directed at the completely new area of electronics. The audion could amplify electrical signals and also had potential as a controlling device—the two key problems in devising a system of talking pictures.

The fame of the kinetophone was short-lived, for after the novelty wore off, movie audiences became impatient with its shortcomings. The playing time of the kinetophone could not accommodate the longer, epic films that were popular in 1913. Audiences wanted their entertainment to last hours, not minutes. Problems with synchronization continued to plague the kinetophone. After another year of unsuccessful experiments and theatrical failures, Edison gave up on the kinetophone and made no further attempt to perfect talking pictures.

Yet he had shown the way and demonstrated the appeal of the talkies to film audiences. Another ten years were to pass before electronic recording and amplification made talking pictures a commercial reality. The sound was picked up by microphones that changed the vibrations of sound into an electrical signal. The sound was recorded onto discs by a recording stylus that was activated by the changes in a magnetic field. The discs were oversized and revolved at low speed, thus creating a long playing time. The electrical signal was reproduced from the record and amplified by vacuum tubes. Audiences heard the sound track through loudspeakers placed about the theater. Fourteen years after Edison announced the coming of talking pictures, *The Jazz Singer* opened up a new era in film entertainment in 1927.

Bibliography

Balio, Tino, ed. *The American Film Industry*. Rev. ed. Madison: University of Wisconsin Press, 1985. A collection of scholarly articles on the early years of the film industry. Several articles deal with the technology of motion pictures.

Conot, Robert. *A Streak of Luck*. New York: Seaview Press, 1979. A popular biography of Edison that seeks to debunk the Edison myth. The section on motion pictures describes the kinetophone and the other attempts at talking pictures. This book stresses the work of others in the field.

Hendricks, Gordon. *The Edison Motion Picture Myth*. Berkeley: University of California Press, 1961. A detailed study of the invention of the motion picture. Hendricks argues that Edison took the credit for the work of others, especially William Kennedy Laurie Dickson.

_____. *Origins of the American Film*. New York: Arno Press, 1972. A concise account of the inventions that created the film industry, written by one of the leading scholars on the subject.

Musser, Charles S. *Before the Nickelodeon: Charles S. Porter and the Edison Manufacturing Company*. Berkeley: University of California Press, 1990. The authoritative history of the part played by Edison and his employees in the early years of film.

Ramsaye, Terry. *A Million and One Nights: A History of the Motion Picture Through 1925*. New York: Simon & Schuster, 1986. A popular history of motion pictures, first published in 1926. The author was closely connected to the film industry and a personal friend of Thomas Edison. He was allowed access to Edison's notes; this book claims to be the authorized history of Edison's invention.

Andre Millard

Cross-References

Fleming Files a Patent for the First Vacuum Tube (1904), p. 255; Zworykin Develops an Early Type of Television (1923), p. 751; Warner Bros. Introduces Talking Motion Pictures (1926), p. 820.

FORD PRODUCES AUTOMOBILES ON
A MOVING ASSEMBLY LINE

Category of event: Applied science
Time: 1913
Locale: Ford Motor Company, Highland Park, Michigan

By applying the principles of mass production, Ford put automobile ownership within the reach of millions and changed a nation, its people, and their habits

Principal personages:

HENRY FORD (1863-1947), an American automobile manufacturer who founded the Ford Motor Company and built the Model T, the world's first mass-produced car

ELI WHITNEY (1765-1825), an inventor who introduced the principle of interchangeable parts to American industry

ELISHA KING ROOT (1808-1865), the man responsible for making division of labor an essential part of modern mass production

OLIVER EVANS (1755-1819), an inventor who developed power conveyors used to achieve continuous flow in the workplace

FREDERICK WINSLOW TAYLOR (1856-1915), an efficiency engineer who strived to eliminate wasted motion from the production process

Summary of Event

Henry Ford produced the first "horseless carriage" in 1896. He built it in his home workshop using traditional handcraft techniques. Three years later, Ford and eleven other investors formed the Detroit Automobile Company to manufacture gasoline-powered motor cars for sale to the general public. This company was not successful, and the business failed.

In 1903, a new automobile manufacturing company—the Ford Motor Company—was born. While other cars at that time were priced at $5,000 to $10,000 each, Ford's first product, the Model A, sold for under a thousand dollars and was well received. Yet, when Ford and his partners tried, in 1905, to introduce a more expensive motor car, sales dropped. Then, in 1907, Ford announced a revised company policy. The Ford Motor Company would build "a motor car for the great multitude." It would be called the Model T.

The Model T was introduced to the general public in 1908. It was everything that Henry Ford said it would be. Ford's Model T was a low-priced (about $850) utility car that came in one color only: black. There were no yearly model changes. Instead, the basic design of the Model T remained unchanged throughout its entire twenty-year production life. Yet, the price of the Model T, or "Tin Lizzie," as it was affectionately called, did not remain constant. Instead, its price dropped over the years to less than half that of the original Model T. As the price dropped, sales increased, and Ford Motor Company quickly became what was then the world's largest automobile manufacturer.

The last of more than 15 million Model T's was made in 1927. In appearance, the 1927 "Tin Lizzie" was remarkably similar to its 1907 predecessor. So, too, was its operation. There, however, the similarity ends, because these two automobiles represent the end products of completely different manufacturing systems: custom production and mass production.

At first, Ford built his cars as every other manufacturer did, one at a time using traditional custom manufacturing techniques. Skilled mechanics would work on a car from start to finish, while helpers and runners brought parts to these highly paid craftsmen as they were needed. After completing one car, the mechanics and their helpers would then begin the next.

Custom manufacturing works well when demand for a product is low and buyers are willing to pay the high labor costs that are required. This was not the case with the automobile. Ford soon realized that his plan to manufacture quality cars in quantity and at a low price depended on finding a more efficient way to produce motor cars. In this regard, he looked to the past and the work of others. He found four principles of production that could be applied to the large-scale manufacture or mass production of his automobiles: interchangeable parts, continuous flow, division of labor, and elimination of wasted motion.

Eli Whitney, the inventor of the cotton gin, is credited with introducing the principle of interchangeable parts to American industry. Prior to the eighteenth century, muskets, like most products, were produced one at a time by highly skilled craftsmen (gunsmiths) who meticulously made and hand-fitted each of the parts together. Although these muskets were usually of high quality, the methods employed in their manufacture left much to be desired. This was especially true with regard to quantity production.

Whitney recognized the inherent disadvantages associated with the custom production method and was determined to overcome them. In 1798, he contracted with the United States government to produce several thousand muskets within a period of two years. Instead of finding and hiring gunsmiths to fabricate the muskets by hand, Whitney devoted the bulk of his resources to the design and construction of specialized machines that were capable of accurately duplicating large quantities of each of the musket parts required. He also developed a number of specialized tools: jigs for positioning materials and/or controlling and guiding cutting tools, dies for cutting and forming materials, gauges for measuring or checking the size of parts, and fixtures for holding work in position while machining. Such tools made it possible for semiskilled, and even unskilled, workers to function successfully at jobs that had formerly been carried out by highly skilled craftsmen.

Through the use of duplicate (interchangeable) parts, Whitney was able to improve the difficult and time-consuming "cut-and-try" method of fitting parts together, which was in use at that time. Thus, he dramatically simplified the process of assembling parts into finished products.

The principle of "continuous flow" is the planned and orderly progression of a product as it undergoes manufacture and is changed and/or assembled into its final form. As the product is fabricated, it passes through a series of production stages, including operation, a stage in which useful work is performed on the product; transfer, when the product is moved from one stage to another; storage, an extended period of time when production is idle; and delay, a temporary form of storage.

Efficient production is accomplished by carefully arranging a product's manufacturing stages so as to result in its continuous flow. Ford borrowed from at least two sources in order to achieve efficient production flow in the manufacture of his Model T: the meat-packing houses of Chicago and an automatic grain mill operated by Oliver Evans.

Ford's idea for a moving assembly line originated in the disassembly lines used by Chicago's great meat-packing houses in the late 1860's. Here, animal carcasses were transported by overhead rail past a series of workers, each performing a specific cutting or packing operation. The introduction of the moving disassembly line in the meat-packing industry resulted in a marked increase in the number of animals that could be butchered and packaged in a single day.

A key ingredient in achieving continuous flow is automatic conveyance of the work to and from the worker. In this regard, Ford looked to Oliver Evans, who is credited with developing three types of conveyor systems—belt, screw, and bucket. In 1783, Evans designed and operated an automatic grain mill. Only two workers were required to run the Evans mill. As one worker poured grain into a hopper at one end of the mill, a second worker filled sacks with flour at its other end. In-between processing was automatic, as Evans' conveyors passed the grain through the various steps of the milling process without human intervention.

The principle of division of labor is simple: By dividing a complex job into several basic operations, certain products can be produced faster, with less chance of error, by workers possessing fewer skills than were previously required. In other words, divide the input and multiply the output.

Elisha King Root is generally credited with developing the division of labor principle. The product that Root applied his principle to was the famous "Colt Six Shooter." In 1849, Elisha Root went to work for Samuel Colt at his Connecticut factory. He proved to be a manufacturing genius. By dividing production operations into very simple steps, each performed by individual workers, Root proved that gun production would increase substantially.

Henry Ford applied Root's principle when he set out to increase engine assembly from the recognized standard, which was then one engine per worker per day. To accomplish his goal, Ford broke down the complex process of assembling an automobile engine into eighty-four separate and distinct operations. He then assigned eighty-four men the task of assembling the engines, with each man performing one of the eighty-four operations. The job of assembling an engine, which once was performed by a single worker, now required the labor of eighty-four different men. Ford proved that this method was efficient. Instead of the 84 engines that might have been expected under the old system, 352 engines were actually assembled. In other words, the production rate was increased by a factor greater than four.

A fact that is quite evident in performing an operation is that wasted motion on the part of the worker is inefficient. It is to industry's advantage, therefore, to eliminate as much wasted motion from production as is possible. Ford found it in the work of Frederick Winslow Taylor.

Frederick Winslow Taylor has been called the "original efficiency expert." In his work, Taylor used both time and motion studies as the basis for improving the production process. His time studies served to establish optimum speeds at which workers could efficiently perform various operations. Taylor proved that, in the long run, doing a job too quickly was as bad as doing it too slowly. According to Taylor, "[C]orrect speed is the speed at which men can work hour after hour, day after day, year in and year out, and remain continuously in good health." He also conducted motion studies, which were designed to streamline worker movements as they performed their assigned tasks. In this way, he was able to keep wasted motion to a minimum.

Impact of Event

Henry Ford was the first to apply the four basic principles of mass production to the large-scale manufacture of a complex product. He did so slowly and with care, testing each new procedure before it was adopted. The changeover from custom to mass production was more an evolution than a revolution. It culminated, in 1913, with the introduction of the first moving assembly line ever used in the manufacture of automobiles. As a result, Ford was able to produce his Tin Lizzies faster than ever before. His competitors soon followed suit. He had achieved his goal of placing automobile ownership within the reach of millions; he changed a nation, its people, and their habits.

Ford's work gave a new push to the Industrial Revolution. It showed the nation that mass production could be used to improve the quality and cut the cost of manufacturing an automobile. In so doing, large amounts of money could also be made. In fact, the Model T was so profitable that in 1914 Ford was able to double the minimum daily wage of his workers. Now, at five dollars per day, even they could afford to buy a Tin Lizzie. Ford prospered even more. Because they were successful, Ford's ideas and manufacturing techniques moved quickly from the Highland Park plant to all phases of American industry and set the pattern of abundance that was to follow.

Although Americans account for only about 6 percent of the world's population, they own about 50 percent of its wealth. The United States makes, builds, sells, buys, and uses more goods and services than any other country in the world. There are more than twice as many radios in the United States as there are people. The roads are crowded with more than 180 million automobiles. Homes are filled with the sounds and sights emitting from more than 150 million television sets. Never have the people of one nation owned so much. Where did all the products—radios, cars, television sets—come from? The answer is industry, which is dependent on the methods developed by Henry Ford.

Bibliography

Fales, James F., et al. *Manufacturing: A Basic Text*. 2d ed. Peoria, Ill.: Bennett and McKnight, 1986. This book on manufacturing discusses introduction to manufacturing, research and development, production, product plans, and tools, materials, and processes. Heavily illustrated, with a glossary.

Ford, Henry, with Samuel Crowther. *My Life and Work*. Garden City, N.Y.: Doubleday, 1923. Ghostwritten by Crowther in a conversational style, Ford's autobiography contains thoughts on the state of the nation and advice on how admiring readers might duplicate their hero's success.

Gelderman, Carol. *Henry Ford: The Wayward Capitalist*. New York: Dial Press, 1981. Gelderman has written a lively biography of Henry Ford. Draws on a wealth of unpublished materials and sources that were unavailable to previous biographers. Contains end notes, references, and a complete index. Illustrated, with some photographs.

Lacey, Robert. *Ford: The Men and the Machine*. Boston: Little, Brown, 1986. The epic story of Henry Ford, the automobile manufacturing company he created, and the dynasty he founded. Spanning more than a hundred years, the book describes the public achievements, the private tragedies, the feuds, and the personalities of the powerful individuals whose ambitions helped to shape modern American society. Supplementing the text are black-and-white photographs (some never before published). A helpful index is also provided.

Swerdlow, Robert. *Student's Guide to Industry*. Rockaway, N.J.: Packaged Educational Programs, 1972. Presents a complete conceptual model of American industry that will prove helpful in understanding production and its relationship to the eleven other elements that are part of a successful business enterprise. This short book is entertaining as well as informative. Cartoons, crossword puzzles, riddles, anecdotes, and interesting experiments and activities are only some of the varied techniques that are used to achieve this goal.

Wik, Reynold M. *Henry Ford and Grass-Roots America*. Ann Arbor: University of Michigan Press, 1972. Based in large part on letters and other materials contained in the Ford archives. The author recreates the era of the Tin Lizzie. Traces and evaluates Ford's activities and ideas in many fields and discusses the impact of the Model T. Contains illustrations.

Robert M. Swerdlow

Cross-Reference

Burton Introduces Thermal Cracking for Refining Petroleum (1913), p. 573.

GEOTHERMAL POWER IS PRODUCED
FOR THE FIRST TIME

Category of event: Earth science
Time: 1913
Locale: Larderello, Italy

Hot springs in northern Italy were used to provide steam to power an electric generator, thus inaugurating the first geothermal power installation

Principal personages:
PRINCE PIERO GINORI CONTI (1865-1939), an Italian nobleman and industrialist who installed the first geothermal electric generator
JOHN DEBO GALLOWAY (1869-1943), an American engineer who directed some of the earliest attempts to drill for geothermal steam in California
SIR CHARLES PARSONS (1854-1931), an English engineer who advanced the first serious proposal for utilization of deep geothermal heat

Summary of Event

It has been known since ancient times that the interior of the earth is hot. Hot springs have been prized for centuries for their supposed curative powers and have been used occasionally for cooking and heating, but attempts to utilize the earth's internal heat on a large scale did not become practical until the twentieth century. Drilling into a reservoir of high-pressure steam requires techniques of protecting drillers during drilling. Also, because most geothermal steam sources are not near large population centers, it was not practical to tap geothermal energy until electric power networks to transport the energy became available.

The first successful use of geothermal energy was at Larderello in northern Italy. The Larderello geothermal field, located near the city of Pisa about 240 kilometers northwest of Rome contains many hot springs and fumaroles (steam vents). In 1777, these springs were found to be rich in boron, and in 1818 Francesco de Larderel began extracting borax from them. Previously, the principal source of borax for Europe had been remote Tibet. In the beginning, wood fires were used to evaporate water from the geothermal brine; but in 1827, Larderel began using steam from the fumaroles as a source of heat as well. Soon afterward, wells were drilled to increase the flow of mineralized water and to obtain more steam. Attempts were made also to use geothermal steam to power steam engines, but these attempts failed because the water was too corrosive. Borax extraction at Larderello continued until 1969.

Shortly after 1900, Prince Piero Ginori Conti, director of the Larderello borax works, conceived the idea of using the steam for power production. An experimental electrical power plant was constructed at Larderello in 1904 to provide electric power to the borax plant. After this initial experiment proved successful, a 250-

kilowatt generating station was installed in 1913 and commercial power production began. As the Larderello field grew, additional geothermal sites throughout the region were prospected and tapped for power. Power production grew steadily until the 1940's, when production reached 130 megawatts; however, the Larderello power plants were destroyed late in World War II. After the war, the generating plants were rebuilt and were producing more than 400 megawatts by 1980.

The Larderello power plants encountered many of the technical problems that were later to concern other geothermal facilities. For example, hydrogen sulfide in the steam was highly corrosive to copper, so the Larderello power plant used aluminum for electrical connections much more than conventional power plants of the time. Also, the low pressure of the steam in early wells at Larderello presented problems. The first generators simply used steam to drive a generator and vented the spent steam to the atmosphere. A system of this sort, called a noncondensing system, is useful for small generators but not efficient to produce large amounts of power. Most steam engines derive power not only from the pressure of the steam but also from the vacuum created when the steam is condensed back to water. Geothermal systems that generate power from condensation, as well as direct steam pressure, are called condensing systems. Most large geothermal generators are of this type. Condensation of geothermal steam presents special problems not present in ordinary steam engines: There are other gases present that do not condense. Instead of a vacuum, condensation of steam contaminated with other gases would result in only a limited drop in pressure and, consequently, very low efficiency. Initially, the operators of Larderello tried to use the steam to heat boilers that would, in turn, generate pure steam. Eventually, a device was developed that removed most of the contaminating gases from the steam. Although later wells at Larderello and other geothermal fields produced steam at greater pressure, these engineering innovations improve the efficiency of any geothermal power plant.

In 1913, the English engineer Sir Charles Parsons proposed drilling an extremely deep (12-kilometer) hole to tap the earth's deep heat. Power from such a deep hole would not come from natural steam as at Larderello, but would be generated by pumping fluid into the hole and generating steam (as hot as 500 degrees Celsius) at the bottom. In modern terms, Parsons proposed tapping "hot dry-rock" geothermal energy. Even now, no such plant has been commercially operated yet, but research is being actively pursued in several countries.

The second geothermal field to produce electric power was Beppu, on the island of Kyushu in southern Japan. Initial studies began in 1919, and a small 1-kilowatt power plant began producing power in 1924. A large number of geothermal power plants have been constructed in Japan, but despite its pioneering role in developing Japanese geothermal power, the Beppu field has never developed into a major energy producer.

In the 1930's and 1940's, geothermal facilities were developed in Iceland and New Zealand. Although geothermal electrical generating plants were built in both countries, much of the geothermal energy was used directly for heating. The two most extensive systems are at Reykjavík, Iceland, and Rotorua, New Zealand, where water is piped from geothermal wells to homes and businesses. More than 60 percent of Iceland's population derives its heat from geothermal sources. Iceland is uniquely suited to exploit geothermal energy because of its small population (about 240,000) and abundant geothermal heat. Somewhat surprisingly, Iceland has been slow in developing geothermal electricity because hydroelectric power has been sufficient to supply its small population.

The first use of geothermal energy in the United States was for direct heating. In 1890, the municipal water company of Boise, Idaho, began supplying hot water from a geothermal well. Water was piped from the well to homes and businesses along appropriately named Warm Springs Avenue. At its peak, the system served more than four hundred customers, but as cheap natural gas became available, the number declined. By 1972, only two hundred customers remained, and the water company was planning to discontinue operations. A citizens' group purchased the water rights to the well and launched a program to expand operations. Klamath Falls, Oregon, has geothermal wells that have been in use since about 1900. The wells have been drilled by individual residents to heat their own buildings.

Although Larderello was the first successful geothermal electric power plant, the modern era of geothermal electric power began with the opening of the geysers geothermal field in California. This field marked the start of commercial geothermal power generation in the United States and the beginning of commercial geothermal power generation on a worldwide basis. Geysers, located about 110 kilometers north of San Francisco, had been known since 1847, when they were discovered by explorer William Bell Elliott. By the end of the century, the geysers had become a resort and tourist attraction visited by Theodore Roosevelt and Mark Twain. Test borings were made in the 1920's by John D. Grant, John Debo Galloway, and Fred Stone, and although the experimental power production was successful, it could not compete with inexpensive power from hydroelectric and fossil fuel power plants. Also, the geysers were too isolated to be a commercially viable source of electric power. In 1955, B. C. McCabe, a Los Angeles businessman, leased 14.6 square kilometers in the geysers area and founded the Magma Power Company. Dan A. McMillan of Thermal Power Company joined with McCabe in exploration. In 1958, McCabe and McMillan contracted with Pacific Gas and Electric Company to produce steam for power generation. The first 12.5-megawatt generator was installed at the geysers in 1960, and production increased steadily from then on. The geysers surpassed Larderello as the largest producing geothermal field in the 1970's, and more than 1,000 megawatts were being generated by 1980. By the end of 1980, geothermal plants had been installed in thirteen countries, with a total capacity of almost 2,600 megawatts, and projects with a total capacity of more than 15,000 megawatts were being planned in more than twenty countries.

Impact of Event

Geothermal power has many attractive features. Because the steam is naturally heated and under pressure, generating equipment can be simple, inexpensive, and quickly installed. Equipment and installation costs are offset by savings in fuel. It is economically practical to install small generators, a fact that makes geothermal plants attractive in remote or underdeveloped areas. Most important to a world faced with a variety of technical and environmental problems connected with fossil fuels, geothermal power does not deplete fossil fuel reserves, produces little pollution, and contributes little to the greenhouse effect.

Although it has been significant to local power production, geothermal power has not had a very great global impact, accounting for less than 1 percent of the world's total electric power production. Despite its attractive features, geothermal power has some limitations. Geologic settings suitable for easy geothermal power production are rare; there must be a hot rock or magma body close to the surface. Although it is technically possible to pump water from an external source into a geothermal well to generate steam, most geothermal sites require a copious supply of natural underground water that can be tapped as a source of steam. In contrast, fossil-fuel generating plants can be built at any convenient location.

The technical difficulties in exploiting geothermal power are considerable. Drilling into hot rock is much more difficult than ordinary drilling; the high temperatures wear out drilling equipment rapidly, and safety precautions are necessary to protect workers during drilling. Fortunately, unlike oil wells, geothermal wells are generally not very deep, usually only a few hundred meters. Geothermal power is not unlimited; excessive consumption of steam can deplete the geothermal reservoir like any other natural resource. The hot underground water is often highly mineralized, capable of corroding or clogging pipes, and even sealing the underground fractures that make the water accessible. If the water is very mineral-laden, disposing of it creates a pollution problem, though it is possible to deal with much of the disposal problem by injecting the fluid back into the ground through disposal wells.

A fundamental limit on geothermal power is set by the second law of thermodynamics, which defines how much useful work can be obtained from any physical process. Any physical process powered by heat converts heat into some other form of energy. In the process, the temperature of the heat source is lowered. The thermodynamic efficiency of any process powered by heat is equal to the temperature drop divided by the original temperature. Fossil-fuel and nuclear power plants are used to create very hot steam so that a large temperature drop is possible, resulting in high efficiency. Most geothermal steam sources are not far above the boiling point of water; geothermal generators cannot achieve a very large drop in temperature and thus have low efficiency. When the unavoidable energy losses because of friction and heat dissipation are counted as well, the actual efficiency of most geothermal power plants is only a few percent.

Bibliography

Armstead, H. Christopher H. *Geothermal Energy: Its Past, Present, and Future Contributions to the Energy Needs of Man.* 2d ed. London: E. and F. N. Spon, 1983.

A general overview of geothermal power and methods of utilizing it. The book begins with a history of geothermal power and describes drilling and power production techniques. Several chapters describe case histories of developed geothermal fields up to the 1980's.

Barnea, Joseph. "Geothermal Power." *Scientific American* 226 (January, 1972): 70-77. An overview of the technology of geothermal power production, describing techniques for locating geothermal heat sources and the methods of extracting power from different types of geothermal fields.

DiPippo, Ronald. *Geothermal Energy as a Source of Electricity: A Worldwide Survey of the Design and Operation of Geothermal Power Plants.* United States Department of Energy Report RA 28320-1. Washington, D.C.: Government Printing Office, 1980. A country-by-country survey of geothermal power projects. The descriptions of the facilities are often quite technical, but there are also historical summaries, maps, and tables of power production.

Garrett, Wilbur E., ed. "Energy: A Special Report in the Public Interest." *National Geographic*, Special Report, February, 1981. A general survey of energy resources, usage, and technology. The principal emphasis is on conventional energy resources, but the report discusses possible future energy sources as well, including geothermal power. An atlas on North American energy resources includes a map of known and potential geothermal fields.

Weaver, Kenneth F. "Geothermal Energy: The Power of Letting off Steam." *National Geographic* 152 (October, 1977): 566-579. A brief survey of geothermal energy resources, their utilization, and possible future impact on energy production. Includes diagrams of the geologic structure of principal types of geothermal heat sources and their geographic distribution.

Steven I. Dutch

Cross-References

Hughes Revolutionizes Oil Well Drilling (1908), p. 396; Steinmetz Warns of Pollution in *The Future of Electricity* (1908), p. 401; Bell Telephone Scientists Develop the Photovoltaic Cell (1954), p. 1487; Manabe and Wetherald Warn of the Greenhouse Effect and Global Warming (1967), p. 1840; Solar One, the Prototype Power Tower, Begins Operation (1982), p. 2216; The Chernobyl Nuclear Reactor Explodes (1986), p. 2321.

GUTENBERG DISCOVERS THE EARTH'S MANTLE-OUTER CORE BOUNDARY

Category of event: Earth science
Time: 1913
Locale: University of Göttingen, Germany

Gutenberg expanded the use of seismographs to the global scale upon his discovery of the boundary between the earth's outer core and the lower mantle

Principal personages:
BENO GUTENBERG (1889-1960), a German-born geologist who discovered the boundary between the earth's lower mantle and outer core
JOHN MILNE (1850-1913), a seismologist who invented the first seismograph in 1883
ANDRIJA MOHOROVIČIĆ (1857-1936), a Yugoslavian meteorologist who discovered the discontinuity between seismograph recordings of earthquake waves leading to the boundary between the earth's crust and upper mantle

Summary of Event

Very little is known about the interior of the earth because of its inaccessibility to modern technology. Based on evidence gained through indirect and secondary research and experiments, scientists have been able to determine that the earth consists of layers. The uppermost layer is the crust, on or in which most life exists. The structure of the remainder of the earth's interior and the size and composition of the deeper layers have been learned through various methods. The original source of information that founded modern understanding of the earth's structure is seismology, the study of earthquakes and vibrations of the earth. The pioneers in the field of seismology used needle and paper seismographs—instruments that measure and record vibrations—to study wave patterns. In 1893, one of the pioneers in the field of seismology, John Milne, perfected the clockwork-powered Milne seismograph, which produced a record of vibrations on light-sensitive film. The Milne seismograph was a self-recording instrument capable of preserving a record of ground movement. Milne discovered that the vibrations from a distant earthquake arrived in a series of separate vibrations traveling at different speeds. The greater the separation between the waves of different types, the farther away the earthquake. The method was identical to that used to calculate the distance of a storm from the time between the arrival of the lightning and the sound of the thunder. The seismograph allowed for the identification of three different kinds of waves. The fastest waves are those of compression, or P waves, which move through the air in a manner similar to sound waves. Another type are shear waves, or S waves, which move by the sideways motion of the particle. Then, the surface waves move along boundaries such as the boundary between the rock and the air or the water. The surface waves are a varied group that behave in a way similar to waves in the sea. Milne's early seismograph allowed for the base recording of earthquake waves. Later improvements on his model were computerized, with the waves recorded in binary code rather than on paper. Although the later models were more precise, recording new waves that aroused new investigations, Milne's early seismograph allowed researchers time to make great discoveries. Later research in the field of seismology used the records—seismograms—to learn the composition of the earth by comparing density curves to wave curves. The results of the research revealed that the innermost section of the earth is composed possibly of pure iron. Surrounding the inner core is the molten outer core, with a radius of approximately 3,500 kilometers and composed of an iron alloy with a metal lighter than nickel. The mantle of the earth is the area between the outer core and crust. Probably the most active area in the layers of the earth, the mantle contains large amounts of the mineral olivine. With a thickness of 3,000 kilometers, the mantle was found to consist of two parts: the lower mantle forming the boundary between the upper mantle and the core, discovered by Beno Gutenberg.

Gutenberg's method of research was first used by Andrija Mohorovičić, a Yugoslavian meteorologist, who was one of the pioneers in the science of seismology. The key event that spurred Mohorovičić's inspiration was a minor earthquake in 1909 in Zagreb, Yugoslavia. Upon examining the seismograph records of the earthquake, Mohorovičić found two primary (P) and two secondary (S) waves recorded for each tremor. The separate groups of P and S waves appeared to be traveling at different velocities. Because the type of material as well as its density changes the rate, and sometimes the direction of the wave's speed, the seismogram indicated the presence of a layer of material under the earth's outer crust that was dense enough to alter the velocity of the second group of P and S waves. Because the second wave group reached the recording stations before the first wave group, Mohorovičić deduced that the boundary—now called the Mohorovičić Discontinuity—was more dense than the crust. Along with the discovery of the boundary between the earth's outer crust and upper mantle, Mohorovičić contributed a new application of seismology in exploring the interior structure of the earth.

Gutenberg, a graduate student in Germany, was encouraged to begin his own studies in seismology two years after the discovery of the Mohorovičić Discontinuity. Gutenberg's area of concentration was the mysterious "shadow zone" of seismology. For some unknown reason, P waves disappeared when passing through a 4,400-kilometer-wide area on the side of the earth opposite to the focus, or epicenter of the earthquake. Gutenberg began a mathematical investigation to explain the temporary disappearance of P waves. The most likely answer was suggested by the work of Richard D. Oldham, a geologist, and Emil Wiechert, a geophysicist. Their independently formed theories proposed that the center of the earth contained a large, dense, and perhaps partially molten core. Assuming they were correct, Gutenberg made mathematical models of the effects a dense core would have on P waves. He positioned his hypothetical core at various depths in the earth, then calculated the course and behavior of P waves in each. After comparing his models to actual seismograph readings, he discovered one that confirmed his work. The model that eventually matched the real graphs was based on a core 2,900 kilometers below the surface of the earth. The shadow zone was the boundary between the lower mantle and outer crust. Later research that continued with Gutenberg's original outline altered the accuracy of his placement only slightly and revealed that the outer edge of the core must be molten. Gutenberg's discovery of the boundary between the lower mantle and the upper core is called the Gutenberg Discontinuity.

Impact of Event

Gutenberg's confirmation of the presence of the earth's core and his discovery of the boundary between the outer core and lower mantle in 1913 solved the old mystery of the shadow zone and raised new questions regarding the composition of these areas. While the discovery of the boundary between the earth's lower mantle and outer core was significant in itself, the research techniques applied in the study opened new venues for tackling old problems, as well as providing a built-in continuation of the original research.

As a sideline to Gutenberg's major discovery, later research indicated that the Gutenberg Discontinuity also marked the lowest edges of the continental plates. Through the use of seismographs, the speed of earthquake waves can be applied to learning the composition of a material through which a random wave will pass. Because the waves traveled more slowly in the lower part of the mantle, Gutenberg postulated that the lower mantle was softer than the upper mantle. This theory shed new light on the study of plate tectonics, for if the lower mantle is the layer in which the plates extend the deepest and it is partially molten, the movement of plates is more easily explained.

With the use of seismic waves, Gutenberg and Mohorovičić revealed the interior structure of the earth. The technology of later years was more sensitive and revealed a previously unrecorded set of P waves in the shadow zone of the earth. Based on Gutenberg's findings, the understanding seismologists had of the core did not coincide with this energy rebound. Using the more sensitive records for her research, Inge Lehmann solved the mystery by proposing the existence of an inner core that could reflect the waves. Through the use of seismic velocities, K. E. Bullen proved that the earth's inner core was solid. Despite his ingenious argument, however, one important wave pattern is missing from the records. If the inner core is solid, there should be an extra wave recorded, but so far, it has not appeared in seismographs. Although the interior of the earth is solid, the outer core is molten. The use of densities, as indicated by wave patterns, is essential in determining the composition of the earth's layers. The easier method of comparing infrared densities in the earth with known densities is inapplicable in this case because of the temperature and pressures found in the earth that cannot be duplicated in laboratories. Thus, comparison of observed seismic wave speeds and estimated densities is the method used.

The seismographs were used again by Gutenberg and Charles F. Richter, professors at the California Institute of Technology. A universal way of judging the absolute size of earthquakes was needed, as well as a scale of earthquakes. Richter developed a way to define the amplitudes of magnitudes of earthquakes. Magnitudes are formed by plotting a curve based on the amplitudes of ground motion against the distance of seismograph recording stations from the epicenter, or heart, of the earthquake. Richter used the logarithms of the amplitudes of the earthquakes as they could be determined to the nearest tenth magnitude. Along with Gutenberg, he developed three scales by which to judge an earthquake, one for near earthquakes, one for distant shallow earthquakes, and one for deep-focus earthquakes.

Bibliography

Bolt, Bruce A. *Inside the Earth: Evidence from Earthquakes.* New York: W. H. Freeman, 1982. Intended as an introductory textbook for students in the field of earth sciences, physics, or engineering. A nonmathematical book that can be understood by students in other fields. Presented from the standpoint of observation, this book gives the reader a clear and basic knowledge of seismology and its uses and discoveries.

Clark, Sydney P., Jr. *Structure of the Earth.* Englewood Cliffs, N.J.: Prentice-Hall, 1971. An introductory volume discussing the structure of the earth and its composition as well as the methods of seismology in determining these. Presented in a clear and easily read format, this volume on geophysics and physical geology is a good source of information for any person interested in learning more about the dynamics of the earth.

Hodgson, John H. *Earthquakes and Earth Structure.* Englewood, N.J.: Prentice-Hall, 1964. An excellent study of the relationship of earthquakes to revelations of earth structure. Depicted in a language understandable to the general reader of the science and applications of seismology.

Jacobs, J. A. *The Earth's Core.* New York: Academic Press, 1975. A book, intended for graduate students and researchers, that discusses the geophysics of the layers of the earth, with a concentration on the core and its special properties. Most useful for understanding the current speculation on the earth's interior based on the technology available.

Phillips, O. M. "Earthquakes and Seismic Waves." In *The Heart of the Earth.* San Francisco: Freeman, Cooper, 1968. A more technical volume based on the science of geophysics. Recommended to those with a serious interest in earth science. This book is geared to those who wish to understand the workings of the earth as a complex machine.

Weiner, Jonathan. "The Living Machine." In *The Planet Earth.* New York: Bantam Books, 1986. This is a companion volume to the PBS television series, which is an introductory-level discussion of earth science in general. In addition to basic information on the earth's interior, there are many other topics for those interested in earth science.

Wood, Robert Muir. *Earthquakes and Volcanoes: Causes, Effects, and Predictions.*

New York: Weidenfeld & Nicolson, 1987. This work on earthquakes and volcanoes is understood easily by the average reader. It has excellent explanations of the science behind earthquakes, the cause, and the actual history of earthquakes. Fully illustrated, with a glossary and list of major earthquakes.

Earl G. Hoover

Cross-References

Wiechert Invents the Inverted Pendulum Seismograph (1900), p. 56; Oldham and Mohorovičić Determine the Structure of the Earth's Interior (1906), p. 340; Wegener Proposes the Theory of Continental Drift (1912), p. 522; Richter Develops a Scale for Measuring Earthquake Strength (1935), p. 1050.

HERTZSPRUNG USES CEPHEID VARIABLES TO CALCULATE THE DISTANCES TO STARS

Category of event: Astronomy
Time: 1913
Locale: Potsdam, East Germany

Hertzsprung used Cepheid variables as a means of measuring stellar distances, which led to discoveries regarding the structure of the Galaxy

Principal personages:

EJNAR HERTZSPRUNG (1873-1967), a Danish astronomer who calibrated the period-luminosity relationship for Cepheid variable stars and determined the distance to the Small Magellanic Cloud

HENRIETTA SWAN LEAVITT (1868-1921), an American astronomer who discovered the relationship between a Cepheid variable's period and its intrinsic brightness or luminosity

EDWARD CHARLES PICKERING (1846-1919), an American astronomer who worked with Leavitt on the period-brightness relationship of Cepheid variables

HARLOW SHAPLEY (1885-1972), an American astronomer who used the Cepheid period-luminosity scale and determined the distance to the center of the Milky Way

Summary of Event

Discovering the distances to heavenly objects traditionally has been a difficult undertaking for astronomers. It is possible to use parallax to determine the distance to relatively nearby stars, and this technique produced the first stellar distance measurement made by Friedrich Wilhelm Bessel in 1838. Parallax is a measurement of how far a star appears to move as Earth follows its orbit around the sun. It relies upon an effect similar to what is seen when a finger is held up at arm's length and viewed first with the left eye only and then with the right eye; the finger appears to shift position relative to background objects because of differing lines of sight. Stars make a similar shift in position when viewed first from one end of the earth's orbit and then again six months later, when the earth is at the opposite point in its orbit. If this shift in position can be measured, one can use trigonometry to calculate the distance of the star. This technique is of limited use, however, since for stars more distant than about 65 light-years (where a light-year is approximately 10 trillion kilometers), the shift is so small as to be unmeasurable.

Another distance technique involves comparing a star's apparent magnitude (its brightness as seen from Earth) and its absolute magnitude (its intrinsic or true brightness). The apparent magnitude, the absolute magnitude, and the distance of a star are all related: An apparently dim star can be either intrinsically dim and relatively close or intrinsically very bright and at a great distance. One can make an analogy between light bulbs and stars: Given the appearance of a light bulb of known wattage, an estimate can be made of its distance; given its distance and its apparent brightness, its wattage can be estimated, which represents its intrinsic or absolute brightness. Similarly, for any star, if any two of the properties (absolute magnitude, apparent magnitude, distance) are known, the third property can be calculated. A star's apparent magnitude is always known; it is the distances and the absolute magnitudes that are difficult to discover. Without a way to deduce a star's absolute magnitude, this distance-calculating technique cannot begin.

Henrietta Swan Leavitt was able to find a key to deducing the absolute magnitudes of some stars. In 1912, Leavitt was working with Edward Charles Pickering at the Harvard College Observatory, studying a particular type of star called a Cepheid variable. Such stars vary in brightness over time in a regular periodic cycle; they are named for the first such star known, which appears in the constellation Cepheus. A Cepheid's light output varies as the star as a whole pulsates, periodically contracting inward and expanding outward. Leavitt discovered that there is a relationship between a Cepheid's period (how long it takes to go from brightest to dimmest and back again) and its apparent magnitude. Leavitt produced a plot of period versus apparent magnitude; if the period for one of the stars Leavitt studied is known, then its apparent magnitude could be inferred from this relationship. Also, one can measure simply the apparent magnitude of a star; the real importance of Leavitt's discovery came when it was found that one could use this relationship to infer the absolute magnitude of a star and from that, its distance. Leavitt studied stars in the Small Magellanic Cloud (a small galaxy visible from the Southern Hemisphere). One can assume that all the stars in this cloud are at approximately the same distance. The absolute magnitude of a star varies according to both its distance and its apparent magnitude; since the distance is approximately constant for these stars, the absolute magnitude relates directly to the apparent magnitude and thus to the period. Leavitt and Ejnar Hertzsprung both realized this fact. Hertzsprung saw that Leavitt's period-luminosity plot needed to be calibrated; that is, the relationship between absolute magnitude and period needed to be found. Then, it could be used to find the absolute magnitude for any Cepheid, given its period, and then, using the apparent and absolute magnitudes, to calculate its distance.

Hertzsprung's task was to find a Cepheid variable for which he could measure the distance in some way. He could then calculate its absolute magnitude and establish the relationship between its magnitude and its period. The simplest thing would be to find a Cepheid close enough to show a measurable parallax. Unfortunately, there were no Cepheid variables close enough for this to work. So, Hertzsprung used statistical techniques to discover the distances for a group of Cepheids. First, he found Cepheids for which the proper motions were known; that is, the apparent movement of the star across the sky had been measured. (Although the stars appear fixed to the casual eye, all are moving, and careful observation and measurement can reveal the motion of some of the ones that are closer, faster moving, or both.) From the stars' proper motions, Hertzsprung was able to deduce the component of the proper motion which, on the average, was caused by parallax. Once he had the parallax for a star, he could calculate its distance and its absolute magnitude. Then, he constructed a plot of absolute magnitude versus period for these Cepheids, which showed the relationship between the two quantities. This was the tool astronomers needed: For any Cepheid, given the period, one could read from the plot the absolute brightness, then the distance could be calculated. A relatively simple measurement of the time it took a star to vary in its brightness thus enabled an astronomer to deduce its distance.

Hertzsprung first used this tool on the Cepheids studied by Leavitt and calculated the distance to the Small Magellanic Cloud, where these Cepheid variables were located. He arrived at the figure of about 33,000 light-years. This was a greater distance than any previously determined distance, which was a surprising and vital result and had implications for the later debate on the size of the Milky Way and of the universe as a whole. Later distance-measuring techniques have given a higher distance measurement for the Small Magellanic Cloud, about five times what Hertzsprung found. There are varying reasons for the discrepancy, chief among them being the fact that starlight is absorbed and dimmed as it passes through the Galaxy. This dimming must be taken into account in the equation involving apparent magnitude, absolute magnitude, and distance; however, in 1913 no one was aware of this fact. Harlow Shapley, in his early work with the period-luminosity scale, recalibrated the period-luminosity plot, using techniques similar to those used by Hertzsprung. He arrived at similar results. Later discoveries regarding interstellar absorption of light led to a more accurate calibration, as did the discovery that there are actually two different types of Cepheids, with two different period-luminosity relationships. The work of Leavitt and Hertzsprung opened a host of new possibilities to astronomers, by giving them a powerful new tool for answering one of astronomy's most difficult questions: How far away are the stars? This led to other answers regarding the nature of the Milky Way and of the universe.

Impact of Event

The Cepheid-variable technique of measuring stellar distances has proved to be extremely powerful and has yielded some vital results that changed the basic beliefs about the structure of the universe. It enabled Shapley to determine the shape and size of the Milky Way galaxy, and it enabled Edwin Powell Hubble to determine that the Milky Way is not the whole universe, but that there are other galaxies that are huge, independent stellar systems. Shapley studied the Cepheid variables he observed in globular clusters of stars, so named for their appearance as tightly packed balls of stars. These clusters are not distributed at random in the sky, but appear to be concentrated about a certain section of the sky in the direction of the constellation Sagittarius. Shapley found this pattern important and guessed that perhaps the clusters were gathered about the center of the galaxy. He made measurements of their distances, used these measurements to make a map of the locations of the clusters, and arrived at a distance scale for the Milky Way galaxy. His results, presented in 1918, gave a first estimate of the size of the Milky Way and also revealed some of the structure of the galaxy.

Hubble was the first to realize that there are Cepheid variables in spiral nebulas, which are now recognized to be spiral galaxies similar to our galaxy. At the time, no one knew for certain the nature of these spiral nebulas; it was not known if they were parts of our galaxy that were relatively close and small. Astronomers also were not certain if they were huge, separate, independent systems, appearing small only because of their great distance. In the beginning of the twentieth century, this was a subject of intense astronomical debate. Shapley's results for the size of the Milky Way indicated that if these objects were indeed similar to our galaxy, they must be very distant to appear as small as they do. This great distance would extend vastly the scale of the known universe and also would shift our galaxy's place in it: If there are other galaxies similar to Earth's, then the Milky Way is not in any special or privileged location in the universe. Hubble was able to settle the debate on this important cosmological question by studying photographic plates taken with the new 254-centimeter Hooker telescope on Mount Wilson. He studied plates of the Andromeda nebula and discovered Cepheid variables in the nebula. By using the period-luminosity scale to deduce the distance of these stars, and assuming the stars were indeed physically part of the nebula, Hubble arrived at a great distance for the nebula, which indicated that it was a separate galaxy. This result settled the debate and gave astronomers important information about the size of the universe and Earth's place in it.

Corrections and modifications have been made to the period-luminosity relationship over the years, notably the correction for the fact that there are really two types of Cepheid variables. In addition, other stars with similar period-luminosity relationships have been discovered and used by astronomers.

Bibliography

Asimov, Isaac. *The Universe: From Flat Earth to Quasar.* Rev. ed. New York: Walker, 1971. A chapter on the galaxy tells, in Asimov's usual lucid and engaging style, the story of the discovery of the Cepheid period-luminosity scale and its use in the discovery of the size and structure of the Milky Way and the nature and distance of external galaxies. Includes some drawings and photographs; brief bibliography.

Kaufmann, William J. *Discovering the Universe.* New York: W. H. Freeman, 1987. Chapters such as "Our Galaxy" and "Galaxies" include the story of the discovery of the size and structure of our Galaxy and the nature and distance of external galaxies. An earlier chapter explains also the physical properties of Cepheids that result in their variability. Written for an introductory astronomy class for nonmajors, includes study aids such as chapter summaries, review questions, and glossary, as well as photographs and drawings.

Mitton, Simon, ed. *The Cambridge Encyclopaedia of Astronomy.* New York: Crown,

1977. A chapter, "Cosmology, the Nature of the Universe," includes the story of the first realization of the size of our Galaxy and the distance to other galaxies. "Variable Stars" discusses the period-luminosity relationship and its physical causes. Contains many lovely photographs, as well as helpful diagrams and drawings. Also includes a brief outline of principles of physics relevant to astronomy.

Struve, Otto, and Velta Zebergs. *Astronomy of the Twentieth Century*. New York: Macmillan, 1962. Cowritten by an astronomer who observed firsthand some of the events the book covers, this account emphasizes the contributions of Shapley more than those of Hertzsprung and explains Shapley's method of recalibrating the period-luminosity scale. Includes discussion of Hubble and Shapley's work with the Milky Way and Andromeda galaxies. Drawings, photographs, glossary, and bibliography.

Vaucouleurs, Gérard Henri de. *Discovery of the Universe: An Outline of the History of Astronomy from the Origins to 1956*. New York: Macmillan, 1957. Includes discussion of Hertzsprung's and Leavitt's work on the discovery of the period-luminosity relationship and its use in distance determination. Discusses the work done by Shapley and Hubble in using Cepheid variables as a tool to studies of our Galaxy and other galaxies. Some drawings and photographs; short bibliography.

Mary Hrovat

Cross-References

Leavitt's Study of Variable Stars Unlocks Galactic Distances (1912), p. 496; Shapley Proves the Sun Is Distant from the Center of Our Galaxy (1918), p. 655; Hubble Demonstrates That Other Galaxies Are Independent Systems (1924), p. 766; Baade Corrects an Error in the Cepheid Luminosity Scale (1952), p. 1449.

SALOMON DEVELOPS MAMMOGRAPHY

Category of event: Applied science
Time: 1913
Locale: Germany

Using a technique derived from X-ray photography, Salomon developed the first X-ray detection procedure to be used in the detection and diagnosis of breast cancer

> *Principal personages:*
> ALBERT SALOMON, the first researcher to use X-ray technology to locate and identify breast cancer lesions without surgical biopsy
> W. VOGEL, the author of a classic document that accurately describes differences in the appearance of various kinds of breast tumors as seen using techniques of mammography
> STAFFORD L. WARREN, a surgeon who discovered that breast tumors could be detected using a fluoroscope
> JACOB GERSHON-COHEN (1899-   ), the first breast cancer researcher to call for widespread screening to detect the presence of breast cancer in women over the age of fifty
> ROBERT EGAN, a surgeon who conducted research concurrent with Gershon-Cohen to test the accuracy of mammography as a diagnostic tool

Summary of Event

Breast cancer has been the focus of medical research for more than a century. At the end of the nineteenth century, techniques for detection were almost nonexistent. By the time breast cancer was detected, it was often too late for the radical surgical procedures prevalent at the time, and those patients who underwent such surgery had a high mortality rate. Therefore, cancer researchers were eager to experiment with X-ray technology after it first appeared in 1896.

The first scientist to use X-ray techniques in breast cancer experiments was Albert Salomon, a German surgeon. Salomon X-rayed more than three thousand breasts that had been excised in breast cancer operations in an effort to develop a biopsy technique that would reflect the cancerous and noncancerous nature of tumors without radical exploratory surgery. In 1913, he published the results of his experiments, demonstrating conclusively that X rays could detect breast cancer. His research predicted the presence of a number of different types of breast cancers based upon the character of the X-ray image. While he is the acknowledged inventor of breast radiology, Salomon never actually used the technique to diagnose breast cancer.

Breast cancer radiology, which came to be known as mammography, was not embraced immediately by the medical community. During the 1920's, further research was conducted in Leipzig, Germany, and in South America. Eventually, the

Leipzig group began to use mammography for diagnosis under the direction of Erwin Payr.

One of the classic documents in breast cancer research emerged from the Leipzig experiments. Published in the 1930's by W. Vogel, it accurately described differences between cancerous and benign tumors as they appeared on X-ray photographs. Included was information about the procedure that was useful to diagnosticians. The detailed descriptions included in the paper remain useful.

Mammography received little attention in the United States until 1926, when a Rochester, New York, physician discovered that a fluoroscope could be used to capture breast tissue images that were similar to Salomon's. Stafford L. Warren developed a stereoscopic technique that he employed in preoperative examinations. Warren published his findings in 1930 in what was the first acknowledgment by the United States of the diagnostic potential of Salomon's procedure. The article also described changes in the character of breast tissue caused by pregnancy, lactation, menstruation, and the onset of breast disease.

In the late 1930's, Jacob Gershon-Cohen became the first clinician to advocate regular screening of all women to detect breast cancer before it became a major problem. He cited the high degree of accuracy achieved by using the technique for diagnosis and the relatively low cost. One of the milestones in breast cancer research came in 1956, when Gershon-Cohen and a number of colleagues began a five-year panel study of more than thirteen hundred women to test the accuracy of mammography in the detection of breast cancer. Each subject was screened once every six months. Of the 1,055 subjects who completed the study, 92 were diagnosed with benign tumors and 23 with malignant tumors. Only one malignant tumor was misdiagnosed as benign, a remarkable record. Concurrently, Robert Egan of Houston began tracking breast cancer X rays. Over a three-year period, one thousand X-ray photographs were used to make diagnoses. When these diagnoses were compared to the results of surgical biopsies in the same period, accurate diagnoses were confirmed in 238 of 240 procedures using mammography. Egan joined the crusade for regular breast cancer screening, noting that most women sought help only after tumors had reached advanced states. This led to a poor recovery rate and an emphasis on early detection.

Once mammography finally was accepted by the medical community as an acceptable diagnostic tool in the late 1950's and early 1960's, attention turned to the need for a technique to teach mammography quickly and effectively to those who might employ it. Following a major study whose results were published in 1965, it was determined that any radiologist could conduct the procedure with five days of training. In the early 1970's, the American Cancer Society and the National Cancer Institute joined forces to coordinate a nationwide breast cancer screening program called the Breast Cancer Detection Demonstration Project. Its goal in 1971 was to screen more than a quarter million women over the age of thirty-five. While the accuracy of the detection of breast cancer continued to remain at an extremely high level, a controversy erupted over possible harmful effects of radiation on patients. In

1976, Ralph Nader issued a call for special consent forms that detailed the risks of breast cancer screening, citing the use of radiological techniques. During the ensuing years, the amount of radiation required to diagnose breast cancer has been reduced through refinement of mammography techniques.

Impact of Event

The progress made in mammography during the twentieth century represents a major improvement in the effort to decrease the mortality rate associated with breast cancer. The disease has always been one of the primary contributors to the number of female cancer deaths that occur annually in the United States and around the world. This high figure stems from the fact that women had no way of detecting the disease until tumors were in an advanced state. Once Salomon's procedure was utilized, physicians had a means by which they could look inside breast tissue without engaging in exploratory surgery, thus giving women a screening technique that was simple, painless, and inexpensive.

Unfortunately, most clinicians working with breast cancer during the first half of the twentieth century were not quick to adopt mammography. The complexity of radiology and the lack of standards for interpreting the images contained in an X-ray photograph of breast tissue led to confusion and skepticism by much of the medical community. In fact, despite efforts by Salomon and Vogel to publish useful information intended to be helpful to the practitioner, efforts by other researchers to duplicate the experiments upon which their articles were based proved difficult; the results were often inconclusive. Some clinicians cited the fact that Salomon never used the procedure in his own practice; therefore, he could not prove its success. It would be decades before work would begin in earnest to make mammography a practical, safe procedure.

Interestingly, the development that brought mammography back into the spotlight occurred by accident. Warren discovered that breast tissue could be viewed through a fluoroscope placed 1.8 meters away from the patient. Warren made the discovery while attempting to use the device to examine heart muscle in a patient. He became interested in mammography and published an article that detailed the results of experimentation conducted by him and his colleagues. Unfortunately, the technique he used was complex and required equipment unavailable to most clinicians of the time. Eventually, he lost interest in mammography and went on to other research, thereby resulting in a second failed attempt at radiology by the medical community.

Gershon-Cohen refined mammography in the late 1930's and began the first effort to get women to engage in preemptive screening for breast tumors. Gershon-Cohen was a controversial figure, however, and his experiments were the subject of much debate in the medical community. Some colleagues considered his methodology and reporting techniques inadequate at best, unacceptable at worst. Many refused to acknowledge his work. Gershon-Cohen was also independently wealthy. He was able to purchase the latest equipment for his research without concern for whether the laboratory in which he was working could afford it. This irritated some colleagues, who questioned the practicality of mammography in the real world. Nevertheless, Gershon-Cohen was able to demonstrate that breast cancer screening represented a dependable technique for detecting breast cancer in its earliest stages, a development that would provide a significant challenge to the high rate of breast cancer mortality.

It is important to note that early experiments with mammography involved significant doses of radiation applied to the skin of the patient. During the 1940's and 1950's, concern began to mount over whether mammography was safe. This concern had the effect of slowing interest in the procedure again. In the 1960's and 1970's, public interest groups began to lobby against mammography based on the purported negative effects of radiation exposure during screenings over the long run. Efforts by some groups to require patients to sign consent forms detailing the risks associated with the procedure led to media attention that further diminished the number of women willing to submit to regular screenings. Still, even that problem turned out to be relatively short-term as the technique was refined further and less and less radiation was required. By 1971, a quarter million women over the age of thirty-five had been screened; twenty years later, the number was in the millions.

Radiology is not a science that concerns only breast cancer screening. While it does provide the technical facilities necessary to practice mammography, the photographic images obtained therein must be interpreted by general practitioners, as well as specialists. Once Gershon-Cohen had demonstrated the viability of the technique, a means of training was devised that made it fairly easy for clinicians to learn how to practice mammography successfully. Once all of these factors—accuracy, safety, simplicity—were in place, mammography became an important factor in the fight against breast cancer.

Bibliography

Baum, Michael. *Breast Cancer: The Facts.* New York: Oxford University Press, 1981. Examines what is known about the causes and treatments for various kinds of breast cancers. Included is a discussion of some of the genetic factors that have been encountered in breast cancer research. Baum's goal is to demystify the disease and its treatment.

Gyllenskold, Karin. *Breast Cancer: The Psychological Effects of the Disease and Its Treatment.* Translated by Patricia Crampton. London: Tavistock, 1982. A good summary of some of the psychological factors that appear in many women who suffer from breast cancer. The approach is to separate the disease from its treatment in order to differentiate between the effects caused by each. The intention is to offer information that might help breast cancer patients make decisions about treatment techniques.

History of Cancer Control Project. *A History of Cancer Control in the United States, 1946-1971.* Book 1 in *A History of Scientific and Technical Advances in Cancer Control.* Washington, D.C.: Department of Health, Education, and Welfare, 1979. An excellent history of mammography that includes a lengthy and thorough discussion of the work of Salomon, Gershon-Cohen, Egan, and Warren. Contains sections on the history of detection techniques for other types of cancer.

Kushner, Rose. *Alternatives: New Developments in the War on Breast Cancer.* New York: Warner Books, 1985. Over the past two decades, the emphasis in the treatment of breast cancer has been on prevention and improved surgical techniques that can replace the radical mastectomy in some patients. This book looks at significant developments in the evolution of mammography and outlines methods in which the disease is being viewed and treated.

Watson, Rita Esposito, and Robert Wallach. *New Choices, New Chances.* New York: St. Martin's Press, 1981. Unlike other books that describe the causes and treatments for breast cancer, this book gives advice on how to deal with the disease from a personal level. The upbeat treatment offers hope and encouragement to sufferers.

Michael S. Ameigh

Cross-References

Röntgen Wins the Nobel Prize for the Discovery of X Rays (1901), p. 118; Barkla Discovers the Characteristic X Rays of the Elements (1906), p. 309; Rous Discovers That Some Cancers Are Caused by Viruses (1910), p. 459; Papanicolaou Develops the Pap Test for Diagnosing Uterine Cancer (1928), p. 864; X Rays from a Synchrotron Are First Used in Medical Diagnosis and Treatment (1949), p. 1336; Horsfall Announces That Cancer Results from Alterations in the DNA of Cells (1961), p. 1682; Hounsfield Introduces a CAT Scanner That Can See Clearly into the Body (1972), p. 1961.

SCHICK INTRODUCES THE SCHICK TEST FOR DIPHTHERIA

Category of event: Medicine
Time: 1913
Locale: University of Vienna, Austria

Schick developed the Schick test, a skin test for determining an individual's susceptibility to diphtheria

Principal personages:
BÉLA SCHICK (1877-1967), a Hungarian microbiologist and pediatrician who studied diphtheria, scarlet fever, and other children's diseases as well as establishing modern pediatrics
EDWIN KLEBS (1834-1913), a German microbiologist who, with Friedrich Löffler, identified *Corynebacterium diphtheriae* as the causative agent of diphtheria
FRIEDRICH AUGUST JOHANNES LÖFFLER (1852-1915), a German microbiologist who, with Edwin Klebs, identified the causative agent of diphtheria
PIERRE-PAUL-ÉMILE ROUX (1853-1933), a French microbiologist who, with Alexandre Yersin, identified diphtheria toxin as the disease's active substance
ALEXANDRE YERSIN (1863-1943), a Swiss microbiologist who, with Émile Roux, identified diphtheria toxin as the disease's active substance
EMIL ADOLF VON BEHRING (1854-1917), a German microbiologist and winner of the 1901 Nobel Prize in Physiology or Medicine for his discovery of diphtheria antitoxin

Summary of Event

Diphtheria is a critical disease of the upper respiratory tract (mouth, nose, pharynx) of humans and other animals. Disease symptoms include a fever, sore throat, and generalized pain all over the body. In many victims, the infection produces a pseudomembrane (false membrane) over the surfaces of the tonsils and interior nose. If the disease is not treated with antibiotics, death can result when the infection spreads and causes irreversible tissue damage in the heart and/or kidneys. Diphtheria is caused by the rod-shaped bacterial species *Corynebacterium diphtheriae*. This bacterium can be transmitted from person to person by direct contact or by droplet infection (for example, sneezing). An infected person or a carrier exhibiting no signs of the disease can spread diphtheria. The bacterium is very resilient, withstanding extremes of temperature and drought. It is more common among children as well as individuals who have poor nutrition and who live in crowded, stressful environments. Once it enters a person's body, the bacterium releases protein toxins which destroy cell membranes and internal cell structures.

The 1800's saw an explosion of research in microbiology—the study of small organisms (microorganisms) too small to be seen with the unaided eye. The work of the eminent microbiologists Louis Pasteur, Robert Koch, and others established the germ theory of disease, which maintains that infectious diseases are caused by microorganisms. Microorganisms include a variety of different species from several different life kingdoms, including bacteria, viruses, fungi (for example, ringworm, athlete's foot), protozoa (for example, malaria), and helminths (for example, tapeworms). For practical purposes, most infectious diseases are caused by certain bacterial species or viruses. Koch was the first scientist to identify a bacterial cause of disease in 1876 with *Bacillus anthracis*, which causes anthrax in humans and cattle.

Diphtheria, typhoid fever, scarlet fever, tuberculosis, and several other diseases were major killers during the nineteenth century, especially among hospital and surgical patients, soldiers in battle, and people living in dilapidated, unsanitary conditions. Following the methods established by Koch for identifying the bacterial causes of disease, an approach now known as Koch's postulates, many microbiologists began seeking the microorganisms that cause various diseases. Their ultimate goal was to discover treatments and cures for these diseases.

In 1883, the German microbiologists Edwin Klebs and Friedrich August Johannes Löffler raised guinea pigs infected with diphtheria. They microscopically observed bacteria growing in blood samples obtained from the infected guinea pigs. For every single guinea pig suffering from diphtheria, a particular rod-shaped bacterium was found. This bacterium was not found in the blood of healthy animals. Furthermore, when this specific rod-shaped bacterium was injected into healthy guinea pigs, they contracted diphtheria and more of the same bacterium was recovered from guinea pig blood samples. Klebs and Löffler clearly demonstrated that this rod-shaped bacterium, which they called *Corynebacterium diphtheriae*, was the causative agent of diphtheria.

Pathogenic (disease-causing) bacteria generally damage their host organism (for example, humans) either by invasiveness—where they multiply in tissues and consume available resources—or by releasing toxins—chemicals that damage host cells—often resulting in irreparable damage to certain organs. Löffler correctly hypothesized that *Corynebacterium diphtheriae* affects its victims by releasing a toxin. In 1888, the microbiologists Pierre-Paul-Émile Roux and Alexandre Yersin, working together at the Pasteur Institute in Paris, separated the diphtheria bacteria from the serum in which they were being grown. Roux and Yersin then injected this cell-free serum into healthy animals. These healthy animals began exhibiting symptoms of diphtheria, even though they contained no diphtheria bacteria. Some substance (that is, toxin) was being released by the *Corynebacterium diphtheriae* into the growth serum; this substance was the active damaging agent of diphtheria, a substance later shown to be a type of protein called an exotoxin.

With the discovery of diphtheria toxin, it was possible for microbiologists to design methods of diagnosing, immunizing, and treating diphtheria victims. In 1890, the German microbiologist Emil Adolf von Behring discovered that the blood of animals infected with diphtheria produced an antitoxin, a chemical that binds to the toxin and inactivates it. The animals were producing defensive, or immune, molecules against the toxin. The antitoxin was later shown to be a type of protein called an immunoglobulin, or antibody, produced by immune system cells called lymphocytes. Behring realized the applications of the antitoxin to producing a vaccine, or immunization, against diphtheria. Because of his insight, he is highly regarded as one of the founders of immunology. He injected animals with heat-attenuated (weakened) diphtheria toxin, thereby stimulating the animals' immune systems to manufacture antitoxin without seriously hurting the animals. Unfortunately, this heat-attenuated diphtheria toxin, called a toxoid, was too dangerous for vaccinating humans. Nevertheless, Behring's work stimulated the later use of diphtheria antitoxin produced in horses as a treatment for human diphtheria victims. In 1923, a safe formalin-treated toxin was used to immunize humans against diphtheria.

In 1908, Béla Schick, a pediatrician and microbiologist from Boglár, Hungary, became an assistant to Theodor Escherich at the University of Vienna, Austria. Schick had received his medical degree in 1900 from the Karl Franz University of Graz, Austria. Schick and Escherich studied various diseases of bacterial origin, including diphtheria and scarlet fever. They discovered a series of allergic reactions which followed incidents of scarlet fever.

In 1913, Schick applied the toxin-antitoxin approach of Behring to the development of a reliable test for determining an individual's susceptibility to diphtheria, the likelihood of an individual contracting the disease. The result was the Schick test, a simple, reliable test for diphtheria. Approximately 0.1 milliliter of a specially prepared attenuated toxin solution is injected subcutaneously (beneath the skin) inside a patient's arm. The toxin is treated so that it will generate localized swelling in susceptible individuals without hurting them. If the patient is susceptible to diphtheria, a reddened, swollen rash will appear around the injection site within a few days. A susceptible person will have a positive reaction with redness and swelling because the toxin is damaging skin cells. A nonsusceptible person will have no reaction because the toxin is producing no damage.

Susceptible individuals who test positive for the Schick test should be immunized. Suitable vaccines include the formalin-treated toxin developed in 1923 and the widely used DPT (diphtheria, pertussis, tetanus) vaccine. The DPT vaccine immunizes against three diseases simultaneously. Diphtheria toxoid and DPT vaccines are recommended for children every few months following birth.

Individuals suffering from diphtheria can be treated with a combination of antibiotics and horse serum antitoxin. Antibiotics such as erythromycin destroy the *Corynebacterium diphtheriae* bacteria. The horse serum antitoxin destroys the diphtheria toxin and confers upon the patient temporary passive acquired immunity until the immune system can generate enough antitoxin.

Schick's test for diphtheria became a valuable tool for identifying the disease and for coordinating immunization efforts against diphtheria. For his important contributions, he was named Extraordinary Professor of Children's Diseases at the University of Vienna in 1918. His test saved thousands of lives, especially among children, one of the groups most susceptible to diphtheria.

Impact of Event

The most immediate and important result of Schick's test for diphtheria was its detection of individuals susceptible to diphtheria so that they could be immunized against the disease. While his discovery of the attenuated toxin skin test for diphtheria occurred in 1913, the real impact of the test would not take effect until the middle to late 1920's, when the first successful toxoid vaccine was brought into widespread use. With the combined Schick test and toxoid vaccine, the number of worldwide diphtheria cases dropped dramatically. During the first two decades of the twentieth century, when the test and vaccine were not available, the United States alone saw approximately 150,000 to 200,000 diphtheria cases per year. By the 1970's, the number of diphtheria cases had dropped to less than ten per year. This tremendous decline in the occurrence of diphtheria was paralleled by declines in other diseases that were being studied by other microbiologists. The same pattern of attack that Schick and others applied to diphtheria was applied to many other deadly diseases. Tests and vaccines/treatments were developed for tuberculosis, measles, pertussis, and sexually transmitted diseases (for example, syphilis and gonorrhea). The top killer diseases of 1900 were mostly eradicated in the United States and Europe by the 1960's.

The work of Schick and others was equally important toward demonstrating the presence of microorganisms everywhere in the environment and their potential to cause disease once they are inside the human body. This knowledge was most applicable to medicine, particularly to surgery. Prior to the 1900's, surgical procedures were usually clean, but they were never sterile (that is, absence of microorganisms). Surgical instruments were not sterilized. The routine cleansing of surgical instruments and equipment did not remove bacteria and viruses that could proliferate once they were inside the human body. Consequently, many patients died following surgery. The implications of late nineteenth and early twentieth century microbiological research included the sterilization of surgical equipment and the use of antiseptic measures in hospitals and food distributions. Water sanitation was an additional outcome of tremendous importance.

The Schick test is similar to tests for other diseases, most notably the Dick test for scarlet fever. Both tests rely upon small amounts of bacterial toxin which reacts or does not react with skin tissue. The tuberculin skin test for tuberculosis is based upon closely related principles. Schick's work was one of the culminating triumphs of the late 1800's to pre-World War II, when important breakthroughs saved countless numbers of lives and advanced the field of medicine into a safer, objective, experimental practice.

Bibliography

Audesirk, Gerald J., and Teresa E. Audesirk. *Biology: Life on Earth.* 2d ed. New York: Macmillan, 1989. This introductory biology textbook for undergraduate majors and nonmajors is a strong introduction to the subject. It is very clearly written and illustrated. Chapter 17, "The Diversity of Life: I. Microorganisms," discusses bacteria; chapter 27, "The Immune System: Defense Against Disease," excellently describes how the human body fights infection.

Breed, Robert S., E. G. D. Murray, and Nathan R. Smith, eds. *Bergey's Manual of Determinative Bacteriology.* 7th ed. Baltimore: Williams & Wilkins, 1957. This information-packed manual for microbiologists is a comprehensive guide for classifying bacteria based upon various bacterial characteristics. Every major group of bacteria is described in detail, including microscopic shape and appearance, growth patterns, and responses to chemical treatments.

Eisen, Herman N. *Immunology: An Introduction to Molecular and Cellular Principles of the Immune Responses.* 2d ed. Philadelphia: J. B. Lippincott, 1980. This introductory immunology textbook for advanced undergraduate and graduate students is a comprehensive, detailed presentation of the cellular biochemistry behind the body's immune system. It describes antibody production, skin responses to certain infections, and how vaccines stimulate the immune system.

Gebhardt, Louis P. *Microbiology.* 4th ed. St. Louis: C. V. Mosby, 1970. This short, concise introductory microbiology textbook for undergraduate students is an excellent survey of the science and its history. While providing comprehensive coverage of every branch of microbiology, it is very understandable to the layperson. The book stresses microbiological applications in everyday life.

Mader, Sylvia S. *Biology.* 3d ed. Dubuque, Iowa: Wm. C. Brown, 1990. This introductory biology textbook for undergraduate majors and nonmajors is written for the layperson and is beautifully illustrated. Chapter 23, "Viruses and Monera," describes viruses and bacteria. Chapter 34, "Immunity," is an excellent introduction to the human immune system.

Raven, Peter H., and George B. Johnson. *Biology.* 2d ed. St. Louis: Times Mirror/ Mosby, 1989. This outstanding introductory biology textbook for undergraduate biology majors is written clearly with beautiful photographs and illustrations. Chapter 30, "Bacteria" and chapter 52, "The Immune System," are excellent presentations of microbiology and immunology for the layperson.

Wallace, Robert A., Jack L. King, and Gerald P. Sanders. *Biosphere: The Realm of Life.* 2d ed. Glenview, Ill.: Scott, Foresman, 1988. This is an excellent introductory biology textbook for undergraduate majors and nonmajors. Excellent diagrams, photographs, and writing make this work very understandable to the layperson. Chapter 40, "Immunity," is a clear introduction to the human body's defense mechanisms against disease.

David Wason Hollar, Jr.

Cross-References

Behring Discovers the Diphtheria Antitoxin (1890), p. 6; Calmette and Guérin Develop the Tuberculosis Vaccine BCG (1921), p. 705; Fleming Discovers Penicillin in Molds (1928), p. 873; Zinsser Develops an Immunization Against Typhus (1930), p. 921; Domagk Discovers That a Sulfonamide Can Save Lives (1932), p. 968; Theiler Introduces a Vaccine Against Yellow Fever (1937), p. 1091.

BURTON INTRODUCES THERMAL CRACKING FOR REFINING PETROLEUM

Category of event: Chemistry
Time: January, 1913
Locale: Whiting, Indiana

Employing high temperatures and pressures, Burton developed a large-scale chemical cracking process, thus pioneering a method that met the need for more fuel

Principal personages:

WILLIAM MERRIAM BURTON (1865-1954), a chemist who developed a commercial method to convert high boiling petroleum fractions to gasoline by "cracking" large organic molecules into more useful and marketable smaller units

ROBERT E. HUMPHREYS, a chemist who collaborated with Burton

WILLIAM F. RODGERS, a chemist who collaborated with Burton

EUGENE HOUDRY, an industrial scientist who developed a procedure using catalysts to speed the conversion process, which resulted in high-octane gasoline

Summary of Event

In January, 1913, William Merriam Burton saw the first battery of twelve stills used in the thermal cracking of petroleum products go into operation at Standard Oil of Indiana's Whiting refinery. Although the process would be quickly modified and more efficient techniques and apparatus would be employed by the early 1920's, the Burton process started a multifaceted revolution within the American petroleum industry not only in terms of products made but also in the sense that university-trained scientists were now recognized as possessing an expertise that could lead to enhanced corporate profits.

Although several individuals played important roles in the development of the Burton process, Burton was instrumental to its success. The scale up and commercialization of the process was the result of his vision, his ability to sense future changes in the market, his persistence in the laboratory, his technical skills, and his forceful determination in convincing skeptical Standard Oil of Indiana executives of the method's merit.

Burton earned a B.A. degree from Western Reserve University in 1886 and then attended The Johns Hopkins University, where he studied organic chemistry under Ira Remsen. After receiving his Ph.D. in 1889, Burton was hired by Standard Oil in Cleveland, and a year later transferred to the Whiting, Indiana, refinery where he set up a two-room laboratory in an old farmhouse overlooking Lake Michigan. Initially, Burton developed methods and fabricated apparatus that physically and chemically tested the refinery's kerosenes, greases, waxes, and lubricating oils; later, he used his chemical knowledge to eliminate unwanted sulfur compounds. In 1896, Burton was promoted to refinery superintendent and other Hopkins-trained chemists took his place in the laboratory. One such scientist was Robert E. Humphreys, who subsequently proved to be a valuable collaborator with Burton in the development of the Burton process. At first, however, Burton and Humphreys would team up to tackle a number of small-scale, yet significant, practical problems that involved research on various kinds of greases and on the conversion of hydroxysteric acid from oleic acid, a product that was used to stiffen candles.

Burton began thinking about a feasible way in which more lighter petroleum materials could be obtained from existing stocks. Clearly, Burton had perceived the vicissitudes of a dynamic marketplace, one that was undergoing a dramatic transformation in the wake of the introduction of the automobile. Less kerosene and more gasoline was needed, and as Burton recognized, Standard Oil of Indiana's position at the beginning of the twentieth century was particularly vulnerable since Midwest oil field production was declining. His process not only would change the refinery product mix, increasing lighter organics and decreasing heavier oils, but also conserve existing stocks by greatly increasing the yield of petroleum's most sought after fraction, gasoline. Burton's idea of converting heavier fractions of petroleum to lighter ones was not new; indeed, by 1910 a number of petroleum refiners were operating the so-called coking process, in which heavy oils were placed in an open still and heated at atmospheric pressure, thereby causing the decomposition of some of these materials into a mixture of products that included kerosene and gasoline. Unfortunately, this process was highly inefficient, as little gasoline was made and considerable quantities of heavy coke lined the bottom of the vessels, insulating their walls.

Beginning in 1909, Burton—along with chemists Humphreys and William F. Rodgers—began investigations using a heated tube and lead bath that were aimed at examining the influence of temperature and reaction time on the cracking of various stocks or petroleum cuts into gasoline. While the yields of gasoline reached 20 percent and more, the scientists realized that the key to success was in keeping the heavy, higher molecular weight gas oil fraction from escaping the still before it could be properly cracked. Furthermore, the gasoline that was produced by this method was of poor quality and plugged fuel lines. To prevent this premature escape during distillation, several process techniques were evaluated, including the use of catalysts and the application of high pressures. While a few catalysts were haphazardly tried in the laboratory, the science of using inert materials to alter the course of a chemical reaction was in its infancy. Thus, Burton and his coinvestigators began to think of using high pressures to alter the reaction, yet this method, like catalysis, was an equally imposing technical challenge at this time.

Unknown to Burton, English chemists James Dewar and Boverton Redwood had demonstrated in 1899 that yields of gasoline increased markedly when heavy petroleum oils were heated under pressure, although Burton and his colleagues intuitively sensed that this result would happen. Using pint-sized "bombs" made of hollowed-out metal, Burton and Humphreys gradually raised the pressure in the small-scale reaction vessels at 2.3 kilograms per square centimeter intervals to 34 kilograms; it was at this pressure—one that was dangerously approaching the limits of safety— that gas oil remained in the still and thus could be cracked into useful compounds of lower molecular weight like gasoline.

Major improvements in reactor design quickly followed this discovery. Humphreys added a long inclined tube to the original arrangement of the apparatus, connecting this so-called run-back between the still and the condensing apparatus and thus separating vaporized kerosene from gasoline. With this innovation, yields and product quality were enhanced, and Burton was now in a position to sell his new process to Standard Oil's management. After more than a year of delays—in part the consequence of managerial resistance and in part the result of Standard Oil's legal difficulties related to antitrust difficulties—a pilot plant was erected. In 1912, construction began on the fabrication of the first set of sixty Burton stills, 9 meters in length and 2.4 meters in diameter, the size of the equipment determined by the largest sheets of steel then available.

Although operational difficulties ensued, refinery workers soon learned proper reaction parameters and equipment limitations. By the end of 1913, 240 stills were in place, and profits soared. For each barrel of gas oil distilled and cracked, the company earned twenty-five cents, and further expansion followed. In 1915, Standard Oil (Indiana) sold more than 2.5 million 189-liter barrels of gasoline made in Burton stills, and five years later output rose to more than 5.8 million barrels.

At first, the company had difficulty in marketing the new product, as it passed a yellow hue and had an offensive odor because of the presence of by-product sulfur compounds. The physical properties of this so-called Motor Spirit were dramatically improved, however, by treating the material with sulfuric acid, and it was later blended with "straight run" gasoline.

As the product's quality was enhanced, the Burton process was modified between 1913 and 1920 in several minor yet important respects. In 1914, false bottom plates were installed in the stills; this minor design alteration increased the vessel's capacity as well as efficiency. The introduction of an air-cooled radiator in 1915 and bubble towers in 1918 led to better fractionation and more and better grades of gasoline.

In short, the Burton process transformed the fortunes of Standard Oil (Indiana) and indeed the entire petroleum industry. Although it was licensed for use in many areas of the world—including Indonesia and Romania—its long-term significance was that it would initiate a wave of technical change in a rather conservative industry, causing tradition-bound methods to be supplanted by science-based techniques. Indeed, a wholly new petroleum industry emerged within two decades of Burton's innovation.

Impact of Event

The Burton process influenced the course of the future petroleum industry both directly and indirectly. As a result of Burton's innovation, the amount of gasoline marketed not only by Standard Oil (Indiana) but also by its competitors increased sharply in the decades immediately after its introduction. Thus, in 1925 more than 23 million barrels of gasoline were produced in Burton stills alone. In addition, the severe demands placed on the apparatus by the high temperatures and pressure employed in the process resulted in the development of new reaction vessels, valves, and fittings that were designed to withstand these extreme conditions, and these improvements were utilized in industrial settings outside the petroleum industry. Furthermore, the work of Burton, Humphreys, and Rodgers demonstrated convincingly the value of scientific and technical expertise within the corporate environment. Within a decade of the adoption of the Burton process, most chemical plants and refineries were under the control of scientists rather than foremen; science-based industry was now a reality.

Although engineers continued to improve the Burton process during the decade following its introduction, its long-term significance lay in its pioneering the technological foundations of what emerged as the rapidly emerging field of petroleum cracking technology. The Burton process was a batch process, but by the 1920's continuous thermal cracking processes were developed. Jesse A. Dubbs and his son Carbon P. Dubbs made the most significant early contributions in this field, and their inventions formed the basis of the Universal Oil Products Company. In 1915, Jesse Dubbs patented a process for an apparatus that broke up stubborn water-oil emulsions, and his son incorporated these ideas on continuous flow with the concept of "clean circulation," in which cracked materials from medium weight fractions were separated from heavy portions by subdividing the steams flowing from the cracking coils. Nevertheless, the Dubbs process had inherent inefficiencies, and these shortcomings could be overcome only by using catalysts. It remained for a French industrial scientist, working with American chemists and chemical engineers, to develop an alternative. As a result of his interest in racecar driving, Eugene Houdry searched for a catalyst that would promote the cracking process and result in an increased yield of high-octane gasoline. In 1931, Houdry came to the United States and formed the Houdry Process Company. Collaborating with chemists and engineers at the Sun Oil Company, Houdry developed a catalytic cracking process using cylindrical horizontally arranged reaction chambers and fast-acting valves to increase yields and quality. Compared to 72 octane gasoline produced by the Burton process, Houdry-process gasoline was 88 octane; it proved vital to the manufacture of high octane aviation gasoline during the early years of World War II. Yet, Houdry's design had several shortcomings, including its expensive apparatus and an inability to process heavy fractions and high-sulfur stocks.

As early as the mid-1930's, chemists and engineers sought to overcome these difficulties by designing a moving-bed method in which cracking of crude oil and regeneration of the catalyst took place simultaneously but in separate vessels. In 1938, Warren K. Lewis and E. R. Gilliland of MIT's Chemical Engineering Department combined the moving-bed design concept with the idea of a finely divided "fluid" catalyst, and the fluid cracking process was first put on stream in 1942. It consisted of a regenerator and a reactor contained within a steel skeleton. Oil vapors were cracked in the reactor, where the reaction was accelerated by the fluidized catalyst and the product was separated in fractionating towers. The spent catalyst first flowed to a hopper and was then sent to the regenerator, where carbon was burned off the catalyst particles. The new manufacturing method was integral to the new petrochemical industry that emerged after World War II and that has created the modern synthetic world of the late twentieth century.

In a very real way, however, this modern synthetic world has its technological legacy in the work of Burton, whose process was perhaps the first in which petroleum was chemically transformed into more useful substances. He applied his scientific understanding to a problem in large-scale chemical manufacturing by harnessing knowledge about the fundamental structural properties of organic molecules and initiated a revolution in synthetic materials that continues to this day.

Bibliography

Enos, John L. *Petroleum Progress and Profits: A History of Process Innovation.* Cambridge, Mass.: MIT Press, 1962. Without a doubt, the best work written on the history of petroleum cracking processes. Enos employed considerable primary source materials, including personal communications with historical individuals, to produce a model for future scholarship. Although this work includes a comprehensive chapter on the Burton process, it also contains exhaustive studies of other competing commercial methods, including the Dubbs, Houdry, and fluid catalytic cracking processes.

Giddens, Paul H. *Standard Oil Company (Indiana): Oil Pioneer of the Middle West.* New York: Appleton-Century-Crofts, 1955. In this definitive history of Standard Oil of Indiana, Giddens describes capably the origins of the Burton process and its economic impact upon the firm. Furthermore, the author traces the complex litigation that followed Burton's 1912 patent as infringement claims were filed by Jesse Dubbs and Texaco Company. The strength of this work is placing Burton's innovation within a broad institutional and economic context.

Haynes, Williams. *This Chemical Age: The Miracle of Man-Made Materials.* New York: Alfred A. Knopf, 1942. In a fascinating chapter entitled "Chemists in Spite of Themselves," the author, who was the first to explore systematically the history of the American chemical industry, deals with scientific efforts to increase the yield of gasoline from petroleum crudes. Readable and easy to understand, the section on the Burton process serves as an excellent introduction to the topic.

Heitmann, John A., and David J. Rhees. *Scaling Up: Science, Engineering, and the American Chemical Industry.* Philadelphia: Center for History of Chemistry, 1984. This informative and well-illustrated work centers on the theme of scaling up chemical processes from test tube to large-scale manufacturing facility. The authors employ several case studies to describe the complexities associated with scale up, and they include a discussion on twentieth century petroleum cracking.

Wendt, Gerald L. "The Petroleum Industry." In *Chemistry in Industry*, edited by

H. E. Howe. New York: The Chemical Foundation, 1924. This essay is particularly valuable because it describes clearly the technology commonly employed in the American petroleum industry at the time of Burton's innovation. In addition to excellent sketches of refining and cracking processes and equipment, the various petroleum products commonly marketed during the 1920's are discussed in this nontechnical treatise.

Wilson, Robert E. "Fifteen Years of the Burton Process." *Industrial and Engineering Chemistry* 20 (October, 1928): 1099-1101. Written by a Standard Oil (Indiana) employee, this short article is extremely valuable, for it not only traces early attempts to "crack" petroleum products but also outlines both the economic significance of Burton's innovation and its long-term technological impact. Wilson maintains that Burton's work convinced management of the importance of scientific expertise in controlling and designing refinery operations.

John A. Heitmann

Cross-References

Hughes Revolutionizes Oil Well Drilling (1908), p. 396; Ford Produces Automobiles on a Moving Assembly Line (1913), p. 542.

FABRY QUANTIFIES OZONE
IN THE UPPER ATMOSPHERE

Category of event: Earth science
Time: January 17, 1913
Locale: Marseilles, France

Fabry determined the amount of ozone in an atmospheric column, leading to discovery of the ozone layer

Principal personages:
CHARLES FABRY (1867-1945), a French physicist who invented the Fabry-Pérot interferometer
FREDERICK ALEXANDER LINDEMANN, VISCOUNT CHERWELL (1886-1957), a scientist who headed the Clarendon Laboratory at the University of Oxford
GORDON MILLER BOURNE DOBSON (1889-1976), the English upper-atmosphere meteorologist who designed and built several instruments and directed the world monitoring of ozone from the University of Oxford for more than fifty years
FRIEDRICH WILHELM PAUL GÖTZ (1891-1954), a Swiss meteorologist who suggested the technique for determining the vertical distribution of ozone in the atmosphere while participating in ozone monitoring work

Summary of Event

Experiments performed in the eighteenth century showed that air is a mixture composed of different substances, rather than being a single element as long supposed. Early study of the major, reactive gases of the atmosphere—oxygen, nitrogen, and carbon dioxide—was followed by investigations of other components.

Ozone is a notable gas because of its sharp odor. Impure ozone is produced easily by a spark in oxygen and can collect in the atmosphere near large electric motors. Curious about the possible concentration of ozone at the earth's surface, Walter Noel Hartley devised chemical procedures for collecting and testing for ozone in the laboratory in 1881. Since the concentration of ozone is extremely low, the volume of air required for such tests is large. Thus, Hartley needed to apply spectroscopy to detect ozone in the higher atmosphere.

The science of spectroscopy was at an early stage of development in the late nineteenth and early twentieth centuries. There were no good light detectors other than photographic film. Though film images were all black and white, people recognized that the dispersion of light into different colors caused by a prism made the different colors fall onto different places on a film. The relative attenuation of light at each wavelength—each position on a film—is characteristic of a particular substance. It can be used to identify the presence and quantity of a substance in a mixture such as air.

By studying films, it was learned that ozone absorbed both visible and ultraviolet light. Virtually complete atmospheric absorption of sunlight at wavelengths below 300 nanometers in the ultraviolet was noticed first by Alfred Cornu. Hartley identified this with ozone; therefore, absorptions in this range are termed the Hartley bands. Other examples of absorptions include Chappuis bands, in the region of visible light, and Huggins bands, in the ultraviolet above 300 nanometers. The Chappuis bands are responsible for the blue color of ozone.

Because surface measurements at high and low altitudes showed little difference in the wavelength of cutoff of sunlight, Hartley suggested that much ozone existed high in the atmosphere. Charles Fabry determined how much ozone existed at that level.

Fabry was a physicist whose life's work involved studies of optics. With Alfred Pérot, he invented an interferometer, which produces a succession of light and dark rings on a screen caused by the interference of different colors of light. The instrument is used to measure short distances with unmatched precision. Fabry's interest in astronomy developed working with his two brothers: Eugene, a mathematician, and Louis, an astronomer. Fabry applied his interferometer to the study of the different wavelengths of light received from the sun and stars. The use of different wavelengths was the key to quantitative determination of ozone in the atmosphere.

The intensity of radiation reaching the earth's surface is a function of the intensity of sunlight reaching the top of the atmosphere, the path length of the light through the atmosphere and thus the angle from the zenith (vertical), the amount of dust and molecular scattering of the light on its way through the atmosphere, and the absorption of light by gas molecules such as ozone. All except dust scattering and path length vary with wavelength.

Working with Henri Buisson, Fabry very carefully measured the absorption coefficients of ozone bands at different wavelengths in the laboratory. They used this information to pick two wavelengths, with a known difference in absorption, at which to view sunlight. By measuring at several angles from the zenith, adjustments for the other variations could be made and the total amount of ozone in a vertical column of the atmosphere determined. The unit in which the result has been reported commonly is the thickness of the ozone if it were held in a pure layer at normal, sea level atmospheric pressure and temperature. A thickness of 0.01 millimeter is known as the Dobson unit. Fabry suggested about 5 millimeters of ozone existed in an atmospheric column.

In 1920, Fabry and Buisson modified their instrument to reduce the amount of stray sunlight reaching the photographic film. They made repeated measurements of ozone and checked several pairs of absorptions to assure that it was indeed ozone they were measuring. They found its concentration steady at 3 millimeters. In discussing their results, Fabry and Buisson showed remarkable insight. They noted that ozone probably formed in the upper atmosphere because of absorption of solar radiation and that the maximum concentration of ozone might be at a height of 40 kilometers.

From his study of meteor tracks in 1921, Frederick Alexander Lindemann (later to become Viscount Cherwell) suggested that the atmosphere above 30 kilometers was much warmer than had been supposed. He believed that absorption of solar radiation by ozone was responsible for the warmth. Since it was already known that the temperature of the stratosphere changes with weather patterns, there was some thought that changes in ozone concentrations might be responsible for these patterns.

Thus, Gordon Miller Bourne Dobson established a program at the University of Oxford for the monitoring of atmospheric ozone. Using a spectrograph he built, based on the design of Fabry and Buisson, Dobson collected a series of measurements from a hill outside Oxford, England, in 1925. From these the annual variation in atmospheric ozone was first seen: a maximum in the spring and minimum in the fall. In the next year and a half, a set of six spectrographs was distributed throughout Europe to investigate the relation between ozone and weather patterns. Dobson found higher concentrations of ozone behind cyclones (large wind systems rotating about a region of low pressure) and ahead of anticyclones (systems around a region of high pressure), further reinforcing interest in ozone measurement.

In 1928 to 1929, the same instruments were sent to sites throughout the world to learn of gross variations in ozone with latitude and location. Concentrations were found to be higher and far more variable at higher latitudes. Later measurement suggests a maximum at roughly 60 degrees latitude, but with considerable variation.

In Dobson's early work, all exposed photographic plates were returned to the University of Oxford for development and analysis. This practice removed a potential source of inconsistency. After 1930, the measurement program continued until World War II, with specially designed spectrophotometers using photomultipliers as detectors in place of film. These were particularly advantageous for measurements at low light levels, such as cloudy days and early or late in a day. These took on great importance after it was found that information about the altitude distribution of the ozone could be gleaned from such measurements.

One of the people producing exposures for Dobson was Friedrich Wilhelm Paul Götz, who was working with Dobson to establish the vertical distribution of ozone. Based on variation of their measurements with zenith angle, they tentatively concluded that ozone might be concentrated in a layer near 50 kilometers above the surface, in rough agreement with the suggestion of Fabry and Buisson.

Since Götz's measurements were made in summer at the far northern island of Spitsbergen, Norway, the sun remained close to the horizon for relatively long periods. Light intensity drops steadily at all wavelengths as the angle of the sun from the zenith increases, since beams must pass through a greater thickness of atmosphere. Götz noted, however, that the ratio of intensity at a short versus a long wavelength went through a minimum near 85 degrees, then, contrary to expectation, increased for observations made overhead while the sun was approaching the horizon.

Light measured in this way has all been scattered. The higher the altitude of scattering, the smaller the opportunity to be absorbed. The longer-wavelength light is effectively scattered from lower altitudes, so its intensity keeps decreasing rapidly as the sun sets. Shorter-wavelength light is scattered above the ozone layer, and so its intensity decreases only slowly. The altitude range of the ozone layer can be determined by measuring this *Umkehr*, or reversal effect. A concentration maximum occurs at roughly 25 kilometers, decreasing rather sharply at higher altitudes and more slowly toward the earth's surface.

The simplicity of the measurement, and the ability to use the instruments already in service determining total ozone in a column, made this the most common approach to locating the ozone layer until recently, when satellite data became widely available. A scattering of balloon and rocket measurements confirmed Götz's conclusion and suggested some variations of ozone concentration, which ground-based measurements could not detect.

One instructive improvement on Dobson's work was based on measurement of the changes in absorption of light by ozone with change in temperature. At the low temperatures of the upper atmosphere, background absorption is reduced. Thus, using wavelengths at absorption bands of ozone allows determination of ozone concentration; measurement of background absorption gives ozone temperatures. Such data confirm a region of high temperatures above 35 kilometers, which is caused by ozone absorption.

The first theoretical model of upper atmospheric chemistry was proposed by Sidney Chapman after attending an informal conference during which Fabry, Dobson, and others presented results of their studies. Oliver R. Wulf and Lola S. Deming demonstrated in 1936 that ozone was produced by photochemical dissociation of oxygen. They also contended that, though ozone is unstable, once formed in the region near its concentration maximum, it could exist long enough to drift lower in the atmosphere, where its concentration is affected by cyclonic wind patterns.

Work in the late twentieth century has focused more on consumption of ozone than its formation. In 1950, the role of radical hydroxyl in the reaction chemistry of ozone was discussed by Marcel Nicolet. In 1970, the picture was further modified by Paul J. Crutzen to include the catalytic and stoichiometric reactions with nitrogen oxides. In the late 1970's and 1980's, concern was raised about the catalytic destruction of ozone by chlorine radicals, especially at high latitudes. This has the potential for increasing the intensity of ultraviolet radiation reaching the earth, changing the temperature patterns of the stratosphere, and thus changing the weather patterns of the world.

Impact of Event

Fabry and Buisson's 1913 publication stimulated little other work in the area. Such research was curtailed sharply during World War I. The experiment was clever, but the result was initially merely a curiosity. The first quantitative determination of ozone in the atmosphere was not Fabry's most notable achievement as a physicist.

The 1921 paper by Fabry and Buisson had a greater effect. The results were more reliable because of improvements on the instrument and more repetition of measurements. More important, the conclusion and discussion could be applied immediately by Lindemann and Dobson to explain their own meteor data. Fabry's paper gave Dobson a basis for believing that an extended series of measurements of atmospheric ozone was not only possible but also potentially useful.

Once started on a program of global monitoring for ozone, Dobson's early results could be used to convince granting bodies that money spent on such measurements was worthwhile. The monitoring results that Dobson reported in 1930 have served as a framework on which all later measurements have been based. Dobson's conclusions proved to be erroneous only in a few points, demonstrating his careful attention to equipment and experimental design.

The studies on ozone helped form or correct the meteorologists' view of the atmosphere, and thus helped keep atmospheric physics and meteorology on a sound footing. For example, the study of ozone offered a means to measure gas temperatures above the altitudes reached by most balloons. The most impressive feature of ground-based ozone study is the long-term and global nature of the information. It was not until rocket observations in the late 1950's and 1960's that a detailed investigation of the stratosphere was possible. Without the comprehensive data base already in place, sensible choice and interpretation of experiments would not have been possible.

Because investigation of matter in the upper atmosphere is so difficult, much effort has been applied to development of mathematical models of atmospheric chemistry and physics. The models consider all the different kinds of molecules and their reactions in attempting to understand what is happening. This work requires actual measurements with which to check the models. Though satellites and high altitude airplane flights have improved Earth's picture of ozone distribution, its scale is not fine enough to appreciate ozone movements near the tropopause. Further improvement of atmospheric models requires even more ozone monitoring, so that local variations are known as well as differences between widely scattered points.

Bibliography

Craig, Richard A. *The Edge of Space: Exploring the Upper Atmosphere.* Garden City, N.Y.: Doubleday, 1968. This book, written for a general audience, discusses the various ways used to measure atmospheric ozone. It was written when understanding of ozone chemistry was far less developed, but is based on an important book in aeronomy, *The Upper Atmosphere: Meteorology and Physics*, which Dr. Craig wrote in 1965.

Dobson, G. M. B. "Forty Years' Research on Atmospheric Ozone at Oxford: A History." *Applied Optics* 7 (March, 1968): 387-405. This is a personal recollection of the development of the global network for ozone monitoring. Gives a fascinating, nonmathematical account of the scientific work. Notes the unexpected observation in 1956 of low concentrations of ozone until late in the Antarctic spring; this phenomenon was intensified in subsequent years by the presence of radical chlorine from chlorofluorocarbons and is known as the ozone hole.

Gribbin, John, ed. *The Breathing Planet*. New York: Basil Blackwell, 1986. There is a section on ozone in this collection of short articles taken from the English journal *New Scientist*. The article "Monitoring Halocarbons in the Atmosphere" by Gribbin suggests the difficulties and uncertainties of monitoring substances in the atmosphere.

_____. *The Hole in the Sky*. New York: Bantam Books, 1988. Details concern the destruction of the ozone layer rather than measurement of ozone. It is the most balanced of books on this topic in the late 1980's.

Kerr, J. B., I. A. Asbridge, and W. F. J. Evans. "Intercomparison of Total Ozone Measured by the Brewer and Dobson Spectrophotometers at Toronto." *Journal of Geophysical Research* 93 (September, 1988): 11129-11140. The plots of carefully taken ozone measurements and the discussion of factors recognized as affecting such measurements over long time periods at one site demonstrate, to the seriously suspicious, the variability that makes spotting trends in stratospheric ozone concentration so difficult.

James A. Carroll

Cross-References

Bjerknes Publishes the First Weather Forecast Using Computational Hydrodynamics (1897), p. 21; Teisserenc de Bort Discovers the Stratosphere and the Troposphere (1898), p. 26; Hewitt Invents the Mercury Vapor Lamp (1901), p. 108; Steenbock Discovers That Sunlight Increases Vitamin D in Food (1924), p. 771; Midgley Introduces Dichlorodifluoromethane as a Refrigerant Gas (1930), p. 916; Rowland and Molina Theorize That Ozone Depletion Is Caused by Freon (1973), p. 2009; The British Antarctic Survey Confirms the First Known Hole in the Ozone Layer (1985), p. 2285.

RUSSELL ANNOUNCES HIS
THEORY OF STELLAR EVOLUTION

Category of event: Astronomy
Time: December, 1913
Locale: Princeton, New Jersey

Russell used the color-luminosity relationship of stars to work out a theory of how stars change over time

Principal personages:

HENRY NORRIS RUSSELL (1877-1957), an American astronomer who discovered the color-luminosity relationship and codeveloped the Hertzsprung-Russell diagram that led to his theory of stellar evolution

EJNAR HERTZSPRUNG (1873-1967), a Danish astronomer and photographer, who established that there is a relationship between a star's color and its luminosity (brightness)

SIR JOSEPH NORMAN LOCKYER (1836-1920), a British astronomer who developed a theory of stellar evolution, which was later elaborated upon by Russell

Summary of Event

Sir William Herschel described the starry sky as a garden, wherein one sees stars in varying stages of their lives, as in a garden or a forest one sees plants and trees in varying stages of early growth, maturity, and death. The assumption of seeing stars of different ages and that stars change as they age was an important prerequisite for the formation of theories of stellar evolution. The advent of increasingly sophisticated techniques for classifying stars in the late nineteenth and early twentieth centuries brought a wealth of data on spectral types from which a theory of stellar evolution could be built.

Sir Joseph Norman Lockyer, working in the late 1800's, used the simple classification systems of Angelo Secchi and Hermann Karl Vogel—which placed stars in one of four categories—to develop a scheme for stellar evolution. This scheme was based on current theory regarding the energy source for stars and the physical forces shaping their life histories. At the time, physicists believed that a star's radiation was heat and light, which was released as the star contracted under the force of gravity. A star was believed to form when enough interstellar matter accumulates in one place to begin to exert gravitational attraction on itself and to form a sphere. The star then begins to contract inward under the force of gravity and to heat up and to shine. Eventually, the collapse is halted when a critical density is reached, and the star begins to cool off and die. Lockyer used the spectral classes of the time to identify a sequence of stages through which it was believed that all stars pass.

Henry Norris Russell had at his disposal a more sophisticated system of classification, involving seven classes of stars. Also, many more stars had been classified while Russell was conducting his research. This was largely the result of a program carried out at Harvard College Observatory under the direction of Edward Charles Pickering at the beginning of the twentieth century, in which stars were given classifications based on their spectra. A star's spectrum, or the bands of color and darkness produced when its light is spread out by a prism or grating, contains dark lines that can be used to classify stars. The researchers at Harvard College Observatory looked at thousands of such spectra and classified their associated stars, producing massive catalogs of information on stellar types. Russell was able to use this information in developing his scheme of stellar evolution.

Since stars cannot be directly examined in the laboratory, astronomers are forced to deduce their characteristics from things that can be observed, such as their spectral type or their brightness. Russell was faced with the question of how to identify a star's characteristics and thus its stage of evolution by its visible characteristics. A star's spectral type was almost universally believed at the time to be linked to its surface temperature and its color, and the different types were the result of differing temperatures; however, no consensus had been reached on the cause of differences in brightness. Russell showed that differences in brightness were a result of variations in density. Thus, spectral type was related to surface temperature and color, and brightness was related to density. Russell plotted data on spectral types versus data on the absolute brightness of stars (that is, a star's true brightness, after its brightness as seen from Earth is corrected for its distance). In 1913, he produced a plot of spectral type versus brightness. (Ejnar Hertzsprung had made a similar diagram in 1911; this type of plot is known today as a Hertzsprung-Russell, or H-R, diagram.) He then used this plot to view the relationship between brightness (and density) and spectral type (and color and temperature).

Russell presented his diagram to the Royal Astronomical Society on June 13, 1913, and to the American Astronomical Society in Atlanta, Georgia, on December 30, 1913. He also offered his interpretation of the diagram, in terms of stellar evolution. Most stars fell either on a diagonal band stretching across the plot (the "main sequence") or on a horizontal strip across the top of the plot (the "giant sequence"). The names given to these two sequences were based on work by Hertzsprung and others which determined that the stars on the giant sequence were much larger than the stars on the main sequence. On the main sequence, stars vary in brightness and color, with stars ranging from bright blue ones to dim red ones. On the giant sequence, stars have a fairly constant brightness but vary in type (color). These two groups or sequences of stars were explained by Russell in terms of the age of stars in each sequence. He used the idea that a star's evolution is driven by gravity alone, and that a star begins its life as cool, red, dim, and diffuse, and grows increasingly dense, bright, and hot (with an associated color change) as it contracts. Once it has contracted as far as it can so that no more gravitational energy is available to it, it begins to cool off and become less bright and more red. Russell hypothesized that the large red stars at one end of the giant sequence are the youngest of stars and that they represent the earliest stages in a star's life, when stars are very diffuse and just beginning their gravitational collapse. As a star collapses, it becomes more dense and begins to change color and spectral type as it moves across the giant sequence; it eventually brightens and leaves the giant sequence for the main sequence. At its hottest point, which Russell believed to be the midpoint of its life, the star was at the top of the main sequence among the brightest and bluest stars. As it then began to cool, while continuing to become denser, it slid down the main sequence from being a hot blue star to being a yellow star like the sun and finally to being a dim red star, very dense and near the end of its life. Thus, this track, along the giant sequence and down the main sequence, was thought to be a path of increasing density and increasing age. There were two sorts of red stars: young, diffuse, large ones of increasing temperature and old, dense, small ones of decreasing temperature. A red star could therefore be at either end of its lifetime; Hertzsprung had demonstrated earlier that the spectra of the two types of red stars were different, and thus enabled astronomers to tell whether a red star was old or young.

Russell presented a concise and straightforward scheme of stellar evolution, which neatly fit the known data in terms of the accepted explanation for why stars shine and how they form, exist, and die. He was able to use his diagram to illustrate succinctly the life-stages of a star as he hypothesized them. His work on the temperature and density of stars, as related to spectral type and brightness, was confirmed by later work. Although his evolutionary scheme later required major revision, it was still an important step in the understanding of the "garden" of varying stars we see.

Impact of Event

Hertzsprung-Russell (H-R) diagrams were used by many astronomers immediately after Russell first presented one in 1913, and they are an important tool in astrophysics today. Walter Baade was able to compare H-R diagrams for groups of stars to show that there are, in fact, two populations of stars (one much older than the other) and that each type has its own distinct H-R diagram. This work had important cosmological implications. The H-R diagrams of clusters of stars in the Milky Way have been studied by Robert Julius Trumpler, Bengt Georg Daniel Strömgren, and Gerard Peter Kuiper, among others, to work out theories of stellar formation and evolution.

The discovery that nuclear fusion powers stars for most of their lifetimes, rather than gravitational collapse, brought about drastic revisions in Russell's scheme. Russell's work was important, however, in that it was an early attempt to deduce, from observable quantities, the life cycles of stars. His use of the diagram was a key step in the developing science of astrophysics. Astronomers' knowledge of the causes of a star's observable properties, as plotted on the diagram, changed as they learned of nuclear fusion and nuclear science. Yet, the method of using the H-R diagram as a clue to a star's properties and life cycle has remained the same. Russell pioneered a practice that continues today.

In his explanation of how the H-R diagram reveals the evolution of stars, Russell gave at least a hint of what was to be discovered later about nuclear power fueling the stars. He suggested that perhaps there is a type of energy release related to radioactivity, which could counteract the gravitational pull inward for a brief period and give a star a longer lifetime than it would have had otherwise. He thought this would not be an important enough effect to change the overall life cycle of the star as he described it.

Today, however, it is known that while a star starts to form because a cloud of material collapses under the influence of gravity, eventually conditions become hot enough in the center of the forming star that nuclear fusion begins to occur. The star then lives out most of its life cycle in one spot on the main sequence, its gravitational pull inward balanced by the pressure outward resulting from energy being released in nuclear fusion. Gravity becomes important again at the end of the star's lifetime, where its fate is determined by the amount of mass it contains. (This is also the factor that determines how long the star lives and where on the main sequence it appears, that is, its brightness and color.)

Much has been learned about such exotic objects as white dwarfs, neutron stars, and black holes, which are the end products of evolution for various masses of stars. Without the H-R diagram, and the foundation of knowledge it offers for the understanding of the interrelationships among a star's density, brightness, temperature, and spectral type, astronomers could not have arrived at their current understanding.

Bibliography

Abell, George O. *Realm of the Universe.* 3d ed. New York: Saunders College Publishing, 1984. Introductory college textbook. Contains sections on properties of stars (including a discussion of the H-R diagram) and on stellar evolution (including information on the use of H-R diagrams to test current theories). Glossary and bibliography, numerous diagrams and drawings, and color plates. Each chapter also includes exercises for the student.

Degani, Meir H. *Astronomy Made Simple.* Rev. ed. Garden City, N.Y.: Doubleday, 1976. Chapter 7 contains useful information on stellar properties, such as temperature and density, plus an explanation of the spectral classes and the Hertzsprung-Russell diagram. Chapter 9 details current knowledge of stellar evolution. Written for the self-motivated learner, includes exercises, drawings, and glossary.

Moore, Patrick. *Patrick Moore's History of Astronomy.* 6th rev. ed. London: Macdonald, 1983. A chapter, "The Life of a Star," gives the history of the theory of stellar evolution, as well as discussions on stellar spectra and different types of stars. Drawings, some color photographs, and a list of landmarks in the history of astronomy. Written for the layperson.

Pagels, Heinz. *Perfect Symmetry.* New York: Simon & Schuster, 1985. Section 1, "Herschel's Garden," contains information about H-R diagrams and the wealth of current information on stellar evolution that has resulted from their use. Written in approachable style for the average reader. Some diagrams, notably a schematic H-R diagram, and bibliography.

Pannekoek, A. *A History of Astronomy*. New York: Barnes & Noble Books, 1961. The chapter, "Common Stars," discusses stellar spectroscopy at the beginning of the twentieth century, Russell's work in constructing H-R diagrams, and his theory of stellar evolution. Includes important diagrams, notably Lockyer's evolutionary scheme and Russell's original diagram. A classic in the history of astronomy.

Rigutti, Mario. *A Hundred Billion Stars*. Translated by Mirella Giacconi. Cambridge, Mass.: MIT Press, 1984. Part 3 is devoted to the story of stellar evolution, including use of the H-R diagram. The H-R diagram is discussed in part 2. Diagrams and some black-and-white photographs. Conversational style; directed at amateurs. Contains some mathematics.

Struve, Otto, and Velta Zebergs. *Astronomy of the Twentieth Century*. New York: Macmillan, 1962. Cowritten by an astronomer who participated in some of the history described, this book contains several chapters on the work of Russell and others in determining the life cycles and natures of stars and the development of the H-R diagram. Diagrams, photographs, glossary and bibliography; end-papers contain a timeline of twentieth century astronomy.

Trefil, James S. *Space, Time, Infinity: The Smithsonian Views the Universe*. New York: Pantheon Books, 1985. Although the emphasis of the book is on the universe, it contains a brief chapter, "We Are Made of Star Stuff," which discusses the H-R diagram and theory of stellar evolution. Many beautiful full-color illustrations, including color schematic H-R diagram.

Vaucouleurs, Gérard de. *Discovery of the Universe*. London: Faber & Faber, 1957. Sections 6 through 9 contain an overview of astronomy from late nineteenth century onward. Gives information on Russell's work, including background and follow-up. Diagrams, drawings, and annotated bibliography.

Mary Hrovat

Cross-References

Hertzsprung Notes the Relationship Between Color and Luminosity of Stars (1905), p. 265; Hertzsprung Describes Giant and Dwarf Stellar Divisions (1907), p. 370; Eddington Formulates the Mass-Luminosity Law for Stars (1924), p. 785; Eddington Publishes *The Internal Constitution of the Stars* (1926), p. 815; Chandrasekhar Calculates the Upper Limit of a White Dwarf Star's Mass (1931), p. 948.

RUTHERFORD DISCOVERS THE PROTON

Category of event: Physics
Time: 1914
Locale: University of Manchester, Manchester, England

Rutherford discovered the proton as part of the nuclear structure of the atom

Principal personages:

NIELS BOHR (1885-1962), a Danish physicist who worked with Rutherford on the structure of the atomic nucleus and was noted for his development of a new model of the atom and discovery of quantum physics

LOUIS DE BROGLIE (1892-1987), a French physicist who proposed that for any atomic particle there is an associated wave property

HANS GEIGER (1882-1945), a German physicist who worked with Rutherford on the scattering patterns of the alpha particle; his name is generally associated with the device used to count subatomic particles

PHILIPP LENARD (1862-1947), a Hungarian-German physicist who explored the nature of cathode rays and the photoelectric effect

WOLFGANG PAULI (1900-1958), an Austrian-American physicist who contributed to the quantum theory and developed the exclusion rules

ERNEST RUTHERFORD (1871-1937), a British physicist who produced the first contemporary model of the atom and was awarded the 1908 Nobel Prize in Chemistry

ERWIN SCHRÖDINGER (1887-1961), an Austrian physicist who used the de Broglie idea of waves and particles to propose that electrons form a wave pattern

FREDERICK SODDY (1877-1956), an English chemist who developed, with Rutherford, an explanation of radioactive decay and coined the term "isotope"

Summary of Event

Until the end of the nineteenth century, atoms were thought to be shaped like hard balls, often visualized as minute billiard balls. This model of the atom had satisfied the laws of physics up to that time and it worked particularly well with the behavior of gases, where the gas atoms bounced off one another. Yet, this model of the atom failed to explain certain new phenomena observed at the beginning of the twentieth century. Philipp Lenard had observed cathode rays penetrating thin layers of material and the photoelectric effect where light falling on certain metals produced electricity. By 1903, Lenard suggested that the atom contained more open space than provided by the earlier billiard-ball model or the revised "plum pudding" model, where the atom was a positive sphere embedded by electrons to make it electrically neutral. Experimental evidence of a new model of the atom had to wait for the work of Ernest Rutherford.

Rutherford was a brilliant student and was awarded a scholarship; he chose to work at Cavendish Laboratory, where Sir Joseph John Thomson was the leading authority in electromagnetism. Rutherford initially worked on problems associated with X rays and then became interested in radioactivity. In 1898, he was appointed professor of physics at McGill University in Montreal, where he continued his work on radioactivity. In 1902, assisted by Frederick Soddy, Rutherford developed the first major breakthrough in nuclear physics: an explanation of radioactive disintegration. They suggested that radioactive decay involved the transmutation of one element to another over a specific half-life period. The half-life of a radioactive element is that period when half of a given amount had changed to a sister element. This half-life can be short or, as in the case of uranium and radium, cover thousands of years. From this beginning, Rutherford produced a number of important papers dealing with the nature of radiation; in 1908, his work culminated in the award of the Nobel Prize.

The process of radioactive decay produced alpha and beta particles, and Rutherford began to concentrate on the characteristics of the more massive alpha particle. By now, Rutherford was convinced that alpha particles were essentially similar to helium atoms and began to use this heavy particle to explore the nucleus of the atom. In 1907, Rutherford began a series of experiments at the University of Manchester on the penetration abilities of the alpha particle. These experiments led Rutherford to his greatest discovery: the nuclear structure of the atom. Rutherford first attempted to measure the number of alpha particles given off from one gram of radium. His associate, Hans Geiger, developed an instrument that could be used for this purpose, known as the Geiger counter. A second series of experiments was set up to measure the scattering of the alpha particles that involved the scintillation method. When an alpha particle strikes a screen of zinc sulfide, the point of contact glows in the dark. Yet, the most successful experiment resulted from the effort of a graduate student, Ernest Marsden, who prepared an experiment to measure the scattering effect of alpha particles directly by bouncing them from foils of different materials. In 1909, this experiment produced dramatic results. Alpha particles were scattered through a number of angles, including some that reversed their directions. Rutherford compared it to firing a cannon shot at a piece of tissue paper and having the cannon ball come back at him. Since alpha particles traveled at more than 16,000 kilometers per second, this was a remarkable effect. By 1913, Rutherford worked out the mathematical probability of the various scattering angles and hypothesized on the size of the positive charge at the center of the atom. These figures indicated an atom that consisted largely of empty space. There was an extremely dense nucleus at the center of the atom containing a number of positively charged protons equal to the negative charges of the electron, rendering the atom electrically neutral. In a series of papers published in 1914, Rutherford described the hypothesis of a new atomic model that included the proton as the nucleus of the atom, although he did not name the proton until later.

The scientific community paid little attention to this new model of the atom. It was too great a departure from the traditionally accepted model and, at the time, several insurmountable problems were associated with the new concept. For one, if the electrons orbited the nucleus, they would emit radiation, which in turn would cause a loss of energy, and eventually the electrons would fall into the center of the atom. While the theoretical foundation of nuclear physics was to come from else-where, Rutherford continued his demonstrations of the validity of his atomic model. In 1917, one experiment involved shooting alpha particles into a container of hydrogen. From the scintillations produced by the collisions, there were indications that hydrogen protons were being hit by alpha particles.

The Rutherford model of the atom gained prominence through the work of Niels Bohr. Bohr saved Rutherford's new model of the atom by proposing a quantum theory, where the energy of the spinning electron emitted energy only in specific quanta. This meant that during stable orbits of the electron, there was no emission of radiation, but when the electron jumped from one orbit to another through in-creasing or decreasing energy of the atom, there would be emissions of radiation. Furthermore, the quantum numbers for the electrons were whole numbers. This idea was supported by the characteristic spectral line of the hydrogen atom, but failed to account for the fine detail of the hydrogen spectrum. Although this model of the atom was later referred to as the "Bohr atom," credit must be given to Rutherford for providing the basic structure of the atom.

Impact of Event

The contributions of Rutherford, Bohr, and their predecessors heralded the age of nuclear physics and quantum mechanics. The 1920's provided one of the most fer-tile, creative, and imaginative periods in the history of physics. As various physicists modified and changed the Bohr atom, the model of the atom that had begun as a miniature version of the solar system now could only be described in mathematical terms without a visual counterpart. In 1925, Wolfgang Pauli formulated the exclu-sion principle, which stated that no two electrons on a specific atom had the same quantum number. By allowing for only four quantum numbers, it was possible to arrange all the elements of the periodic table into shells and sub-shells around the nucleus. This classification of elements provided chemists with a useful model for the purposes of interpreting chemical reactions. For physicists, however, this model did not account for problems in the spectral lines of elements. Two major contribu-tions in 1925 drastically altered the form and methodology of nuclear physics. First, Werner Heisenberg decided to abandon all attempts to create visual representations of the atoms and proposed only mathematical relationships between the electrons and the spectral lines of the elements. Then, Louis de Broglie argued that matter and radiation both possessed properties of wave motion as well as particles. In 1926, Erwin Schrödinger brought these developments together and placed the electron into a cloudlike shell, where it was no longer possible to detect the precise location of the particle, but only its wave motion.

Meanwhile, exploration continued of the nucleus of the atom. By 1920, Rutherford not only had discovered the proton but also had proposed the neutron. The proton provided a positive charge and half the atomic weight of the element, while the neutron held no electrical charge, but provided the other half of the atomic weight. In 1932, Rutherford's student, James Chadwick, supplied the experimental evidence for the existence of the neutron. Both Rutherford and Chadwick had pioneered the method of bombarding the atomic nucleus with particles of higher and higher energy. These experiments marked the beginning of high-energy physics and the discovery of about one hundred subatomic particles. Nuclear physics had finally arrived as a field of study with military and commercial consequences.

Bibliography

Broglie, Louis de. *The Revolution in Physics: A Non-Mathematical Survey of Quanta*. Translated by Ralph W. Niemeyer. New York: Noonday Press, 1953. A highly recommended text for those seeking nontechnical information on quantum mechanics. This book attempts to provide a popular explanation of the rapidly changing world of physics and makes the difficult subject of quantum mechanics accessible to the general reader.

Crowther, J. G. *The Cavendish Laboratory, 1874-1974*. New York: Science History Publications, 1974. This work covers the history of the laboratory. The focus is on Thomson, who provided the foundations and research directions of this institution for many years. Eight chapters provide information on his successor, Ernest Rutherford.

Einstein, Albert, and Leopold Infeld. *The Evolution of Physics: The Growth of Ideas from Early Concepts to Relativity and Quanta*. New York: Simon & Schuster, 1938. This is probably one of the most accessible single-volume histories on the development of modern physics available to the general reader. There are virtually no technical terms, and no mathematics background is required. The sections of the book on the decline of the mechanical view and on quanta are highly recommended.

Jammer, Max. *The Conceptual Development of Quantum Mechanics*. New York: McGraw-Hill, 1966. This work traces both the physics and the conceptual framework of quantum theory. The sections dealing with the formative development of quantum theory are moderately accessible for the general reader.

Segrè, Emilio. *From X-Rays to Quarks: Modern Physicists and Their Discoveries*. San Francisco: W. H. Freeman, 1980. Segrè was one of the few physicists who both participated directly in nuclear physics (for which he received a Nobel Prize) and wrote a number of popular accounts on the history of physics. The earlier sections of this volume cover the discoveries and theories of those who produced a coherent picture of the atom. Consequently, it is possible to appreciate the full significance of Rutherford's contribution to the field of nuclear physics.

Trefil, James S. *From Atoms to Quarks: An Introduction to the Strange World of Particle Physics.* New York: Charles Scribner's Sons, 1980. An excellent introductory text to the world of subatomic particles. Chapter 4 on antimatter, chapter 6 on accelerators, and chapter 7 on the discovery of particles are highly recommended.

Victor W. Chen

Cross-References

Becquerel Wins the Nobel Prize for the Discovery of Natural Radioactivity (1903), p. 199; Thomson Wins the Nobel Prize for the Discovery of the Electron (1906), p. 356; Bohr Writes a Trilogy on Atomic and Molecular Structure (1912), p. 507; Rutherford Presents His Theory of the Atom (1912), p. 527; Lawrence Develops the Cyclotron (1931), p. 953; Chadwick Discovers the Neutron (1932), p. 973.

THE FIRST TRANSCONTINENTAL
TELEPHONE CALL IS MADE

Category of event: Applied science
Time: April, 1915
Locale: Jekyll Island, Georgia; New York; San Francisco, California

Bell and Watson, inventors of the telephone, officially opened long-distance telephone service coast to coast

> *Principal personages:*
> ALEXANDER GRAHAM BELL (1847-1922), the inventor of the telephone
> THOMAS A. WATSON (1854-1934), an electrical engineer and Bell's assistant when the telephone was invented

Summary of Event

It would be difficult to dispute the assertion that the telephone is the single most important invention to come out of the nineteenth century. Alexander Graham Bell and Thomas A. Watson opened a new era in communications with their talking machine, making it possible for people to converse over long distances instantaneously for the first time. During the last two decades of the nineteenth century and the first decade of the twentieth century, the American Telephone and Telegraph (AT&T) Company continued to refine and upgrade telephone facilities, introducing such innovations as automatic dialing and long-distance service.

One of the greatest challenges faced by Bell engineers was to develop a way to maintain signal quality over long distances. Telephone wires were susceptible to interference from electrical storms and other naturally occurring phenomena, and electrical resistance and radiation caused a fairly rapid drop-off in signal strength, so that a long-distance telephone conversation was often barely audible, and even more often unintelligible.

By 1900, Bell engineers had discovered that signal strength could be improved somewhat by wrapping the main wire conductor with other, thinner wires, called loading coils, at prescribed intervals along the length of the cable. Using this procedure, Bell extended long-distance service from New York to Denver, Colorado, then considered the farthest point accessible with acceptable and reliable quality. Still, the result was less than satisfactory, as the quality of the signal was unreliable. The Bell company recognized a need for some form of amplification of the signal along the line to improve the quality and make it more reliable.

A breakthrough came in 1906 when a young scientist, Lee de Forest, invented the audion tube, a device capable of sending and, for the first time, amplifying radio waves. Bell scientists recognized immediately the potential the new device had for improving long-distance telephone circuitry and began building repeaters, or amplifiers, to be placed strategically along the long-distance wire network.

Work progressed so quickly that by 1909, Bell officials were predicting that the first transcontinental long-distance service, between New York and San Francisco, was imminent. In that year, Bell President Theodore N. Vail went so far as to promise organizers of the Panama-Pacific Exposition, scheduled to open in San Francisco in 1914, that coast-to-coast telephone service would be available by that date and that the Bell company would offer a demonstration at the Exposition. The promise was risky, because technical problems associated with sending a telephone signal over a 4,800-kilometer-long wire had not been solved yet. De Forest's audion was still a crude device, less capable of meeting the needs of long-distance amplification of telephone signals in the practical sense than in the theoretical sense. Nevertheless, progress was being made.

Two more breakthroughs came in 1912, when de Forest improved on his original concept and a Bell engineer, Harold D. Arnold, improved upon de Forest's concept. The Bell company bought rights to de Forest's vacuum tube patents in 1913 and completed construction of the New York-to-San Francisco circuit, using both loading coils and repeaters. The last connection was made at the Utah-Nevada border on June 17, 1914.

The network was tested successfully on June 29, 1914, but the official demonstration of it was postponed until January 25, 1915, to accommodate the Panama-Pacific Exposition, which also had been postponed. On that date, a circuit was established between Jekyll Island, Georgia, where Theodore Vail was recuperating from an illness, and New York City, where Alexander Graham Bell was standing by to talk to his former associate, Watson, in San Francisco. Once everything was in place, Bell spoke into the telephone. The conversation that took place was: Bell: "Hoy! Hoy! Mr. Watson? Are you there? Do you hear me?" Watson: "Yes, Dr. Bell, I hear you perfectly. Do you hear me well?" Bell: "Yes, your voice is perfectly distinct. It is as clear as if you were here in New York."

The first transcontinental telephone conversation over wire was followed quickly by another that was transmitted via radio. Although the Bell company was slow to recognize the potential of radio wave amplification for "wireless" transmission of telephone conversations, by 1909 the company had made a significant commitment to research in radio telephony. On April 4, 1915, a wireless signal was transmitted by Bell technicians from Montauk Point on Long Island to Wilmington, Delaware, a distance of more than 320 air kilometers. Shortly thereafter, a similar test was conducted between New York and Brunswick, Georgia, via a relay station at Montauk Point. Total distance of the transmission was more than 1,600 kilometers. Finally, in September, 1915, Vail placed a successful transcontinental radio-telephone call from his office in New York to Bell engineering chief J. J. Carty in San Francisco. The first transcontinental call of its kind, it represented the final event in the conquest of the continental United States by the builders of the nationwide telephone network.

Only a month later, the first telephone transmission across the Atlantic Ocean was accomplished via radio from Arlington, Virginia, to the Eiffel Tower in Paris. The signal was detectable, although the quality was poor. It would be ten years before true transatlantic radio-telephone service would begin.

The Bell company recognized that, by creating a nationwide long-distance network, it would increase the total volume of telephone calls simply by increasing the number of destinations reachable from any one telephone station on the system. As the network expanded, each subscriber would have more reason to use the telephone more often, thereby enhancing revenues. Thus, the strategy became one of tying local and regional networks together into one great system. There are several reasons for its implementation. In the early days of long-distance telephony, AT&T refused to grant many independent telephone companies access to its long-distance network, in some cases forcing those operators to deploy their own long-distance lines from city to city. Eventually, Bell company officials began to recognize the possibility that their own refusal to grant long-distance access to competing companies might encourage serious long-distance competition. The company reversed the decision and offered to lease long-distance lines to all telephone companies, including the independents. The result was an immediate upsurge in the volume of calls and a stronger relationship between AT&T and the independent companies.

The political climate of the time also encouraged the company to rethink its policies. There was growing antitrust sentiment that included calls in Congress for the breakup of the near monopoly, and company officials sought a way to appease critics who said it was growing too big too fast. Some said the issue was not the amount of the growth, but the methods used to accomplish it. In the early years of the twentieth century, AT&T gained a reputation for ruthlessness in the acquisition of independent telephone companies. During that period, the company was owned primarily by the famous financier J. P. Morgan, who, critics said, often forced independent telephone companies to sell out to Bell at low prices by cutting off their financing. Eventually, Congress became alarmed at the possibility that nationwide telephone service might soon be controlled by a monopoly capable of setting its own rates without concern for the public welfare. The decision by AT&T to make its long-distance facilities available to independent telephone companies saved it from a government-mandated restructuring that might have been similar in impact to the 1982 consent decree that eventually broke up AT&T. The decision to open the long-distance network to all comers proved to be a boon to the company and all telephone subscribers.

Impact of Event

Just as the railroads had interconnected centers of commerce, industry, and agriculture all across the continental United States in the nineteenth century, the telephone promised to bring a new kind of interconnection to the country in the twentieth century: instantaneous voice communication. During the first quarter century after the invention of the telephone and during its subsequent commercialization, the emphasis by telephone companies was to set up central office switches that would provide interconnection among subscribers within a fairly limited geographical area. Large cities were wired quickly, and by the beginning of the twentieth century most were served by telephone switches that could accommodate thousands of subscribers.

Long-distance service, or interconnection among central offices, developed less quickly and almost exclusively under the aegis of the Bell company. There were many independent local telephone companies, but few provided long-distance service to subscribers. Over time, as telephone service providers and subscribers became increasingly sophisticated in the use of telephone technology, demand for long-distance services increased. Many independent companies sought access to AT&T long-distance lines to provide that service but were rebuffed by the company. At the same time, AT&T was gaining a reputation as a ruthless competitor, intent on taking over independent telephone companies by pressuring their bankers to squeeze them financially, then buying them out at bargain-basement prices.

In the first decade of the twentieth century, the federal government began to question whether AT&T was becoming an undesirable monopoly that should be regulated. The company, feeling threatened, agreed to open its long-distance network to independent companies, in part to protect itself from antitrust litigation by the federal government. Ironically, the company soon learned that providing long-distance network access to outside companies was good business that resulted in significantly increased revenues brought on by the increase in the volume of long-distance traffic.

Still, long distance was fairly regional in 1910. Major cities in the East and the Midwest were interconnected, but loading coil and repeater amplification technology was not yet refined. Also, some regions were still isolated from one another by the lack of workable long-distance circuitry. Once the issue of access was solved, Bell engineers began to seek aggressive ways to amplify telephone signals so that they could be transmitted over great distances. With the invention by de Forest of the audion tube and advances in the conductivity of wire, it was merely a matter of time before the first transcontinental telephone conversation would occur in 1915.

This event became a milestone in the evolution of telephony for two reasons: First, it was a practical demonstration of the almost limitless application of this innovative technology. Second, for the first time in its brief history, the telephone network took on a national character. It was clear that large central office networks, even in large cities such as New York, Chicago, and Baltimore were but relatively small parts of a much larger, universally accessible communication network that spanned a continent. The next step would be to look abroad, to Europe and beyond, as instantaneous communication became a reality around the world.

Bibliography

Brooks, John. *Telephone: The First Hundred Years.* New York: Harper & Row, 1976. An excellent corporate history of the Bell system. Includes many anecdotes and colorful stories about the early years of telephony, giving life and context to what could otherwise be described as a highly technical description of the birth and development of one of the world's most remarkable companies. Includes pictures of principal telephone pioneers and early facilities and equipment. Contains a partial transcript of the conversation between Bell and Watson during their transcontinental telephone call.

Casson, Herbert. *The History of the Telephone*. Chicago, Ill.: F. G. Browne, 1913. A rare glimpse into the early days of telephony as described by many of the innovators who participated in the development of the nationwide telephone network.

Danielian, Noorbar R. *AT&T: The Story of Industrial Conquest*. New York: Vanguard, 1939. A good look at some of the personalities involved in the development of the world's largest telephone network. Provides a strong backdrop for understanding how and why decisions were made regarding the adoption of technical innovations at AT&T through the years.

Fagen, M. D., ed. *A History of Engineering and Science in the Bell System: The Early Years (1875-1925)*. New York: Bell Telephone Laboratories, 1975. A large work prepared by members of the technical staff at the Bell Telephone Laboratories as part of a multivolume set tracing the corporate and technical history of the company.

Rhodes, Frederick Leland. *Beginnings of Telephony*. New York: Harper & Bros., 1929. Describes many of the key developments in the evolution of the telephone and related technology, much of it gleaned from interviews with individuals who were there at the time.

Michael S. Ameigh

Cross-References

Strowger Invents the Automatic Dial Telephone (1891), p. 11; Transatlantic Telephony Is First Demonstrated (1915), p. 620; The First Transatlantic Telephone Cable Is Put Into Operation (1956), p. 1502; Direct Transoceanic Dialing Begins (1971), p. 1934; The First Commercial Test of Fiber Optic Telecommunications Is Conducted (1977), p. 2078.

THE FOKKER AIRCRAFT ARE THE FIRST AIRPLANES EQUIPPED WITH MACHINE GUNS

Category of event: Space and aviation
Time: May, 1915
Locale: Schwerin, Germany

Fokker designed a cam-operated interrupter gear, connected it to the oil-pump drive of an Oberursel engine and the trigger of a Parabellum machine gun, and synchronized the gun to fire through a moving propeller

Principal personages:
> ANTHONY HERMAN GERARD FOKKER (1890-1939), a Dutch-born American entrepreneur, pilot, aircraft designer, and manufacturer
> ROLAND GARROS (1888-1918), a French aviator and the first flier to score a victory over an enemy aircraft by firing through a propeller
> MAX IMMELMANN (1890-1916), a German aviator credited with the first victory using an aircraft mounted forward-firing synchronized machine gun
> RAYMOND SAULNIER (1881-1964), a French aircraft designer and manufacturer
> FRANZ SCHNEIDER (1871-?), a German inventor and aircraft designer

Summary of Event

The first true aerial combat of World War I opened in 1915. Until that time, defensive and offensive weapons attached to airplanes were inadequate for any real combat work. Hand-held weapons and clumsily mounted machine guns were used by pilots and crew members in attempts to convert their observation planes into fighters. In the spring of 1915, the German army had 230 frontline aircraft to the Allies' 500. On April 1, 1915, this situation became more lopsided. From an airfield near Dunkerque, France, a French airman, Lieutenant Roland Garros, was armed with a device that would make his plane the most feared weapon in the air at that time. Prior to the war, Garros had been an acclaimed exhibition pilot, holding the world altitude record and becoming the first person to fly across the Mediterranean. As a combat pilot, however, Garros was frustrated by the inability to maneuver his aircraft into a position where either he or his observer could bring his weapons to bear on the enemy.

During a visit to Paris, Garros met with Raymond Saulnier, a French aircraft designer. In April of 1914, Saulnier had applied for a patent on a device that mechanically linked the trigger of a machine gun to a cam on the engine shaft which, theoretically, would allow the machine gun to fire between the moving blades of the propeller. Unfortunately, the available machine gun Saulnier used to test fire his device was a Hotchkiss gun, which tended to fire at an uneven rate. The low-quality ammunition produced for the guns resulted in a large number of delay-fired rounds. No device could eliminate the Hotchkiss gun from mistiming and destroying the propeller. On Garros' arrival, Saulnier showed him a new invention: a steel deflector that, when fastened to the propeller, would deflect the small percentage of mistimed bullets that would otherwise destroy the blades. The first test firing was a disaster, shooting the propeller off and destroying the fuselage. Modifications were made to the deflector braces, streamlining its form into a wedge shape with gutter-channels for deflected bullets. The invention was attached to a Morane-Saulnier monoplane; on April 1, Garros took off alone toward the German lines. For the first time, a fast, maneuverable airplane—of a design suited for aerial combat—was armed so that the pilot could use his plane for aiming directly at a target.

Success was immediate. Garros shot down a German observation plane that morning. It was the first time a flier ever aimed an aircraft as a weapon and shot through the propeller to bring down an enemy. During the next two weeks, Garros shot down five more German aircraft. The German High Command, frantic over the effectiveness of the French "secret weapon," sent out spies to try to steal the secret and also set up armament committees to develop a similar weapon. Nevertheless, luck was with them. On April 18, 1915, despite warnings by his superiors not to fly over enemy-held territory, Garros was forced to crash-land behind German lines with engine trouble. Before he could destroy his aircraft, Garros and his plane were captured by German troops. The secret weapon was revealed.

The Germans were ecstatic about the opportunity to examine the new French weapon. Unlike the French, the Germans had the first air-cooled machine gun, the Parabellum, which shot continuous bands of one hundred bullets and was reliable enough to be adapted to a timing mechanism.

In May of 1915, the German High Command sent a message to Anthony Herman Gerard Fokker, who at that time was building airplanes for the German Signal Corps in Schwerin, and asked if he could produce a forward-firing machine gun mount similar to the one used by the French. Fokker was shown Garros' Morane plane and was ordered to copy the idea. Instead, Fokker and his assistant designed a new firing system. The design was similar to an interrupter gear patented in 1913 by German designer Franz Schneider, who had devised a method of shooting through the airscrew shaft in the same year. Both these inventions were overlooked by the military.

It is unclear whether Fokker and his team were already working on a synchronizer or to what extent they knew of Saulnier's previous work in France and Schneider's in Germany. Within several days, however, they had constructed a working prototype and attached it to a Fokker *Eindecker 1* airplane. The design consisted of a simple linkage of cams and push-rods connected to the oil-pump drive of an Oberursel engine and the trigger of a Parabellum machine gun.

The technical problem encountered by Fokker was to shoot between the rotating propeller blades. The two-bladed propeller revolved twelve hundred times a minute, so a blade would pass a given point twenty-four hundred times a minute. The firing rate of the Parabellum was six hundred rounds a minute. The solution to the problem involved how to keep the pilot from pulling the trigger when the propeller blade was directly in front of the muzzle. The answer was to make the propeller shoot the gun.

During the testing trials, Fokker attached a small knob to the propeller, striking a cam as it revolved. The cam was attached to the hammer of the machine gun. By slowly rotating the propeller, it was discovered that the gun shot between the blades. To set the timing, a plywood disc was attached to the propeller and test firing continued until an even pattern of bullet holes appeared between the blades. One blade-mounted cam was found to be sufficient to operate the system, because the gun could shoot only six hundred times a minute, while the blades passed a given point twenty-four hundred times a minute. Fokker then attached a knee lever to the cam, which operated a spring-held push-rod. A piece of the rod striking the gun hammer was hinged so the pilot could engage the device when he was ready to shoot.

Fokker took his invention to Doberitz air base, and after a series of exhausting trials before the German High Command, both on the ground and in the air, he was allowed to take two prototypes of the machine-gun-mounted airplanes to Douai in German-held France. At Douai, German pilots crowded into the cockpit with Fokker and were given demonstrations of the plane's capabilities. The airmen were Oswald Boelcke, a test pilot and veteran of forty reconnaissance missions, and Max Immelmann, a young, skillful aviator who was assigned to the front. When the first two combat-ready versions of Fokker's *Eindecker 1* were delivered to the front lines, one was assigned to Boelcke, the other to Immelmann. On August 1, 1915, with their aerodrome under attack from nine English bombers, Boelcke and Immelmann manned their aircraft and attacked. Boelcke's gun jammed, and he was forced to cut off his attack and return to the aerodrome. Immelmann succeeded in shooting down one of the bombers with his synchronized machine gun. It was the first victory credited to the Fokker-designed weapon system.

Impact of Event

At the outbreak of World War I, military strategists and general high commands on both sides saw the wartime function of airplanes as a means to supply intelligence information behind enemy lines or as airborne artillery spotting platforms. As the war progressed and aircraft flew more or less freely across the trenches, providing vital information to both armies, it became apparent to ground commanders that while it was important to obtain intelligence on enemy movements, it was important also to deny the enemy similar information. Early in the war, the French used airplanes as strategic bombing platforms. As both armies began to use their air forces for strategic bombing of troops, railways, ports, and airship sheds, it became evident aircraft would have to be employed against enemy aircraft to prevent reconnaissance and bombing raids.

No aircraft in service to either army at the outset of World War I was intended officially for fighting. It was left to the pilot in a single seat scoutcraft or to the observer in a two-seat observation plane to take a pistol or rifle in order to defend himself and his craft if he encountered an enemy aircraft during a mission. Pistols, rifles, and shotguns loaded with chains, grenades, fléchettes (steel darts), rocks, and grappling hooks were all used in attempts to down enemy aircraft. It was apparent to most aviators that the ideal weapon for aerial combat was the machine gun. The problem was that no airplane in service at the war's start was designed to carry such a weapon. Airplanes at that time were so fragile that the extra weight of a machine gun was enough to hamper their performance.

Two types of aircraft were in service to both armies: pusher style planes with a propeller in the rear and tractor types with the propeller in the front. While tractor types were faster, there was no means of mounting a machine gun in front of the pilot, where he could take aim, without shooting off the blades of his propeller also. Pusher planes, on the other hand, with machine guns mounted on the front, offered the observer a wide field of fire forward, but his field to the sides and rear was obstructed by wings, struts, and wires. He also was forced to rely on the pilot to place him in proper firing position. Experiments at mounting machine guns on the sides of aircraft fuselages, on wing tops, and on swivel mounts all denied the aviator the ability to use his aircraft as a means of aiming at a target.

With the invention of the synchronized forward-firing machine gun, pilots could use their aircraft as attack weapons. A pilot finally could coordinate control of his aircraft and his armaments with maximum efficiency. This conversion of aircraft from nearly passive observation platforms to attack fighters is the single greatest innovation in the history of aerial warfare. The development of fighter aircraft forced a change in military strategy, tactics, and logistics, and ushered in the era of modern warfare. Fighter planes are responsible for the battle-tested military adage: Whoever controls the sky, controls the battlefield.

Bibliography

Batchelor, John, and Bryan Cooper. *Fighter: A History of Fighter Aircraft*. New York: Charles Scribner's Sons, 1974. A beautifully illustrated book on the history of fighter aircraft. It contains a set of diagrams showing the principles of the Fokker interrupter gear and the Garros Wedge.

Bowen, Ezra, and the Editors of Time-Life Books. *Knights of the Air*. Alexandria, Va.: Time-Life Books, 1980. A richly illustrated volume documenting the rise of aerial warfare during World War I. Clear and readable, it gives a good overview of the facts surrounding the development of the synchronized machine gun.

Fokker, Anthony H. G., and Bruce Gould. *Flying Dutchman: The Life of Anthony Fokker*. New York: Holt, 1931. This book, the autobiography of Anthony Fokker, is easily read and well illustrated. Fokker has been noted by his contemporaries and historians as a person of immense ego. In the chapter entitled "I Invent the Synchronized Machine-Gun," Fokker claims total credit for the idea, with no reference to the work of others.

Grey, Charles G. *The History of Combat Airplanes*. Northfield, Vt.: Norwich University, 1942. Highly opinionated book by a contemporary of Fokker. A good reference point to learn about the military and political climate surrounding the invention of the synchronized machine gun.

Phelan, Joseph A. *Heros and Aeroplanes of the Great War, 1914-1918.* New York: Grosset & Dunlap, 1970. This book documents the lives and exploits of many early innovators in aerial combat tactics and illustrates the progression in fighter aircraft design throughout World War I.

Randall L. Milstein

Cross-Reference

The Germans Use the V-1 Flying Bomb and the V-2 Goes into Production (1944), p. 1235.

CORNING GLASS WORKS TRADEMARKS PYREX AND OFFERS PYREX COOKWARE FOR COMMERCIAL SALE

Category of event: Applied science
Time: May 20, 1915
Locale: Corning, New York

After developing heat-resistant borosilicate glass in 1915, Corning Glass Works named the material and began marketing it for bakeware and laboratory applications

Principal personages:
> JESSE T. LITTLETON (1888-1966), the chief physicist of Corning Glass Works' research department and eventual vice president and director of research
> EUGENE G. SULLIVAN (1872-1962), the founder of Corning's research laboratories in 1908
> WILLIAM C. TAYLOR (1886-1958), the assistant to Sullivan in developing heat-resistant borosilicate glass

Summary of Event

The first use of Corning's heat-resistant glass for cooking occurred in 1913. Various stories abound; one version is of Jesse T. Littleton's wife breaking a casserole in which she was about to bake a pudding, and substituting the only vessel available, the cut-off bottom of a battery jar made of heat-resistant glass. The result was "so surprisingly good" that trials were immediately instituted, with glass dishes furnished to others in the laboratory to be used in all kinds of baking. Therefore, the marketing of Pyrex bakeware began in 1915. The actual event was somewhat less serendipitous and more systematic. To place it in perspective, it is necessary to review the history of Corning Glass Works to see why the company produced a heat-resistant glass with no apparent plans to use it in the kitchen or the laboratory.

By the beginning of the twentieth century, Corning had a reputation as an industry that cooperated with the world of science to improve existing products and develop new ones. In the 1870's, the company had hired university scientists to advise on improving the optical quality of glasses, an early example of today's common practice of academics consulting for industry. The company had worked with Thomas Alva Edison to produce blanks for his new incandescent lamps. The company also made lenses for railroad signal lanterns, and Corning's colorants for lens glass were accepted in 1908 by the Railway Signal Association as the standard for the industry. This is the avenue that led to the heat-resistant glass. Lenses for oil or gas lanterns were vulnerable to weather damage; that is, they could shatter if they were heated too much by the flame that produces the light then sprayed by rain or wet snow. This changed a red "stop" light to a clear "proceed" signal and caused many accidents or near misses in railroading in the late nineteenth century.

When Eugene G. Sullivan established Corning's research laboratory in 1908 (the first of its kind devoted to glass research), the task that he undertook with William C. Taylor was that of making a heat-resistant glass for railroad lantern lenses. The problem was that ordinary flint glass (the kind in bottles and windows, made by melting together silica sand, soda, and lime) has a fairly high thermal expansion, but a poor heat conductivity. This means that when it is heated, the outer parts can expand greatly, long before the inner parts are heated at all; or when it is cooled, the outer parts can contract before the inner parts cool. Either situation can cause the glass to break, sometimes violently. Two solutions were possible: to improve the thermal conductivity or to reduce the thermal expansion. The first is what metals do; most metals have an expansion with heat much greater than that of glass, but they conduct heat so quickly that they expand nearly equally throughout and seldom lose structural integrity from uneven expansion. Glass, however, is inherently a poor heat conductor, so this approach was not possible. A formulation had to be found that had little or no thermal expansivity. Pure silica (one example is quartz) fits this description, but it is expensive and, with its high melting point, very difficult to work. The formulation that Sullivan and Taylor devised was a borosilicate glass, essentially a soda-lime glass with the lime replaced by borax, with a small amount of alumina added. This gave the low thermal expansion needed for signal lenses. It also turned out to have good acid-resistance, which led to its being used for the battery jars required for railway telegraph systems and other applications. The glass was marketed as "Nonex" (for "nonexpansion glass").

Littleton joined Corning's research laboratory in 1913. The company had a very successful lens and battery jar material, but no one had even considered it for cooking or other heat-transfer applications, because prevailing opinion was that glass absorbed and conducted heat poorly. This meant that in glass pans, cakes, pies, and the like would cook on the top, where they were exposed to hot air, but would remain cold and wet (or at least undercooked) next to the glass surfaces. Stove burner operations were out of the question. As a physicist, Littleton knew that glass absorbed radiant energy very well. This solved the heat-conduction problem by giving a source of heat in the glass vessel. It would also give glass a significant advantage over metal in baking. Metal bakeware mostly reflects radiant energy to the walls of the oven, where it is lost ultimately to the surroundings. Glass would absorb this radiant energy and conduct it evenly to the cake or pie, giving a better result than that of the metal bakeware. Moreover, glass would not absorb and carry over flavors from one baking to the next, as some metals do.

Littleton took a cut-off battery jar home and asked his wife to bake a cake in it. He took it to the laboratory the next day, handing pieces around and not disclosing the method of baking until all had agreed that the results were excellent. With this agreement, he was able to commit laboratory time to developing variations on the Nonex formula that were more suitable for cooking. The result was Pyrex, patented and trademarked in May of 1915. Today, the patents have long since expired, but the trademark remains the property of Corning. The etymology of the name is interesting. The association with the Greek root *pur* (fire) is fortuitous. The original intent was to model the name on the existing "Nonex," with the word "pie" substituted before the suffix, as the first piece explicitly fabricated as a baking dish was a pie plate.

Initial sale of Pyrex bakeware took place at the Jordan Marsh department store in Boston in 1915. In addition to the pie plate, the company offered cake pans, custard cups, and bread pans. Within a short time, Americans overcame their distrust in glass as a cooking material, and in 1919 more than 4.5 million pieces of bakeware were sold. In the 1930's, Pyrex "Flameware" was introduced, with a new glass formulation that could resist the increased heat of stovetop cooking. The cookery revolution was complete.

In the same year that Pyrex was marketed for cooking, it was also introduced for laboratory apparatus. Laboratory glassware came from Germany at the beginning of the twentieth century; World War I cut off the supply. Corning filled the gap with Pyrex beakers, flasks, and other items, and, by the end of the war, these items were so well entrenched that they remained. Today, Corning-style glassware is found in laboratories all over the world.

Impact of Event

The effect of placing Pyrex cookware on the market was to introduce an entire range of products, in an entirely new material, to the American kitchen and, within a very few years, to kitchens in England and Europe and around the world. In the half century since Flameware was introduced, Corning has gone on to produce a variety of other products and materials: tableware in tempered opal glass; cookware in Pyroceram, a glass product made crystalline by heat treatment with such mechanical strength as to be virtually unbreakable; even hot plates and stoves topped with Pyroceram. It is possible to outfit a kitchen and dining room exclusively in heat-resistant glasses or glass-ceramics, although most households continue to mix these with dishes and cookware in metals and conventional ceramics. The revolution in the kitchen, then, is a revolution by way of addition to existing materials and methods.

In the laboratory, the revolution was one of total replacement. The delicate blown glass equipment that came from Germany was completely displaced by the more rugged and heat-resistant machine-made Pyrex ware. Any number of operations are possible with Pyrex that cannot be performed safely in flint glass: Test tubes can be thrust directly into burner flames, with no preliminary warming; beakers and flasks can be heated on hot plates, which (because contact and heat transfer occur at only a few points) almost inevitably shatters flint glass vessels; materials that dissolve with evolution of heat, like sodium or potassium hydroxide, can be made into solutions directly in Pyrex storage bottles, a process which, if carried out in regular glass, would leave the benchtop and the floor covered with hot caustic solution; thermometers can be placed directly into heating baths 300 degrees or more above room temperature. The list can be expanded indefinitely of heating and cooling operations in Pyrex or other borosilicate vessels (for example, Kimble's "Kimax") that cannot be done in regular glass. It is safe to say that in any laboratory where "wet chemistry" is done (that is, syntheses and analyses in solution in water or other solvents), if all glassware were replaced overnight with that of a century ago, work would immediately stop. Weeks would go by while chemists and technicians retrained themselves in different techniques and slowly reached their previous level of activity. Pyrex revolutionized the laboratory.

Pyrex has found other unique applications since its introduction in 1915. It has proved to be the material of choice for lenses in the great reflector telescopes, beginning in 1934 with that at Mount Palomar. By its nature, astronomical observation must be done with the scope open to the weather. This means that the mirror must not change shape with temperature variations, which rules out metal mirrors. Silvered (or aluminized) Pyrex serves very well, and Corning has developed great expertise in casting and machining Pyrex blanks for mirrors of all sizes. Finally, Pyrex is usually the glass of glass fibers, whether for insulation or as a component in glass-plastic construction materials. Pyrex is less brittle than regular glass and has less of a tendency to break into tiny, needlelike shards.

Bibliography

Hollister, George B. "The Battery Jar That Built a Business." *Gaffer*, July, 1946, 3-6, 18. An account of the original development of Pyrex bakeware, followed by much information on manufacturing and marketing practice. *Gaffer* is an in-house publication of the Corning Glass Works.

_____. *Historical Highlights, Corning*. Pamphlet. Corning, N.Y.: Corporate Communications Division, Corning Glass Works, 1982. A useful chronology from 1851 to 1981 of major events in the company's history. Both technical and managerial advances are given.

_____. "Pyrex Brand Glass Found Suitable for Oven Cooking—1913." In *Historical Records of Corning Glass Works, 1851-1930*. Corning, N.Y.: Corning Glass Works, Archives and Records Division, 1931. Good technical historical background to the material of this article. A typescript from the Archives and Records Division of Corning Glass.

_____. "The Story of Pyrex and Heat Resistant Glass." *Leader*, October 21, 1968, B6. Although a newspaper account, the paper is that of the town of Corning. Article is authoritative if brief, with some information not found in the other references.

Morey, George W. *The Properties of Glass*. New York: Reinhold, 1938. Gives technical material, in tabular and discussion form, of types of glass, including Pyrex. Discusses formulations and chemical, physical, and engineering properties.

Uhlmann, Donald R., and Norbert J. Kreidl, eds. *Glass: Science and Technology*. 4 vols. San Diego, Calif.: Academic Press, 1979-1990. Widely available for interested readers. Discussion of glass formulas.

Robert M. Hawthorne, Jr.

Cross-References

Schmidt Invents the Corrector for the Schmidt Camera and Telescope (1929), p. 884; Lyot Builds the Coronagraph for Telescopically Observing the Sun's Outer Atmosphere (1930), p. 911; Fluorescent Lighting Is Introduced (1936), p. 1080; Reber Builds the First Intentional Radio Telescope (1937), p. 1113; Hale Constructs the Largest Telescope of the Time (1948), p. 1325; The First Commercial Test of Fiber Optic Telecommunications Is Conducted (1977), p. 2078.

McLEAN DISCOVERS THE
NATURAL ANTICOAGULANT HEPARIN

Category of event: Medicine
Time: September, 1915-February, 1916
Locale: Johns Hopkins University, Baltimore, Maryland

McLean, while studying cephalin in liver tissue, accidentally discovered the natural anticoagulant heparin

Principal personages:
JAY MCLEAN (1890-1957), an American physician who discovered heparin and later became a recognized authority on cancer
WILLIAM H. HOWELL (1860-1945), an American physiologist who directed research studies on coagulation
CHARLES H. BEST (1899-1978), a Canadian physiologist who headed the Toronto research team that purified and standardized heparin, making human clinical applications possible

Summary of Event

Jay McLean, a young medical student at Johns Hopkins University, accidentally discovered the natural anticoagulant heparin in 1916 while working on a physiology research project for William H. Howell. McLean wished to become a surgeon with a strong basis in physiology. He asked to be assigned a problem he could finish and publish in a year. He specifically requested that he be allowed to work on the problem alone in order to prove to himself that he had the ability to accomplish a complex task on his own. For more than thirty years, Howell had been studying the various aspects of the coagulation of blood. At the time, he was performing blood clotting experiments involving a substance known as cephalin. Howell considered cephalin to be the thromboplastic substance of the body, meaning that cephalin caused the blood to clot. The problem Howell assigned McLean was to develop a method to prepare cephalin in a highly purified form and to determine if it enhanced the clotting process. The method of obtaining cephalin previously employed by Howell used macerated brain tissue, which contains large amounts of cephalin. This brain tissue was dried on glass plates and then taken through a series of complex, time-consuming steps, using extraction by ether and alcohol precipitation in order to separate out the cephalin.

As McLean began work on his project, he also began taking an advanced course in German. While reading in German chemical literature, he learned of work in Germany in which substances similar to cephalin were being extracted from heart and liver tissue. McLean suggested to Howell that it might be advantageous to use other organs in his experiments. Subsequently, he found that extracts from heart and liver tissue did indeed possess thromboplastic activity, but apparently the extracts were not pure cephalin. This was demonstrated by the fact that the precipitates from the heart and liver tissue had different appearances from the cephalin precipitate from brain tissue. McLean referred to the extract from the heart as cuorin and the extract from the liver as heparphosphatid, the terms used in the German literature. In the course of his experiments, McLean also found that with time the thromboplastic activity of cephalin deteriorated in these tissues. It was while he was attempting to determine how long the thromboplastic activity lasted that McLean discovered that at a certain point, not only did the liver extract fail to cause blood to clot, but it actually prevented the blood from clotting. McLean concluded that this inhibition of coagulation was apparently the result of the substances mixed with the cephalin in the heparphosphatid extract.

Since this discovery was not a part of the assigned problem, McLean did not inform Howell immediately. He instead repeated the experiment several times to prove that the conclusion was correct. When McLean informed Howell of his finding, Howell was understandably skeptical that McLean had discovered a naturally occurring anticoagulant. In order to convince Howell, McLean added some of his extract to the freshly drawn blood of a laboratory cat, and as McLean predicted, the blood failed to clot. Even though Howell still was not totally convinced, he realized the importance of McLean's work and decided to continue research on the project.

The first presentation concerning the anticoagulant at a scientific meeting was made February 19, 1916, before the Society of the Normal and Pathological Physiology at the University of Pennsylvania. In June, 1916, McLean submitted his work on the thromboplastic action of cephalin for publication in *The American Journal of Physiology*. Howell had discouraged McLean from mentioning the discovery of the anticoagulant substance, which McLean called heparphosphatid. In a letter to Charles H. Best, McLean stated that Howell did not think that he should include anything about the discovery of the anticoagulant in his paper, but that it should be studied thoroughly and a separate paper written on it later. McLean argued that the finding was made during 1915-1916, and he believed that its discovery should be included as a record of the work done during that period. Howell finally agreed to permit its inclusion in the body of his paper. Further, in his letter to Best, McLean stated that Howell was very skeptical that he had found a true anticoagulant. This was because McLean was using a very weak solution of the anticoagulant and that it was only through very careful records and the systematic saving of little tubes and repetition that he was aware that he had an actual anticoagulant.

After McLean left Johns Hopkins University, Howell, working with Emmett Holt, continued McLean's work. Howell and Holt, after evaluating many variations of McLean's methods, developed a technique that would yield a reliable preparation of the anticoagulant. In their publication in *The American Journal of Physiology* submitted in October, 1918, Howell and Holt first introduced the word "heparin" for the heparphosphatid which McLean had discovered. In this article, they also described how heparin could be prepared from lymph glands, as well as from heart and liver. They described the antagonism between heparin and cephalin in the clotting mechanism. Howell later published papers in 1922 and 1925 describing the preparation of heparin in a more purified form. In 1928, he published a detailed paper on the chemical and physiological reactions of heparin. Meanwhile, Best, working at the University of Toronto, had been concerned with the preparation of insulin for administration to diabetic patients; after learning of Howell's work, he recognized the potential clinical applications of heparin. Realizing that clinical trials of heparin must be preceded by extensive work on its chemical preparation, Best organized a group of scientists to study its chemistry and physiology. From 1928 through 1936, numerous discoveries concerning heparin came from the University of Toronto. Working under the direction of Best, David Scott and Arthur Charles discovered that heparin could be extracted from beef lung, a much less expensive source. These investigators also developed methods of purifying, concentrating, and standardizing heparin. At this time, it was demonstrated also that heparin was an effective anticoagulant in dogs.

Impact of Event

The first clinical trials with heparin were done by E. C. Mason in 1924 and Howell in 1928 in blood transfusion studies. These trials were largely unsuccessful because of the undesirable reactions in the patients. As soon as a purified, concentrated form of heparin became available in 1935, Gordon Murray began clinical trials in Toronto. His results, published in 1937, clearly indicated treatment with heparin could prevent some types of clinical thrombosis. The availability of heparin also made possible a large number of experimental studies. These resulted in the first exchange transfusion in 1938 and the development of the artificial kidney in 1944. Also, in the 1940's, large-scale clinical experiments with anticoagulant therapy in the United States, Sweden, and Switzerland were begun. These experiments involved heparin treatment of medical conditions such as leg thrombosis, thrombophlebitis of deep veins, and pulmonary embolism. The success of these studies firmly established the use of heparin in medical practice. It was not until 1966, however, that studies were done to demonstrate the use of heparin in the prevention of postoperative thrombosis, a frequent cause of complications and mortality following surgery. In a study by J. G. Scharnoff, patients receiving small doses of heparin subcutaneously prior to surgery had a lower incidence of thromboemboli. Because of the fact that this study did not have proper controls, it was not widely accepted as valid. Beginning in the early 1970's, however, numerous other studies demonstrated conclusively the benefit of prophylactic administration of heparin.

The role of heparin is important in both the treatment and prevention of thrombosis. The drug cannot be given orally and therefore must be administered either by continuous or intermittent intravenous infusion or by subcutaneous injection. It may be administered in either low, medium, or high dosage. Low-dosage therapy is indicated for the prevention of deep-vein thrombosis of the lower extremities, especially in high-risk surgical patients. A medium dose is given to patients with active phlebitis, with pulmonary emboli, and to patients undergoing total hip replacement surgery. A high dose is administered to patients with massive pulmonary embolism.

Even though heparin is tremendously valuable in reducing sickness and death, it is not without its problems. Since clotting is a natural protective mechanism of the body, its inhibition by heparin can lead to excessive bleeding. Heparin-associated complications are prevalent. A 1977 study by J. Porter indicated that heparin was the most common cause of drug-related deaths of hospitalized patients. Heparin also has uses in medical science beyond treatment and prevention of thrombosis. It makes possible the maintenance of blood circulation outside the body which is necessary in heart surgery and in renal dialysis. Heparin is used also to prevent clotting in devices implanted in a vein for the intermittent injection of medication or the withdrawing of blood for laboratory testing.

Bibliography

Best, Charles H. "Preparation of Heparin and Its Use in the First Clinical Cases." *Circulation* 19 (January, 1959): 79-86. A very interesting article written with a historical perspective by one of the early investigators of heparin. The article was written as a part of a Historical Symposium on Anticoagulants. It includes excerpts from McLean's and Howell's letters and makes reference to other early investigators of heparin.

Howell, W. H., and Emmett Holt. "Two New Factors in Blood Coagulation—Heparin and Pro-antithrombin." *The American Journal of Physiology* 47 (1918): 328-341. This is a technical article in which Howell expanded McLean's work and first introduced the term "heparin." Howell also describes other factors involved in the coagulation process and correctly identifies the role of heparin to prevent intravascular coagulation.

McLean, Jay. "The Thromboplastic Action of Cephalin." *The American Journal of Physiology* 41 (1916): 250-257. In this article, McLean first reported his discovery of the natural anticoagulant. Although written in fairly technical language, it gives considerable insight into the extent and complexity of McLean's work.

Triplett, Douglas A., ed. "Heparin: Clinical Use and Laboratory Monitoring." In *Laboratory Evaluation of Coagulation.* Chicago: American Society of Clinical Pathologists Press, 1982. This chapter provides a thorough yet readable description of heparin's biochemistry, biological actions, and clinical applications. Includes a very thorough list of 172 references.

Wintrobe, Maxwell M. *Hematology, the Blossoming of a Science: A Story of Inspiration and Effort.* Philadelphia: Lea & Febiger, 1985. A very impressive work that covers the historical development of the study of blood. Although little is devoted to heparin itself, anyone interested in the history of medicine will find this book informative.

Deborah L. Rogers

Cross-References

Abel Develops the First Artificial Kidney (1912), p. 512; Gibbon Develops the Heart-Lung Machine (1934), p. 1024; Barnard Performs the First Human Heart Transplant (1967), p. 1866; DeVries Implants the First Jarvik-7 Artificial Heart (1982), p. 2195.

TRANSATLANTIC RADIOTELEPHONY IS FIRST DEMONSTRATED

Category of event: Applied science
Time: October, 1915
Locale: Arlington, Virginia; and Paris, France

Telephone engineers sent radio messages from the United States to Europe

Principal personages:

REGINALD AUBREY FESSENDEN (1866-1932), an American electrical engineer who pioneered radio communication with continuous radio waves

LEE DE FOREST (1873-1961), an American inventor who produced one of the first vacuum tubes and played an important role in the development of radio

HAROLD D. ARNOLD (1883-1933), an American physicist who significantly improved the audion as an electronic amplifier

JOHN J. CARTY (1861-1932), an American electrical engineer who led the research effort of the telephone companies as chief engineer

THEODORE NEWTON VAIL (1845-1920), an American businessman who helped establish the American Telephone and Telegraph Company and became its president in 1907

Summary of Event

The idea of commercial transatlantic communication was first raised by Guglielmo Marconi, the pioneer of wireless telegraphy. Marconi used a spark transmitter to generate radio waves, which were interrupted, or modulated, to form the dots and dashes of Morse code. The rapid generation of sparks created an electromagnetic disturbance that sent radio waves of different frequencies into the air—a broad, noisy transmission that was difficult to tune and detect. The inventor Reginald Aubrey Fessenden produced an alternative method that became the basis of radio technology in the twentieth century. His continuous radio wave kept to one frequency, making it much easier to detect at long distances. Furthermore, the continuous waves could be modulated by an audio signal, making it possible to transmit the sound of speech.

Fessenden was faced with the problem of generating continuous waves. He found the answer in the alternator that produced electric current for use in the home and workplace. Fessenden's alternator was designed to generate electromagnetic waves at the high frequencies required in radio transmission. It was specially constructed at the laboratories of the General Electric Company. The machine was shipped to Brant Rock, Massachusetts, in 1906 for testing. Radio messages were sent to a boat cruising offshore, and the feasibility of radiotelephony was thus demonstrated. Fessenden followed this success with a broadcast of messages and music between Brant Rock and a receiving station constructed at Plymouth, Massachusetts.

The equipment installed at Brant Rock had a range of about 160 kilometers. The transmission distance was determined by the strength of the electric power delivered by the alternator, which was measured in watts. Fessenden's alternator was rated at 500 watts, but it usually delivered much less. Yet, this was sufficient to send a radio message across the Atlantic. Fessenden had built a receiving station at Machrihanish, on the west coast of Scotland, to test the operation of a large rotary spark transmitter he had constructed. An operator at this station picked up the voice of an engineer at Brant Rock, sending instructions to Plymouth. The first radiotelephone message had been sent across the Atlantic by accident. Fessenden decided not to make this startling development public. The station at Machrihanish was destroyed in a storm, making it impossible to carry out further tests. The successful transmission undoubtedly had been the result of exceptionally clear atmospheric conditions that might never again favor the inventor. Fessenden decided to concentrate on perfecting and marketing a system of radiotelephony that joined ships at sea with stations on the shore. He set up companies to exploit his invention and continued experiments with radio wave generation.

One of the parties following the experiments in radiotelephony was the American Telephone and Telegraph Company (AT&T). Fessenden entered into negotiations to sell his system to the telephone company, but the sale was never made. AT&T was more interested in finding a way of improving its wired communications than branching out into radio. The strategy followed by AT&T president Theodore Newton Vail was to dominate telephone communication in the United States with one integrated system and one universal service. This ambitious plan required control of all technologies related to long-distance communication. Subsequently, AT&T consolidated its research and development effort into a department led by John J. Carty, formerly chief engineer of the New York Telephone Company. After the financial panic of 1907 had been overcome, Carty was given the resources and scientific personnel to initiate a program of impressive technical development of the telephone system. His laboratory became one of the leading industrial research organizations in the United States. The technical problem facing Carty was to extend the reach of long-distance telephone service. Vail's strategy of one system was based on transcontinental service and Carty had promised a demonstration of a coast-to-coast telephone call for the Panama-Pacific Exposition scheduled for 1914. Carty's laboratory searched for a means to amplify telephone messages so that they could travel longer distances. After examining magnetic and electromechanical devices, Carty's research staff decided that electronic amplification promised better results. This led them to examine the newly developed vacuum tube.

The English physicist John Ambrose Fleming invented a two-element (diode) vacuum tube in 1904 that could be used to generate and detect radio waves. Two years later, the American inventor Lee de Forest added a third element to the diode to produce his "audion" (triode), which was a more sensitive detector. Announcements of this progress in radio technology had made the stockholders of the telephone companies fear that wired communications soon might be replaced completely by radio. AT&T wanted to gain a foothold in radio in case rapid technical advance made it a better form of communication than the telephone.

The research laboratory of the telephone companies had carefully examined the new devices produced for radio. Carty became convinced that the amplification problem in telephony and radio had the same solution. An electronic amplifier could be used to increase the strength of telephone signals, and it could generate continuous radio waves that could travel long distances. On Carty's advice, AT&T purchased the rights to de Forest's audion. A team of about twenty-five researchers, under the leadership of physicist Harold D. Arnold, were assigned the job of perfecting the triode and turning it into a reliable amplifier. The improved triode was responsible for the success of transcontinental telephone service introduced in January, 1915. Also, the triode was the basis of AT&T's foray into radio telephony. Carty's research plan called for a system composed of an oscillator (to generate the carrier wave), a modulator (to impose the audio signal on the carrier), and an amplifier (to transmit the modulated carrier wave through the air). Arnold designed the power amplifier around banks of triodes arranged in parallel. The test transmitter constructed in 1915 consisted of a modulator and a three-hundred-tube parallel amplifier. As each tube gave out 25 watts, the total power output of the transmitter was 7,500 watts, enough to send the radio waves over thousands of kilometers.

The apparatus was installed in the United States Navy's radio tower in Arlington, Virginia, in 1915. Radio messages from Arlington were picked up at a receiving station in California, a distance of 4,000 kilometers, then at a station in Pearl Harbor, Hawaii, which was 7,200 kilometers from Arlington. AT&T's engineers had succeeded in joining its telephone lines with the radio transmitter at Arlington; therefore, president Vail could pick up his telephone and talk directly with someone in California. The next experiment was to send a radio message from Arlington to a receiving station set up in the Eiffel Tower in Paris. After several unsuccessful attempts, the telephone engineers in the Eiffel Tower finally heard Arlington's messages on October 21, 1915. The AT&T receiving station in Hawaii also picked up the messages. The acknowledgments of receipt of the messages had to be sent by telegraph to the United States because both stations were set up to receive only. The Arlington-to-Paris transmission was a one-way transmission. Two-way radio communication was still years in the future.

Impact of Event

The announcement that messages had been received in Paris was front-page news that brought about an outburst of national pride in the United States. The demonstration of transatlantic radio telephony was more important as publicity for AT&T than as a scientific advance. The national attention and media response were fixed firmly on the Arlington-to-Paris transmission, despite the fact that the Arlington-to-Hawaii transmission was longer and involved the more difficult task of sending radio waves across land. The great publicity given to the receipt of messages in France achieved AT&T's goal of taking the high ground of radio technology and imprinting this on the public mind. Telephone stockholders would not concern themselves any longer with the threat that radio posed to wired communication. AT&T announced a transcontinental radio telephone service in 1915, although it had no intention of replacing its wires; radio was to complement the universal service.

Vail ensured that all the credit went to AT&T and to Carty's laboratory. Both Fessenden and de Forest attempted to draw attention to their contributions to long-distance radio telephony, but to no avail. The Arlington-to-Paris transmission was a triumph for corporate public relations and corporate research. The development of the triode had been achieved with large teams of highly trained scientists—a contrast to the small-scale efforts of Fessenden and de Forest, who had little formal scientific training. Carty's laboratory was an example of the new type of industrial research that was to dominate the twentieth century. The golden days of the lone inventor, in the mold of Thomas Edison or Alexander Graham Bell, were gone. Only the large corporation had the resources to develop new technology and market it. It was significant that all the businesses started by Fessenden and de Forest failed. The pioneers of radio got little financial reward for their efforts.

In the years that followed the first transatlantic radio telephone messages, little was done by AT&T to advance the technology or to develop a commercial service. The equipment used in the 1915 demonstration was more a makeshift laboratory apparatus than a prototype for a new radio technology. The messages sent were short and faint. There was a great gulf between hearing "hello" and "good-bye" amid the static and setting up reliable and affordable communication. Subsequently, the many predictions of a direct telephone connection between New York and other major cities overseas were premature. It was not until 1927 that a transatlantic radio circuit was opened for public use. By that time, a new technological direction had been taken, and the method used in 1915 had been superseded by shortwave radio communication.

Bibliography

Aitken, Hugh G. J. *The Continuous Wave: Technology and American Radio, 1900-1932*. Princeton, N.J.: Princeton University Press, 1985. The authoritative work on the development of radio technology written by the leading scholar in the field. Following on his *Syntony and Spark* (which covered the early years of radio), Aitken provides a detailed and comprehensive account of the technology and the business affairs of radio.

Brooks, John. *Telephone: The First Hundred Years*. New York: Harper & Row, 1976. A popular account of the growth of the communications industry that provides clear technical explanations for the general reader. This overview is useful for putting technical events into a broader context.

De Forest, Lee. *Father of Radio: The Autobiography of Lee de Forest*. Chicago: Wilcox & Follett, 1950. This firsthand account of the early years of radio provides many insights into the interaction of business and technology. As the author is highly biased, only his version of the events is described.

Fagen, M. D., ed. *A History of Science and Engineering in the Bell System: The Early Years (1875-1925)*. New York: Bell Laboratories, 1975. This is the official history of the work carried out by the laboratories of the telephone companies. The chapters are arranged by topic. "The Advent of Radio" describes the development of this technology in detail.

Reich, Leonard S. *The Making of American Industrial Research: Science and Business at GE and Bell, 1876-1926*. Cambridge, England: Cambridge University Press, 1985. This book concentrates on the operation of industrial research and the business strategy that lay behind it. Gives a detailed analysis of the work done by Carty and Arnold in the AT&T laboratory.

Andre Millard

Cross-References

Marconi Receives the First Transatlantic Telegraphic Radio Transmission (1901), p. 128; Fleming Files a Patent for the First Vacuum Tube (1904), p. 255; Fessenden Perfects Radio by Transmitting Music and Voice (1906), p. 361; The First Transcontinental Telephone Call Is Made (1915), p. 595; The Principles of Shortwave Radio Communication Are Discovered (1919), p. 669.

LANGEVIN DEVELOPS ACTIVE SONAR
FOR SUBMARINE DETECTION AND FATHOMETRY

Categories of event: Physics and earth science
Time: October, 1915-March, 1917
Locale: Toulon, France

*Langevin developed the first active ultrasonic underwater sonar transducer for
detecting reflected sound from submerged objects and the seafloor*

> *Principal personages:*
> PAUL LANGEVIN (1872-1946), a French physicist, engineer, and educa-
> tional reformer
> CONSTANTIN CHILOWSKI, a Soviet engineer working in France

Summary of Event

The concept of detecting submerged objects using acoustic waves impinging on
and reflected from an underwater vessel has been argued as inherent in any detailed
understanding of acoustic wave propagation in the ocean, sound velocity in liquids,
viscous frictional damping of underwater sound, and sound radiation and diffraction
patterns. Sir Isaac Newton's *Philosophiae Naturalis Principia Mathematica* (1687)
gives a formula for approximately calculating the depth of a water well from the
elapsed time for a falling stone to be heard striking the water. Following the experiments by French physicists Daniel Colladon and Charles-François Sturm on Lake
Geneva in 1826, employing submerged bells to measure acoustic sound velocity in
water, the French astronomer François Arago proposed that it would be possible
also to find the depth of a lake or ocean location by noting the round-trip travel time
for a strong acoustic impulse to be reflected or echoed from the bottom. This suggestion apparently was tested first by the U.S. Navy in 1838, a study that confirmed
the greater velocity, clarity, and constancy of a bell signaling underwater as compared with air. Later experiments in 1841 showed that whereas the acoustic selfnoise from the paddlewheels and propellers of steamboats could not be heard by an
underwater listening trumpet beyond about 0.5 kilometer, the noise of a ship's chain
or underwater bell could be detected distinctly at ranges exceeding 2 kilometers.

As reported by Sir William Henry Bragg, an English physicist heavily involved in
the development of uni- and bidirectional hydrophones for passive underwater sound
detection, after serious U-boat attacks on military and commercial shipping of August to October, 1914, numerous suggestions were debated for detecting reliably
hostile submarines in shallow coastal and adjacent ocean waters. The basic operational detection requirement for the Allied Navy was reliable detection within about
0.75 kilometer from the defending vessel, to permit evasive navigation and artillery/
depth charge response. With underwater sound remaining the most ready expedient
having at least some precedent, specific questions remained as to whether the me-

chanical propeller and flow noises generated by target submarines as signal, and by the listening vessel as unwanted background noise, could be discriminated reliably to permit estimation of submarine distance, angular bearing, and speed. As was discovered soon by onshore coastal listening experiments in the English Channel, unless more than one listening station was used, passive "asdic" (Anti Submarine Detection Investigation Committee), at best, provided information only on the probable presence of an underwater acoustic sound source, which detectability could be lost easily if the target submarine reduced or listening vessel increased speed.

In 1914, John Joly and others reported on experiments with ship-to-ship underwater signaling and telephony, using multiple-controlled sound sources and listening hydrophones. After visual or audible sighting of a submarine by one or more listening vessels, additional sweeper craft would explode a small depth charge, whose position could be found relative to submerged hydrophones near the coast, giving the submarine's prior position and bearing. This early echo-sounding, or active insonification, approach for detecting a submerged sound-reflecting surface had been proposed previously and patented by American inventor Reginald Fessenden in 1889 and tentatively developed by him and others in the early 1900's by the Submarine Signal Company of Portsmouth, Rhode Island. Underwater bells, or vibrators, operated electrically, pneumatically, or by wave action, were located near lighthouses, shoals, and wrecks. Under favorable ocean conditions, their signals were received by ships at ranges of up to 15 kilometers using hydrophones fitted to or suspended from a ship's bow. By about 1912, these technologies were in use in the United States, England, France, and Germany, not only for communication but also for navigational use. All these devices, however, generated acoustic signals of frequencies less than about 600 cycles per second, in a frequency band filled with generally strong competing noises that could not, in general, be screened against or distinguished.

Fessenden's method, one of the most widely used (for example, by the German navy), was the first electroacoustic transducer based on an oscillator constructed from a reciprocating electromagnetic induction motor moving a steel membrane. The year before its introducton in 1913, the sinking of the *Titanic*, after hitting a submerged iceberg, caused intense international interest in reliable advance detection of navigational obstacles. Unfortunately, Fessenden's oscillator was not very effective, since it did not produce enough power or sufficiently sharp sound impulses required for reliable timing and ranging. It was soon realized by English and French antisubmarine warfare engineers that considerable improvement in performance and reliability would require greater acoustic output intensity as well as a pulse width smaller than the shortest conceivable two-way acoustic travel time. Although various ideas were proposed originally by English physicists Lord Rayleigh and E. G. Richardson after the *Titanic* sinking, in 1912, a Soviet engineer working for the French navy, Constantin Chilowski, built the first prototype ultrasonic source unit, whose output intensity, however, was still too weak to permit reliable insonification and detection of reflected signals for objects more than about 100 meters distant. After initial work for the French artillery ranging service in developing acoustic detectors for explosions, French physicist Paul Langevin joined Chilowski in mid-1915.

Langevin was well known in Europe for his numerous contributions to the study of X rays (1897 to 1898), of ionization in gases and kinetic theory (1899 to 1912), and notably of the electromagnetic properties of dielectric and paramagnetic/diamagnetic solids (1903 to 1913). During World War I, the latter still was considered esoteric pure research of little applicability, although it proved crucial to Langevin's sonar transducer work. In 1880, French physicists Jacques Curie and Pierre Curie discovered the change in dimensions of crystals subjected to electromagnetic fields. The effect on quartz and Rochelle salt was one of alternating compression and expansion when subjected to an alternating electric current. As the field oscillates, the crystal slab will vibrate longitudinally in the three axes of optical symmetry. When the crystal dimension in either direction is a whole-number multiple of half an acoustic wavelength, an electromechanical resonance is set up, resulting in greatly increased output amplitude. Although Rochelle salt has a higher Curie constant and, hence, greater sensitivity to smaller signal voltages, it is readily dissoluble in water. Thus, late in 1915, Langevin had the idea of exciting one or more quartz crystals in ultrasonic resonance, using a tuned amplifying circuit of the type invented by William du Bois Duddell in 1900. Langevin's first experiments with an electrostatic spark generator and carbon button (telephone type) receiver were not successful. After several false starts, an improved thermionic valve amplifier finally became available in France in early 1917. The comparatively weak reflected signals were no longer swamped by amplifier selfnoise, and in April, 1917, Langevin finally received the first acoustic echoes from a piezoelectric quartz transmitter and hydrophone receiver. Sound ranging in seawater is limited by intensity decreases, because of inverse square geometric spreading and by the thermo-viscous absorption of acoustic energy by water molecules, which above 5,000 cycles per second results in roughly 10 decibels loss per 1,000 meters. Although tests over the 20 to 150 kilocycles band were conducted, based on tradeoffs between lower in-water sound attenuation and wider acoustic beams with decreasing transducer frequency, operational frequencies between 30,000 and 40,000 cycles per second were chosen.

Close technical liaison was established between English and French scientists coordinated with, but independent of Langevin. In 1918, English physicist Ernest Rutherford and Canadian physicist R. W. Boyle obtained echoes in the field from a submarine at a range of almost 0.5 kilometer using a separate single-quartz crystal transmitter/receiver combination with a French electronic amplifier. In the meantime, Langevin had developed a more efficient piezoelectric quartz transducer from a composite block including a number of quartz crystals in series cut relative to their optical axis, with thickness of one-fourth the desired acoustic output wavelength, firmly mounted between iron slabs. Much care was needed in coupling the thermionic amplifier to the crystal to prevent unwanted "pinging" effects from extraneous mechanical shocks. Notable increases in acoustic radiated efficiency resulted over single crystal designs, limited predominantly by dielectric and elastic hysteresis effects (which still govern active sonar design). The total quartz oscillator area was of the order of 400 square centimeters, permitting interception of considerable reflected acoustic energy by the same surface (in receive mode). In June, 1918, using basically this multicrystal transducer, improved results over Rutherford and Boyle's techniques were obtained. Shortly before the Armistice, a prototype active asdic unit housed in a canvas dome was fitted for secret sea trials aboard a shallow-water trawler. Final operating frequencies could be selected between 20,000 and 50,000 cycles per second; at vessel speeds of 15 knots, the final prototype had an effective underwater echo detection range of more than 2.7 kilometers.

Impact of Event

Concurrently with French-English efforts, several civilian and military research groups in the United States concentrated on lower-noise thermionic amplifiers (M. I. Pupin at Columbia University), improved transducer reliability and focusing (A. P. Willis, I. Langmuir, A. W. Hull, and C. E. Eveleth at General Electric Company), as well as collateral prototype system development using water-shielded Rochelle salt crystals (Western Electric Company, Wesleyan University). Shortly after the end of World War I, these transducers were tested successfully at the Naval Experimental Station in New London, Connecticut, with reliable acoustic echoes detected from an armored schooner streaming past a sending/listening ship at distances of more than 400 meters. Although a joint Allied sonar research conference was held in Paris in October, 1918, to plan further cooperative development of "the Langevin apparatus for supersonic signalling and detection of submarines by echo," when the war ended, the exchange of scientific information ceased.

During the interwar years, American, English, and French active sonar research progressed along strikingly similar lines. Within about three and one-half years of Langevin's final prototype, Boyle demonstrated successfully ultrasonic detection of submerged icebergs, rocky reefs, shipwrecks, and undersea topographic features, giving birth to what has since been designated as acoustic fathometry. Soon after, an improved piezoelectric quartz oscillator was employed, with operating frequencies of up to 500,000 cycles per second, to make the first systematic investigations in vivo of chemical and biological effects of ultrasound—the starting point for the acoustic subdiscipline of ultrasonics. In 1919, the Rochelle salt was used as a more efficient pickup receiver, replacing cactus needles and tungsten stylii in gramophone transmitters. By the late 1920's, routine surveys by the U.S. Coastal and Geodetic Survey, and the German Oceanographic "Meteor" Survey, were employing active sonar fathometry for comprehensive sounding of the midatlantic ridge area, and soon thereafter 14 to 25 kilocycle dual frequency active sonar units were deployed for commercial whale and fish school location. Although limited by ocean and seafloor medium conditions that have become progressively a major focus of supporting research, since World War II, active sonar has continued to play a critical role in under-ice navigation, bathymetric mapping, and antisubmarine warfare, the basic physics of which was established by Langevin and his colleagues.

Bibliography

Bragg, William Henry. *The World of Sound: Six Lectures Delivered Before a Juvenile Auditor at the Royal Institution*. London: G. Bell & Sons, 1930. Bragg, a major developer of underwater acoustic hydrophones during World War II, presents then declassified aspects of the Royal Navy's work on directional acoustic detection of ship, submarine, and artillery-generated sounds.

Crandall, Irving B. *Theory of Vibrating Systems and Sound*. New York: D. Van Nostrand, 1926. Although intended as an intermediate-level physics text, this is an invaluable reference. The bibliography captures a significant portion of American, English, French, and German literatures from both world wars.

Hackmann, Willem Dirk. *Seek and Strike: Sonar, Anti-Submarine Warfare, and the Royal Navy, 1914-1954*. London: Her Majesty's Scientific Office, 1984. Comprehensive study of the specific military requirements and technological possibilities and limits imposed on underwater acoustic transduction in submarine detection. Well conveyed and illustrated. Hackmann succeeds in communicating to a general audience the central technical, as well as military-political, issues.

Hunt, Frederick V. *Electroacoustics: The Analysis of Transduction and Its Historical Background*. Cambridge, Mass.: Harvard University Press, 1954. Although comparatively technical in focus, Hunt's volume is the acknowledged central reference of choice. Especially convenient are its nearly complete references to English and foreign-language publications, reports, and patents.

Richardson, Edward G. *Sound: A Physical Textbook*. London: E. Arnold, 1929. Elementary reference. Includes specific discussions of the impact of the war on ocean acoustics.

Urick, Robert J. *Principles of Underwater Sound*. 3d ed. New York: McGraw-Hill, 1983. A central source for the principles and applications of underwater acoustic transduction and propagation.

Gerardo G. Tango

Cross-References

Anschütz-Kaempfe Installs a Gyrocompass onto a German Battleship (1906), p. 303; The First German U-Boat Submarine Is Launched (1906), p. 350; Fessenden Perfects Radio by Transmitting Music and Voice (1906), p. 361; Beebe and Barton Set a Diving Record in a Bathysphere (1934), p. 1018.

EINSTEIN COMPLETES HIS THEORY OF GENERAL RELATIVITY

Category of event: Physics
Time: November 25, 1915
Locale: Berlin, Germany

Einstein proposed that physical laws appear the same in any reference frame, even one accelerated under the influence of gravitational fields

Principal personages:

ALBERT EINSTEIN (1879-1955), a German physicist who founded the modern gravitational theory, seminal figure in quantum and statistical physics, and winner of 1921 Nobel Prize in Physics for his explanation of the photoelectric effect

MARCEL GROSSMAN (1878-1936), a Swiss mathematician who collaborated with Einstein on an important, but incorrect, early version of general relativity

SIR ISAAC NEWTON (1642-1727), an English scientist who proposed that physical laws do not depend on the absolute velocities of observers and derived first equations of motion of bodies; his theories were unchallenged for two hundred years

JAMES CLERK MAXWELL (1831-1879), a Scottish physicist whose theory of electricity and magnetism violated the relativity principle of Newton and gave Einstein a clue to the structure of special relativity

ERNST MACH (1838-1916), an Austrian physicist and philosopher whose book on mechanics asserted that all motion is relative and inspired Einstein's bold generalization of special relativity to the general form

Summary of Event

When Albert Einstein was young, there already existed a two-hundred-year-old principle of relativity. This principle stated that there is no standard of absolute motion or rest. The velocities of all objects are defined only in relation to other objects; this is a statement of Galilean relativity, named after Galileo (1564-1642).

On the other hand, changes in velocity, or accelerations, do not depend on the observer's velocity. Suppose there is a train moving at 100 kilometers per hour and two observers: one in a car traveling alongside the train at 60 kilometers per hour and one standing on a station platform. If the observer on the platform observes the train accelerate by 20 kilometers per hour to 120 kilometers per hour, the observer in the car will also see that the train has accelerated by 20 kilometers per hour, to 60 kilometers per hour. Thus, while velocities have only a relative meaning, accelerations have an absolute one.

From these two facts, Sir Isaac Newton deduced, in 1687, that the physical laws of nature must be based on the acceleration of objects, not their velocities. Thus, the physical laws of nature (or, in mathematical terms, the equations of motion) appear the same to all observers each moving at any arbitrary velocity, as long as their velocities do not change with time. Such special observers are said to be in inertial frames of reference.

Yet, in 1865, the Scottish physicist James Clerk Maxwell presented his theory of electricity and magnetism, which required that the speed of light be the same number for an observer moving at *any* constant velocity. Here, a velocity (the speed of light) has an absolute meaning. If a light beam is thought of as a train racing at a speed of 300,000 kilometers per second, then no matter how fast an observer flies in a rocket ship alongside this light-train, the light-train will always be moving 300,000 kilometers per second *faster* than the rocket ship.

Scientists, quite confused, proposed that there was an absolute standard of rest, an ether filling space, and that somehow this ether explains why Galilean relativity breaks down. This ether had originally been proposed as the medium that carries the electromagnetic waves. In 1887, experiments by scientists Albert Abraham Michelson and Edward Williams Morley revealed no evidence of this ether. Meanwhile, the correct equations of transformation between inertial frames were worked out by the Irish physicist George Francis FitzGerald (1889) and the Dutch physicist Hendrik Antoon Lorentz (1899). Yet, a proper understanding of these equations was lacking.

Einstein dismissed the ether conjecture and reaffirmed that the laws of physics should appear the same in all inertial reference frames; excepting the velocity of light, all velocities are again relative. Still, there was a twist. In order to account for the fact that the speed of light is the same in any inertial frame, Einstein proposed that measurements of both length and time are different for observers in different inertial frames. Observer A will find that objects in Observer B's inertial frame shrink in the direction of relative motion, and that Observer B's wristwatch runs slower than Observer A's. Observer B will, with equal justification, say that objects in Observer A's inertial reference frame appear shorter in the direction of motion, and Observer A's wristwatch appears to be running slower. This theory is now referred to as special relativity.

Another profound consequence of special relativity is that it is impossible to accelerate a body from rest or from sublight velocities up to the speed of light. The equations that Einstein derived predict that it would take an infinite amount of energy to do so. The faster a body is moving, the harder it is to accelerate the body further. A popular interpretation is that the mass of an object increases as it gains velocity, becoming infinitely massive as the speed of light is reached. More generally, mass is merely another form of energy and can be converted back and forth.

Unfortunately, the conclusion that nothing can be accelerated past the speed of light conflicted with the then-current understanding of gravitation. According to Newton, given two objects with a gravitational force between them, if one of the objects is moved slightly, the other object instantly feels a shift in the gravitational force between them. The line of force between the two objects is always a straight line connecting them. Aided by the insights of special relativity, Einstein realized that information on the movement of the first object cannot travel instantly to the second. At the fastest, this information may travel at the speed of light. The line of force between two objects must curve if one of the objects experiences a push. There must be a lag time before the second object realizes the first has moved. The reconciliation between special relativity and gravitation forms Einstein's theory of general relativity.

After some first steps toward the general theory, between 1905 and 1907, mathematical difficulties and an increasing interest in the new quantum physics caused Einstein to defer work on gravitation. Between 1905 and 1911, Einstein made stunning contributions in statistical and quantum physics. Then, between 1912 and 1913, he returned to the study of gravitation, collaborating with his old school friend, Marcel Grossman. Although their theory proved incorrect, Grossman, a mathematician, introduced Einstein to differential geometry, essential to the mastering of curved space. Finally, in the summer of 1915, Einstein discovered his errors, and after furious work, presented his general theory in its final form on November 25, 1915. (David Hilbert, a mathematician, discovered the errors the same time that Einstein did and presented the fundamental equation only five days before Einstein; however, the physical principles behind the general theory and the vision of its existence are usually credited to Einstein.)

The resolution of the conflict between special relativity and Newtonian gravitation came in the form of gravity waves, which carry information about the motion of masses at the speed of light, in much the same way that electromagnetic waves carry information about the motion of electrical charges. Thus, far-off objects do not instantly perceive changes in the position of a nearby object, but must wait for gravity waves from the nearby object to reach them.

Yet, there is more than one way to formulate a theory of gravity waves. Einstein made one further assumption (partly inspired by the assertion of Austrian physicist and philosopher Ernst Mach) that *all* motions possess only relative meaning, not simply inertial (constant velocity) motion. Einstein required that physical laws should appear the same regardless of one's frame of reference, even one accelerated under the influence of gravitational fields. Yet, again there was a twist, this time requiring a generalization of what is meant by inertial motion and a revolution in the concept of the structure of space and time.

Impact of Event

Both general relativity and special relativity revolutionized ideas about the structure of space and time. Special relativity introduced the concept of four-dimensional space-time, wherein measurements of the spatial dimensions of an object cannot be made independently of a measurement of the temporal dimension—that is, the velocity with which the object is moving to or away from the observer. Objects that move away very quickly will shrink along the direction of motion.

General relativity introduces the idea that space-time is curved; that is, the presence of mass or other forms of energy distorts space-time, in much the same way that a bowling ball placed on a trampoline distorts the surface of the trampoline. What appears as gravitational force is not, within general relativity, a force at all; it is simply the motion of bodies in curved space-time along paths as nearly straight as possible. Thus, the motion of Earth around the Sun, which appears in three dimensions as a circular orbit, in curved four-dimensional space-time is actually a straight line. Thus, a marble placed on the trampoline will roll toward the bowling ball not because it is gravitationally attracted to the bowling ball but because the trampoline is not flat. Einstein generalized the concept of an inertial frame to curved space-time.

One of the most important results of this generalization is a proof of the equivalence of inertial and gravitational mass, which had puzzled scientists since the time of Newton. Inertial mass is the resistance a body gives to force. A larger inertial mass means it is harder to accelerate a body to a given speed. Gravitational mass is a measure of a body's gravitational force field. The larger the gravitational mass, the more strongly it feels the gravitational force of other mass. Since motion in a gravitational field is a generalized inertial motion in curved space-time, there is no gravitational force, per se, in general relativity. Hence, there is actually only inertial mass, no gravitational mass.

Predictions based on general relativity, now confirmed by experiment, include the bending of light rays on passing massive celestial objects, the shift of light frequency in a gravitational field (the gravitational redshift), an additional rotation of the elliptical orbit of Mercury around the Sun (the precession of the perihelion of Mercury), the existence of black holes (regions of such enormous mass density that even light cannot escape), and the expansion of the universe.

Light rays bend toward massive objects because space is deformed around them, and the light rays simply follow the straightest contours of space-time by them. A black hole occurs when the deformation of space is so great that the light ray is continually bent toward the gravitational source, never able to escape. Light frequencies shift in the neighborhood of strong gravitational fields because the passage of time is also distorted by the deformation of space-time. Wristwatches, for example, will appear to run slower in strong gravitational fields. (Light cycles through phases much as one's common alternating current electrical outlet. Its frequency is hence a measure of time, much like a wristwatch with a variable-speed secondhand.) The additional rotation of the elliptical orbit of Mercury and the expansion of the universe come from analysis of Einstein's new equations of motion.

There is also a practical significance to general relativity in the field of satellite communications, since measurements of time and space are different when observed from high-altitude satellites and when observed on the surface of the earth. For example, highly accurate satellite-based navigation systems would send oceangoing ships off course by several kilometers if relativistic corrections were not taken into account.

Bibliography

Bergmann, Peter G. *The Riddle of Gravitation.* New York: Charles Scribner's Sons, 1968. A clear, full presentation of gravitation from the ancient Greeks through special and general relativity and the consequences of quantum mechanics. No mathematical background is required. Insightful relations are worked out in five appendices, requiring high school-level algebra. Many illustrations, diagrams, and photo-reproductions. Helpful bibliography, glossary, and index. Gives names and dates of many relevant personalities.

Einstein, Albert. *Relativity: The Special and General Theory.* 15th ed. Translated by Robert W. Lawson. London: Methuen, 1954. This book is intelligible and elegantly written but fairly demanding for readers accustomed to light popular reading. High school algebra helpful but not essential. No discussion of black holes or quantum effects. A few diagrams; also contains an index and bibliography.

Gamow, George. *Biography of Physics.* New York: Harper & Row, 1961. Chapter 6 is devoted to relativity. Chatty, with amusing anecdotes, helpful diagrams, and a few equations. Presents basic ideas, but no discussion of black holes or quantum effects. Fairly light reading. Indexed; no bibliography or references; table of contents terse.

Hawking, Stephen W. *A Brief History of Time.* New York: Bantam Books, 1988. Excellent for the nonspecialist: Clear and well organized, with vivid explanations of basic principles. The first two chapters provide historical background and the major concepts of relativity. Succeeding chapters deal with black holes, quantum effects, particle physics, time, and the unification of physical laws. Interesting short biographies on Einstein, Galileo, and Newton; helpful diagrams, glossary, and index; no references or bibliography. Contains only one equation.

Pais, Abraham. *"Subtle Is the Lord . . .": The Science and Life of Albert Einstein.* New York: Oxford University Press, 1982. Meticulously referenced biography of Einstein. Features detailed chronology of Einstein's life, good subject index, and exhaustive name index. Account of Einstein's intellectual efforts includes mathematics at the level of a physics graduate student. Does not devote comparable space to Einstein's political acts and thoughts.

David Hsu

Cross-References

Einstein States His Theory of Special Relativity: $E = mc^2$ (1905), p. 297; Gamow and Associates Develop the Big Bang Theory (1948), p. 1309; The Mössbauer Effect Is Used in the Detection of Gravitational Redshifting (1960), p. 1640; Wheeler Names the Phenomenon "Black Holes" (1968), p. 1881; Georgi and Glashow Develop the Grand Unified Theory (1974), p. 2014.

SCHWARZSCHILD DEVELOPS A SOLUTION TO THE EQUATIONS OF GENERAL RELATIVITY

Category of event: Astronomy
Time: 1916
Locale: Potsdam, Germany

In 1916, Schwarzschild developed an exact solution to Einstein's equations of general relativity, which describes a gravitational black hole

> *Principal personages:*
> KARL SCHWARZSCHILD (1873-1916), a German physicist who was the first to derive the exact solution to the equations of the theory of general relativity
> ALBERT EINSTEIN (1879-1955), a German physicist who is best known for his theories of special and general relativity
> SIR ISAAC NEWTON (1642-1727), an English scientist-philosopher who developed many pioneering concepts in the physical sciences and mathematics

Summary of Event

In 1915, Albert Einstein published his theory of general relativity. This revolutionary new concept of curved space-time stood in opposition to the universal law of gravitation, which had been developed by Sir Isaac Newton in 1665. According to Newton, gravity is an attractive force acting between all particles of matter in the universe. Einstein believed that gravity is a consequence of the shape of space-time. Local space-time, according to the theory of general relativity, is distorted by the presence of a large mass such as a star or a planet. Objects traveling in close proximity to a massive body would therefore travel in a curved path, hence, the appearance of a gravitational field.

When the theory of general relativity was first proposed, its mathematics were thought to be beyond comprehension. In fact, it was frequently stated that only about twelve or so scientists in the world completely understood the theory. To appreciate the complexity, consider that the theory contains sixteen separate equations. Each of these equations is a nonlinear partial differential equation for sixteen separate unknown functions. In addition, problems arise even after the equations are solved because interpretation of the solutions is extremely difficult. Even today, many of its implications remain to be understood.

The first person to find an exact solution to the equations of the theory of general relativity was the German physicist Karl Schwarzschild. Prior to the work of Schwarzschild, the only solutions to the equations had been approximations. In 1916, when Schwarzschild was working on his solution, Germany was at war. Because of his patriotism, the forty-year-old Schwarzschild insisted upon serving in the German armed forces. Various campaigns took him to Belgium, France, and finally to Russia. While serving in Russia he contracted the fatal disease, pemphigus. Although he became too ill to continue in the military service, he continued to work on the equations. Shortly after his return to Germany, he completed his paper and sent a copy to Einstein. Within a few months, Schwarzschild died. His paper entitled "Über das Gravitationsfeld eines Mass enpunktes nach der Einstein Theorie" (on the field of gravity of a point mass in the theory of Einstein) was published in the 1916 edition of *Sitzungsberichte der Preussichen Akademie der Wissenschaften zu Berlin* (the journal of the Royal Prussian Academy of Sciences).

Schwarzschild had sought to investigate what would happen if gravity around a spherical body became infinitely powerful. He was also concerned with finding the least complex explanation. The result is known as the Schwarzschild solution. This solution describes a bizarre object: a black hole.

The French astronomer Pierre-Simon Laplace first considered the possibility of an object so dense that light itself could not escape from its surface. Unfortunately, at the time (1796), there was no way to test his ideas, and they soon became discarded. When Schwarzschild derived his solution to Einstein's equations, it was not readily recognized by the scientific community that, like Laplace, he was describing a model for a black hole. Difficulties in interpreting the Schwarzschild solution cast some doubt upon its validity until the 1960's when its true significance was recognized. The formation of a black hole is believed to be the final stage in the decay of a massive star. During its life, the star produces energy in its core by the process of nuclear fusion. The resulting outward flow of heat and energy enables the various layers of the star to balance the inward force of gravity. When nuclear fuel is exhausted in the core, the star begins its decay stage. The exact sequence of events depends entirely on the mass of the star. Toward the end of its life, a massive star will go through the supernova stage, where much of its outer material is blasted off into space. The core—no longer producing energy to counteract the crushing force of gravity—begins to collapse. If the star's mass is 1.4 or fewer solar masses, the final decay product will be a white dwarf. At this stage, the pressure exerted by the electrons of the atoms making up the core is sufficient to stop the collapse. This hot carbon mass will eventually cool to become a black dwarf. If the mass of the decayed star is between 1.4 and 3.1 times the mass of the sun, gravity will cause a much more extensive collapse. At this point, the pressure is so great that electrons cannot support the core. Electrons and protons combine to form neutrons in a process termed neutronization. The result will be a neutron star. If the remnant is greater than 3.1 solar masses, neutrons will not be able to counteract the force of gravity and the star will continue to collapse. As this collapse continues, the surface gravity for the collapsed star will become greater and greater. As a result, the velocity needed to escape this gravitational body increases. When the escape velocity reaches the velocity of light, further collapse results in the formation of a black hole. This distance, at which the escape velocity is equal to the velocity of light, is the distance calculated by Schwarzschild in his solution to Einstein's equations; it is known as the Schwarzschild radius or the event horizon. Beyond this point, there is no way of determining events. It is an area that is totally disconnected from our space and time. When a star collapses within its Schwarzschild radius, it becomes a black hole. The term "black hole" comes from the fact that no visible light or any other form of electromagnetic radiation can escape from such an object. It therefore cannot be detected optically. In theory, any object could become a black hole if it were compressed enough. If the earth were shrunk to slightly less than a centimeter in radius, it would become a black hole. If the sun were to be compressed to a radius of less than three kilometers, it would become a black hole also.

The diameter of the Schwarzschild radius of a black hole depends on the mass of the decayed stellar core. For example, a decayed core with a mass five times greater than the sun will have an event horizon with a radius of 30 kilometers. A stellar remnant of 20 solar masses would have an event horizon with a 60-kilometer radius. Within this boundary, however, the remains of the star continue to collapse to a point of infinite pressure, infinite density, and infinite curvature of space-time. This point is known as the Schwarzschild singularity.

The Schwarzschild solution describes a black hole that has neither electrical charge nor rotation, but only mass. Consider a body falling toward such an object. As the object passed through the Schwarzschild radius, it would feel nothing unusual. For observers of this object watching from some distance away, however, the situation would appear quite different. The effects on time predicted by the theory of general relativity would be noticed by the observer. As the first body approached the event horizon, its onboard clock would appear to slow. When the body reached the event horizon, it and its clock would both appear to stop, frozen in time. The object would enter the event horizon and plunge—at nearly the speed of light—toward the singularity. At this point, what happens is not possible to predict because the laws of physics are no longer valid. An interesting solution to this problem was presented in the 1930's: The Einstein-Rosen bridge interpretation described space-time warped into a tunnel or a bridge to another universe or to some other part of the universe. At this time, however, infinite space-time warps can be little more than interesting speculation for cosmologists.

Impact of Event

In 1916, Schwarzschild published his exact solution to the equations of general relativity. At the time, the work was thought to be somewhat of an exercise in mathematics without any actual application. Schwarzschild believed that his solution would have no more application in the natural sciences than the approximate solution that had been previously worked out by Einstein. The true significance of Schwarzschild's work would not be recognized until more study had been done on stellar structure and evolution. An important step was taken in 1931 when the astronomer Subrahmanyan Chandrasekhar completed calculations that described the interior of a white dwarf star. At that time, he did not consider the fate of very massive stars, but English astronomer Arthur Stanley Eddington proposed that massive stars in their death stages continue to radiate energy as they become smaller and smaller. At some point, they reach equilibrium.

In 1939, the American physicist J. Robert Oppenheimer and his student Hartland Snyder showed that a star that possesses enough mass will collapse indefinitely. This paper actually expanded upon the work of Schwarzschild and proposed that black holes may exist in the universe. It is now fully recognized that the Schwarzschild solution describes a black hole. The type of black hole described by the Schwarzschild equations is static. A static black hole does not rotate and has no electric charge. The only property possessed by such a body is mass.

Based upon the work of Schwarzschild, Oppenheimer, Chandrasekhar, and others, a model for the formation of a black hole has been formulated. Although there is some debate on the lower limit of solar masses necessary for black hole formation, a value of about 3.1 is generally acceptable. This means that if the decayed star has a mass of 3.1 solar masses or greater, it will become a black hole. As the stellar remnant begins to collapse, gravity compresses the star's matter into a smaller and smaller volume. The curvature of space-time around the body becomes more pronounced and, as a result, beams of light no longer leave the surface in a straight path. As the gravitational collapse continues, more light beams are drawn back to the surface. When the star collapses within the Schwarzschild radius, light can no longer escape; the object has become a black hole. The object described by Schwarzschild consists of only one event horizon or Schwarzschild radius. Within this boundary lies the singularity, the point which is the remains of the collapsed star.

Variations on the work of Schwarzschild have produced such theoretical objects as rotating black holes, black holes with electrical charge, and those with both charge and rotation. At this time, there is no actual proof that these objects exist. Astrophysicists, however, have identified several objects in the universe that may be black holes. Further research will determine if the Schwarzschild solution describes a real object or if it was only an exercise in theoretical mathematics.

Bibliography

Asimov, Isaac. *The Collapsing Universe*. New York: Walker, 1977. A very readable volume describing such topics as the forces of nature, planets and planetary formation, and the stages of stellar evolution. The book is suitable for the layperson.

Greenstein, George. *Frozen Star*. New York: Freundlich Books, 1983. This volume discusses the topics of pulsars, black holes, and stellar evolution. The reader should have some general physics and astronomy background to fully comprehend the material.

Kaufmann, William J., III. *Black Holes and Warped Spacetime*. New York: W. H. Freeman, 1979. This well-illustrated volume deals with stellar evolution and the warped space-time of general relativity. The study of the structure and properties of black holes is well presented. The book is suitable for the average reader.

Krane, Kenneth S. *Modern Physics*. New York: John Wiley & Sons, 1983. A highly technical treatment of selected topics in modern physics such as special and general relativity, quantum mechanics, and nuclear physics. The volume was intended as a textbook for an advanced undergraduate course in modern physics.

Shipman, Harry L. *Black Holes, Quasars, and the Universe.* Boston: Houghton Mifflin, 1976. This volume covers such topics as stellar evolution, galaxies, active galaxies, cosmology, and astrophysics. The reader should have some background in elementary physics and astronomy.

Sullivan, Walter. *Black Holes: The Edge of Space, the End of Time.* Garden City, N.Y.: Doubleday, 1979. This well-illustrated volume describes the evolution of the concept of black holes from early theory to modern cosmology. The volume is suitable for the general reader.

David W. Maguire

Cross-References

Russell Announces His Theory of Stellar Evolution (1913), p. 585; Einstein Completes His Theory of General Relativity (1915), p. 625; Einstein's Theory of Gravitation Is Confirmed over Newton's Theory (1919), p. 684; The Mössbauer Effect Is Used in the Detection of Gravitational Redshifting (1960), p. 1640; Wheeler Names the Phenomenon "Black Holes" (1968), p. 1881.

BIRDSEYE DEVELOPS FREEZING AS A WAY OF PRESERVING FOODS

Category of event: Applied science
Time: 1917
Locale: Gloucester, Massachusetts

Birdseye developed a technique for quick-freezing fresh foods and fathered the frozen foods industry

Principal personages:
> CLARENCE BIRDSEYE (1886-1956), a scientist and inventor who was one of America's leading authorities on food
> WETMORE HODGES, the son of Charles H. Hodges (vice-president of the American Radiator Company) who was responsible for helping Birdseye refinance his General Foods Company
> DONALD K. TRESSLER (1894-   ), the coauthor of *The Freezing Preservation of Foods* and a researcher at Cornell University

Summary of Event

In 1917, Clarence Birdseye developed an inventive process for quick-freezing meat, fish, vegetables, and fruit without substantially changing their original tastes. His system of freezing was called by *Fortune* magazine "one of the most exciting and revolutionary ideas in the history of food." Birdseye went on to refine and perfect his freezing method and to promote the frozen foods industry until it became a commercial success nationwide.

Even as a boy, Birdseye was interested in preserving things, animal skins in particular. By the time he was a teenager, he considered himself an authority in taxidermy and placed an advertisement in a sports magazine, announcing courses at his newly founded American School of Taxidermy. Later, he worked as a fur trader in Labrador, where his interest in quick-frozen foods first began. During one of his Labrador trips, Birdseye's new wife and five-week-old baby accompanied him. In order to keep his family well fed, he placed barrels of fresh cabbages in salt water and then exposed the vegetables to freezing winds. Successful at this, he went on to freeze a winter's supply of ducks, caribou, and rabbit meat. This was the start of the frozen-food industry as it is known today. In the following years, Birdseye experimented with many freezing techniques. He started with only seven dollars, with which he purchased an electric fan, cakes of ice, and buckets of salt brine. His earliest experiments were on fish and rabbits, which he froze and packed in old candy boxes. By 1924, he borrowed on his life insurance and was fortunate enough to locate three partners to invest in his new General Seafoods Company (later renamed General Foods), located in Gloucester, Massachusetts.

Although it was Birdseye's genius that put the principles of quick-freezing to work, he did not actually invent quick-freezing. The scientific principles involved had been known for some time. In the mid-1800's, ice-salt systems were used to freeze foods. As early as 1842, a patent for freezing fish was granted to H. Benjamin in England, and later in 1861 to Enoch Piper in Maine. Nevertheless, the commercial exploitation of the freezing process could not have happened until the end of the 1800's, when mechanical refrigeration was invented. Yet, even with the refrigerator, Birdseye had to overcome major obstacles. By the 1920's, there still were few mechanical refrigerators in American homes. Therefore, it took years before adequate facilities for food freezing and retail distribution had sprung up across the United States. By the late 1930's, frozen foods had, indeed, found their role in commerce. Despite this fact, frozen foods still were not important competitors with canned or fresh foods. Birdseye had to work tirelessly as a prime mover of the industry, writing and delivering numerous lectures and articles to advance their popularity. Simultaneously, his efforts were aided by scientific research conducted at Cornell University by Donald K. Tressler, coauthor of *The Freezing Preservation of Foods*, and by C. R. Fellers at the then Massachusetts State College. Also, war conditions advanced public acceptance of quick-frozen packaged foods by at least five years. Rationing, combined with a shortage of canned foods, contributed to the demand for frozen foods. The armed forces made large purchases of these items as well.

Although Birdseye's new company was not the first to freeze whole fish commercially, General Foods was the first to use a system of extremely rapid freezing of perishable foods in packages. Under the Birdseye system, fresh foods, like berries or lobster, were packaged snugly in convenient square containers. Then, the packages were pressed between refrigerated metal plates, under pressure at 50 degrees below zero. The types of freezing machines used commercially by General Foods were the "double belt" and "multiplate" Birdseye freezers. The former consisted of two metal belts that ran through a 15-meter freezing tunnel, while calcium chloride brine was sprayed on the surfaces of the belts. This double-belt freezer was used only in permanent installations and was soon replaced by the multiplate freezer, which was portable and required only 11.5 square meters of floor space compared to the double belt's 152 square meters. The multiplate freezer also made it possible to bring quick-freezing to seasonal crops. People were able to transport these freezers easily from one harvesting field to another, where they were used to freeze crops such as peas, fresh off the vine. The handy multiplate freezer consisted of an insulated cabinet equipped with refrigerated metal plates. Placed one above the other, these plates were capable of being opened and closed, to receive food products and to compress them with evenly distributed pressure. Each aluminum plate had internal passages through which ammonia flowed and expanded at a temperature of −3.8 degrees Celsius, thus causing foods to freeze.

A major benefit of the new frozen foods was that their taste and vitamin content were not lost, as had been the case previously. Ordinarily, when food is frozen slowly, ice crystals form, which slowly rupture food cells, thus altering the taste of the food. Yet, at 50 degrees below zero, cellular rupturing is minimized because the ice crystals formed are one one-hundredth the size of the slowly frozen crystals. Consequently, texture, flavor, color, and odor of the product are retained; there is no shrinkage from loss of water. Also, quick-freezing cuts down bacterial growth and retards oxidation, as compared to slow-freezing.

Up until 1925, financial problems plagued Birdseye's commercial efforts. Later, Wetmore Hodges, son of the vice president of the American Radiator Company, had the foresight to interest J. P. Morgan and Company in refinancing General Foods. By 1928, Hodges had convinced two other corporations that Birdseye's process had a sales potential of $1 billion a year. Within the year, these companies negotiated the purchase of Birdseye's system with its 168 patents. Soon, the scientist-inventor's frozen foods began to appear on the market under the trademark Birdseye Frosted Foods. Birdseye, by then a millionaire, continued to act as a consultant to General Foods, while promoting the frozen food industry with his articles and lectures on food preservation.

In later years, Birdseye turned his attention to developing an improved method of dehydrating foods, which he called "anhydrous." Relying on the same principle of speed that had served him well in the quick-freezing industry, he discovered that rapidly dehydrated foods retain their cell structure in this new quick-drying method. His technique extracted water from fresh-picked fruits and vegetables in one-tenth the time used by other methods and was said to retain color, flavor, texture, aroma, and nutritional qualities. This was Birdseye's second major contribution to the field of food preservation.

Impact of Event

During the months between one food harvest and the next, humankind requires trillions of pounds of food for sustenance. If a year's food supply for every person on Earth was packaged into one pound units and placed side by side, it would pave a circle around Earth, out to the Moon and back. In many parts of the world, an adequate supply of food is available; elsewhere, much food goes to waste and many go hungry.

Methods of food preservation such as those developed by Birdseye have contributed immensely to reducing the number of malnourished in the world. Since all foods are highly perishable, any means for preserving their food value extends their season of availability, thus increasing the quantity and variety of foods that people can eat. Birdseye fathered a whole new industry, which has had a major impact on the world's modern-day lifestyle. People can keep their freezers stocked with fresh frozen foods as well as prepared foods. This time-saving option has given people more leisure time, since food preparation time is minimal. In addition, the variety of foods available to people in even the most remote towns has been increased greatly by virtue of the frozen foods industry. In all parts of the world, tropical and arctic delicacies can be eaten in any season of the year.

The importance of frozen foods in daily life is evident in other areas as well. In a free market system, frozen foods have successfully competed with fresh and canned foods. To the consumer, this has meant better foods at lower prices, whether fresh, frozen, or canned. Economically, frozen foods have become important items of commerce. As an example, 90 percent of Iceland's export trade is frozen fish. The frozen foods industry brought new possibilities to many industries. The shellfish industry was revolutionized by Birdseye's contributions. The prepared frozen foods industry came into being as a natural offshoot of groundwork laid by General Foods.

With the advent and subsequent popularity of frozen "fast" foods, nutritionists began to study the nutritive value of quick-frozen foods. Research has shown that health-wise, fresh is best. It may be many decades before scientists know the long-term effects on generations raised primarily on frozen foods. Research needs to be conducted to see if the convenience of frozen foods has undermined a nation's best asset: the health of its citizens. In an industrial nation with large concentrations of people, the distribution of fresh commodities is most difficult. Whether or not Birdseye contributed to the ultimate health of humankind, he did contribute to the variety and quantity of foods available to people in all areas of the world. For this achievement, he will always be known as father of the food preservation revolution.

Bibliography

Birdseye, Clarence. "Bringing Quick-Freezing to Seasonal Crops." *Food Industries* 3 (1931): 490-491. This article gives the first authentic description of the multiplate freezer. Includes a discussion of how this portable unit is an improvement over Birdseye's earlier model.

_____. "Freezing Foods." In *Refrigeration Data Book*. Vol. 1. New York: American Society of Refrigeration Engineers, 1932. Includes a discussion on biological and chemical aspects of freezing, thermal considerations, low temperature refrigerating machinery, storage, and packaging. The book concludes with an excellent bibliography.

_____. "Preparation and Distribution of Frozen Perishable Products." *Refrigeration Engineering* 19 (1930): 173. Birdseye discusses the benefits of quick-freezing. He briefly covers packaging, equipment for storage and display, and the difficulties encountered in thawing.

Carlton, Harry. *The Frozen Food Industry*. Knoxville: University of Tennessee Press, 1941. The chapter "Freezing Methods" presents an overview of a variety of freezers designed by engineers since Birdseye's original models. Includes a detailed description of how each of these freezers work.

Desrosier, Norman W. "Principles of Food Freezing." In *The Technology of Food Preservation*. Westport, Conn.: AVI, 1959. This text presents the elements of the technology of food preservation founded in the physical and biological sciences. Chapter 5, in particular, gives a thorough presentation of the physical, chemical, and biological changes occurring during the freezing and thawing of foods.

Tressler, Donald K., and Clifford F. Evers. *The Freezing Preservation of Foods*. 2d rev. ed. New York: AVI, 1947. The first general treatise on the subject, this book covers the freezing of not only fruits, fruit juices, and vegetables but also meat, poultry, fish, shellfish, and dairy products. Includes a section on the economic status of the food freezing industry, with comments on its importance and probable trends. Illustrations of Birdseye's multiplate freezer and "gravity froster" are accompanied by a thorough explanation of how these freezers work.

Tressler, Donald K., Clifford F. Evers, and Lucy Long. *Into the Freezer, and Out.* New York: AVI, 1946. Gives additional background information on the home freezing of foods, and is a companion work to *The Freezing Preservation of Foods* (cited above).

Weil, B. H., and Frances Sterne. *Literature Search on the Preservation of Food by Freezing.* Atlanta: Georgia School of Technology, 1946. A comprehensive bibliography of articles dealing with frozen foods and techniques of freezing.

Nan White

Cross-References

Hopkins Suggests That Food Contains Vitamins Essential to Life (1906), p. 330; Geothermal Power Is Produced for the First Time (1913), p. 547; Corning Glass Works Trademarks Pyrex and Offers Pyrex Cookware for Commercial Sale (1915), p. 605; Steenbock Discovers That Sunlight Increases Vitamin D in Food (1924), p. 771; Midgley Introduces Dichlorodifluoromethane as a Refrigerant Gas (1930), p. 916; Manabe and Wetherald Warn of the Greenhouse Effect and Global Warming (1967), p. 1840.

INSECTICIDE USE INTENSIFIES WHEN ARSENIC PROVES EFFECTIVE AGAINST THE BOLL WEEVIL

Category of event: Earth science
Time: 1917
Locale: Tallulah, Louisiana; Lake Village, Arkansas; Scott, Mississippi

Entomologists discovered a technique to poison the cotton boll weevil, reinforcing the widespread use of insecticides and discouraging further support of cultural and biological controls

> *Principal personages:*
> BERT RAYMOND COAD (1890-   ), a United States Department of Agriculture entomologist who was in charge of the boll weevil laboratory at Tallulah, Louisiana
> LELAND OSSIAN HOWARD (1857-1950), a major figure in entomology, and chief of the Division of Entomology at the United States Department of Agriculture
> CHARLES VALENTINE RILEY (1843-1895), a naturalist and entomologist who served as the first state entomologist of Missouri, on the United States Entomological Commission, and was the first chief of the Division of Entomology at the United States Department of Agriculture

Summary of Event

The use of chemical insecticides in the United States intensified during the 1920's following the discovery of a technique to poison the cotton boll weevil, one of the nation's worst agricultural pests. Insecticides had become established in the nineteenth century, when exotic pest insects arrived on the steamers of European immigrants and on cargo ships. As early as 1868, an unknown farmer discovered that Paris green (a bright colored dye often used to paint window shutters) could kill the Colorado potato beetle. The active toxic ingredient in Paris green was arsenic, a poison also employed in insecticides developed later, such as London Purple and lead arsenate. In a letter to the editor of the *Galena Gazette* on May 28, 1869, a Wisconsin farmer informed Illinois potato growers that an early morning dusting of Paris green mixed with flour would kill beetle larvae. This advice was repeated in the July issue of *The American Entomologist*, and the practice of using Paris green on the potato beetle rapidly gained acceptance. In the 1870's, Paris green was found to be effective against other pests as well and it soon became a standard insecticide for the American farmer.

There was a serious need for insect control in the nation's agricultural industry. In 1870, for example, journalist Horace Greeley estimated that the average annual loss to farmers from insect damage exceeded $100 million. Assisted by the Division of Entomology in the United States Department of Agriculture (USDA), farmers found themselves with three basic strategies for fighting pest insects: insecticides, biological controls, and cultural controls. By the 1920's, however, insecticides had emerged as the principal means of insect control. The reasons for this can be grasped by reviewing the bureau's experience with three pests: the cottony-cushion scale, the gypsy moth, and the cotton boll weevil.

The cottony-cushion scale had been accidentally imported from Australia or New Zealand in the 1870's. Arsenicals had limited effect on the pest, so there was little to prevent the rapid spread of the scale through the orange and lemon groves of California in the 1880's. Charles Valentine Riley, first chief of the USDA Division of Entomology, noted that the cottony-cushion scale posed a significant problem in New Zealand. He concluded that the species was native to Australia and had been kept in check there by natural enemies, so it was neither abundant nor injurious. Riley sent his assistant, Albert Koebele, to Australia to search for natural predators. Koebele returned in 1889 with a small beetle that preyed upon the scale. Known as the Australian ladybird, or vedalia beetle, the new predator became so effective that the scale was brought under control in the first season after its release. The results of this experiment aroused great enthusiasm among farmers and entomologists, many of whom saw biological control as the solution to the war on insects, boldly predicting that spraying would no longer be necessary. By 1920, however, this confidence in biological control had been subrogated largely by a renewed faith in insecticides.

The gypsy moth had been introduced into the United States in 1869 by Leopold Trouvelot, a French-born astronomer with an avocation in the breeding of silkworms. He imported from Europe the eggs of the gypsy moth—a leaf-eating insect known to be harmful to trees. Some of the insects escaped from Trouvelot's laboratory and gradually became established near his home in Medford, Massachusetts. Twenty years after the accidental release, their population exploded. Writing in 1930, the bureau's chief, Leland Ossian Howard, described the infestation of caterpillars that invaded the town in 1889: "The numbers were so great that in the still, summer nights the sound of their feeding could plainly be heard, while the pattering of their excremental pellets on the ground sounded like rain." The caterpillars created a nightmare for Medford, defoliating trees, covering sidewalks and fences, and invading food and bedding inside houses. They were found to be resistant to Paris green and able to consume nearly ten times the amount of arsenic required to kill caterpillars of other species. Increasing the proportion of arsenic merely burned the foliage. Relief came in 1892 when the chemist F. C. Moulton found that lead arsenate could kill the caterpillar without as much injury to foliage as that produced by Paris green. Lead arsenate proved effective on the moth and on other insects; in the early 1900's, it became the most popular insecticide until it was replaced by dichloro-diphenyl-trichloro-ethane (DDT) in the 1940's.

After the California experience with the vedalia beetle, however, many believed that ultimate control of the gypsy moth would come when a suitable insect predator was found. Financed by state and federal funds, Howard traveled to Europe to search for natural enemies. Progress was slow. In Europe, the gypsy moth was kept in check by fifty parasites, and control in the United States might require importing all of them. Finally, in 1930, Howard concluded that biological control was far more complicated than entomologists had believed twenty years earlier and that the successful experience with the vedalia beetle had been an exceptional case. Although some control was eventually achieved through the introduction of natural enemies, the gypsy moth generally was kept in check through the use of lead arsenate.

The boll weevil problem furnishes an example of why cultural insect controls largely failed in American agriculture. The USDA was alerted to the boll weevil problem in 1894, when it received word from Corpus Christi, Texas, that a peculiar weevil had destroyed much of the "top crop" of cotton (a late harvest possible whenever the first frost arrives late). Local farmers found that ordinary poisons had no effect on the pest. Howard immediately dispatched entomologist C. H. Tyler Townsend to investigate the infestation. Townsend reported extensive crop damage and recommended cultural control measures, such as burning or flooding the stalks after the main harvest to eliminate the weevil's food source prior to hibernation; and a fifty-mile wide noncotton zone along the Texas international border to prevent further in-migration of the insect from Mexico. By the end of the next year, the boll weevil had spread well into Texas. Strong opposition from constituent farmers forced state legislators to decide against a noncotton zone on the Mexican border. Other cultural control measures recommended by the bureau also were rejected by farmers for socioeconomic reasons. Destruction of the crop after the main harvest, for example, would deprive farmers of the chance for a top crop, and thus posed an immediate economic cost with no guarantee of a more profitable harvest the next year. Furthermore, if neighboring farmers did not employ the same measures, the weevils would continue to thrive in nearby fields.

It was known that weevils fed from the cotton squares and bolls through deep punctures, thus avoiding poisons which would remain on the surface tissue of the plant. Nevertheless, Texas farmers used an estimated twenty-five boxcarloads of Paris green during a three-month period of 1904 in futile attempts to destroy the boll weevil. A breakthrough finally occurred in 1914 when bureau entomologist Bert Raymond Coad saw the possibility of poisoning the insect by means of the dew on the leaves of cotton plants. Over the next three years, he experimented with this idea on cotton plantations in Louisiana, Arkansas, and Mississippi. The results of these tests were highly encouraging. Numerous large-scale experiments were conducted in 1917 and 1918, and the success of these tests led to USDA guidelines on poisoning the boll weevil. Coad had found calcium arsenate to be more poisonous to the insect than other arsenicals. Coad's experimental work also verified his theory that the weevils could be poisoned by their habit of drinking from water on the plant's surface. He recommended that dusting be done at night when plants were especially moist from the dew. The combination of the new insecticide and the approach of poisoning weevils through their drinking rather than their feeding habits proved effective in controlling cotton damage caused by the pest. An insecticide again had provided the most convenient form of insect pest control.

Impact of Event

During the 1920's, farmers became increasingly reliant upon the utility offered by insecticides. No other method, it seemed, would stop insects as effectively as chemicals. New techniques were developed to increase the ease and efficiency of insecticide application. In 1922, for example, Coad demonstrated the possibility of dusting cotton crops from the air; by 1927, one aerial crop-dusting company had contracts to treat one-half million acres of cotton. The manufacture of insecticides developed into a large industry, which provided further encouragement and support to farmers inclined to dust and spray. Prior to 1918, for example, there was only one manufacturer of calcium arsenate. The total annual production of the compound was about fifty thousand pounds. Two years later, there were twenty-five manufacturers with a combined output of more than 10 million pounds per year. The sharp increase in production reflected the new demand for calcium arsenate as an insecticide for the boll weevil. From the time of Coad's discovery in 1917, production continued to grow until calcium arsenate became the second leading arsenical insecticide in use, next to lead arsenate. The annual production of lead arsenate had increased from 11.5 million pounds in 1919 to more than 37 million pounds in 1931. Annual production of calcium arsenate by 1931 had climbed to more than 26 million pounds.

In 1924, A. G. Ruggles, president of the American Association of Economic Entomologists, complained that young entomologists were not dedicating enough time to the study of insects; they were experimenting with insecticides to control pests even before thoroughly learning about the life cycles of those insects. Publicly funded economic entomologists were under pressure to ground their recommendations on control methods they knew would produce immediate results, and chemical insecticides had become the most efficient weapon in the war on insects.

Public health concerns about chemical residues on food were expressed shortly after Paris green first gained popularity as an insecticide. Tolerance levels for arsenic and lead residues, however, were not set by the government until the 1920's and 1930's. Levels were set by the USDA, and were based more on what the department believed industry could achieve through washing rather than on safe exposure levels. With few exceptions, government officials were looking for evidence of acute poisoning rather than chronic health effects from long-term exposure to spray residues. The potential for cumulative impacts from lifetime ingestion of these chemicals did not become an important issue for public debate until after the publication of Rachel Carson's *Silent Spring* in 1962.

The popularity of arsenical insecticides prepared the way for the rapid, almost indiscriminate, acceptance of DDT when it became available after World War II. By 1945, insecticides were already well established in the social and technological framework of American agriculture. It was not until the 1960's, however, that the general public became aware of indirect health effects resulting from insecticides that washed off the land into streams and lakes, poisoning fish, wildlife, and humans.

Bibliography

Dunlap, Thomas R. *DDT: Scientists, Citizens, and Public Policy*. Princeton, N.J.: Princeton University Press, 1981. An excellent, highly readable source for the DDT story in historical context. While focusing on the interaction of science and politics in the DDT controversy and the Wisconsin hearings in particular, the book also provides a background on insecticides, entomology, and public health prior to DDT. Includes bibliography and index.

Howard, L. O. *A History of Applied Entomology (Somewhat Anecdotal)*. Washington, D.C.: Smithsonian Institution, 1930. A valuable resource for the student of the history of entomology. Howard's highly personal account ranges from biographical sketches of important figures such as Riley to the use of beneficial predatory insects in thirty-two countries. Although Howard does not thoroughly discuss insecticides, the volume is a useful synthesis of the early development of economic entomology by a man with more than fifty years of government service. Includes illustrations and an index.

Perkins, John H. *Insects, Experts, and the Insecticide Crisis: The Quest for New Pest Management Strategies*. New York: Plenum, 1982. A useful source for students of the post-World War II era interested in the history of science and technology as they apply to entomology and insecticides. The book traces the movement toward integrated pest management strategies and the role of the entomological expert in American agriculture. Includes figures and an index.

Rudd, Robert L. *Pesticides and the Living Landscape*. Madison: University of Wisconsin Press, 1964. Although some historical background is included in this book, Rudd's primary purpose is to address the environmental hazards of chemical pest control. In addition to describing the kinds of pesticides, he summarizes their regulation and economics. Rudd argues for the diversification of pest control measures with limited use of chemicals. Includes tables, bibliography, and an index.

Whorton, James. *Before Silent Spring: Pesticides and Public Health in Pre-DDT America*. Princeton, N.J.: Princeton University Press, 1974. A good source for the early history of insecticide use, recognition of public health problems from spray residues, and the federal regulation of insecticides as these health problems became increasingly apparent. Whorton does a thorough job of explaining the background to the DDT controversy, providing examples ranging from careless spraying to health policy decisions that were driven primarily by economic considerations. Contains an index.

Robert Lovely

Cross-References

Müller Discovers That DDT Is a Potent Insecticide (1939), p. 1146; Carson Publishes *Silent Spring* (1962), p. 1740; The United States Government Bans DDT Use to Protect the Environment (1972), p. 1982.

HALE OVERSEES THE INSTALLATION OF
THE HOOKER TELESCOPE ON MOUNT WILSON

Category of event: Astronomy
Time: November, 1917
Locale: Mount Wilson, Pasadena, California

Hale oversaw the installation of the 254-centimeter Hooker telescope on Mount Wilson, the world's largest until 1948

Principal personages:
GEORGE ELLERY HALE (1868-1938), an American astronomer who observed and interpreted heavenly objects
JOHN DAGGETT HOOKER (1838-1911), an American businessman who donated money for the Mount Wilson telescope
GEORGE WILLIS RITCHEY (1864-1945), an American optician who began the grinding of the mirror for the Hooker telescope
WALTER SYDNEY ADAMS (1876-1956), an American astronomer who contributed to the design of the Hooker telescope

Summary of Event

Since Galileo first used a telescope to view celestial objects in 1609, astronomers have worked to make bigger and better telescopes. Galileo's first telescope was a refracting telescope; that is, it worked by using lenses to bend, or refract, the light. Sir Isaac Newton and N. Cassegrain in the seventeenth century worked to perfect reflecting telescopes, which worked by using mirrors to reflect starlight.

There is a limit to how big a refracting telescope can be, because a lens, supported only around its edges, will distort under its own weight once it gets too large. The largest refracting telescope is the 102-centimeter telescope at Yerkes Observatory in Wisconsin. Reflecting telescopes can be made much larger than this, however, since the mirror is supported across its whole lower surface. Astronomers want to have big telescopes because the bigger a telescope's aperture (width of the primary mirror or lens receiving the starlight), the more light is gathered by the telescope. Since stars are extremely small and faint sources of light as seen from Earth, the more light-gathering capacity the telescope has, the better.

In 1906, George Ellery Hale, at the Mount Wilson Observatory in California, was overseeing the construction of a 153-centimeter reflecting telescope. With characteristic enthusiasm and energy, he described to John Daggett Hooker how a larger telescope would perform even greater wonders than the 153-centimeter telescope could. Hooker, a wealthy businessman who had contributed money for the initial expedition to set up a telescope on Mount Wilson, was excited to hear this, and immediately offered $45,000 to the observatory to have a 213-centimeter mirror cast. He decided later to fund a 254-centimeter mirror instead. He wanted the telescope to be the biggest in the world and thought that a 254-centimeter mirror would not be easy for anyone else to surpass in size.

The Saint-Gobain Company in France was the only company willing to cast such a large mirror. They had to melt the glass for the mirror in three separate batches, which were all poured into the mold simultaneously. The meeting of the three streams of molten glass formed large clouds of air bubbles in the glass, and the glass also crystallized partially during its cooling. Nevertheless, the Saint-Gobain Company shipped the disk to Hoboken, whence it was shipped to New Orleans, and then sent the final leg of its journey to Pasadena, where it arrived on December 7, 1908. Both Hale and Hooker were disappointed with the quality of the mirror blank, and George Willis Ritchey—who was to be responsible for the mirror grinding—believed that the glass would never hold the necessary shape. The Saint-Gobain Company accepted financial responsibility for the failure and proceeded to cast another disk. The second disk broke during the cooling, and further tries at casting a new disk were also unsuccessful. The advent of World War I halted the attempts.

Ritchey and Hooker were both reluctant to use the original disk, which they thought was worthless. (In fact, Hooker refused to give any more financial support to the enterprise, and the remainder of the expenses were paid by a gift from Andrew Carnegie.) Walter Sydney Adams had carried out tests on the original disk and decided that his results showed that it could be ground to the proper shape. Despite Ritchey's disagreement, in 1910, Hale told Adams that the polishing of the mirror was to begin. The blank contained roughly 51,000 square centimeters of surface, each of which had to be polished and shaped accurately to within millionths of a centimeter. This painstaking job was begun by Ritchey and completed by W. L. Kinney.

Meanwhile, the construction of the mounting and controls for the telescope also was being carried out. The mounting design was Ritchey's, which received major revisions from Hale, Francis Pease, and F. L. Drew. The mounting was a huge rectangular steel cradle and was built in Quincy, Massachusetts; it was shipped to San Pedro Harbor in California by way of the Panama Canal. The finer parts of the instrumentation, such as the driving mechanisms that would enable the telescope to track an object across the sky, were crafted by the machinists in the observatory's workshops. The dome was designed by Daniel Hudson Burnham of Chicago. The motions of the telescope and dome were controlled by more than thirty electric motors, which worked to control smoothly and accurately the motion of the massive mirror and mounting, so that the telescope could track and photograph an object with no blurring of the image.

The telescope was designed to have several "foci," or places where the light is focused and observed. Newton had developed a telescope in which the light was reflected from the main mirror (the primary) up to a much smaller secondary mirror, which reflected it out the side of the telescope, where it was brought to focus and observed. Cassegrain had developed a telescope in which the light, after leaving the primary, was reflected from a secondary at the opposite end of the telescope and then back down to the vicinity of the primary. The Hooker telescope utilized both of these types of focus: The Newtonian focus was used for photography and the recording of spectra, and various instruments were used at the Cassegrain foci. Each focus has different characteristics that make it suitable for a particular type of work.

By early 1916, the grinding and testing of the mirror were completed, the great piers to hold the mounting and telescope were ready, and the trip up Mount Wilson could begin. Getting the huge mirror and its massive mounting and machinery to the observatory site was a harrowing task, requiring the building of a special road and involving some physical danger to the participants. On July 1, 1917, the mirror was safely carried up the mountain, and in November, 1917, the telescope was assembled. The astronomers and technicians were ready for first light, the first trial of the telescope.

On the evening of November 1, 1917, Hale pointed the telescope at Jupiter. Despite the 90,000 kilogram weight of the telescope, it moved smoothly. Unfortunately, the image of Jupiter was distorted disastrously. Rather than one clear image, there were six or seven overlapping images. The horrified astronomers attempted to guess what could have gone wrong with their new telescope. The dome had been open during the day and the sun had warmed the mirror; perhaps this warming and the subsequent cooling it was undergoing were distorting the mirror's shape and thus the image. The only way to test this idea was to wait and let the mirror cool further. This process took several hours. The astronomers waited, even attempting to go home and get some sleep. Hale could not sleep, however, and returned to the Observatory at around 2:30 A.M., where he was joined by Adams. Jupiter had set, and Hale moved the telescope to the bright star Vega. One can only imagine how delighted Hale must have been to see at last a clear, sharp image of this star in the telescope. This was the beginning of the long and useful career of the Hooker telescope.

Impact of Event

The Hooker telescope began immediately to prove its worth. Photographs of the moon and of nebulas revealed previously unseen details of great fineness. The great light-gathering capacity of the huge mirror allowed the study of the spectra of very faint stars (the stars' light, broken down into its component wavelengths by a prism or grating). Over the years of its use, the telescope contributed a vast amount of information to the knowledge of the stars and their properties.

Rather than make many unrelated observations with the new telescope, Hale organized the first observing program to focus on one of the great controversies of the time: whether the spiral nebulas visible in the sky were relatively nearby parts of the Milky Way or whether they were huge, distant, independent systems. The Hooker telescope was used to make photographs of the Andromeda nebula. Edwin Powell Hubble studied these photographs; the detail they showed enabled him to identify a star of a type known as Cepheid variables. These stars vary in light output, and the period of variation is related to the absolute brightness of the star; the absolute brightness can be compared to the brightness as seen from Earth and this comparison used to calculate the star's distance. Hubble calculated the distance of this star, and thus of the entire Andromeda nebula; the distance was very great and this proved to be decisive evidence in the controversy over the spiral nebula. They are, indeed, remote separate galaxies that are not part of the Milky Way. The Hooker telescope was crucial in the resolution of this basic question, which changed astronomers' view of the universe and Earth's place in it.

After this 1924 discovery, Hubble and Milton Humason worked with the Hooker telescope and gathered the data that would enable them to conclude that all the galaxies are receding from one another, and the speed of their recession can be used to measure the age of the universe.

The Hooker telescope also measured the diameter of a star. Stars are so tiny as seen from Earth that the measurement of their diameter is an exceedingly difficult task. Albert Abraham Michelson had developed a method of measuring star diameters, and in 1920, Francis Pease and J. A. Anderson carried out the measurements for the bright red star Betelgeuse in the constellation Orion. Ejnar Hertzsprung had used indirect means to deduce that Betelgeuse was a giant star; this measurement confirmed his deduction, giving the result that the diameter of Betelgeuse was about 350 times that of the sun.

This work and other work being done with the Hooker telescope led to results that could not be investigated further without a larger telescope. Thus, the success of this instrument led to Hale's plans for the 508-centimeter Hale telescope, which was eventually built on Mount Palomar and completed in 1948.

Bibliography

Asimov, Isaac. _Eyes on the Universe: A History of the Telescope._ Boston: Houghton Mifflin, 1975. Written in Asimov's customary engaging style, this book focuses on the development of the telescope. The chapter "Reflectors Take Over" covers the period during which the Hooker telescope was built and briefly discusses its construction and some of the astronomical advances to which the Hooker telescope contributed. Includes photographs.

King, Henry C. _The History of the Telescope._ Cambridge, Mass.: Sky, 1955. Contains a chapter that discusses the various telescopes of Mount Wilson, including the Hooker telescope. Gives drawings, diagrams, and technical details on the mounting and optics of the telescopes. Also includes photographs; references are given for each chapter. Recommended for those interested in the technical aspects of the Hooker telescope.

Struve, Otto, and Velta Zebergs. _Astronomy of the Twentieth Century._ New York: Macmillan, 1962. Contains some discussion of the building of the Hooker telescope and discusses the work of Hubble and Shapley in which this telescope played a part. Discussion of Hale and Mount Wilson, however, emphasizes solar work rather than the Hooker telescope. Contains photographs, drawings, bibliography, and glossary.

Wright, Helen. _Explorer of the Universe: A Biography of George Ellery Hale._ New

York: E. P. Dutton, 1966. Excellent source for the story of Hale's work on Mount Wilson, including the building and use of the Hooker telescope. Heavy use of letters and other original documents to convey the thoughts and hopes of the astronomers of the time. Includes photographs, drawings, and bibliographies. For the nontechnical reader.

Wright, Helen, Joan N. Warnow, and Charles Weiner, eds. *The Legacy of George Ellery Hale: Evolution of Astronomy and Scientific Institutions, in Pictures and Documents.* Cambridge, Mass.: MIT Press, 1972. Includes some discussion of the Hooker telescope, although emphasis is on the larger Hale telescope and on solar telescopes. Interesting and useful for the many photographs and references to original letters, newspapers, and other documents.

Mary Hrovat

Cross-References

Hale Establishes Mount Wilson Observatory (1903), p. 194; Michelson Measures the Diameter of a Star (1920), p. 700; Hubble Demonstrates That Other Galaxies Are Independent Systems (1924), p. 790; Hale Constructs the Largest Telescope of the Time (1948), p. 1325; Construction of the World's Largest Telescope Begins in Hawaii (1985), p. 2291; NASA Launches the Hubble Space Telescope (1990), p. 2377.

NOETHER SHOWS THE EQUIVALENCE OF SYMMETRY AND CONSERVATION

Categories of event: Physics and mathematics
Time: 1918
Locale: The Institute of Mathematics, Göttingen, Germany

Noether wrote one of the most beautiful chapters in mathematical physics by disclosing the necessary and sufficient connection between a symmetry and a conserved quantity

Principal personages:
   EMMY NOETHER (1882-1935), a German-Jewish mathematician who was the founder of modern abstract algebra
   DAVID HILBERT (1862-1943), a German mathematician whose interest in relativity and contribution to the invariants motivated Noether
   FELIX KLEIN (1849-1925), a German mathematician known for his *Erlanger Programm* (1872), with which he gave his influential abstract definition of a geometry
   ALBERT EINSTEIN (1879-1955), a German-Swiss-American physicist whose influential work motivated Göttingen mathematicians to pursue the theory of invariants

Summary of Event

As an achievement of theoretical physics, Emmy Noether's 1918 theorems were the upshot of developments in mathematics and physics along several lines. With the proof of these theorems, Noether succeeded in bringing together various threads, whose close mutual connections scientists had not suspected. These physics "threads" included conservation laws, the "symmetry principle," and Einstein's theory of gravitation (general relativity). On the side of mathematics, they were the theories of invariants, the notion of transformation groups, and an abstract concept of geometries. The idea of symmetry, which was being processed by theoreticians into a precise, abstract, and useful formulation was another theorem.

Noether was the daughter of Max Noether, professor of mathematics of the University of Erlangen and a specialist in algebra. For mathematicians, Erlangen had been famous for Felix Klein's *Erlanger Programm*, which was proclaimed in 1872. Klein unified the proliferating family of geometries by declaring that, defined by a group of transformations, a geometry investigates everything that is invariant under the transformations of this given group. Nevertheless, Noether did not start with an abstract approach. Her Ph.D. adviser was Paul Gordan, an old-fashioned specialist on the algebraic theory of invariants. After 1907, Noether became known as a theoretician on invariants. In 1915, Klein and David Hilbert invited Noether to join them at Göttingen University because they were interested in Albert Einstein's theory of general relativity and because they wanted Noether, with her expertise in invariants, to make contributions in this regard.

"Invariant" means constant, unchangeable. From the nineteenth century, in both physics and mathematics, scientists became increasingly interested in unchangeable characteristics in either a physical system or a mathematical entity. Beginning from the law of the conservation of matter, a list of conservation laws began to take shape: energy, momentum, angular momentum, electric charge, and the like. Physicists realized that it was important to ask under what conditions what quantities maintained constant values. The conservation of energy was officially titled the first law of thermodynamics. At the same time, physicists became aware that heat itself was hardly a conserved quantity (even under most usual physical conditions). The conservation of electric charge was confirmed as a basic principle; in the meantime, it was realized that "magnetic charges" did not exist, much less as conserved quantities.

In mathematics, by the middle of the nineteenth century, Arthur Cayley and James J. Sylvester began to develop the idea of invariants. For example, Cayley showed that the order of points formed by intersecting lines is always unchangeable, regardless of spatial transformation. It is ironic that in the late 1820's, the seminal idea of group theory occurred independently to two tragically short-lived mathematical prodigies: a Norwegian, Niels H. Abel, and a Frenchman, Évariste Galois. When they attacked the same problem of algebra, their approaches took similar paths. In 1824, Abel proved the impossibility of solving the quintic equation—general equation of the fifth degree—by "radicals" (algebraically). Before Galois was killed in a duel, he devised a more general solution: the clarification of the conditions that an equation must satisfy in order for it to be solvable algebraically. By the middle of the nineteenth century, Cayley was most responsible for furthering the idea of transformation groups. Later, Marius Sophus Lie, in collaboration with Klein, discovered the fundamental importance of the concept of continuous transformation groups, because, for example, it can be used to classify mathematical theories. Moreover, in physics, one has to make transformations from one reference system to another; those are continuous transformations.

Beginning with the twentieth century, Einstein became concerned with a fundamental question of physics. A physicist measures physical phenomena and formulates physical laws in relation to a reference system. Yet, there are possible an infinite number of reference systems. They are not all equally good. This line of inquiry would lead to the relatively late idea of the "symmetry of physical laws," or the "symmetry principles." Einstein noticed that there existed a certain incongruity between dynamics (Newtonian mechanics) and electrodynamics (Maxwellian electromagnetism): Dynamical laws are valid for all the "inertial systems," whereas electrodynamic laws appear to be valid in only one of these infinitely many "inertial systems." He solved this problem by establishing the theory of special relativity. Now, dynamics and electrodynamics are unified on a common basis: They are both valid for all inertial systems. In other words, the symmetry principle of the theory of special relativity requires that physical laws are symmetrical—invariant, unchanged—under any transformation from one inertial system to another.

After establishing the theory of special relativity in 1905, Einstein saw the need of generalizing his result to include all possible reference systems. Previously, he had found electromagnetic laws in his way, as if they posed a hurdle; now, he found a barrier in the traditional gravitational law. Prior to 1916, Einstein made a great effort to reform the theory of gravitation. Göttingen mathematicians were aware of and very interested in his work. In 1915, Hilbert independently derived the basic equations of the theory of general relativity.

Both Hilbert and Klein welcomed Emmy Noether at Göttingen because she was able to help them with her invariant-theoretic knowledge. In fact, her work on the theory of general relativity ended in its most general mathematical formalism. On the basis of such eminent work, in 1918, Noether proved two theorems: One theorem is about the symmetry of a physical system. If it is symmetrical, there must exist a conserved quantity corresponding to this specific symmetry, and vice versa. The second theorem is about the symmetry of a physical law. Starting from a certain physical condition, which is decided by physical measurements, the requirement that the physical law is invariant under a transformation group leads to the quantitative law itself. Thus, Noether's theorems represent a high degree of generalization. Physicists had begun already to realize the equivalence between a symmetry and a conservation law; Noether collected all these specific cases under the designation of her first theorem. Physicists had begun to realize the symmetry principle. Noether stated the "principle" in a general, rigorous, and succinct mathematical formulation.

Impact of Event

For three decades, most physicists were not aware of Noether's significant contribution. During the several years following 1918, only the mathematicians at Göttingen introduced or extended her theorems. Ernst Bessel-Hagen applied Noether's results to dynamics and electrodynamics (1921). Hermann Weyl mentioned them in his book *Raum, Zeit, Materie* (1918; space, time, matter); so did Wolfgang Pauli in his *Relativitätstheorie* (1921; *Theory of Relativity*, 1958). Hilbert included them in his *Methoden der Mathematischen Physik* (1924; the methods of mathematical physics), which was coauthored by Richard Courant.

Around 1950, physicists began to cite Noether's theorem—a trend in which Soviet mathematicians and physicists played an influential role. Since the middle of the 1950's, because of the revolutionary impact of the confirmation of parity-nonconservation, "Noether equations" have been applied frequently either in the context of general theory of relativity or, in most cases, the exposition of quantum field theories. In textbooks, sometimes, neither the title of the theorem nor its inventor is explicitly mentioned.

Richard P. Feynman, Nobel laureate and distinguished teacher, gave a long series of lectures (*Feynman Lectures on Physics*) on the new college physics between 1961 and 1963 at the California Institute of Technology. From the published lecture notes,

Feynman discussed the "Symmetry and Conservation Laws." Symmetry is important because, according to Feynman, one can examine "some of the even more remarkable symmetries of the universe—the symmetries that exist in the basic laws themselves." In quantum mechanics, for each of the rules of symmetry, there is a corresponding conservative law. There is "a definite connection" between the laws of conservation and the symmetries of physical laws. This "definite connection" is the Noether theorem.

In 1983, the First International Meeting of the History of Scientific Ideas was held; the thesis chosen for this scholarly gathering was "Symmetries in Physics (1600-1980)." The major speaker on the Noether theorem was Hans A. Kastrup from Aachen, Germany, who published thereafter in the proceedings of the conference (1987) "The Contributions of Emmy Noether, Felix Klein, and Sophus Lie to the Modern Concept of Symmetries in Physical Systems."

In 1981, an anthology, *Emmy Noether: A Tribute to Her Life and Work*, was published to commemorate her one hundredth birthday. Thus, this great scientist is now very well known; her personal stories have been told through a number of magazine articles. One of these articles is entitled "Emmy Noether: She Did Einstein's Math." That part of her math is her 1918 achievement, but many specialists point out that that encompasses only a minor part of her total mathematical creations.

Bibliography

Brewer, James, and Martha Smith, eds. *Emmy Noether: A Tribute to Her Life and Work*. New York: Marcel Dekker, 1981. An anthology including articles by several specialists, Noether's former colleagues. A valuable volume for the history of twentieth century mathematics. Shortly before Joseph Stalin was to push his Great Purge to its climax, Paul S. Alexandroff still could say that Noether saw in Soviet scientific successes the refutation of all the predictions that "Bolsheviks are destroying culture."

Dick, August. *Emmy Noether, 1882-1935*. Translated by Heide I. Blocher. Boston: Birkhauser, 1981. Noether's earliest, authoritative biography in a single volume. Weyl's often-quoted memorial address is included. It is not clear if anyone has ever pointed out the self-contradiction between Weyl's harsh words about Gordan's computational style (which have been echoed by every biographical writer thereafter) and his own epistemological observation made in 1931.

Feynman, Richard P., Robert B. Leighton, and Matthew Sands. *The Feynman Lectures on Physics*. Vols. 1 and 3. Reading, Mass.: Addison-Wesley, 1963-1965. Geared for college physics students. Reads like a verbatim record of Feynman's lively language.

Kastrup, Hans A. "The Contributions of Emmy Noether, Felix Klein, and Sophus Lie to the Modern Concept of Symmetries in Physical Systems." In *Symmetries in Physics (1600-1980)*, Proceedings of the First International Meeting on the History of Scientific Ideas, edited by Manuel G. Doncel, Armin Hermann, Louis

Michel, and Abraham Pais. Barcelona, Spain: Universitat Autonoma de Barcelona, 1987. Although technical, this is an excellent piece of "internal history" of science. Because of its historical character, the essay can be recommended to general readers.

Kramer, Edna E. *The Nature and Growth of Modern Mathematics.* New York: Hawthorn, 1970. Outstanding mathematicians around Noether are introduced. The topic of invariants is also discussed. Unfortunately, the two theorems are missing, as is the topic of conservation. Ponderous, anthologic, and weak in conceptual clarity.

Weyl, Hermann. *Symmetry.* Princeton, N.J.: Princeton University Press, 1952. In view of the fact that the late 1950's witnessed feverish discussion on symmetries among physicists, this brief popular book can be described as a timely, even prophetic, book. By reminding the readers of the prevalence of symmetry in nature and the arts, and from reviewing the usual understanding of the idea, Weyl introduces the general, abstract notions of group, geometry, symmetry, and the like.

Wen-yuan Qian

Cross-References

Einstein States His Theory of Special Relativity: $E = mc^2$ (1905), p. 297; Einstein Completes His Theory of General Relativity (1915), p. 625; Einstein's Theory of Gravitation Is Confirmed over Newton's Theory (1919), p. 684; Noether Publishes the Theory of Ideals in Rings (1921), p. 716.

SHAPLEY PROVES THE SUN IS DISTANT FROM THE CENTER OF OUR GALAXY

Category of event: Astronomy
Time: January 8, 1918
Locale: Mount Wilson Observatory, California

From his studies of star clusters, Shapley deduced the size of the Milky Way galaxy and Earth's location within it

Principal personages:

HARLOW SHAPLEY (1885-1972), an American astronomer, humanitarian, and civil libertarian who was the winner of the Rumford Medal and the Gold Medal of the Royal Astronomical Society

JACOBUS CORNELIS KAPTEYN (1851-1922), a Dutch astronomer famous for his studies of the motions and distribution of stars

ADRIAAN VAN MAANEN (1884-1946), a Dutch-American astronomer who was noted for his studies of stellar motions

HEBER DOUST CURTIS (1872-1942), an American astronomer who proved that there are numerous galaxies beyond the Milky Way

HENRIETTA SWAN LEAVITT (1868-1921), an American astronomer who discovered the relationship between the period and the brightness of the Cepheid variable stars

Summary of Event

Over the centuries, the question of what humans' place in the universe is has been a very fruitful question to address for both science and religion. After giving the matter long and careful thought, the ancient Greek philosopher Aristotle concluded that Earth lay in the center of the universe and that the universe visible to humans ended at the sphere of stars that lay just beyond the planets. He considered the possibility that Earth might move around the sun but could find no evidence to support this idea. Thus, it seemed that the universe was a cozy abode for humans and was focused on humans at its center as the Greeks supposed their gods had intended. Some nineteen hundred years later, Nicolaus Copernicus established the sun as the center of the universe. Since it seemed that the sun was largely here for our benefit, human beings could still consider themselves special because of their location in the universe.

At about this same time, Christian scholars began to suggest that God, being infinite, must have a domain far more extensive than Earth and the heavens that surround it. The English astronomer Thomas Diggs supposed that the stars were distributed throughout an infinite universe and that myriad planets orbited these stars and were inhabited by the creations of God. Several astronomers attempted to discover how stars were distributed throughout space by doing "star counts." These efforts culminated in the work of Jacobus Cornelis Kapteyn. In its simplest form, the star-counting method requires counting the number of stars seen in a patch of the sky. Some stars will look faint and others bright. If it is assumed that all stars would be equally bright if they were all placed at the same distance from Earth, then the faint stars are faint only because they are farther away. After this process has been repeated for many patches across the sky, one can construct a model of the galaxy.

. Suppose one had the means to place tiny sparks in the surrounding air and suppose that they would stay put. Using the data from the star counters, the model would be shaped rather like a grindstone, a squat cylinder many times wider than thick. The sun would be about in the center. In order to establish a scale for the model, it is assumed that all the stars are as bright as the sun. It must then be deduced how far away they must be in order to look as dim as they do in the sky.

All stars do not have the same brightness as the sun. Some are brighter, but most are fainter. In order to improve the model, a better method is needed to estimate distances to stars. This was Kapteyn's specialty. He began by using parallax to determine distances to nearby stars. Parallax is the apparent change in position of an object produced by a real change in position of the viewer. Perhaps the most familiar example of parallax is that objects near the road appear to move rapidly as one drives past, while the farther from the road an object is, the more slowly it seems to move. In a similar fashion, as Earth moves around the sun, nearby stars appear to move as seen from Earth. Measuring how much the stars seem to move allows one to find the accurate distance to nearby stars. The parallax of even the nearby stars is quite small and can be detected only with cameras and telescopes. This explains why Aristotle was unable to detect stellar parallax even though he searched carefully for it.

Knowing the distances to many stars, one can now calculate the brightness of different kinds of stars. That information can be used to estimate how far away distant stars of a given type are. Kapteyn's "grindstone" galaxy, also called "Kapteyn's universe," was ragged around the edges and had the sun just off center. Overall, it was 30,000 light-years across and 6,000 light-years thick. (A light-year is the distance light can travel in one year. For comparison, it takes light slightly more than eight minutes to make the trip from the sun to Earth.)

Harlow Shapley took a different approach. Scattered throughout the sky are ball-shaped groups of stars called globular clusters. Rich clusters contain tens to hundreds of thousands of stars and, therefore, can be seen even when they are relatively distant. To determine how far away the clusters were, Shapley used a new method involving a rare type of star called a variable star. Variable stars grow bright and dim as they swell in size and then shrink. Some variable stars have very regular periods of hours, days, or months. In 1908, Henrietta Swan Leavitt of the Harvard Observatory discovered that for certain variable stars, the brighter the star, the longer was its period. These particular stars are called Cepheid variables because the first star of this kind was found in the constellation Cepheus.

Shapley supposed the Cepheids to be the same as the variable stars he found in globular clusters. He measured their periods and used Leavitt's results to calculate how bright these cluster variables should be. Comparing this value with how bright they looked, Shapley could then calculate how far away they must be.

If globular clusters were placed on the grindstone galaxy model, one would find that none of them fit into the grindstone. Instead, the clusters would float above and below the grindstone and would occupy a roughly spherical volume. Two other aspects of the model would be striking: First, the sphere of globular clusters would be ten times the size of Kapteyn's grindstone. Second, the center of the cloud of clusters would be well off to one side of the grindstone. Assuming that the globular clusters reflected the structure of the galaxy, Shapley found the galaxy to be 300,000 light-years across, with its center 50,000 light-years from the sun in the direction of the constellation Sagittarius.

Later, Shapley would write in his book, *The View from a Distant Star* (1963), "It was a shocking thought—this sudden realization that the center of our universe was not where we stood but far off in space, that our heliocentric picture of the universe must be replaced by a strange sort of eccentric universe." Shapley's results were summarized on January 8, 1918, in a letter to Sir Arthur Stanley Eddington, a well-known English astronomer and physicist.

Impact of Event

The full impact was years in coming because it took that long to separate truth from error. The relevant questions were brought into focus by the "great debate" held between Shapley and another astronomer, Heber Doust Curtis, in April of 1920. One important issue was that of the nebula. "Nebula" is Latin for cloud, a meaning it retains in the word "nebulous." In 1920, astronomers were mostly concerned with two kinds of nebulas: irregular patches of glowing gas near hot stars and glowing patches with a somewhat spiral shape.

Curtis championed Kapteyn's view of our galaxy. He further supposed that spiral nebulas were galaxies like our own Milky Way but that they were so far away that their individual stars could not be discerned. Curtis eventually found support for his position when novas were observed in a few of these spiral nebulas. A nova is a star that explodes with tremendous energy. For many days it can shine with the brightness of billions of stars. If these novas were similar to those that occur in our galaxy, then their distances could be estimated. It followed that spiral nebulas must be galaxies themselves, and they must be far beyond our own galaxy.

A close associate of Shapley, Adriaan van Maanen, attempted to measure the speed at which spiral nebulas rotate. He found that they rotated and that they did so in a fashion predicted by some of the leading theorists of the day. Shapley pointed out that if spiral nebulas were very far away, van Maanen should not have seen evidence of their rotation over the few years for which photographs were available. It was later proved that van Maanen's measurements were in error. These measurements were beyond the capabilities of the equipment available to him.

Another important factor was interstellar dust. A handful of dust particles scattered throughout a volume of cubic kilometers is not enough to change it from a good vacuum. Yet, thousands of light-years of such dusty vacuum is enough to dim, or even to block, starlight. Shapley looked for evidence of dust, but by chance, looked in a direction in which there was little. The chief effect dust was to have on Shapley's measurements was to explain why he did not see globular clusters close to the plane of the Milky Way, which is dusty. The effect of dust was far greater on Kapteyn's results. The sun appeared to be near the center of the galaxy only because he could see into the dust about the same distance in all directions. Also, since his view was limited by dust, "Kapteyn's universe" was only a fraction of the real Milky Way galaxy.

The final block fell into place when Shapley discovered an error in the calibration of the distances to variable stars. Shapley had originally supposed that our galaxy was an "island universe" containing all the stars and nebulas that exist surrounded by an infinite dark space devoid of gas, dust, stars, and humans. Today, it is recognized that the universe is filled with other galaxies—islands like the Milky Way.

Modern measurements yield 80,000 light-years for the diameter of the visible part of our galaxy. This is roughly three times Kapteyn's number and only one-fourth of Shapley's original number. Yet, Shapley's philosophical legacy remains. The Milky Way is not at the center of the galaxy. That lies 25,000 light-years away in the direction of the constellation Sagittarius. The Milky Way galaxy is vast beyond anything Kapteyn had imagined.

Bibliography

Berendzen, Richard, Richard Hart, and Daniel Seeley. *Man Discovers the Galaxies.* New York: Science History Publications, 1976. This is an ideal book. It is written in an engaging, nontechnical style and is filled with historical photographs and drawings. There are biographies of all the principals, extensive bibliographies to each section, and even thought questions for those who would match wits with people of the past. It covers the period from Thomas Wright (1750) to Albert Einstein and the expanding universe.

Ferris, Timothy. *Galaxies.* New York: Stewart, Tabori & Chang, 1982. For anyone wanting a modern view of galaxies, this book is outstanding. It is a magnificent collection of some of the finest pictures of galaxies ever published. It begins with objects in our galaxy and moves outward to the universe. The lucid text is a browser's delight; one can begin almost anywhere. There are also several helpful diagrams and a useful glossary.

Harrison, Edward R. *Masks of the Universe.* New York: Macmillan, 1985. This book covers the various notions held about the galaxy and the universe from the dawn of time up to 1985. It shows how culture and science influence each other. While Shapley's work receives only short coverage here, this book will help place it within the panorama of the ten-thousand-year-long reach for the stars. The book is for the layperson and is fascinating.

Shapley, Harlow. *Galaxies.* Rev. ed. Cambridge, Mass.: Harvard University Press,

1961. While written for the layperson, this book contains some technical material. It reviews the work of Shapley and others on galaxies and summarizes what was known then about our galaxy, neighboring galaxies, and the expanding universe. Contains many helpful pictures and charts.

_____. *Through Rugged Ways to the Stars.* New York: Charles Scribner's Sons, 1969. This is an "informal" autobiography that grew from interviews done for an oral history project. It includes chapters on finding the center of the Milky Way and on the great debate. It also includes Shapley's studies of ants, which he performed while waiting for nightfall. For the general reader.

_____. *The View from a Distant Star: Man's Future in the Universe.* New York: Basic Books, 1963. Shapley was a popular speaker and writer. This book is a collection of many of his lectures and articles. One chapter deals with his discovery of the vastness of the galaxy. Other topics covered are humans' place in the universe, the educational system, astrology, and water dowsing. For the general reader.

Charles W. Rogers

Cross-References

Kapteyn Discovers Two Star Streams in the Galaxy (1904), p. 218; Leavitt's Study of Variable Stars Unlocks Galactic Distances (1912), p. 496; Hubble Demonstrates That Other Galaxies Are Independent Systems (1924), p. 790; Oort Proves the Spiral Structure of the Milky Way (1927), p. 830; Oort and Associates Construct a Map of the Milky Way (1951), p. 1414.

ASTON BUILDS THE FIRST MASS SPECTROGRAPH
AND DISCOVERS ISOTOPES

Category of event: Physics
Time: 1919
Locale: Cavendish Laboratory, Cambridge, England

Aston invented the first mass spectrograph to measure the mass of atoms and discovered that the atomic mass of elements is a combination of isotopes

> *Principal personages:*
> FRANCIS WILLIAM ASTON (1877-1945), an English physicist who developed and perfected the mass spectrograph and was awarded the 1922 Nobel Prize in Chemistry
> SIR JOSEPH JOHN THOMSON (1856-1940), an English physicist who discovered the electron
> WILLIAM PROUT (1785-1850), an English biochemist who first proposed that the atomic weights of elements were whole number multiples of the weight of hydrogen
> ERNEST RUTHERFORD (1871-1937), a leading physicist who contributed fundamental knowledge toward radioactivity and the structure of the atom

Summary of Event

Isotopes are one or more forms of a chemical element and act similarly in chemical or physical reactions. Isotopes differ in two ways: They possess different atomic weights and radioactive transformations. In 1803, John Dalton proposed a new atomic theory of chemistry that claimed that chemical elements in a compound combined by weight in whole number proportions to one another. By 1815, William Prout had taken Dalton's hypothesis one step further and claimed that the atomic weights of elements were integral multiples of the hydrogen atom. For example, if the weight of hydrogen was 1, then the weight of carbon was 12 and oxygen, 16. Over the next decade, several carefully controlled experiments were conducted to determine the atomic weights of a number of elements. Unfortunately, these results did not support Prout's hypothesis. For example, the atomic weight of chlorine was found to be 35.5. It took a theory of isotopes, developed in the early part of the twentieth century, to justify Prout's original theory.

After the discovery of the electron, Sir Joseph John Thomson, the leading physicist at Cavendish Laboratory, devoted much of his remaining research years to determining the nature of "positive electricity." As a result, without specifically looking for isotopes, Thomson became one of the first to confirm the possibility of isotopes of elements. The phenomenon of positive electricity was first identified by Wilhelm Wien, and Thomson then began developing an instrument sensitive enough to analyze the positive electron. Francis William Aston, as a result of the combination of these events, was pivotal to the discovery of isotopes.

Aston was ideally suited for the line of research that would eventually win for him a Nobel Prize. He was an experimenter who could patiently repeat a series of experimental procedures many times while making minute adjustments in his instruments. He possessed the mechanical skills to make instruments that produced the desired results—particularly glassblowing; Aston created the discharge tubes necessary for atomic research. The publication in 1903 of Thomson's book *Conduction of Electricity Through Gases,* opened up a world of new challenges for Aston. He was captured by the new phenomena of cathode rays and X rays. He became interested in an effect called "Crookes' dark space," which exists between the cathode and the negative glow. By designing a discharge tube with a movable cathode, Aston was able to define mathematically one of the dark spaces; it was subsequently named for him. Aston continued to work on the variables between current, pressure, electrode materials, and dark space until 1923.

Thomson had a reputation for inviting gifted scientists to work at the Cavendish Laboratory. The invitation to Aston in 1910 was such a case. Recommended by J. H. Poynting, who had taught Aston physics at Mason College, Aston began a lifelong association at Cavendish, and Trinity College became his home. By 1906, Thomson had discovered the electron and turned his attention to positive rays generated by the cathode of the discharge tube. When the electrons are stripped from an atom, the atom becomes positively charged. Through the use of magnetic and electrical fields, it is possible to channel these positive rays into parabolic tracks. By examining photographic plates of these tracks, Thomson was able to identify the atoms of different elements.

Aston's first contribution at Cavendish was to improve this instrument by blowing a spherical discharge tube with a finer cathode; he developed a more efficient pump to create the vacuum. He also devised a camera for sharper photographs of the parabolic tracks. By 1912, the improvements to this apparatus provided proof that the individual molecules of a substance have the same mass. While working on the element neon, Thomson obtained two parabolas, one with a mass of 20 and the other with a mass of 22. Aston was given the task of resolving this mystery. To separate the two constituents of neon, Aston decided to try fractional distillation and diffusion. The fractions of the distillation were in such minute quantities, however, that he had to invent a new balance to measure the differences. The quartz microbalance used a sealed quartz bulb balanced on a liquid of known density. By measuring the degree to which the bulb floated or sank, it was possible to compare the density of a known gas with that of an unknown one. Aston started with a quantity of neon and after several thousand operations was able to extract a minute amount of the heavier element of neon. The change in density was barely outside experimental error, however, and hence too doubtful to prove his case.

During World War I, Aston worked as a chemist at the Royal Aircraft Factory at Farnborough, improving the dope of the canvas that covered the aircraft. These were productive years; a number of scientists, housed at the same facility, were able to discuss the latest developments in physics and chemistry. Aston, who was normally shy, was encouraged to discuss his work. In addition, neon discharge tubes were a source of research in the factory because they were an excellent source of light for the stroboscope. After the war, Aston continued his attempts to distill the heavier part of neon but failed to achieve the necessary results.

In 1919, Aston began to build a mass spectrograph, an idea he had developed while at Farnborough. The idea was to treat ionized or positive atoms like light. He reasoned that just as light can be dispersed into a spectrum and analyzed through its constituent colors, the same could be achieved with atoms of an element such as neon. By using magnetic fields to focus the stream of particles, he was able to create a mass spectrum and record this on a photographic plate. The heavier mass of neon was collected on one part of a spectrum and the lighter neon showed up on another. This was a magnificent apparatus: The masses could be analyzed without reference to the velocity of the particles, which was a problem with the parabola method devised by Thomson. Neon turned out to possess two isotopes: one with a mass of 20 and the other with a mass of 22 in a ratio of 10:1. When combined, this gave the atomic weight 20.20, which was the accepted weight of neon.

Aston's accomplishment in developing the mass spectrograph was recognized immediately by the scientific community. It was a simple device and one capable of accomplishing a large amount of research quickly. Following Aston's pioneering work, the field of isotope research played an important part in other areas of physics.

Impact of Event

The years following 1919 were highly charged with excitement, as month after month new isotopes were announced. Chlorine had two; bromine had isotopes of 79 and 81, which gave an almost exact atomic weight of 80; krypton had six isotopes; xenon had even more. In addition to the discovery of nonradioactive isotopes, the "whole number rule" for chemistry was verified: Protons were the basic building blocks of different atoms, and these occurred in whole numbers. In 1920, Aston found that the mass of the hydrogen atom was about 1 percent greater than a whole number. At the time, it was thought reasonably certain that when four atoms of hydrogen were brought together, they would produce one atom of helium. This means that in "packing" the nucleus, about 1 percent of the mass would be lost.

Aston's original mass spectrograph had an accuracy of 1 in 1,000. In 1927, he built an even more accurate instrument, which gave ten times greater accuracy. Using this instrument, he was able to determine the packing fractions of a large number of elements. The apparatus was also sensitive enough to measure Albert Einstein's law of mass energy conversion during a nuclear reaction. Between 1927 and 1935, Aston reviewed all the elements that he had worked on earlier and published updated results. He also began to build an instrument with ten times greater accuracy; this instrument proved to be of great value to nuclear chemistry.

The discovery of isotopes opened the way to further research in nuclear physics and completed those speculations begun by Prout during the previous century. Even though radioactivity was discovered separately, isotopes played a central role in the field of nuclear physics and chain reaction.

Bibliography

Aston, F. W. *Mass-Spectra and Isotopes.* Rev. ed. New York: Longmans, Green, 1941. This book is an expanded and reedited edition of Aston's earlier work *Isotopes.* Large sections require technical knowledge, but the physics is described in terms that can be understood by general readers. Particularly valuable for those who wish to experience Aston's precise and clearly focused mind at work.

Chalmers, T. W. *Historic Researches, Chapters in the History of Physical and Chemical Discovery.* New York: Charles Scribner's Sons, 1952. There are a number of chapters on experimental work done through the 1920's. Although Aston is only briefly mentioned, the book provides an overview of experimental work during this period. Aston remarked in 1935 that he doubted if his researches would have passed any planning committee. It was a telling remark, as his work was done during more informal and less controlled times.

Crowther, J. G. *The Cavendish Laboratory, 1874-1974.* New York: Science History Publications, 1974. Though this work covers the history of the laboratory, and has limited material bearing directly on Aston, there are extensive sections on Aston's actual working environment. Includes extensive sections on Thomson and his work on the electron, which led directly to Aston's investigations.

Ihde, Aaron J. *The Development of Modern Chemistry.* New York: Harper & Row, 1964. This is a long and comprehensive history of the different aspects of chemistry. Aston's contribution is brief. Chapter 18 covers the developments in radiochemistry that led directly to Aston. These topics include the Dalton atom, gas discharge tubes, X ray and X-ray spectra, radioactivity, and isotopes.

Thomson, George Paget. *J. J. Thomson and the Cavendish Laboratory in His Day.* London: Thomas Nelson, 1964. This volume details the work done by Thomson and his associates. Describes experiments in great detail and provides excellent drawings of the experimental equipment and photographs of the results. The illustrations provide an added dimension for those who find it difficult to comprehend verbal descriptions of complicated equipment and experiments.

Victor W. Chen

Cross-References

Becquerel Wins the Nobel Prize for the Discovery of Natural Radioactivity (1903), p. 199; Thomson Wins the Nobel Prize for the Discovery of the Electron (1906), p. 356; Thomson Confirms the Possibility of Isotopes (1910), p. 471; Bohr Writes a Trilogy on Atomic and Molecular Structure (1912), p. 507; Rutherford Presents His Theory of the Atom (1912), p. 527; Rutherford Discovers the Proton (1914), p. 590.

MISES DEVELOPS THE
FREQUENCY THEORY OF PROBABILITY

Category of event: Mathematics
Time: 1919
Locale: Dresden, Germany

Mises developed the first precise empirical interpretation of probability, using the concept of relative frequency

Principal personages:

RICHARD VON MISES (1883-1953), an Austrian-American mathematician and physicist who originated the first precisely formulated frequency theory of probability

ALONZO CHURCH (1903-   ), an American logician and philosopher who refined Mises' theory using Turing computability (general recursive functions)

SIR KARL RAIMUND POPPER (1902-   ), an Austrian-British philosopher of science and Fellow of the Royal Society who invented the propensity theory of probability

A. N. KOLMOGOROV (1903-1987), a Soviet mathematician who axiomatized probability theory and provided it with a set-theoretical foundation

BRUNO DE FINETTI (1906-   ), an Italian mathematician who was one of the originators of the subjective Bayesian interpretation of probability

Summary of Event

The classical theory of probability, the earliest detailed analysis of probability, was developed by Pierre-Simon Laplace, in 1820. Laplace proposed his Principle of Indifference as the foundation for understanding probabilities. This principle stipulates that the probability of an event is the number of favorable outcomes of the event divided by the total number of cases possible, given no particular reason to prefer any of those cases. Thus, the probability of heads on a coin toss is ½, since there is one favorable case out of two "equipossible" cases. Laplace's theory served quite well in systematizing earlier work by Blaise Pascal and others on the probabilities of gambling devices. Over the course of the nineteenth century, however, it was gradually realized that games of chance formed an artificial set of problems, where the outcomes of, say, the roll of a die were already fixed to be equiprobable. When the Principle of Indifference is applied to other situations, a variety of absurdities may result. For example, consider the probability of its raining tomorrow. The two outcomes of interest are rain and no rain, so the Indifference Principle suggests an assignment of equal probabilities to each, namely ½. If one then asks "What is the probability of its snowing tomorrow?," the answer must come out the same. Therefore, the probability of rain or snow is one.

Such difficulties led John Venn (in his *Logic of Chance*, 1866), Charles Sanders Peirce, and other nineteenth century thinkers to identify probabilities with the observed frequencies of an outcome relative to a reference class, or relative frequencies. Thus, the probability of a sunny day tomorrow would be identified with the empirical frequency of sunny days in the given location. Probabilities cannot be identified with frequencies within a finite sample, however. For example, if a coin is tossed ten times, one may get a frequency of heads of $4/10$. A second series may yield six heads. Clearly, the probability of heads is not both $4/10$ and $6/10$; indeed, it is most likely neither. Frequency theorists instead equated the probability with the relative frequency in "the long run," that is, what happens if the sampling is continued without limit. Unfortunately, the frequentists of the nineteenth century did not provide an unambiguous account of long-run frequencies. Therefore, in 1921, John Maynard Keynes regretted that he could not find a careful analysis of the frequency theory to criticize. About that time, Richard von Mises was developing such a detailed exposition, initially in technical papers (1919) and subsequently in the book *Probability, Statistics and Truth* (1928).

Mises conceived of his task as replacing a commonsense, vague notion of probability by a scientific, precise concept. For this purpose, he restricted himself to considering "mass phenomena," that is, the infinite sequences that would be formed by indefinitely repeating an experiment or event. Such a sequence is a collective only in the case that it satisfies two requirements: the axiom of convergence and the axiom of randomness. The axiom of convergence postulates that as a sequence is extended, the proportion of outcomes having a specified property shall tend toward a definite mathematical limit. This corresponds to what Mises called the "Empirical Law of Large Numbers": that repeating experiments tends to produce stable frequencies of outcomes.

The axiom of randomness was Mises' most original contribution to the definition of probability. The idea behind it is that probabilities depend on more than merely stable frequencies in the limit. Thus, the sequence of heads and tails (T, H, T, H, T, H, . . .) will yield the limiting frequency of $1/2$ for heads; however, the probability of an H in the Nth location is not $1/2$, but either 1 or 0, depending upon whether the index N is even or odd. To eliminate such trivialization, one must disallow sequences open to useful predictions based upon their initial outcomes; in other words, one must rule out the possibility of successful gambling systems. The axiom of randomness is designed to do so. It requires that the limits of the relative frequencies be unaltered by any place selection, where place selections are subsequences whose members are chosen only on the basis of their index numbers in the original sequence and knowledge of prior members of the sequence. The sequence of H's and T's is not a collective, since the place selection of even-numbered outcomes has a different limiting frequency of heads (namely, one) from that of the original sequence.

A problem with this definition of place selection is that it imposes no clear restriction on which subsequences count as a place selection and which do not. Any subsequence will be selected by some infinite binary number, where each digit "1" is used to indicate that the corresponding element of the original sequence goes into the subsequence and the digit "0" indicates the element is excluded. Alonzo Church answered this objection in 1940. He restricted the allowable place selections to those that are Turing computable (calculable by a computer), given the index of the element and prior outcomes. Thus, a sequence is a collective only in the case that none of the computable place selections alters its limit frequencies.

Limiting frequencies within collectives are provable probabilities in the sense of the modern mathematical theory; that is, they satisfy the axioms of probability theory put forward by A. N. Kolmogorov in 1933. Mises had succeeded in providing an objective and empirical conception of probability: Rather than attempting to identify probabilities with a priori analyses of the state of ignorance, like Laplace, he defined them in terms of an idealization from observed frequencies. The task of statistics would be to identify what kinds of experiments are capable of generating collectives and to educe the associated probabilities.

Mises' theory, however, has remained highly controversial. If a probability is identified with a limit in an infinite sequence, then any finite sequence can be attached to the front of the sequence without affecting the probability in the least. For example, if the probability of heads in a collective is ½, then it will remain ½ if one puts any number of heads, say one trillion, in front of the sequence. The unfortunate consequence of this mathematical result is that any observation of finite frequencies is compatible with any probability at all, so it seems that statistics can find no foundation in Mises' theory.

Mises attempted to defend his theory by invoking the Law of Large Numbers: Assuming a hypothetical probability (limit frequency) for a sequence, then given a large enough sample from that sequence, it can be deduced that there is a high probability that the sample frequency will be very close to the hypothetical probability—that the sample estimate will be good. This argument has not been accepted because it leads immediately to an infinite regress: The "high probability" of getting a good sample must itself be understood as a limit frequency on Mises' account, and so is again compatible with any finite number of bad samples that diverge arbitrarily from the probability being estimated.

The price of Mises' insistence on considering only mass phenomena was that it left probability statements impossible to confirm or falsify. It also led Mises to the implausible view that ascriptions of probability to individual events are strictly meaningless.

Impact of Event

Problems of this kind led Sir Karl Raimund Popper to introduce (in the 1950's) a related conception, the propensity interpretation of probability. He criticized Mises' theory on the ground that if he introduced even one toss of a biased coin into an infinite sequence of fair tosses, then the probability of heads for that toss must be different from $\frac{1}{2}$, regardless of the limit frequency. Popper then identified probabilities with the individual experiments, rather than infinite repetitions of experiments. The individual experiment has the disposition or propensity to produce a limiting relative frequency if it were to be repeated indefinitely. Popper's theory is thus empirical in the same sense as Mises', but it directly applies to finite cases. Objections have been raised to this theory as well, among them the problem of the reference class: It is unclear what to count as a repetition of the same experiment. Different descriptions of an experiment lead to very different infinite sequences and therefore conflicting propensities for a single experiment.

Another influential competitor to the frequency view is the subjective interpretation of probability (Bayesianism). This view identifies probabilities with rational degrees of belief. It is possible to discover how strongly a person believes something by finding the odds he would accept for a bet on that proposition. Furthermore, using certain natural assumptions, it has been proved that rational degrees of belief obey Kolmogorov's axioms of probability. Nevertheless, there remain many objections to simply identifying probabilities with the strength of beliefs. Subjectivism fails to do justice to the common intuition that the flip of a coin merely has a probability $\frac{1}{2}$ of heads. In 1937, Bruno de Finetti attempted to answer this with a convergence theorem: In the long run, the probabilities hypotheses scientists ascribe to will converge, as long as they update those probabilities with empirical evidence using Bayesian theories. Yet, if two scientists start out with radically divergent probabilities, then even an enormous number of experiments will fail to bring their assessments together. In actual practice, however, agreement is normally reached within decades rather than millennia, so there must be some rational constraint in prior probabilities that subjectivism does not acknowledge. The subjective Bayesian view is at least incomplete.

The frequency theory arose in the context of the logical positivist philosophy of science propounded by the "Vienna Circle," of which Mises was a member. Frequentism has continued to appeal to empiricist philosophers who wish to find a foundation for scientific knowledge in empirical observation and has been defended by, for example, Hans Reichenbach and Wesley Charles Salmon. The frequency interpretation has been attractive to statisticians also, satisfying their intuition that there should be a connection between frequencies and probability. In practice, however, statisticians use any function obeying Kolmogorov's probability axioms, ignoring the question of whether it corresponds to limiting relative frequencies.

Despite the intellectual achievements of Mises and others, a consensus has not emerged. How to understand probabilities and their relation to the world remains an open and perplexing issue in philosophy and the foundations of statistics.

Bibliography

Howson, Colin, and Peter Urbach. *Scientific Reasoning: The Bayesian Approach*. La Salle, Ill.: Open Court, 1989. Elaborates and defends the subjective Bayesian approach to probability. Attempts to incorporate Mises' work on collectives into a subjectivist framework. Without hiding their biases, the authors provide a clear survey of competing views, including classical statistical inference.

Kyburg, Henry E., Jr. *Probability and Inductive Logic*. New York: Macmillan, 1970. Excellent survey of the different interpretations of probability in philosophy and science. Each chapter ends with extensive bibliographical notes. Includes exercises.

Mises, Richard von. *Mathematical Theory of Probability and Statistics*. Edited by Hilda Geiringer. New York: Academic Press, 1964. A collection of Mises' lectures and papers on probability and statistics, organized and supplemented with notes by his widow. Attempts to provide a rigorous, objective foundation to the methods of statistical inference. Highly technical.

_____. *Positivism: A Study in Human Understanding*. New York: George Braziller, 1956. A readable presentation of the logical positivist worldview. Applies positivism to a broad spectrum of issues, including language, science, probability, and art.

_____. *Probability, Statistics, and Truth*. 2d rev. ed. London: George Allen & Unwin, 1957. A semipopular and clearly written account of Mises' frequency interpretation of probability and its implications for science. A classic exposition of the frequentist view.

Popper, Karl R. *Realism and the Aim of Science*. Edited by W. W. Bartley III. Totowa, N.J.: Rowman & Littlefield, 1983. Part of a "postscript" to Popper's influential *Logic of Scientific Discovery* (1934); written, but not published, in the 1950's. Part 2 describes and defends the propensity interpretation at length.

Salmon, Wesley C. *Scientific Explanation and the Causal Structure of the World*. Princeton, N.J.: Princeton University Press, 1984. Applies a version of Mises' definition of probability to a philosophical analysis of the nature of statistical explanations in science. Also examines the role of causality in explanation and in quantum mechanics.

Kevin B. Korb

Cross-References

Lebesgue Develops a New Integration Theory (1899), p. 36; Markov Discovers the Theory of Linked Probabilities (1906), p. 335; Turing Invents the Universal Turing Machine (1935), p. 1045.

THE PRINCIPLES OF SHORTWAVE RADIO COMMUNICATION ARE DISCOVERED

Category of event: Applied science
Time: 1919
Locale: Europe and North America

Theoretical principles proposed and tested by physicists, coupled with technological and empirical experimentation, made possible reliable long-distance radio communication via short waves

Principal personages:

JAMES CLERK MAXWELL (1831-1879), a Scottish physicist who developed a theory describing the movement of electromagnetic waves in space

SIR OLIVER JOSEPH LODGE (1851-1940), an English physicist who originated a theory of the "ether," through which electromagnetic waves traveled, developed, and refined the coherer, and proposed and stressed the importance of "syntony," or tuned resonance

HEINRICH HERTZ (1857-1894), a German physicist whose research interests included electromagnetic waves

GUGLIELMO MARCONI (1874-1937), an Italian engineer and inventor who was the first to exploit electromagnetic wave radiation as radio communications over long distances

HIRAM PERCY MAXIM (1869-1936), an amateur radio experimenter who obtained governmental approval for amateur enthusiasts to return to the airwaves after World War I

Summary of Event

When James Clerk Maxwell first postulated the theory that the flow of an electric current created an accompanying electromagnetic force, he did so without recourse to empirical experimentation and as an enlargement upon his theories of light waves and optics. His mathematical and theoretical suppositions were published in the celebrated 1864 article, "A Dynamical Theory of the Electromagnetic Field," in which he maintained that electromagnetic waves operated under the same laws and in the same manner as light. As a theoretician, Maxwell neither proposed nor foresaw any practical uses for the electromagnetic (radio) waves his formulas described.

Heinrich Hertz, however, was a physicist with a distinctly experimental approach. In part based upon Maxwell's theories, he designed and built what is generally acknowledged to have been the first practical demonstration of transmitted and received radio waves. His design consisted of a spark gap oscillator and a loop receiving aerial, in which a small opening allowed the received "signal" to spark. Because of the space limitations of his laboratory, the aerials he constructed were relatively small. In fact, his initial experiments, which demonstrated the practical ability to transmit radio waves and detect them at a distance from the transmitter, were conducted in what is now called the Very High Frequency (VHF) range; that is, the waves oscillated approximately 100 million times per second or at a frequency of 100 megahertz. Because his experiments were carried out at a frequency that operates best in direct, line-of-sight fashion, his apparatus was more important for the physical phenomenon it demonstrated, not as an immediately useful communications device.

In the years after Hertz's results were published, much work was done in extending the sensitivity of radio wave devices; as a result, the range over which such waves could be sent and received was increased. Particularly important was the work of Sir Oliver Joseph Lodge, who developed and refined the radio wave detector, then called a "coherer," a device that would complete an electrical circuit (which, in turn, might be used to ring a buzzer) in the presence of radio waves of sufficient intensity. Second, Lodge emphasized the significance of "syntony," or tuned resonance, in the radio wave spectrum. The design of spark gap transmitters used at the time was such that their radiated energy was spread over a broad number of frequencies. Lodge's insistence on tuning circuits to "focus" transmitted and received radio wave energy was an important step in making simultaneous communications between many stations practical. In fact, Lodge received patents for both of these achievements.

The progress made by Lodge was the basis on which Guglielmo Marconi (whose name is associated most often with the early days of "wireless" technology) was able to establish a corporation whose sole product was radio equipment and communications services. Marconi relied less on theoretical physics than on empirical research; that is, he tried what worked and refined it as best he could, even if such an approach led him to investigate unproductive ideas. His refinements of the coherer, his use of resonant circuits, and his practical experiments with transmissions on low frequencies enabled him to conduct the first transatlantic radio transmission on December 12, 1901, thus demonstrating the possibilities the medium offered. Despite the distance covered in that demonstration (nearly 2,700 kilometers from England to Newfoundland), however, the first practical application of early radio was in maritime communications between ships at sea and ship to shore at distances up to 300 kilometers. Beyond that range, communications were not reliable.

The establishment of reliable, long-distance radio communications became Marconi's goal. He found little guidance from theoretical physics in this area. Nineteenth century physicists had supposed earlier that electromagnetic forces necessarily traveled through some sort of medium, which, although of unknown composition, they called the "ether." Only at the beginning of the twentieth century did the experience of radio communicators suggest that the particular frequency range of a given radio wave had much to do with the distance it seemed to cover and that no other medium was necessary to account for electromagnetic wave propagation. Today, the radio frequency spectrum is divided into various "bands," or ranges of frequencies, that share similar propagation characteristics. At the dawn of the radio age, however, it seemed clear only that radio waves with wavelengths greater than 200 meters were the most reliable for communications up to 300 kilometers. Consequently, frequencies in the Very Low Frequency (VLF, 10 to 30 kilohertz), Low Frequency (LF, 30 to 300 kilohertz), and Medium Frequency (MF, 300 to 3,000 kilohertz) were employed by corporations and by governments for their commercial and military communications. Prior to 1919, the wavelengths below 200 meters (that is, frequencies above 1.5 megahertz) were held to be of no commercial value. This band of frequencies from 3 to 30 megahertz (the High Frequency, or HF band) is known as the "short wave" band since their wavelength was, in comparison with wavelengths then generally in use, considerably shorter.

Prior to World War I, there was virtually no governmental regulation of radio transmissions. Thus, many individuals with sufficient inclination, money, and an interest in this new technology built their own transmitting and receiving apparatus. When the war broke out, amateurs in Europe and the United States were forbidden to use their equipment. It was only with the active lobbying of amateur investigators such as Hiram Percy Maxim that, on October 1, 1919, hobbyist radio experimenters in the United States were allowed once again to make their broadcasts to one another.

Amateur operators undertook the same types of communications experiments on the higher frequencies as Marconi's corporation was conducting. It soon became clear that as one went higher in frequency (that is, as the wavelength became shorter), greater distances could be covered. A combination of improved antennas, more powerful transmitters, and more sensitive and selective receiving equipment proved that transatlantic communications were possible. As continuing experiments were to reveal, there is a region of electrically charged ions and electrons located about 50 to 400 kilometers above and encircling the earth. This region is called the ionosphere and it acts to refract or bend radio waves below 30 megahertz. (The ionosphere is a complex series of differing layers whose electrical charges vary on a daily basis as well as in response to the eleven-year cycle of sunspot activity.) Whereas VLF, LF, and MF waves tend to radiate along the ground and will follow the curvature of the earth, HF waves—short waves—are bounced back by the ionosphere, generally at distances quite far from the transmitting station. If an operator chooses carefully a frequency of operation within the shortwave band, even low-power transmitters can be heard around the world as a consequence of waves reflected multiple times (or "hops") by the ionosphere.

Impact of Event

Throughout history, humanity has continually sought ever faster and more reliable means of communication. With the rise in scientific and engineering research that preceded and accompanied the industrial age in Europe and North America came not only the ability but also the perceived need to send messages over great distances. Samuel F. B. Morse's invention of the telegraph system in the 1860's thus found ready acceptance and, by the beginning of the twentieth century, undersea cables linking the United States to Europe were already in operation. Radio communications were seen initially as little more than an oddity inasmuch as early radio systems had limited range, were not always easy to operate, and were not secure (because radio waves were transmitted through open air, anyone within range of a transmitter and inclined to build a receiver could intercept those radiotelegraphic signals).

The business of radio communications was first limited primarily to maritime use. The sinking of the *Titanic* in 1912 provided dramatic evidence of how useful such communications could be and impetus toward further refinement of the technology. As the *Titanic* began to sink, its wireless operator transmitted an emergency call for aid. A ship about 130 kilometers distant happened to be equipped with radio as well and, although it took hours, came to assist the ship, saving hundreds of lives. As a result of this incident, in both the United States and Europe, laws were passed equipping ships with operating networks of shore stations. Nevertheless, such communications were limited to relatively short distances. It was to be the role of the shortwave band to encourage long-distance radio communications.

Among those "amateur" experimenters were most of the noted engineers and scientists of radio who communicated their findings in their amateur radio journal, *QST*. In the 1920's, AM (amplitude modulation) radio broadcasting became an important part of everyday life. Broadcasters were quick to realize that the shortwave frequencies offered them the chance to transmit not only to a local audience in a given city but also to a large area. Because it has always been impractical for one transmitter on any one shortwave frequency to service adequately the entire world, both nations and individual corporations soon erected numerous transmitting sites and appropriate directional antennas operating on different frequencies.

In order to increase the amount of information that could be sent by shortwave radio and in order to "encode" that data to keep all but the most determined from listening in on transmissions, alternate forms of communication were developed. Radioteletype, for example, uses mixtures of two different tones in patterns not at all like the Morse code to transmit data quickly; it soon became standard for international news services, telegraph companies, and governments (who further encrypted their messages using ciphers). The airline industry found shortwave radio communications to be of considerable value in keeping in touch with airplanes en route and in communicating with foreign airports to learn of weather conditions. Facsimile devices were invented in the 1930's and allowed international transmission of pictures and diagrams. In short, the shortwave band was exploited quickly for its ability to provide long-distance radio communication.

By the mid-1930's, it became clear that uncontrolled radio use, especially in the shortwave band, was growing in an alarming fashion. Thus, nations enacted laws to regulate the limited radio spectrum at home. Because radio waves—especially the far-reaching short waves—do not respect borders, however, an international organization was formed to divide the shortwave spectrum into various subbands for different uses (commercial, amateur, governmental, international maritime, and the like) in different regions. Today, World Administrative Radio Conference (WARC) meetings are held in plenary session each decade to plan radio spectrum use.

An alternative technology has been developed that would deemphasize the importance of the shortwave band. Geosynchronous satellites, which reliably carry the broad signals necessary for television transmissions and for multiplexed voice and computer data transmissions, are in widespread use. Nevertheless, demands made on the shortwave spectrum have scarcely diminished. Whereas international telephone and television transmissions have been shifted to satellite systems, the shortwave band provides a reliable and inexpensive medium for individuals or small organizations and nations with limited financial resources. Indeed, the fact that there are so many international shortwave broadcasts intended for individual listeners around the world demonstrates the interest and use this technology still engenders.

Bibliography

Aitken, Hugh G. J. *The Continuous Wave: Technology and American Radio, 1900-1932*. Princeton, N.J.: Princeton University Press, 1985. A continuation of Aitken's earlier book; concentrates on the establishment of broadcast services and the development of the technologies employed in the late 1980's. Accounts for the economics of radio as well by following the rise of large American technology and broadcasting corporations. Well illustrated and indexed.

_____. *Syntony and Spark: The Origins of Radio*. New York: John Wiley & Sons, 1976. Discusses both the physical and experimental basis of the discovery of spark gap radio communications, the earliest phase of radio. Emphasizes the processes by which physics at first anticipated the discovery of radio waves and, later, was surprised by the discovery of the ionosphere. Numerous diagrams and illustrations; indexed.

Hale, Bruce S., ed. *The 1991 American Radio Relay League Handbook for the Radio Amateur*. Newington, Conn.: American Radio Relay League, 1990. Updated annually since its first appearance in 1922; a massive volume that covers virtually all aspects of radio (and television) communication for the enthusiast. Includes heavy emphasis on shortwave frequency communications, construction and alignment of equipment, erection of various antennas, and more. Fundamentals of electricity, waves and their propagation, and electronics also taught as well as amateur operating principles. Well illustrated and indexed.

Maclaurin, W. Rupert, and R. Joyce Harman. *Invention and Innovation in the Radio Industry*. New York: Macmillan, 1949. Readable account of the early history of radio communications. Includes discussion of figures not mentioned elsewhere. Illustrated and indexed.

O'Hara, J. G., and W. Priche. *Hertz and the Maxwellians*. London: Peter Peregrinus, 1987. A short but eminently readable history of the discovery of electromagnetic waves. A brief introduction is followed by excerpts from the correspondence of Hertz and the scientists with whom he discussed and evaluated his findings. Illustrations and photographs.

Terman, Frederick E. *Radio Engineering*. 3d ed. New York: McGraw-Hill, 1947. Explanations of radio technology of historical interest only; discussions of radio wave propagation and antennas as valid in the 1990's as at the time of publication. Well illustrated.

Joseph T. Malloy

Cross-References

Marconi Receives the First Transatlantic Telegraphic Radio Transmission (1901), p. 128; Kennelly and Heaviside Propose the Existence of the Ionosphere (1902), p. 174; Fleming Files a Patent for the First Vacuum Tube (1904), p. 255; Fessenden Perfects Radio by Transmitting Music and Voice (1906), p. 361; The First Transcontinental Telephone Call Is Made (1915), p. 595; Transatlantic Radiotelephony Is First Demonstrated (1915), p. 615; Armstrong Perfects FM Radio (1930), p. 939; A Secret English Team Develops Colossus (1940's), p. 1155; The First Transatlantic Telephone Cable Is Put into Operation (1956), p. 1502; The St. Lawrence Seaway Is Opened (1959), p. 1608.

BJERKNES DISCOVERS FRONTS
IN ATMOSPHERIC CIRCULATION

Category of event: Earth science
Time: 1919-1921
Locale: Bergen, Norway

Bjerknes named the line of intersection of the interface between the cold and warm currents in the front part of a storm, the warm front

Principal personages:
>VILHELM BJERKNES (1862-1951), a Norwegian meteorologist who was a pioneer in modern weather forecasting
>JACOB BJERKNES (1897-1975), a Norwegian meteorologist who was the developer of the polar front theory of cyclones, which explained much about global origins of weather
>CARL-GUSTAV ARVID ROSSBY (1898-1957), a Swedish-American meteorologist who pioneered the study of the upper atmosphere
>TOR BERGERON (1891-), a Swedish meteorologist who discovered the importance of ice crystals in the initiation of precipitation in supercooled clouds

Summary of Event

Vilhelm Bjerknes, a Norwegian geophysicist and meteorologist, knew in the early 1900's that accurate forecasting of weather was dependent upon ample data. He also knew that the weather in one place was part of a huge mass that covered the world. With this knowledge as a basis, he formulated a theory to explain it. Prior to his return to Norway, he had tenure at the University of Stockholm from 1895 to 1907, and during his stay, he proposed that movements in the atmosphere are stimulated by heat from the sun, while at the same time these motions radiate heat as the result of friction of air masses rubbing against one another. When Bjerknes returned to Bergen, Norway, in 1917 (after his stay at the University of Leipzig in Germany), he was motivated by the need for improved weather prediction for commercial fishing and agriculture. In part, the urgency arose from restrictions of imports and communications as a result of World War I. He persuaded the Norwegian government to help set up strategically located observing stations. In addition to the stations, he founded a school at Bergen, which attracted meteorologists from all over the world, including his son Jacob Bjerknes; Carl-Gustav Arvid Rossby, a Swedish-American meteorologist; and Tor Bergeron, a Swedish meteorologist. He also developed the theory of electromagnetic wave resonance, which was an important link in the development of wireless telegraphy. He influenced his son, Jacob, in the origination of the polar-front theory of cyclones, which formed the basis of modern weather forecasting.

Weather types and changes, along with moving masses of diverse air and their interaction, had been studied and noted through many centuries. More than a century ago, Luke Howard, an English physicist, in his book *Climate of London* (1818-1820) referred to northerly and southerly winds blowing alongside each other, with the colder wedging in under warmer and the warmer gliding up over the colder and giving extensive and continued rains. In 1852, evidence was found of an advancing polar wind underrunning a warm, nearly saturated tropical wind and pushing it up with the production of cumulus clouds.

Vilhelm Bjerknes was a pioneer in the development of a mathematical theory of fronts and their effects. In addition, along with his son, he was the first to use an observational basis for the present concept of the extratropical cyclone and its practical use in weather forecasting. Extratropical cyclones are tropical cyclones that may cross an ocean in ten days, lose most of their intensity, and then develop again into large and vigorous storms. In the years following World War I, Norwegian meteorologists had a fairly good understanding of the action in the big storms sweeping across the Atlantic. From this observation, Vilhelm Bjerknes postulated a clashing of two air masses, one warm, the other cold, along a well-defined boundary as the main essence of storm development. His theory did not take into account the pumping effect of the jet streams aloft. Aside from the frontal concept, his view of cyclone development produced another concept: In the life cycle of a storm, at the start there is an undisturbed state in which cold and warm air masses flow side-by-side, separated by a straight front line. Each air mass flows along its proper side of the front, the flow paralleling the extent of the front lines. This flow is suddenly interrupted by a small disturbance that causes the warm air to produce a small impression in the straight front line leading to a wave disturbance. It starts to spread and amplify, especially as surface pressures begin to fall near the apex of the newborn wave, and at the same time air motions try to spiral into the low-pressure area. As this wave develops, the original stationary front starts to advance. Along one portion of the front, cold air tries to push ahead, marking the cold front. Along one frontal portion, warm air starts to advance, marking the warm front. Normally, the cold front moves faster than the warm front; therefore, it tends to catch up with the latter. As a consequence, as one storm grows deeper, the cold front becomes more pronounced. The whole process from the time the prong of polar air encounters the northward flow of warm air to the final, complete occlusion and filling up of the area of low pressure is known as the life cycle of a frontal system, according to the wave theory as originally developed by Vilhelm Bjerknes in 1921.

In 1919, when this work began, upper atmosphere studies were limited by primitive aeronautics and the lack of such things as radar images, lasers, computers, and satellites. Vilhelm Bjerknes showed that the atmosphere was not homogeneous or continuous but, in fact, was a composition of distinct masses of air converging at various places to produce different meteorological effects. He published the study, entitled *On the Dynamics of the Circular Vortex with Applications to the Atmosphere and Atmospheric Vortex and Wave Motion*, in 1921.

Impact of Event
The pioneering weather forecasting stations established by Vilhelm Bjerknes in the 1920's were a monumental accomplishment considering the limited data basis and the lack of high-speed, worldwide communications and the fact that all computations were done without the assistance of a computer to analyze and model the data. In the 1980's, the National Meteorological Center (NMC) used national, international, public, and private resources to predict the weather. Throughout the Northern Hemisphere, approximately two thousand stations regularly transmit weather data to national or regional collecting centers four times a day, seven days a week. Data recorded and sent by radio or satellite consist of barometer readings, thermometer readings, rain and wind gauges, and hygrometer readings. All these data are fed into a computer. On an average day, the NMC picks up about thirty-two hundred ship reports on weather throughout the seven seas, about one thousand reports from commercial aircraft in flight, and at least two hundred reports from scheduled reconnaissance flights by military aircraft.

Bjerknes' research efforts did not have the advantage of satellites and high-flying aircraft; however, his work was well developed and reasoned regarding hydrodynamics and the application of its principles to meteorology. In the 1980's, scientists used working models of an actual atmospheric process for close study in the laboratory. These miniature laboratories can model the circulation of air over a hemisphere. There are other miniatures that can create a test-tube tornado. A model of the atmosphere can be created entirely from numbers by entering the data into a computer. Although the programs are very complex, the simulation of one day of weather requires only a few hours of computer time.

During the International Geophysics Year (IGY), 1957 to 1958, the first organized instrumental exploration of the upper atmosphere took place using an upper-atmosphere sounding rocket. The purpose of this research was to look into the region of ozone layers, X rays, ultraviolet rays, meteoric dust, weirdly illuminated clouds, and bitter cold. It also studied sunspots to determine their effect on earth's weather. In 1960, the world's first all-weather satellite, Tiros (television infrared observation satellite), was launched. Although weather forecasting was the primary benefactor, subsequent satellites were launched that enhanced research: infrared radiation, examining the anatomy of a cloud, and measuring clouds.

Great progress has been made as a result of new technology and a universe of data, but it was pioneers such as Vilhelm Bjerknes who paved the way.

Bibliography
Humphreys, W. J. *Physics of the Air*. New York: Dover, 1964. A college textbook on physical meteorology for upper-level and graduate students. Although the book has numerous mathematical formulas, it is still a good reference for the advanced high school and lower college-level student. Well illustrated; however, there are no supplementary reference sources.

Koeppe, Clarence E., and George C. DeLong. *Weather and Climate*. New York:

McGraw-Hill, 1958. This is written by geographers, and as a result there is a minimum of mathematics and physics. It should be a good reference source for the high school and college student. Copious illustrations, as well as an extensive reference list for additional reading.

Lutgens, Frederick K., and Edward J. Tarbuck. *The Atmosphere: An Introduction to Meteorology.* 2d ed. Englewood Cliffs, N.J.: Prentice-Hall, 1982. An introduction to meteorology for the college student; however, this book can be used by the advanced upper-level high school student as well. Well illustrated and has a glossary and a good appendix covering the explanation and decoding of the daily weather map. Of particular interest is the chapter on weather patterns.

Neiburger, Morris, James G. Edinger, and William D. Bonner. *Understanding Our Atmospheric Environment.* San Francisco: W. H. Freeman, 1973. Can be used as a reference for the high school and college student. It has very few references to mathematics or physics. Its purpose is to provide the student with the physical explanations of atmospheric phenomena. Well illustrated and has a section after each chapter devoted to questions, problems, and projects. There is also an appendix giving weather map symbols.

Reiter, Elmar R. *Jet Streams: How Do They Affect Our Weather?* Garden City, N.Y.: Doubleday, 1967. An excellent reference for the high school and lower-level college student. It is a popular survey on how jet streams are formed, how they move, and what effect they have on weather and climate. Illustrated, with a short suggested reading list.

Schaefer, Vincent J., and John A. Day. *A Field Guide to the Atmosphere.* Boston: Houghton Mifflin, 1981. An excellent reference for the high school and lower college-level student. There are numerous color and black-and-white photographs as well as drawings to help clarify the physical principles. Includes twenty appendices and a very good bibliography after each chapter.

Thompson, Philip D., and Robert O'Brien. *Weather.* New York: Time-Life Books, 1968. Primarily a general-interest reference for the general public, this book is well written and enjoyable to read. Copiously illustrated with photographs, drawings, and graphics to assist in understanding the basic principles. Includes a list of references.

Earl G. Hoover

Cross-References

Bjerknes Publishes the First Weather Forecast Using Computational Hydrodynamics (1897), p. 21; Teisserenc de Bort Discovers the Stratosphere and the Troposphere (1898), p. 26; Kennelly and Heaviside Propose the Existence of the Ionosphere (1902), p. 174; Fabry Quantifies Ozone in the Upper Atmosphere (1913), p. 579; Piccard Travels to the Stratosphere by Balloon (1931), p. 963; Tiros 1 Becomes the First Experimental Weather Reconnaissance Satellite (1960), p. 1667; The British Antarctic Survey Confirms the First Known Hole in the Ozone Layer (1985), p. 2285.

FRISCH DISCOVERS THAT BEES
COMMUNICATE THROUGH BODY MOVEMENTS

Category of event: Biology
Time: Spring, 1919
Locale: Munich Zoological Institute, Munich, Germany

Frisch discovered that honeybees returning to the hive use a so-called round dance to communicate to their comrades that food is within about 50 meters of the hive

Principal personage:
KARL VON FRISCH (1886-1982), an Austrian physiologist and student of animal behavior who was a cowinner of the 1973 Nobel Prize in Physiology or Medicine

Summary of Event

Karl von Frisch was an early student of animal physiology and behavior. His early career in the first decades of the twentieth century saw the beginnings of an experimental approach to the study of animal behavior. In fact, he can be credited, in part, for several lines of experimentation, such as the study of color perception in bees and hearing in fish, which hastened the development of comparative physiology and the comparative study of animal behavior. It was his study of communication in bees, however, that brought him world fame and eventually a Nobel Prize in 1973, which he shared with Konrad Lorenz and Nikolaas Tinbergen.

Many observers, including Aristotle, have noticed that when honey or sugar water is placed near a hive, it may be many hours before a wandering bee discovers the food. Yet, once the food is discovered, soon thereafter hordes of bees descend upon the new find. Obviously, in some way, the forager bee communicates information about the presence of food to other members of the hive. A few naturalists noticed the dancing movements of bees and speculated as to what its meaning might be, but it remained for Frisch to perform the many years of exacting experiments to substantiate that dancing in bees is actually a form of communication.

In his autobiography, *Erinnerungen eines Biologen* (1962; *A Biologist Remembers*, 1967), Frisch recounts the experiment that led to the most far-reaching observation of his life. At the time, he was teaching at the Munich Zoological Institute. The institute building had a central garden courtyard which Frisch used for experiments with honeybees. He was studying bees in a queen-breeding cage, which is a type of cage that holds a single piece of honeycomb and that has glass sides so that all the bees can be seen easily. Working alone, Frisch put out a dish of sugar water to feed foraging bees from the little glass-sided hive. He marked the bees that fed on the sugar water with small dots of red paint. He then removed the dish of sugar water, and the bees came less and less frequently. Finally, he once again put the sugar water out and allowed a bee to feed. He watched the behavior of the bee once it returned to the hive. As Frisch describes in his autobiography, "I could scarcely believe my eyes. She performed a round dance on the honeycomb which greatly excited the marked foragers around her and caused them to fly back to the feeding place." As soon as the school term ended, Frisch and his family went to Brunnwinkl, Austria, where he continued his studies of the round dance as a form of communication in honeybees. The results of these early studies were published in 1920.

First, it should be emphasized that the round dance in particular is used to communicate the fact that food has been found near the hive, that is, within about 50 meters for Carniolan honeybees and within about 10 meters for Italian honeybees. The round dance does not indicate the direction of the food, and the recruited foragers search equally in all directions within the region around the hive. When the dancing bee performs the round dance, it moves in a tight circle to the right and then to the left, describing between one and two circles in each direction, and repeating the turning movements for half a minute or longer. The sweeter the food source, the more vigorous the dancing becomes. Typically, a group of bees surround the dancing bee and extend their antennae over the body of the dancing bee. This behavior allows the new recruits to detect odors adhering to the dancer's body. These odors enable the recruits to find the particular species of flower that is producing nectar. During pauses in the dance, the dancer regurgitates nectar from her honey stomach and feeds the bees around her. This nectar carries the scent of the flower that was visited. The honeybee has a scent organ, or "Nasinov gland," near the end of the abdomen which exudes a scent that can be used to mark an odor trail near the food site. The degree to which each of these factors is important has been resolved by hundreds of careful experiments by Frisch and his coworkers.

Frisch also demonstrated that bees have color vision and can learn to seek out a given color that they have associated with food. He found that bees cannot distinguish red from black, and they can see ultraviolet as a distinct color. The patterns of color on flowers thus appear different to bees than to humans. Individual bees use color vision to locate flowers they have already visited, but there is no indication that they can communicate colors to other bees.

Within three years of his discovery of the round dance in bees, Frisch was convinced that he understood communication by dance in bees. He had always placed feeding stations near the hive for convenience. Nevertheless, approximately twenty years later, he discovered that he had missed part of the cycle. Over the years, he had noticed a so-called wagging dance that was often performed by bees returning from a distance with loads of pollen. Upon closer inspection of bees fed 400 meters north of their hives at Brunnwinkl in June of 1945, he discovered that this more elaborate dance communicates much more information than the round dance. The wagging dance, used for distances greater than 50 meters from the hive, indicates both direction and distance. In the wagging dance, the dancing bee moves in a figure-eight pattern. In the darkness of the hive, the surrounding bees follow her movements with their outstretched antennae. Frisch discovered that the greater the distance to the food, the slower the tail-wagging was when the bee crossed the straight stretch of the figure-eight. The dance was usually performed on a vertical comb, and it was found that the angle of the straight stretch to gravity was the same as the angle the bee flew with respect to the sun. If the tail-wagging part of the dance was upward, then the food was toward the sun, and if the tail-wagging part was downward, the food was away from the sun. The biological clock of the bee gradually corrected the dance for changes in the apparent position of the sun.

The discovery of the significance of the round dance in 1919 was a fundamental new discovery. The additional discovery of the wagging dance in 1945 was remarkable, but essentially it was a more elaborate version of the round dance. The scientific community could accept the existence of the round dance far more easily than the more complex wagging dance. Fortunately, Frisch's reputation was well established by the time he announced the additional discovery.

Impact of Event

Frisch's publication of his 1919 observations on the round dance as a form of communication did not result in either immediate fame or controversy, although eventually both would come. It was the steady stream of scientific papers on animal physiology and behavior, especially on fish and bees, that eventually established Frisch as the most widely known German biologist. By the time of World War II, his reputation allowed him to continue his work for a time, even though his mother was partially of Jewish descent. Later, forced into isolation at Bunnwinkl, Frisch continued his research during the war years. It was there in 1943 that Frisch discovered the importance of the more elaborate wagging dance in bees.

The discovery of the round dance's role in communication undoubtedly prepared Frisch's mind for unraveling the meaning behind the wagging dance. Early studies on the round dance honed the experimental techniques that were later applied to the wagging dance. The work with the round dance generally furthered Frisch's reputation, and it played a role in the development of the slowly emerging field of animal behavior. It was the work with the wagging dance, however, that was so unique, and at times difficult to believe, that brought the greatest fame, controversy, and the sharing of the Nobel Prize.

The controversy did not appear on the surface until 1967 when the first of a series of critical papers appeared in *Science*, the most prestigious American science journal. The articles were by Adrian Wenner and Patrick Wells, American professors who taught in California. Their basic claim was that the dance patterns shown by bees were meaningless movements that conveyed no information. Any coordinated behavior among the bees, according to Wenner and Wells, was in response to odors on the bees or in the environment. Various experiments were reported that supported their conclusions. By this time Frisch was in his eighties and limited in his ability to perform new experiments to silence his critics. Frisch cited many of his past experiments to rebuke various lines of reasoning used by his opponents. The controversy gained wide renown, in part, because of Frisch's great stature and some lingering thoughts that he could be wrong. Few scientists had actually worked with dancing bees and second-hand opinions were limited in their value. Eventually, a series of new experiments by James L. Gould and others largely supported Frisch's findings. Gould, in 1976, reviewed all the experiments by himself and others in *The Quarterly Review of Biology* and found that Wenner's claims for the importance of odors were already recognized by Frisch as an important factor. The various experiments by Wenner and Wells used odors that were typically ten times stronger than the odors used by Frisch. The experiments by Frisch's critics were not as rigorous as they first appeared. Gould's own experiments also uncovered especially convincing evidence for Frisch's interpretations. Frisch's careful and meticulous years of research survived its great challenge. Dancing in honeybees continues to be recognized as one of the great discoveries of the twentieth century.

Bibliography

Frisch, Karl von. *Bees: Their Vision, Chemical Senses, and Language.* Ithaca, N.Y.: Cornell University Press, 1950. A small, pocket-sized book gives a quick overview of Frisch's honeybee research. Based on revised notes for his lecture tour of the United States in 1949. Well illustrated and presented in a simple and readable fashion.

_____. *A Biologist Remembers.* Translated by Lisbeth Gombrich. New York: Pergamon Press, 1967. A chronicle of Frisch's long and productive life with insights into how a scientist uses experiments to test various competing hypotheses. Of great human interest because of his love and importance of family in nurturing his fascination with nature. Includes the drama of trying to maintain a professional career in Austria and Germany during World Wars I and II.

_____. *The Dance Language and Orientation of Bees.* Translated by Leigh E. Chadwick. Cambridge, Mass.: The Belknap Press of Harvard University Press, 1967. A rather technical review of Frisch's scientific findings; filled with many diagrams and many references to the scientific literature. The best access to Frisch's scientific papers short of reading the original German articles. Only for the motivated and patient reader who wants the details of Frisch's experimental methods and procedures.

_____. *The Dancing Bees.* Translated by Dora Ilse. New York: Harcourt, Brace & World, 1955. The most readable English book on Frisch's research as well as the natural history of honeybees, with a chapter on ants, wasps, and bumblebees. Written for the layperson and filled with line drawings and photographs, the book reveals Frisch's elegant ability to simplify his scientific findings from decades of research and reflection.

Gould, James L. "The Dance-Language Controversy." *The Quarterly Review of Biology* 51 (June, 1976): 211-244. A detailed analysis of all the experiments relating to how bees communicate and find their way. Adequately discusses the details of Wenner's objections to claims by Frisch that bees communicate by dances and ultimately dismisses the contention by Wenner and Wells that olfaction by itself can account for the experimental results. This review is considered to be the decisive vindication of Frisch's discovery of communication by dance in bees.

Gould, James L., and Carol Grant Gould. *The Honey Bee.* New York: Scientific American Library, 1988. A semitechnical survey of all aspects of the natural history of honeybees, their evolution, types of learning, communication, and navigation. A chapter on the role of dancing in communication gives the latest positive assessment of Frisch's research. The book has beautiful colored illustrations and has an excellent list of selected readings for each chapter.

John T. Burns

Cross-References

Ramón y Cajal Establishes the Neuron as the Functional Unit of the Nervous System (1888), p. 1; Pavlov Develops the Concept of Reinforcement (1902), p. 163; Bayliss and Starling Discover Secretin and Establish the Role of Hormones (1902), p. 179; Sherrington Delivers *The Integrative Action of the Nervous System* (1904), p. 243.

EINSTEIN'S THEORY OF GRAVITATION
IS CONFIRMED OVER NEWTON'S THEORY

Categories of event: Physics and astronomy
Time: November 6, 1919
Locale: Burlington House, London, England

Measurements made during an eclipse showed that the sun's gravitational field bent the path of starlight

Principal personages:
ALBERT EINSTEIN (1879-1955), a German-Swiss-American physicist who was the best-known scientist since Isaac Newton
SIR ARTHUR STANLEY EDDINGTON (1882-1944), an English astronomer and physicist who was an early supporter of Einstein's theory of general relativity and led an eclipse expedition which confirmed the predicted bending of starlight by the sun
SIR FRANK DYSON (1868-1939), the English Astronomer Royal who sent out the eclipse expeditions to check Einstein's prediction of the bending of starlight
WILLEM DE SITTER (1872-1934), a Dutch astronomer who introduced Einstein's work to Eddington; first to show that Einstein's theory implied an expanding universe

Summary of Event

In the summer of 1687, Sir Isaac Newton's *Philosophiae Naturalis Principia Mathematica* (mathematical principles of natural philosophy) was published. Usually referred to as the *Principia*, it is one of the most influential scientific books ever written. Taking the works of those who preceded him, molding them into a coherent whole, and adding his own genius, Newton set out his laws of motion and law of gravitation. Newton's law of gravitation states that every mass (every object composed of matter) attracts every other mass through gravitation, and that this force of attraction depends directly upon the product of the masses being considered and inversely upon the square of the distance between their centers. (To simplify matters, it is assumed the masses are uniform spheres.) In other words, the more massive the bodies, the stronger the gravitational force between them; the farther apart the bodies, the weaker the force between them. Newton's laws were extremely successful; they were used to predict the motion of falling apples, as well as the orbits of planets and comets and ocean tides. In spite of all the successes, however, there were problems with the law of gravitation. Newton called the notion absurd that one body could exert a force on another body some distance away. It was a puzzle how one body could "sense" the presence of a second body. Newton had no explanation.

To avoid this action-at-a-distance problem, scientists began to speak of a mass modifying the space around it by establishing a gravitational field. A second mass interacted with the field at its location and not directly with the first mass. How mass can establish a field was not explained. For example, suppose the first mass changes position. The second mass, which is attracted to it, must experience a force pulling it in a new direction toward the new position of the first mass. Yet, the questions of how fast changes in the gravitational field propagate and how long it will be before the second mass "knows" that the first mass moved still remained.

Newton's theory of gravitation was incomplete. Einstein would take gravitational theory a giant step forward. Taking a hint from the well-known result that all objects—no matter how massive—accelerate at the same rate when acted upon by gravity, Einstein deduced that gravitation and acceleration are equivalent in some fashion. He thought about how a beam of light might look to someone moving upward in an elevator. If the light beam were actually parallel with the floor as it entered the elevator to a passenger accelerating upward with the elevator, the light beam would appear to bend downward. Assuming equivalence between acceleration and gravitation, presumably gravity must also deflect light rays downward. Since light has no mass, as one normally thinks of it, this result was completely unexpected.

Einstein was now at an impasse. He was perplexed as to why a light beam took a curved path when traversing a gravitational field in an otherwise empty space. After all, the path taken by a light ray in empty space is the definition of a straight line. Yet, when is a straight line also a curved line? The answer is clear when it is drawn on a curved surface, such as a globe. For example, one may travel in a straight line along the earth's equator and eventually return to the starting point without ever turning around.

Still to be resolved was how long it takes for one mass to "sense" that another mass has moved. First, Einstein went back to the beginning and reformulated his theory in terms of curved space-time. (He discovered that space and time had to be included together on an equal basis.) It proved to be an arduous task. In 1905, he had published data on the theory of special relativity, which deals with measurement made by observers moving relative to one another. In 1915 and 1916, Einstein published key papers on the theory of general relativity. The theory of general relativity was similar in intent, but included the additional effects of gravitation and acceleration. Einstein was successful in interpreting gravitation not as a force, but as the result of curved space-time. The answer as to how long it takes for one mass to "sense" that another mass has moved was the time it would take light to travel between the masses. For example, a moving mass produces a ripple in the curvature of space-time which propagates at the speed of light. A weak gravitational field corresponds to almost no curvature of space-time. Where space-time is nearly flat, both Einstein's and Newton's theories agree quite well. Differences appear only when the field is very strong or the measurement is very accurate.

Einstein suggested three effects that could be measured to see if his theory was more accurate than Newton's: the gravitational redshift of light, the advancement of the perihelion of the planet Mercury, and the deflection of starlight by the sun. The strongest gravitational field nearby is that of the sun. Einstein calculated that a ray of starlight just grazing the sun should be deflected by only 1.75 seconds of arc. Stars cannot normally be seen when the sun is out, so Einstein suggested the measurement be made during a total solar eclipse.

In 1916, with Germany and England at war, international scientific cooperation was difficult. Einstein sent a copy of his work to astronomer Willem de Sitter, in the neutral country of Holland. De Sitter was favorably impressed by the work, and he sent a copy to the astronomer Sir Arthur Stanley Eddington in England. Both de Sitter and Eddington became ardent supporters of Einstein. Next, Eddington made a convert of Sir Frank Dyson, the British Astronomer Royal.

A total solar eclipse is visible only from a small part of the earth. Dyson sent out two expeditions to photograph the eclipse of May 29, 1919. Charles Rundle Davidson led one expedition to Sobral in northern Brazil, while Eddington headed the other expedition to Príncipe Island in the Gulf of Guinea. Eddington's expedition had good weather for a month while they set up and tested their equipment. The day of the eclipse, however, began with a heavy rain, which did not stop until noon. Finally, at 1:30 P.M., after the eclipse had already begun, they got their first glimpse of the sun. During the next few minutes, they took sixteen photographs, which kept them so busy that no one had an opportunity to view the eclipse. Eddington developed some of the film on the spot and found only a few of the photographs to be useful. Comparing one of them with another photograph of the same star field taken six months earlier when the sun was not present, Eddington was delighted to find the star images shifted by the same amount Einstein had predicted.

Until various cross-checks were completed, the scientists were not ready to make a public announcement of the result, but word was sent to Einstein. Finally, on November 6, 1919, the announcement was made to the public. A joint meeting of the Fellows of the Royal Society and of the Fellows of the Royal Astronomical Society was held at Burlington House in London. Dyson reported on the eclipse expeditions. Then, Joseph John Thomson, credited with the discovery of the electron and then president of the Royal Society, termed Einstein's theory "one of the greatest achievements in the history of human thought."

Impact of Event

The confirmation of Einstein's theory of general relativity had an immediate social impact of great magnitude. The public was eager to learn more about Einstein and the general theory. Within one year, more than one hundred books on the subject had been published.

Leopold Infeld, who coauthored a book with Einstein on relativity, suggested that the intensity of the public reaction was a result of the timing—World War I had just ended. "People were weary of hatred, of killing. . . . Here was something which captured the imagination . . . [t]he mystery of the sun's eclipse and of the penetrating power of the human mind." The theory of general relativity was a great achievement in which humankind took pride. It was also a way to heal war wounds between nations.

The scientific impact was even more profound. While popular reaction was very intense, it was relatively short-lived. Although the members of the scientific community were not all immediate converts, scientific interest not only has been enduring but also has increased since the technological developments of the 1950's. More important, Einstein's theory is more correct than Newton's because it is more attuned to nature.

Einstein's theory of gravitation will continue to be tested under any circumstance that can be devised, for that is the nature of science. The theory of general relativity has passed the three tests (gravitational redshift, perihelion advance of Mercury, and bending of starlight) with flying colors as well as many more tests using radar, radio telescopes, pulsars, and quasars.

Einstein has shown that space is not simply an empty place. Space and time are not independent, but must be considered together; furthermore, they are curved by mass. Perhaps most exciting is that the theory of general relativity is a theory of cosmology. Knowing only a few basic numbers such as the average density of matter in the universe, general relativity predicts the size and fate of the universe. Ironically, when Einstein's theory led to the conclusion that the universe was expanding, he rejected it at first. De Sitter was the first to accept the expanding universe model. Later, in 1929, Edwin Powell Hubble offered experimental evidence to show that the universe is, in fact, expanding. While it is unclear yet what the properties are of the universe as a whole, there is every reason to suppose that they will be consistent with the theory of general relativity.

Bibliography

Bernstein, Jeremy. *Einstein*. New York: Viking Press, 1973. Although biographical, this book concentrates on the scientific ideas of Einstein. Bernstein's strength is in making the esoteric theories of Einstein understandable to the general reader. The book is composed of sections on special relativity, general relativity, gravitation, cosmology, and quantum theory.

Clark, Ronald W. *Einstein: The Life and Times*. Cleveland: World Publishing, 1971. Among the hundreds of books published on the subject, this one remains a classic. It is a comprehensive story of Einstein's life interwoven with his scientific theories. It is easily read by the layperson. Includes many historical photographs.

Eddington, A. S. *Space, Time, and Gravitation*. Cambridge, England: Cambridge University Press, 1920. This delightful classic has been reprinted numerous times up through 1978. Eddington was one of the original researchers of general relativity and was one of the first to understand it. This book is for the well-informed reader and will give as much insight into general relativity as can be had without mastering the mathematics of tensor calculus.

Goldsmith, Maurice, Alan Mackay, and James Woudhuysen, eds. *Einstein: The First*

Hundred Years. Elmsford, N.Y.: Pergamon Press, 1980. One of numerous centennial volumes, it is a collection of various papers by experts. They are grouped under five headings: the man, the impact on science, society, world affairs, and the arts. Useful for the general reader.

Hoffmann, Banesh, and Helen Dukas. *Albert Einstein: Creator and Rebel.* New York: Viking Press, 1972. Dukas was Einstein's personal secretary for many years, and she brings some interesting insights to his work. The authors present "the essential flavor of the man and his science." Many historical photographs are included. .

Schilpp, Paul Arthur, ed. *Albert Einstein: Philosopher-Scientist.* Evanston, Ill.: Library of Living Philosophers, 1949. Collection of various essays about Einstein and his work. Most of the essays should be useful to the well-informed layperson. Of special interest are the autobiographical notes by Einstein in volume 1 and the extensive bibliography of Einstein's works in volume 2.

Will, Clifford M. *Was Einstein Right?* New York: Basic Books, 1986. This fascinating work is geared for the informed layperson. It reviews the classic three tests of relativity and includes results such as the time-delay effect measured by beaming radar waves past the sun and reflecting them from Venus, gravitational radiation from a binary pulsar system, and measuring the gravitational redshift using gamma rays and the Mössbauer effect.

Charles W. Rogers

Cross-References

Einstein States His Theory of Special Relativity: $E = mc^2$ (1905), p. 297; Einstein Completes His Theory of General Relativity (1915), p. 625; Hubble Confirms the Expanding Universe (1929), p. 878; The Mössbauer Effect Is Used in the Detection of Gravitational Redshifting (1960), p. 1640.

SLIPHER PRESENTS EVIDENCE OF REDSHIFTS IN GALACTIC SPECTRA

Category of event: Astronomy
Time: The early 1920's
Locale: Lowell Observatory, Flagstaff, Arizona

Slipher pioneered the spectroscopy of galaxies, discovering that most galaxies are receding with high velocities

Principal personages:
VESTO MELVIN SLIPHER (1875-1969), an American astronomer who served as director of the Lowell Observatory from 1916 to 1952
PERCIVAL LOWELL (1855-1916), an American astronomer who was the founder of the Lowell Observatory and who initiated the search which led to the discovery of Pluto
EDWIN POWELL HUBBLE (1889-1953), the American astronomer who demonstrated that spiral nebulas were systems of stars outside the Milky Way galaxy and that the universe is expanding
MILTON L. HUMASON (1891-1972), the astronomer who extended Slipher's observational work on galactic spectra, leading to Hubble's discovery of the expansion of the universe
ALBERT EINSTEIN (1879-1955), the German-born physicist whose theory of general relativity predicts that the universe can be dynamic and evolving

Summary of Event

The general view held by astronomers in the first two decades of the twentieth century was that the universe consisted of a single aggregation of stars, the Milky Way galaxy, which was a system of stars estimated to be about 10,000 light-years in diameter. All objects that were visible in the heavens through the largest telescopes were thought to be part of our galaxy; beyond, a trackless, undifferentiated void extended infinitely far. By the early part of the twentieth century, astronomers had compiled extensive catalogs listing the visible constituents of the galaxy which included numerous stars and various nebulas, misty patches of light in the sky whose complete nature was not understood then but were presumed to consist primarily of gases. Photographs of nebulas showed that some had irregular shapes but that many had a distinctly spiral structure.

Percival Lowell was keenly interested in the study of the spiral nebulas. A member of a prominent Boston family, Lowell was able to finance the construction of his own observatory in Flagstaff, Arizona, dedicated to the study of planets. Lowell's interest in the spiral nebulas lay in the notion, held by nearly all astronomers at the beginning of the twentieth century, that they were planetary systems in the process of formation. The study of spiral nebulas, Lowell hoped, would disclose valuable clues to the origin of the solar system.

In 1901, Lowell hired Vesto Melvin Slipher as an observer at Lowell Observatory and assigned him to a project on spiral nebulas. Slipher was to take spectra of the brighter ones and look for Doppler shifts in their light, which would reveal motions taking place within them. Lowell expected the results to support the theory that the spiral nebulas were rotating, contracting clouds of gas which would eventually form a planetary system or a cluster of stars. Slipher thought this was unlikely; he believed the spirals were probably systems of stars outside our own galaxy.

By late 1912, and using the 61-centimeter refractor at the Lowell Observatory, Slipher had photographed four separate times the spectrum of the Andromeda nebula, one of the largest and brightest of the spirals. Because of the slowness of the photographic emulsions of the time, Slipher found it necessary to expose each photograph for twenty to forty hours, spread over several nights. When examined, the spectra were found to be similar to those of stars like the sun, a band of colors from blue to red crossed by dark lines which are characteristic of the elements found in the stars. Slipher had provided the first hint that a spiral nebula was a system of stars rather than a collection of gases. Without knowing the distance to the Andromeda nebula, however, Slipher was not able to demonstrate conclusively that the nebula was external to the Milky Way. Slipher interpreted, as did many other astronomers who learned of his work, the failure to detect individual stars in the spirals as an indication of their large distances.

In the spectra of the Andromeda nebula, Slipher noticed that there was a systematic shift of all the dark lines toward the blue end of the spectrum. Such a Doppler shift of all the lines toward either the red or blue was attributed to a systematic motion of the emitting nebula as a whole. If the object is moving toward the observer, the shift is toward the blue end of the optical spectrum and is called a blueshift. If the object is moving away, there is a corresponding redshift. The size of the shift in the position of the dark lines provides a direct measure of the speed with which the object is moving toward or away from the observer. In the case of the Andromeda nebula's blueshift, Slipher's data indicated that it was approaching at the speed of 300 kilometers per second, a speed greater than that of any astronomical object measured at the time.

Slipher extended the work on spiral nebulas and by 1914 had analyzed the spectra of twelve additional spirals, making a total of thirteen spirals whose Doppler shifts had been measured. Two of the spectra displayed a blueshift (one was that of the Andromeda nebula), but the other eleven were all redshifts, indicating that these nebulas were receding. If the spirals were part of the Milky Way galaxy, astronomers expected that roughly half would be approaching and half would be receding. Moreover, the speeds of recession measured by Slipher ranged up to an astounding 1,100 kilometers per second. A pattern was beginning to emerge, and astronomers began to suggest openly that the spirals must be stellar systems outside of our galaxy. The speeds of the spiral nebulas seemed to be too great for them to be gravitationally bound to our galaxy. Slipher's results helped direct attention to the spiral nebulas and to the theory that space is populated by visible galaxies.

Slipher was fastidious, methodical, and careful. Although his results up until 1914 were suggesting that most spirals were in recession, he believed it necessary to continue this line of inquiry and extend the survey further; a sample of thirteen Doppler shifts was not convincing. By 1923, Slipher had measured Doppler shifts in forty-one different nebulas; thirty-six had redshifts, and the remaining five had blueshifts. Meanwhile, other astronomers had added four more to the list; these were all redshifts. When it was discovered in 1925 that the Milky Way galaxy as a whole was rotating and that the sun, because of the rotation, was moving with a speed of 250 kilometers per second in a direction generally toward the Andromeda nebula, the Doppler speeds of the nebulas, as measured by Slipher, were corrected for the rotation of the galaxy. Thus, the 300 kilometers per second approach of the Andromeda nebula is composed of a 250 kilometers per second motion of the sun toward the spiral and an intrinsic 50 kilometer per second approach of the spiral. When so corrected, of the total of forty-five nebular Doppler shifts measured, forty-three were redshifts. Slipher had demonstrated clearly that the general trend was for the spiral nebulas to exhibit redshifts in their spectra, indicating that they were receding from the Milky Way galaxy and from one another. The two exceptions were the largest spirals, and therefore probably the nearest. Nevertheless, Slipher's work forcefully showed that spirals were probably galaxies in their own right, external to the Milky Way, and that the overwhelming preponderance of redshifts indicated that galaxies were all rushing away from one another.

Impact of Event

Slipher's pioneering work on the redshifts of the spiral nebulas provided the foundation for a coherent picture of the evolution of the universe. In the late 1920's, Slipher's evidence was juxtaposed, along with the cosmological arguments that were being discussed by astronomers. It provided the impetus for a major new project to determine the distances to the galaxies.

Following the construction of the giant 254-centimeter telescope on Mount Wilson, California, Milton L. Humason and Edwin Powell Hubble were able to study the spiral nebulas in much greater detail than had been possible for Slipher. In fact, with the new telescope, individual stars could be discerned in some of the larger spirals, the Andromeda nebula in particular. Now, all doubt was removed regarding the spiral nebulas: They were galaxies, vast systems of stars similar to the Milky Way of which the sun is a part. With individual stars available for study, they could be compared with stars in the Milky Way, and the distance to the galaxy could be estimated. The Andromeda galaxy lay at a distance of 750,000 light-years, far outside the Milky Way. Other spirals had even greater distances. Using the redshift data inherited from Slipher, Hubble combined those results, together with the distance measurements based on his and Humason's observations to arrive at a relationship between distance and recessional velocity: The greater the recessional velocity of a galaxy, the greater is its distance.

To astronomers of the time, the cause of the recession was now clear. To explain the rush of galaxies away from one another, the universe must be expanding. Such an idea had its roots in the theory of general relativity published by Albert Einstein in 1916. Since that time, Einstein and other astronomers and physicists examined the consequences of the theory and found that the universe should generally be in a state of either expansion or contraction. Slipher's redshift measurements and Hubble's correlation with distance demonstrated that the universe is expanding, an observation of central importance to cosmology. Since as time progresses, the universe expands, it must have been the case that in earlier epochs the galaxies were very close together and, at one time, entirely coalesced. Astronomers reached the startling conclusion that the universe was born in a titanic explosion which hurled the material from which the galaxies eventually formed. The high-speed rush of galaxies away from one another is direct evidence of that genesis.

Humason extended the redshift work, and by 1935 had added 150 measurements to Slipher's list. Recessional speeds now were up to 40,000 kilometers per second. When distances were determined for the galaxies, Hubble's redshift-distance relation still held. By the mid-1930's, astronomers pictured a universe full of galaxies that were rushing apart from one another as a result of a fiery birth in the distant past. This model of the universe has remained fundamentally unchanged to the present.

Bibliography

Barrow, John D., and Joseph Silk. *The Left Hand of Creation*. New York: Basic Books, 1983. This book by two internationally renowned astronomers deals with the early epochs of the universe and its subsequent evolution. The authors draw on advances up to 1983 to present the general reader with a popular account of the origins and evolution of the universe. The authors are concerned primarily with developments in cosmology made after the 1930's. Contains an extensive glossary, an index, and suggestions for further reading.

Ferris, Timothy. *The Red Limit: The Search for the Edge of the Universe*. New York: William Morrow, 1977. This well-presented volume discusses the history of the major discoveries in astronomy and pays particular attention to those individuals who made these discoveries. A comprehensible, accurate, up-to-date discussion of astronomy written in an engaging style. Directed to readers who have not previously encountered modern cosmological ideas. Includes an extensive glossary of astronomical nomenclature, an index, a selected bibliography, and a small collection of rare photographs of the personalities involved in the major discoveries of the twentieth century.

Sagan, Carl. *Cosmos*. New York: Random House, 1980. This visually stunning book with more than 250 color illustrations is based on Sagan's thirteen-part television series. Written with Sagan's remarkable ability to make scientific ideas both comprehensible and exciting, the book is about science in its broadest human context:

how science and civilization grew up together. Sagan often focuses on the forces and individuals who helped shape modern science. Contains an index and suggestions for further reading.

Silk, Joseph. *The Big Bang*. New York: W. H. Freeman, 1989. This volume is a revised and updated version of an earlier edition. Silk presents a sweeping account of the formation and evolution of the universe. He recounts the history of astronomical speculation about the universe and examines evidence for the big bang theory. The treatment is extensive and includes many details. The book does not include mathematics, except in an appendix. A glossary and index are also included.

Wilson, Colin. *Starseekers*. Garden City, N.Y.: Doubleday, 1980. Wilson's book charts the history of the discovery of the universe from ancient to modern times. Often looking at the lives of seminal thinkers involved in understanding the universe, Wilson weaves in elements of history, religion, philosophy, and science. One section, "The Exploding Universe," is an account of the era of the rapid pace of discovery witnessed in the twentieth century. Imaginatively illustrated in color and black and white, with a bibliography and an index.

Anthony J. Nicastro

Cross-References

Leavitt's Study of Variable Stars Unlocks Galactic Distances (1912), p. 496; Slipher Obtains the Spectrum of a Distant Galaxy (1912), p. 502; Einstein Completes His Theory of General Relativity (1915), p. 625; Shapley Proves the Sun Is Distant from the Center of Our Galaxy (1918), p. 655; Hubble Demonstrates That Other Galaxies Are Independent Systems (1924), p. 790; Lemaître Proposes the Big Bang Theory (1927), p. 825; Hubble Confirms the Expanding Universe (1929), p. 878.

MILLIKAN NAMES COSMIC RAYS AND INVESTIGATES THEIR ABSORPTION

Categories of event: Physics and astronomy
Time: 1920-1930
Locale: United States

Millikan and his colleagues proved that upper atmospheric radiation was of extraterrestrial origin, named it, and led in its exploration

Principal personages:
ROBERT ANDREWS MILLIKAN (1868-1953), an American physicist who won the 1923 Nobel Prize in Physics, named cosmic rays, and spent years examining them
VICTOR FRANZ HESS (1883-1964), the Austrian physicist who won the 1936 Nobel Prize in Physics with Carl David Anderson and who first discovered cosmic radiation
ARTHUR HOLLY COMPTON (1892-1962), the physicist who won the 1927 Nobel Prize in Physics and who discovered the latitude effect
WERNER KOLHÖRSTER (1887-1946), the German physicist whose balloon flights confirmed Hess's findings
GEORGE HARVEY CAMERON (1902-1977), the Millikan assistant who helped perform the decisive absorption experiments
CARL DAVID ANDERSON (1905-   ), the Millikan protégé who won the 1936 Nobel Prize in Physics with Hess for his discovery of the positron
IRA SPRAGUE BOWEN (1898-1973), the director of the Mount Wilson Observatory who helped with Millikan's early balloon flights

Summary of Event

The 1920's were a time of great excitement in the world of physics. Albert Einstein's theory of relativity had just passed its first critical test in 1919. Scientists struggled with the problems of the wave-particle duality of light. They attempted to discern the structure of the atom. Quantum mechanics was invented to explain many of these problems, and physicists spent even more time solving the new problems that this "solution" raised. While the experimental and theoretical work on these and other problems was done on Earth, problems in another area of research were occurring in the heights of the atmosphere. This area of research was the study of cosmic radiation.

Cosmic radiation had initially been discovered by the Swiss physicist Albert Gockel in 1910. It was the Austrian physicist Victor Franz Hess, however, who first proposed that the radiation was of extraterrestrial origin. Hess had been working on the problem of air ionization, a phenomenon known since the beginning of the century. It was initially supposed that this slight ionization was caused by radioactive elements in the earth. This meant that at greater altitudes the radiation should decrease. Yet, in 1911, when Hess ascended in a balloon to 5,200 meters and took measurements, he found that the radiation increased above 2,000 meters and that above 3,000 meters there was an even sharper rise in intensity. Hess concluded that the "penetrating radiation," as it was then known, entered the atmosphere from above. Hess's work was confirmed in 1913 by Werner Kolhörster, a German physicist who made a balloon ascent to 9,000 meters.

Not all physicists believed the explanation Hess and Kolhörster gave, however, and even the very existence of the radiation remained in some doubt. The idea that a strong enough source of radiation existed in outer space was simply unimaginable to some scientists. Some still believed that radioactive uranium and thorium in the soil caused the radiation. Others believed that the equipment used by Hess was flawed. Still others sought a compromise position, believing that the radiation was produced somewhere higher up in the earth's atmosphere, something that Hess admitted was a possibility. Robert Andrews Millikan, the American physicist, decided to try and settle the matter.

Millikan had just completed the work on determining the charge of the electron for which he would be awarded the 1923 Nobel Prize in Physics. He became interested in the cosmic ray controversy through his interest in radioactivity. His first attempt to clarify the situation was made in the winter of 1921-1922. With the assistance of Ira Sprague Bowen, Millikan launched a number of sounding balloons, weighing only 190 grams with payload, from Kelly Field in San Antonio, Texas. Each balloon carried a barometer, thermometer, and electroscope, all of which were self-recording, along with photographic film. The flights, attaining altitudes of up to 15,500 meters, failed to show the increase in the penetrating radiation that Hess's hypothesis, and Kolhörster's data, suggested (caused, it is now known, by the earth's magnetic field). The results, however, were not inconsistent with the compromise position, so Millikan planned further tests. These further tests, conducted during 1922 and 1923, took place atop Mount Whitney in California and Pikes Peak in Colorado. There tests were also inconclusive and marred further by nearby storms. In a 1924 paper, Millikan concluded that the experiment showed that the radiation was not penetrating radiation but rather was of local origin, although he drew no conclusion as to how it got into the upper atmosphere.

In the summer of 1925, Millikan designed an experiment to determine the penetrating power of the rays, which had not yet been measured. If the rays were of external origin, they would have to have a penetrating power great enough to get through the atmosphere, which was equivalent to penetrating 10 meters of water. The strongest rays produced by known radioactive elements could not penetrate more than about 2 meters of water. With his assistant, George Harvey Cameron, Millikan took measurements from two California lakes, Muir Lake (elevation 12,000 feet), near Mount Whitney, and Lake Arrowhead (elevation 5,000 feet).

At Muir Lake, Millikan and Cameron lowered their electroscopes into the water; they found that the radiation, coming exclusively from above, was eighteen times greater than that of the hardest known gamma ray (the strongest of the three types of radioactive emissions). This radiation was strong enough to penetrate the atmosphere, proving that the radiation certainly could come from space. At Lake Arrowhead, Millikan and Cameron found that the readings were identical to the Muir Lake readings at a level 6 feet lower. (Six feet is the water equivalent in absorbing power of the 7,000 feet of atmosphere between the elevations.) This proved to Millikan that the atmosphere played no part in the propagation of the rays and acted merely as an absorbing medium. Millikan now believed that the rays came from space.

In late 1925, before a meeting of the National Academy of Sciences, Millikan announced his findings, calling the new radiation "cosmic rays." He believed, since the strongest radiation previously known was that produced in radioactive transformations, these cosmic rays were the result also of some sort of nuclear charge. The strongest rays on Earth were photons (particles of electromagnetic radiation), produced when helium was produced from hydrogen atoms, and when an electron was captured by a light nucleus. Millikan inferred, therefore, that cosmic rays were photons produced from some type of atom formation.

Millikan next tested his assumption that cosmic rays were composed of high-energy photons. In a 1926 trip to Lake Titicaca in South America, he noticed almost no difference between findings there and at Muir Lake. If cosmic rays had been composed of charged particles, the earth's magnetic field would have affected their distribution across the globe. Measurements on the return boat trip from Peru to Los Angeles also showed no variation.

Further developments also served Millikan's theory of cosmic ray origin. Using his own data beginning with the 1922 surveys, Millikan and Cameron plotted cosmic ray intensity against depth. They argued that the curve could be represented by three different curves, since no one coefficient of absorption could account for the curve. After using the formula for absorption through Compton scattering (the scattering of photons after collision with electrons), which was introduced in 1926 by Paul Adrien Maurice Dirac, Millikan noted that the energies of these three curves matched the energies produced when helium, oxygen, and silicon were formed from hydrogen atoms. These elements were among the most abundant in the universe, and Millikan concluded from this that cosmic rays were photons produced when the higher elements were formed; in the words of the popular press of the day, they were the "birth cries" of atoms. In 1928, the Klein-Nishina formula for Compton scattering absorption seemed to support Millikan's views further.

Impact of Event

The public attention that Millikan received from his discoveries was enormous. He was canonized in *The New York Times*, whose editors proposed calling the new radiation "Millikan rays." He was featured on the cover of *Time*. He became the leading spokesman for American science almost overnight. Popular belief even held that he had discovered the new radiation, a claim that Millikan himself never made and one that he was sorry to see made.

Yet, while the public was infatuated with Millikan, many of his scientific colleagues were moving away from his theories. While many scientists accepted Millikan's assertion that cosmic rays were indeed composed of photons, they were much less enamored of his atom-building hypothesis. There was no conclusive proof that there were only three curves which accounted for all cosmic rays. And the Klein-Nishina formula, which worked at the one energy level Millikan tested, had not been proved for other energy levels.

Then, in 1929, the notion that photons were the primary constituents of cosmic rays was challenged. Kolhörster and Walther Bothe, after a series of experiments with a Geiger-Müller counter, concluded that cosmic rays were, in fact, composed of charged particles. Following this work, many physicists turned to the problem of determining which model was correct.

The decisive experiment was made by Arthur Holly Compton, the Nobel laureate who had explained the photon scattering problem. He turned again to the question of what effect, if any, the earth's magnetic field had on cosmic ray intensities. Even though Millikan, and later Kolhörster, failed to notice any appreciable difference, a growing body of work, beginning in 1927, pointed toward a "latitude effect." In 1932, Compton organized a massive survey of the globe, trying to detect such an effect. By September, 1932, the results of the survey showed that there was, in fact, a latitude effect, and thus that cosmic rays were composed of charged particles. From this point on, Millikan was in retreat. He fought a very public battle with Compton about the existence of the latitude effect. When in 1933, Millikan's student, Henry Victor Neher, confirmed the existence of the latitude effect, Millikan was forced to admit that charged particles accounted for at least a portion of cosmic radiation.

By 1935, Millikan was forced also to reject his atom-building hypothesis. Data accumulated from manned and unmanned balloons, as well as on Earth, showed that the energies of most cosmic radiation were too great to be related to the building up of the abundant elements. Millikan now turned to an atom-annihilation hypothesis that had been suggested earlier. By 1947, with the discovery of the pion, even this was made untenable.

One positive aspect of Millikan's later work in cosmic ray research was his work with Carl David Anderson. In 1931, recognizing a need to determine cosmic ray energies directly, he appointed Anderson to analyze the trajectories of charged particles in a cloud chamber enclosed in a magnetic field. Anderson's results led to his determination that cosmic ray absorption resulted from nuclear encounters as well as Compton scattering. The next year, only a few months after James Chadwick discovered the neutron, Anderson's cloud chamber pictures showed him another new particle: the positron, or positive electron. These events helped to develop a new branch of physics: nuclear, or particle physics.

Bibliography

DeVorkin, David H. *Race to the Stratosphere: Manned Scientific Ballooning in America*. New York: Springer-Verlag, 1989. The definitive history of the manned scientific ballooning by the curator of the National Air and Space Museum. Focuses on Auguste and Jean Piccard, with extensive coverage of the cosmic ray experiments conducted with Millikan and Compton. Scholarly, but very readable. Strong bibliography, notes, index, and photographs.

Friedlander, Michael W. *Cosmic Rays*. Cambridge, Mass.: Harvard University Press, 1989. A popular account by a practicing researcher. Includes a good bit of history in discussing all aspects of cosmic ray research. Photographs, illustrations, bibliography, and index.

Kargon, Robert H. *The Rise of Robert Millikan: Portrait of a Life in American Science*. Ithaca, N.Y.: Cornell University Press, 1982. A selective scholarly biography by a historian of science. Focuses on themes in American science as illuminated by Millikan's life. Much material on the public side of cosmic ray research. Some photographs; also contains notes and index.

Kevles, Daniel J. *The Physicists: The History of a Scientific Community in Modern America*. New York: Alfred A. Knopf, 1977. A scholarly but easily readable work by a historian of science. Tells the story of the development of the physics community in America from its origins through supercolliders. Contains some material on the Millikan-Compton controversy, and places the field in its larger context. Extensive bibliographic essay, notes, and index.

Millikan, Robert Andrews. *Electrons (+ and −), Protons, Photons, Neutrons, Mesotrons, and Cosmic Rays*. Rev. ed. Chicago: University of Chicago Press, 1947. A revision of Millikan's 1937 edition; all but the last five chapters are largely unrevised. Presents much of what was known about particle physics; however, the sections on cosmic rays are extremely self-justifying, and were recognized as such by other physicists. Should be read with the Kargon book (cited above). Photographs, illustrations, and index.

Pomerantz, Martin A. *Cosmic Rays*. New York: Van Nostrand Reinhold, 1971. A semipopular account aimed at the college undergraduate; should be read only with some science or mathematics background. Historical chapter is more approachable. Covers all aspects of research. Contains illustrations, photographs, and index.

Rossi, Bruno. *Cosmic Rays*. New York: McGraw-Hill, 1964. Popular account by a pioneer researcher. Very readable. Photographs, illustrations, index.

Segrè, Emilio. *From X-Rays to Quarks*. San Francisco: W. H. Freeman, 1980. Impressionistic account of the development of physics by a practitioner. Some material on cosmic rays. Photographs, annotated bibliography, index.

Sekido, Yataro, and Harry Elliot. *Early History of Cosmic Ray Studies: Personal Reminiscences with Old Photographs*. Boston: D. Reidel, 1985. A collection of papers by a number of early cosmic ray researchers. Especially good on Hess and his predecessors, weak on Millikan. Includes a piece by Anderson. Essays, many of which are translated, are of varying quality. Contains photographs, illustrations, notes, and index.

George R. Ehrhardt

Cross-References

Becquerel Wins the Nobel Prize for the Discovery of Natural Radioactivity (1903), p. 199; Barkla Discovers the Characteristic X Rays of the Elements (1906), p. 309; Thomson Wins the Nobel Prize for the Discovery of the Electron (1906), p. 356; Geiger and Rutherford Develop the Geiger Counter (1908), p. 412; Hess Discovers Cosmic Rays Through High-Altitude Ionizations (1912), p. 532; Rutherford Discovers the Proton (1914), p. 590; Chadwick Discovers the Neutron (1932), p. 973; Anderson Discovers the Positron (1932), p. 983.

MICHELSON MEASURES THE DIAMETER OF A STAR

Category of event: Astronomy
Time: December 13, 1920
Locale: Mount Wilson Observatory, California

Michelson made the first precise measurement of a star other than the sun

Principal personages:

SIR ARTHUR STANLEY EDDINGTON (1882-1944), an English astronomer and physicist who created a theoretical structure for the interiors of stars based on the forces of radiation and gravity

EDWIN POWELL HUBBLE (1889-1953), an American astronomer who characterized the expansion of the universe

GEORGE ELLERY HALE (1868-1938), an American astronomer who invented a device to photograph the spectral line of the sun and organized the funding and building of the Yerkes, Mount Wilson, and Mount Palomar Observatories

HENRIETTA SWAN LEAVITT (1868-1921), an American astronomer who invented a means of measuring distances of stars by their brightness

ALBERT ABRAHAM MICHELSON (1852-1931), a German-American physicist, working with Edward Williams Morley, who tried to prove that light traveled in an "ether"; more successful in his optical studies for which he was the first American to receive a Nobel Prize in Physics

EDWARD WILLIAMS MORLEY (1838-1923), an American chemist who worked out the relative weights of oxygen and hydrogen; he later began a long-term collaboration with Michelson on light experiments

Summary of Event

Albert Abraham Michelson ranks as a distinguished scientist who was one of the finest instrument makers and experimental physicists of his time. Over several centuries, a body of scientific experiments had accumulated which demonstrated that light traveled in a wave pattern. Since other wave motions, such as sound and water waves, travel in a medium, light was given a medium called "ether." One method of proving the existence of ether was to demonstrate the effect produced by the medium. For example, the sound of a train whistle traveling toward an observer will have a higher pitch than one moving away from the observer. This happens since the speed of sound added to the speed of the train results in a higher velocity as it is carried toward the observer and a lower velocity while it is moving away. Since it was thought that the earth and all celestial objects move in an ether substance, then the speed of light traveling in different directions in this ether therefore must have different values.

In 1878, Michelson became interested in measuring the speed of light. While working on this problem, he developed an instrument called an interferential refractometer, which he used to measure the effect of the ether. By splitting a beam of light so that two sections traveled at right angles to each other, with the movement of the earth through the ether, one of the two beams would be affected by the ether. Although this instrument was extremely sensitive, it produced no measurable results. Michelson's attempts to measure the effect of the ether faced two major problems: First, a debate on whether the ether itself was stationary or moving, hence producing different results; second, the possibility that the instrument itself produced experimental errors.

Undaunted by these setbacks, Michelson teamed up with Edward Williams Morley in 1885 to redesign the experiment. In the process of developing instruments for the experiment, Michelson and Morley undertook the challenge of determining the length of the international meter bar in Paris. By providing an exact length of the meter bar in terms of the light wavelength of cadmium, Michelson transformed light into a standard of measurement. As a result of the precise nature of the experiment, Michelson achieved international recognition.

During this period, Michelson developed another instrument called an interferometer. This device showed the interference patterns for light waves when light waves intersect each other. For example, when light waves hit a screen with two small pin holes, the pattern behind the screen shows alternate patterns of light and dark areas. Similarly, light waves that arrive at different times also will show an interference fringe. Yet, no such fringe was found. In 1905, Albert Einstein published his theory of special relativity, which held that the speed of light was a constant in a vacuum. There was no longer a need for the ether. Over the course of his life, however, Michelson attempted to refine his experiment and prove the existence of the ether.

In 1918, at the end of World War I, Michelson was sixty-six years old but still filled with ideas on new experiments and instruments. Yet, even though he was saddled with increasing administrative responsibilities at the University of Chicago, Michelson began to travel to California for the summers. He divided his time between the California Institute of Technology and the Mount Wilson Observatory. One of his experiments was a return to the ether problem, yet another project used the interferometer to measure the size of a star. Earlier, George Ellery Hale had obtained the funds and had overseen the building of the Mount Wilson Observatory. By 1908, Hale had constructed a 152-centimeter reflecting telescope. Not satisfied with this achievement, he constructed the 254-centimeter Hooker telescope, which was the largest telescope in the world until he built the Palomar Observatory in 1929. Michelson saw the possibility of using this instrument, along with a redesigned interferometer, to measure the diameter of a star. He chose Betelgeuse (Orionis) in the constellation of Orion.

In 1920, the British astronomer, Sir Arthur Stanley Eddington, had made a calculation on the size of Betelgeuse based on surface radiation. This figure, however, was based on theoretical deductions rather than a direct instrumental measurement. Consequently, Michelson's measurement not only served to corroborate Eddington's figure but also to substantiate part of the theoretical foundations of astronomy. For the experiment, Michelson blacked out all the star except for the extreme edges; his interferometer picked up the light of these edges through slits. On December 13, 1920, while Michelson was in Chicago, his assistant, Francis Pease, reported the final readings that Betelgeuse had a diameter of 386 million kilometers. This figure turned out to be very close to the one calculated by Eddington.

Although astronomers expected this result, there was an immediate reaction from the public. The idea that a star had a diameter equal to the orbit of Mars was almost beyond comprehension. For scientists, this heralded a new era in which an instrument could measure with precision an object 150 light-years away. The formal announcement was made by Michelson at a joint meeting of the American Physical Society and the American Association for the Advancement of Science on December 29, 1920.

The measurement of the diameter of a star was only one interlude in a rich and full life. Mount Wilson was also the site where Michelson performed one of the best optical measurements of the speed of light. In 1926, an American physicist, Dayton C. Miller, claimed to have obtained experimental evidence of the effects of ether on light. This spurred Michelson to perform a number of fruitless experiments to duplicate the results. Until his death, he held onto the belief that light must travel in a medium.

Impact of Event

When Hale erected the Hooker telescope, it was his intention to foster a revolution in astronomy. For a discipline that extends thousands of years back to the ancient Babylonians, little was known about the evolution of stars, the form and shape of the universe, or the matter within it. Michelson's measurement of the diameter of a star was one step in the realization of that vision. In 1928, the members of the Optical Society of America named their annual meeting after Michelson in celebration of the fiftieth anniversary of his first paper on the speed of light. In dedicating the meeting to him, the Society said that Michelson had established light as a standard or "measuring rod" of the physical sciences. If light traveled in a medium, then its speed would depend on the relative motion of its source. Therefore, the absolute value of the velocity of light in a vacuum can be used as a device to measure the universe.

The task of measuring the universe occupied the talents and activities of astronomers for the first half of the twentieth century. In 1912, while studying a cluster of stars (Cepheids) in the constellation Cepheus, Henrietta Swan Leavitt discovered that it was possible to determine distances by comparing the true brightness of the stars. In 1920, while using this Cepheid method, Harlow Shapley used the Hooker telescope and determined the size and shape of our galaxy. As Hale had promised during the construction of the Hooker telescope, the revolution in astronomy was about to begin. In 1924, Edwin Powell Hubble led the charge by measuring the distance to the Andromeda nebula (soon to be classified as a galaxy). By 1929, he theorized the Hubble law, which claimed that galaxies receded from us in proportion to their distance from Earth. These discoveries ended the notion that had existed for thousands of years that the earth was not only at the center of our galaxy but also at the center of the universe.

The Michelson interferometer played an important role in this new age of astronomy. The resolving power of this instrument was limited only by the size of the rigid and vibration-free grid which can be constructed. In addition, during adverse sighting conditions, the instrument can continue to separate the light source distinctly. Yet, Michelson's contributions to more precise measurements of the universe did not end a series of debates on the theoretical foundations of astronomy, such as the rate of expansion and the age and formation of the universe. Toward the end of the 1940's, the "big bang" theory—that the universe began 2 billion years ago—was one resolution of these problems. Still, a number of details of Michelson's theory remain to be worked out.

Bibliography

Jaffe, Bernard. *Michelson and the Speed of Light*. Garden City, N.Y.: Doubleday, 1960. A solid source on a number of Michelson's experiments. Specifically, the work details the scientific debates involving the speed of light. There are some technical areas, but suitable for the general reader.

Livingston, Dorothy Michelson. *The Master of Light: A Biography of Albert A. Michelson*. New York: Charles Scribner's Sons, 1973. Michelson's daughter has written an amusing, gossipy, and highly readable account of her father. Includes her collection of papers and memorabilia.

Millikan, Robert A. "Biographical Memoirs of Albert Abraham Michelson 1852-1931." *Biographical Memoirs*. National Academy of Sciences 19 (1938): 120-147. Millikan, a highly respected scientist, was both Michelson's student and colleague. This article covers Michelson's career and offers some observations on his contributions to science.

Swenson, Loyd S., Jr. *The Ethereal Aether: A History of the Michelson-Morley-Miller Aether-Drift Experiments, 1880-1930*. Austin: University of Texas Press, 1972. This work focuses less on Michelson than on the resolution of solid and creative scientists to prove a theory. Parts of the book are technical and more suited for the advanced reader.

Wright, Helen. *Explorer of the Universe: A Biography of George Ellery Hale*. New York: E. P. Dutton, 1966. Hale made Mount Wilson Observatory possible and directed its construction. The book describes the life and activities of one of the pioneers in the development of large-scale, high-technology science.

Victor W. Chen

Cross-References

Leavitt's Study of Variable Stars Unlocks Galactic Distances (1912), p. 496; Shapley Proves the Sun Is Distant from the Center of Our Galaxy (1918), p. 655; Hubble Demonstrates That Other Galaxies Are Independent Systems (1924), p. 790; Eddington Publishes *The Internal Constitution of the Stars* (1926), p. 815; Lemaître Proposes the Big Bang Theory (1927), p. 825; Hubble Confirms the Expanding Universe (1929), p. 878.

CALMETTE AND GUÉRIN DEVELOP
THE TUBERCULOSIS VACCINE BCG

Category of event: Medicine
Time: 1921
Locale: Pasteur Institute, Lille, France

Calmette and Guérin cultured an avirulent (nondisease) strain of bovine tuberculosis bacilli for use as a vaccine

Principal personages:
> ALBERT CALMETTE (1863-1933), a French microbiologist and student of Louis Pasteur who directed the Pasteur Institute in Lille, France, from 1896 to 1919
> CAMILLE GUÉRIN (1872-1961), a French veterinarian and microbiologist who studied human and bovine tuberculosis with Calmette at the Pasteur Institute in Lille
> ROBERT KOCH (1843-1910), a German physician and microbiologist who identified several bacterial disease agents and developed the tuberculin skin test

Summary of Event

Tuberculosis, often called consumption, is a deadly, contagious disease of humans and other mammals, including primates and cattle. The disease is caused by the bacterium *Mycobacterium tuberculosis*, first identified by the eminent German physician Robert Koch in 1882. The bacterium can be transmitted from person to person by physical contact or droplet infection (for example, sneezing). The bacterium can survive in moist or dried sputum for up to six weeks. Once inside the body, the tuberculosis bacterium, called the tubercle bacillus because of its rod shape, invades lung tissue. Amoeba-like immune system cells called phagocytes attack and engulf the tubercle bacilli, destroying some of the bacteria. Other tubercle bacilli, however, destroy the phagocytes and reproduce to form new bacilli. Bacilli activity eventually damages and inflames large lung regions, causing difficulty in breathing and failure of the body to deliver sufficient oxygen to various tissues. The tubercle bacilli can spread to other body tissues, where further complications develop. Without treatment, the disease progresses, disabling and eventually killing the victim. Tuberculosis normally is treated with a combination of antibiotics and other drugs.

During the late 1800's, many microbiologists, principally Pasteur and Koch, established the germ theory of disease, which maintains that microorganisms such as bacteria are responsible for infectious diseases. In 1876, Koch became the first scientist to isolate a bacterial cause of disease with *Bacillus anthracis*, the causative agent of anthrax in humans and cattle. The approach he developed and used for identifying *Bacillus anthracis* is now referred to as Koch's postulates: Blood samples are taken from animals infected with a particular disease, bacterial species found in the blood of all infected animals are isolated for further study, each individual bacterial species is tested by injection into healthy animals, and the bacterial species that produces the disease in healthy animals—along with new bacteria in the bloodstreams of these animals—is the causative agent of the disease.

Koch developed his approach for identifying bacterial pathogens (disease producers) with simple equipment, primarily microscopy. He identified numerous other bacterial agents of disease and classified hundreds of microorganisms (for example, bacteria, protists, fungi), both pathogens and nonpathogens. In 1882, he identified *Mycobacterium tuberculosis* as the causative agent of tuberculosis in humans from phlegm and lung abscesses of diseased victims. Koch reported his discovery to the Physiological Society of Berlin in March, 1882. In subsequent years, he made additional contributions to microbiology, although he continued to place special emphasis upon tuberculosis. In 1890, he discovered that a chemical released from tubercle bacilli elicits a hypersensitive (allergic) reaction in individuals previously exposed to or suffering from tuberculosis. This chemical, called tuberculin, was isolated from culture extracts in which tubercle bacilli were being grown.

When small amounts of tuberculin are injected into a person subcutaneously (beneath the skin), a reddened, inflamed patch approximately the size of a quarter develops if the person has been exposed to or is suffering from tuberculosis. The infected person's body produces antibodies against foreign objects such as tubercle bacilli and foreign chemicals (for example, tuberculin) released from tubercle bacilli. Injection of tuberculin into an uninfected person yields a negative response (that is, no inflammation) because the person's immune system has never been stimulated to produce antibodies against any aspect of tuberculosis. Tuberculin does not injure tested patients because it is only an extract derived from tubercle bacilli. It is targeted by the immune systems of infected individuals because it is a foreign object. Therefore, Koch's discovery of the tuberculin skin test was extremely valuable to medicine because it became a diagnostic tool for identifying unknowing victims and carriers of the disease, thereby limiting further spread of the disease. Today, two tuberculin preparations are used in the tuberculin skin test: Old Tuberculin and Purified Protein Derivative. Old Tuberculin, developed by Koch, is an extract from sterilized (killed) *Mycobacterium tuberculosis*. Purified Protein Derivative is the isolated tuberculin protein from the Old Tuberculin preparation and is the more accurate skin test for the disease. Both preparations are administered subcutaneously, injected beneath the skin of the upper arm. If a reaction occurs, inflammation should be visible around the injection site within forty-eight hours. A positive result should be followed by a chest X ray and treatment with antituberculosis drugs such as rifampin, streptomycin, parazinamide, isoniazid, and para-aminosalicylic acid.

The first vaccine to prevent tuberculosis was developed in 1921 by two French microbiologists, Albert Calmette and Camille Guérin. Calmette was a student of the eminent French microbiologist Louis Pasteur at Pasteur's Institute in Paris. Guérin was a veterinarian who joined Calmette's laboratory at Lille in 1897. At Lille, Calmette and Guérin focused their research upon the microbiology of infectious diseases, especially tuberculosis. In 1906, they discovered that individuals who had been exposed to tuberculosis or who had mild infections were developing resistance to the disease. They found that resistance to tuberculosis was caused by the body's immune response to tubercle bacilli located within the body. They also discovered that tubercle bacilli grown in culture over many generations become progressively weaker and avirulent, losing their ability to cause disease.

From 1906 through 1921, Calmette and Guérin cultured tubercle bacilli from cattle (*Mycobacterium bovis*). With proper nutrients and temperature, bacteria can reproduce by binary fission (that is, one bacterium splits into two bacteria) in as little time as thirty minutes. Calmette and Guérin cultivated tubercle bacilli in a bile-derived food medium for thousands of generations over fifteen years, periodically testing the bacteria for virulence by injecting them into cattle. After many generations, the tubercle bacilli lost their virulence, their ability to cause disease. Nevertheless, these avirulent tubercle bacilli still stimulated the production of antibodies by the cow immune system. Calmette and Guérin had successfully bred a strain of avirulent tubercle bacilli that could not cause tuberculosis in cows but could stimulate immunity against the disease, thereby making the cows immune to virulent tubercle bacilli. Cows that had been vaccinated with the avirulent tubercle bacilli did not develop tuberculosis when they later were injected with virulent tubercle bacilli. The cows had been immunized against tuberculosis.

There was considerable concern over whether the avirulent tubercle bacillus strain was harmless to humans. Calmette and Guérin continued cultivating weaker versions of the avirulent tubercle bacillus strain that retained antibody-stimulating capacity. By 1921, they had isolated an avirulent antibody-stimulating tubercle bacillus strain that was harmless to humans, a strain they called Bacillus Calmette-Guérin (BCG). In 1922, they began BCG-vaccinating newborn children against tuberculosis at the Charité Hospital in Paris. The immunized children exhibited no ill effects from the BCG vaccination. Calmette and Guérin's vaccine was so successful in controlling the spread of tuberculosis in France that it attained widespread use in Europe and Asia beginning in the 1930's. Furthermore, Calmette devised a skin test for detecting tuberculosis that was very similar to Koch's tuberculin test. Unfortunately, Calmette did not live to see very widespread use of the BCG vaccine.

Most bacterial vaccines involve the use of antitoxin or heat-/chemical-treated bacteria. BCG is one of the few vaccines that use specially bred live bacteria. Its use sparked some controversy in the United States and England, where the medical community questioned its effectiveness and postponed BCG immunizations until the late 1950's. Extensive testing of the vaccine was performed at the University of Illinois before it was adopted in the United States. Its effectiveness is questioned by some physicians to this day.

Impact of Event

Calmette and Guérin's development of the BCG vaccine against tuberculosis saved thousands of lives across Canada, Europe, and Asia, from the 1920's to the 1940's and worldwide from the 1950's onward. Tuberculosis affects primarily newborns, children, and white males forty years of age and above, although nonwhites have a higher mortality rate from the disease. The disease is more prominent among impoverished individuals and alcoholics. BCG played a very important role in saving many of these individuals.

Whereas the BCG vaccine was derived from bovine tuberculosis, it is equally effective in inducing antibody production in humans against human tuberculosis, because of the two bacterial species' structural similarities. The human immune system produces antibodies that attack either species of tubercle bacilli. The two bacterial species are shaped similarly and produce nearly identical proteins upon which human antibodies are targeted. Therefore, the BCG vaccine is interspecies-specific. The procedure is somewhat similar to English physician Edward Jenner's 1796 historic treatment of human smallpox using matter from cowpox sores on infected cattle.

When a person is injected with BCG, he/she cannot contract tuberculosis because this particular bacterial strain cannot damage lung tissue. It is avirulent. Once inside the body, however, its shape and the proteins it produces stimulates human immune system cells called lymphocytes to produce and release special proteins called immunoglobulins (antibodies). The antibodies bind to the BCG bacteria and associated BCG proteins, followed by phagocytic engulfment of the bacteria. Some lymphocytes multiply to become "memory" cells so that the body will have a large supply of anti-BCG antibodies. If the vaccinated person is exposed to virulent tubercle bacilli, then these memory cells will release these anti-BCG antibodies to inactivate the bacteria; the exposed person will not contract tuberculosis.

The avirulent, antibody-stimulating BCG vaccine was controversial in the United States because of its inadvertent conflict with the tuberculin skin test. The tuberculin skin test is designed to identify people suffering from tuberculosis so that they can be treated. A BCG-vaccinated person will have a positive tuberculin skin test like a tuberculosis sufferer. If a physician does not know that a patient has had a BCG vaccination, it will be presumed that the patient has tuberculosis. Nevertheless, the BCG vaccine has been invaluable in curbing the worldwide spread of tuberculosis, although it has not eradicated the disease.

With the worldwide acceptance of the BCG vaccine in the late 1950's, medical science obtained a complete set of weapons for battling tuberculosis, a disease that still is prevalent in lesser developed countries. Infected individuals can be identified from the tuberculin skin test, a part of most routine physical examinations. Tuberculosis victims can be treated with a variety of drugs and antibiotics. BCG vaccinations can be given to people in high-risk groups and to health-care workers. Together, these approaches have held tuberculosis in check, at least in the developed countries of North America and Europe.

Bibliography

Alberts, Bruce, et al. *Molecular Biology of the Cell.* New York: Garland, 1983. This lengthy introductory molecular biology textbook for undergraduate biology majors is a thorough survey of the science by several leading molecular biologists and biochemists. It is clearly written, contains excellent photographs and diagrams, and has valuable reference lists. There is extensive coverage of prokaryotes (bacteria) and the human immune system.

Breed, Robert S., E. G. D. Murray, and Nathan R. Smith. *Bergey's Manual of Determinative Bacteriology*. 7th ed. Baltimore: Williams & Wilkins, 1957. This information-packed manual for microbiologists is a comprehensive guide for classifying bacteria based upon various bacterial characteristics. Every major group of bacteria is described in detail, including microscopic shape and appearance, growth patterns, and responses to chemical treatments.

Eisen, Herman N. *Immunology: An Introduction to Molecular and Cellular Principles of the Immune Responses*. 2d ed. Philadelphia: J. B. Lippincott, 1980. This introductory immunology textbook for advanced undergraduate and graduate students is a comprehensive, detailed presentation of the cellular biochemistry behind the body's immune system. It describes antibody production, skin responses (for example, hypersensitivity) to certain infections, and how vaccines stimulate the immune system.

Gebhardt, Louis P. *Microbiology*. 4th ed. St. Louis: C. V. Mosby, 1970. This short, concise introductory microbiology textbook for undergraduates is an excellent survey of the science and its history. While providing comprehensive coverage of every branch of microbiology, it is very understandable to the layperson. The book stresses microbiological applications in everyday life.

Lechevalier, Hubert A., and Morris Solotorovsky. *Three Centuries of Microbiology*. New York: McGraw-Hill, 1965. This outstanding book is a detailed history of microbiological research from the 1600's to the present, including the many famous experiments of Pasteur, Koch, Calmette and Guérin, and others. Chapter 3, "Koch," is a lengthy tribute to the German physician's great discoveries. Chapter 6, "Immunology: Humoral," describes Calmette and Guérin's work on the BCG vaccine in detail.

Mader, Sylvia S. *Biology*. 3d ed. Dubuque, Iowa: Wm. C. Brown, 1990. This introductory biology textbook for undergraduate majors and nonmajors is clearly written for the layperson and is beautifully illustrated. Chapter 23, "Viruses and Monera," describes viruses and bacteria. Chapter 34, "Immunity," is an excellent survey of the human immune system.

Tortora, Gerard J., Berdell R. Funke, and Christine L. Case. *Microbiology: An Introduction*. 3d ed. Redwood City, Calif.: Benjamin/Cummings, 1989. This excellent introductory microbiology textbook for allied health-care majors is a thorough, but uncomplicated presentation of the subject. It is well written, organized, and illustrated. Chapter 22, "Microbial Diseases of the Respiratory System," describes various bacterial, viral, and protozoan pathogens of the respiratory tract, including the *Mycobacteria*.

Wistreich, George A., and Max D. Lechtman. *Microbiology*. 5th ed. New York:

Macmillan, 1988. This tremendous microbiology book is both an outstanding reference work and an excellent introductory textbook for undergraduate biology students. It covers every aspect of microbiology in extensive detail, supported by a plethora of charts, diagrams, tables, and excellent, although sometimes gruesome, photographs. It provides disease case histories and up-to-date reference lists. It is a must book for the serious microbiologist.

David Wason Hollar, Jr.

Cross-References

Behring Discovers the Diphtheria Antitoxin (1890), p. 6; Schick Introduces the Schick Test for Diphtheria (1913), p. 567; Fleming Discovers Penicillin in Molds (1928), p. 873; Zinsser Develops an Immunization Against Typhus (1930), p. 921; Domagk Discovers That a Sulfonamide Can Save Lives (1932), p. 968; Theiler Introduces a Vaccine Against Yellow Fever (1937), p. 1091.

LARSON CONSTRUCTS THE
FIRST MODERN POLYGRAPH

Category of event: Applied science
Time: 1921
Locale: Berkeley, California

Larson developed the modern version of the lie detector, an instrument that revolutionized the administration of criminal justice in the United States

Principal personages:
>JOHN A. LARSON (1892-1967), a California police officer who became a forensic psychiatrist and criminologist
>LEONARDE KEELER (1887-1949), a police patrolman who developed Larson's first mechanism into an advanced instrument that bears his name
>AUGUST VOLLMER (1875-1940), the founder and chief of Berkeley's "scientific" police department
>CESARE LOMBROSO (1836-1909), a celebrated Italian criminologist and early pioneer in lie detection techniques

Summary of Event

The first attempt to utilize a scientific instrument for the purpose of lie detection occurred in 1895. Cesare Lombroso, a celebrated Italian criminologist, published an account of several experiments he had conducted on criminal suspects whose truthfulness or deception he sought to determine by recording fluctuations in blood pressure or pulse rate when the suspects were questioned about the offense under investigation. The instrument that Lombroso used—called a "hydrosphygmograph"—had been invented and developed by other scientists for medical purposes and was not originally intended for use as an instrument for detecting deception. Essentially, the instrument consisted of a small, water-filled tank into which the subject's hand was placed. The immersed fist was then sealed across the top of the tank by a rubber membrane. Changes in pulse pattern and blood pressure in the fist were transferred to the water, then changes in the water level were transferred to an air-filled tube leading to a revolving drum.

Although Lombroso reported successful results in his experiments, his research ended with the publication of his book in 1895; and it was not until 1915 that further experiments with blood pressure changes were conducted by any other investigator. In 1915, William Moulton Marston began his research in the field of lie detection. Marston was a student of Hugo Munsterberg, a well-known Harvard pioneer in criminal psychology and author of *On the Witness Stand* (1908). In this book, Munsterberg discussed the effects of emotional changes upon blood pressure, respiration, galvanic skin reflex, and other physiological processes, and he pointed out the possibilities of utilizing such reactions in detecting deception.

Marston's technique consisted essentially of the use of an ordinary sphygmoma-nometer—the same type of instrument used by physicians in determining a patient's blood pressure—by means of which he obtained periodic, discontinuous blood pressure readings during the course of a test. Marston also recorded the respiration and noted the time of the subject's verbal responses. Furthermore, he experimented with the galvanometer to record skin resistance changes and a gripping device to record tension. The questioning technique he used, initially an obscure word association test, was abandoned later in favor of a narrative-type answer and a cross-questioning of the subject regarding his or her statements. Marston reported some very successful results with this technique.

In the early 1920's, further experiments in lie detection were conducted by three members of the California Police Department: John A. Larson, a police officer in the city of Berkeley; August Vollmer, the founder and chief of the Berkeley "scientific" police department; and Leonarde Keeler, a patrolman. While a police officer in Berkeley under Chief Vollmer, Larson began experimenting with measurement of blood pressure and respiratory changes during the questioning of criminal suspects. Encouraged by Vollmer, Larson assembled the first continuous-recording interrogation polygraph; and some of its first practical applications were outstandingly successful. A female college student had been shoplifting in a local store. The shop clerk knew only that the thief lived in a certain dormitory but could not identify her further. Larson was able to question all thirty-eight residents of that dormitory (during sixteen hours in one day) using what later was known as the relevant-irrelevant, or R/I technique, a mixture of irrelevant questions and relevant ones. One of the young women responded much more strongly to the relevant questions than did any of the others, and she subsequently made a full confession.

Larson's instrument, which he named a polygraph, used pens to record, on a moving strip of graph paper, the changes in a subject's heart rate, blood pressure, respiration, and electrical skin reaction as the individual underwent continuous questioning. The lie detector operated on the theory that if the subject was lying, his or her emotional and physical stress would cause the lines on the graph to move above previously established normal levels.

After a preliminary interview, the subject was seated in a chair specially constructed to permit the attachment of the various measuring devices. The pneumograph tube was tied to the subject's chest, the blood pressure cuff was wrapped around the upper arm, and a net of electrodes was attached to the hands. The subject was directed to look straight ahead. The examiner was seated to one side behind a desk containing a set of controls the subject could not see. These instruments began a continuous graphic recording when the examination commenced. The questions asked were based upon the results of the preliminary interview, along with available facts and circumstances forming the basis of the accusation. They also varied somewhat with each person questioned.

Some of the team's first experiments provoked severe criticism from those who did not comprehend the technique. These critics argued that tension and nervousness resulting from the mere realization that a crucial test was being performed would naturally produce false and misleading indications on the graph. The team was quick to explain, however—as later polygraphists did—that testing always begins with a long series of deliberately innocuous questions, or control inquiries. Not until the subject has established a normal level of graphic reactions does the examiner subtly and with no change of voice or facial expression introduce the crucial question that refers directly to the offense. The graphic results, when examined and interpreted by an expert, would presumably indicate whether the subject was lying.

Although Larson is credited with the development of the modern lie detector, it was Keeler who later refined Larson's original equipment. The Keeler polygraph included, in addition to units for recording blood pressure-pulse and respiration changes, a galvanometer for recording what is known as the "galvanic skin reflex" (GSR), or electrodermal response. Galvanic skin response is obtained by fastening electrodes to the fingertips; the fingertips are believed to show evidence of perspiration when a person is under emotional stress or speaking falsely.

Impact of Event

In view of the overwhelming enthusiasm and extravagant claims of his associates and successors, Larson's attitude toward the polygraph's effectiveness in detecting deception remained scientifically skeptical. During the first half century after 1915, when Marston's "lie detector" was becoming entrenched in American criminology circles, Larson was the only investigator to report an objective study of the accuracy of the diagnosis of deception using polygraph recordings obtained from criminal suspects. In a 1938 paper, Larson told of examining sixty-two suspects, whose records were then evaluated independently by nine psychologists. The number of records classified by the different judges as indicating deception ranged from five to thirty-three, though sixty-one of the suspects were, in fact, truthful. Larson later said that he originally hoped that instrumental lie detection would become a legitimate part of professional police science. He believed that it was becoming little more than a psychological "third degree" aimed at extorting confessions not unlike the old method of physical beatings. He even stated that at times he regretted ever participating in the development of the polygraph.

It should be emphasized that Larson's experience and at least some of his disillusionment was focused on the relevant/irrelevant test format and that other interrogation techniques, notably the control-question lie test and the guilty knowledge test, were developed later. Until about 1950, the R/I procedure was standard in the field, though it continued to be taught in one major school of polygraphy and continued to be used by many older examiners—especially promoted by C. D. Lee and Keeler of the Berkeley Police Department.

Although questions about its reliability continue to be raised and debated, the lie detector is used in criminal investigation and security applications in Canada, Israel, Japan, South Korea, Mexico, Pakistan, the Philippines, Taiwan, and Thailand. Employee screening applications, however, are almost exclusively North American. Western European police agencies have remained skeptical about the value of the polygraph.

Current experts in the field maintain that no machine can detect lying; there is only a form of interview or test employing a polygraph, a machine that provides certain data that the examiner uses in reaching a diagnosis of truthful or deceptive. Because several different types of lie detectors exist, researchers continue to investigate the appropriate methods of interpreting data (and demonstrating its reliability and validity) with each type of detector.

Bibliography

Block, Eugene. *Lie Detectors: Their History and Use*. New York: David McKay, 1977. Block traces the development of lie detection techniques from ancient times to the present. Through a discussion of a variety of often landmark cases, he illustrates what he believes to be the value, dangers, and limitations of lie detectors. Concludes with a look into the future use of the polygraph in criminal and noncriminal settings. For a wide audience.

Gale, Anthony, ed. *The Polygraph Test: Lies, Truth, and Science*. Beverly Hills, Calif.: Sage, 1988. An excellent and extensive source of information on the polygraph's use in three contexts: criminal investigation, security screening, and personnel selection. Although based on a report conducted in England, the work covers polygraph use in the United States and elsewhere. Aside from the basic facts about the instrument and its accuracy, psychological, legal, and civil rights issues are raised. An annotated bibliography, a guide for students, and a glossary of terms are useful.

Lykken, David T. *A Tremor in the Blood: Uses and Abuses of the Lie Detector*. New York: McGraw-Hill, 1981. This informative work presents the first critical appraisal of the history, theory, and practices of polygraphic interrogation. Accessible to the general and specialized reader alike. Especially effective is Lykken's examination of the lie detector industry from the point of view of the citizen as well as from what he calls the lie detector industry.

Reid, John E., and Fred E. Inbau. *Lie Detection and Criminal Interrogation*. 3d ed. Baltimore: Williams & Wilkins, 1953. Intended as a practical and useful manual not only for criminal investigators but also for those who have an interest in the "art" of lie detection and criminal investigation. The first part discusses the methods used in the detection of deception; the second part focuses on various techniques that may be used by law enforcement officials in order to elicit information. Each part is supplemented with a treatment of the legal aspects of the subject matter. Contains numerous graphs, charts, and illustrations.

_____. *Truth and Deception: The Polygraph ("Lie-Detector") Technique*. 2d ed. Baltimore: Williams & Wilkins, 1977. This is one of the best and most detailed sources of information for those interested in learning about the polygraph technique. The authors' years of experience in the field of lie detection give the reader not only a general overview of the historical development of the instrument but also a clear picture of how the test is administered and interpreted. Legal, moral, and philosophical issues surrounding the polygraph test are discussed. Includes graphs, appendices, and a selected bibliography.

Genevieve Slomski

Cross-References

Einthoven Develops the Forerunner of the Electrocardiogram (1900's), p. 41; Berger Develops the Electroencephalogram (EEG) (1929), p. 890; Gibbon Develops the Heart-Lung Machine (1934), p. 1024; Cerletti and Bini Develop Electroconvulsive Therapy for Treating Schizophrenia (1937), p. 1086.

NOETHER PUBLISHES THE THEORY
OF IDEALS IN RINGS

Category of event: Mathematics
Time: 1921
Locale: University of Göttingen, Germany

Noether's theory of ideals in rings furthered Richard Dedekind's studies of polynomic root solutions and laid the foundations for much of abstract algebra

Principal personages:
EMMY NOETHER (1882-1935), a German mathematician and educator
RICHARD DEDEKIND (1831-1916), a German mathematician

Summary of Event

It is almost a hopeless task to give a nonesoteric account of certain highly abstract and technical developments in areas of higher mathematics, such as the ring and ideal theory in modern algebra. This results from the fact that many key developments are highly formalized and have few or no equivalents in ordinary mathematics. It is necessary from the start to limit one's treatment and focus instead primarily on the status and impact of these developments.

A set of elements for which the binary operations of addition and multiplication are defined, so as to satisfy the basic axioms of commutativity, associativity, and distributivity, is known as a ring. The common integer counting numbers for a ring, as do the polynomials of all degrees N are defined as $f = f(x) = a_0 + a_1x + a_2x^2 + \ldots + a_nx^n$. The term "ring" derives from the operation of wrapping a segment of the lineal real number line around a circle to obtain a modular mapping. The German mathematician Ernst Eduard Kummer (1810-1893) tried to solve the famous polynomic problem of Pierre de Fermat's last equation in number theory; that is, to prove $x^n + y^n = z^n$ for all n. Kummer made the unwarranted assumption that a hypothesis called the unique factorization theorem is always true in rings of algebraic integers. A number in the complex field is called an algebraic integer if it satisfies an algebraic equation with rational integer coefficients not greater than 1. The algebraic integers in an algebraic number field are said to form an integral domain. Although Kummer's unsuccessful effort did not arrive at a proof of Fermat's theorem, the theory of ideal numbers that arose subsequently (through Richard Dedekind's efforts) did make it possible to establish the general conditions under which the Fermat equation would be unsolvable by means of integers. Kummer defined what Dedekind later independently termed "ideal" numbers, such that composite numbers made from the new species satisfied Carl Friedrich Gauss's unique factorization theorem into so-called prime ideal factors.

Gauss first applied number theory factorization concepts to the ring of all complex numbers, defined by $a + bi$. The further development of ideals by Dedekind arose as a result of his subsequent efforts to restore unique factorization in some algebraic domains. Faced with this problem, Dedekind had the insight that, instead of considering the single number 3, for example, one could consider the set $A = 3x$ and $B = 2 + \sqrt{-5}\, y$, where both x and y are in a common set Z. The sets A and B are examples of what Dedekind calls ideals. An integral domain is a ring in which the nonzero elements constitute a semigroup of the multiplicative semigroup. Any set equipped with an operation (such as multiplication) satisfying the conditions eg $= ge = g$ and $g^{-1}g = e$, is called a group. The integral domain Z defined by $Z = x + y\sqrt{-5}$ does not have the property of factorization into unique prime numbers. Nevertheless, as Dedekind demonstrated, it is possible to develop unique factorizations in some kind of prime quantities for general algebraic fields. If D is an integral domain, a nonempty set of D, K is called an ideal, if it satisfies the following conditions: that $b_1 + b_2$ is a part of K, that $b_1 - b_2$ is a part of K, and that $r \times b$ is a part of K, or the equivalent condition that K is a group with respect to addition.

An ideal is not itself a number, but a set of numbers qualifying as a special kind of subring of a ring. If R is a ring, a subring of R is a subset, which is a ring with respect to addition and multiplication in R. Multiplication and other operations with ideals can also be defined. Some mathematicians have ascribed the rather odd choice of the name "ideal" to a prophetic intuition of the future formal axiomatics of David Hilbert.

With Emmy Noether, the ideals first invented for use in number theory became a more fundamental tool of wider use in higher algebra and elsewhere. Noether was the daughter of Max Noether, a noted mathematician who played an important role in contributing to the Erlangen school's development of the theory of algebraic functions. During the 1903 to 1904 semester, despite official opposition because of her gender, Noether was permitted to enroll as an auditor in courses at the University of Göttingen given by Hilbert, Felix Klein, and Hermann Minkowski. Hilbert and Klein recognized her potential. After further studies at the University of Erlangen under Paul Gordan, she received her Ph.D. in 1907; her thesis extended Gordan's finiteness problem of invariants for two variables. After 1911, Noether turned toward Hilbert's formal and abstract methodology. In 1915, she was invited by Hilbert and Klein to work at Göttingen. She stayed there as an untenured associate professor until dismissed by the Nazi regime in 1933.

In addition to Dedekind's work, the research of Steinitz on the theory of abstract fields was also of great importance for Noether's work, particularly during and following World War I. Beginning with her correspondence in 1917 with German mathematician E. Fischer and through her study of the arithmetic theory of algebraic fields from 1918 to 1919, Noether initially became familiar with Dedekind's theory of modules and ideals. Noether's first work in algebra, dating from 1919, culminated in her 1921 publication in the *Mathematische Annalen* of what many mathematicians consider to be her most significant and wide-reaching paper: "Idealtheorie in Ringbereichen" (theory of ideals in rings). Noether developed a more general theory of ideals using the formal axiomatic basis of Hilbert to include all prior examples, as well as extend the range of ideals. The chief innovation of this work is the so-called ascending-chain-axiom, which states that a chain of ideals, a_1, a_2, a_3, . . . a_n, necessarily comes to an end after a finite number of steps, if each term a_1 includes the preceding term a_{1-1} as a so-called proper part. Noether's ascending chain condition can be shown to be equivalent to Hilbert's earlier theorem of the finite ideal basis. More generally, through this and several later papers, Noether showed how it is possible to derive the polynomial ideals of Kummer in the same axiomatic fashion and to retrieve all Dedekind's classical results on ideals in algebraic number fields, the latter requiring the condition of the ring to be "integrally closed." A closed ring is a set of numbers where there is no means to obtain a number outside the set by any means of addition, multiplication, and the like.

Many of Noether's later discoveries were notably furthered by her students of the "Noether school," including Wolfgang Krull, Gottfried Koethe, and notably B. L. van der Waerden. Van der Waerden's two-volume text on advanced algebra remained the standard for many decades. The widespread modern tendency of viewing algebraic structures as groups with operators can be traced directly to Noether's publications and those of her associates. Instead of operating with definite or even formal expressions, the simple properties of the operations, for example, of addition and multiplication to which they lend themselves, were reformulated as initial axioms, forming the basis for further deductions. Noether's particular strength, acknowledged by many of her contemporaries and students, lay in her uncanny ability to operate abstractly with concepts alone within the framework of her drive toward axiomatic purity.

Impact of Event

The notion of ideals in other new versions played a decisive role in Noether's theory of noncommutative algebras and their representation. Although most common operations with numbers in multiplication are commutative ($a \times b = b \times a$), in the more general interpretation of multiplication provided by abstract algebra, noncommutative algebra was derived abstractly by Noether between 1924 and 1928. In Noether's abstract approach, traditional calculational tools, like matrices and determinants, used so successfully by her contemporary I. J. Schur in 1926, are discarded entirely in favor of purely abstract concepts. In intensive cooperation with mathematics colleagues, Noether carefully investigated the detailed structure of noncommutative algebras and applied this theory further to the ordinary commutative number fields and their arithmetics by means of her so-called cross-product method. The important influence of many of these later efforts by Noether is clearly visible in the influential textbook by physicist-intuitionist mathematician Hermann Weyl *Gruppentheorie und Quantenmechanik* (1928; *The Theory of Groups and Quantum Mechanics*, 1950), who also made notable contributions to the algebraic theory of numbers.

The dissemination and development of Noether's work was ensured by the twelve doctoral students under her directorship, as well as by a host of French, German, and Soviet mathematicians with whom she frequently visited and corresponded. By eliminating some of Noether's original axioms, van der Waerden and Emil Artin later obtained further generalizations of her ideal theory. The most far-reaching generalizations of the Dedekind-Noether theory of ideals were produced by German mathematician, logician, and philosopher Paul Lorenzen. A special subtype of ideals has been named "Noetherian" in her honor.

As Nicolas Bourbaki notes in the *Éléments de mathématique* (1939; elements of mathematics), the wider penetration of general algebraic ideas and methods into the diverse network of mathematical and physical subdisciplines became possible only after the publications of Noether. The effects of Noether's work on the theory of ring-ideals can be judged by comparing the organization, methods, and focus of van der Waerden's theory to modern algebra of 1930 with the pre-Noetherian treatment of algebra.

Bibliography

Dick, Auguste. *Emmy Noether, 1882-1935.* Translated by H. I. Blocher. Boston: Birkhäuser, 1970. One of the most widely available accounts of Noether's life.

Jones, Burton W. *An Introduction to Modern Algebra.* New York: Macmillan, 1975. Gives a general account of modern ring and ideal theory.

Robinson, Abraham. *Numbers and Ideals: An Introduction to Some Basic Concepts of Algebra and Number Theory.* San Francisco: Holden-Day, 1965. A unique introductory text treating ideals with minimum prerequisites.

Srinivasan, Bhama, and Judith Sally. *Emmy Noether in Bryn Mawr: Proceedings of a Symposium.* New York: Springer-Verlag, 1983. A presentation of eulogies and studies giving important retrospectives on Noether's accomplishments.

Weil, Andre. *Number Theory: An Approach Through History from Hammurabi to Legendre.* Boston: Birkhäuser, 1984. A unique presentation of abstract arithmetic by one of the founders of the Bourbaki circle.

Gerardo G. Tango

Cross-References

Hilbert Develops a Model for Euclidean Geometry in Arithmetic (1898), p. 31; The Study of Mathematical Fields by Steinitz Inaugurates Modern Abstract Algebra (1909), p. 438; Noether Shows the Equivalence of Symmetry and Conservation (1918), p. 650; The Bourbaki Group Publishes *Éléments de mathématique* (1939), p. 1140.

BANTING AND MACLEOD WIN THE NOBEL PRIZE FOR THE DISCOVERY OF INSULIN

Category of event: Medicine
Time: 1921-1923
Locale: University of Toronto, Canada

Banting and Best, in Macleod's laboratory, isolated the pancreatic antidiabetic hormone insulin, which saved the lives of countless patients suffering from diabetes

Principal personages:

SIR FREDERICK GRANT BANTING (1891-1941), a Canadian physician who discovered the pancreatic hormone insulin, for which he was awarded the Nobel Prize in Physiology or Medicine in 1923

CHARLES HERBERT BEST (1899-1978), a graduate student in the Department of Physiology of the University of Toronto who codiscovered insulin with Banting

JAMES BERTRAM COLLIP (1892-1965), a professor in the Department of Biochemistry of the University of Alberta, Edmonton, who collaborated on the purification of insulin

JOHN JAMES RICKARD MACLEOD (1876-1935) a Scottish professor, head of the Department of Physiology at the University of Toronto, and cowinner of the Nobel Prize in Physiology or Medicine in 1923

Summary of Event

"Sugar disease" (diabetes mellitus) has been known since ancient times. The disease in its juvenile form is induced by a deficiency of the pancreatic islets of Langerhans, which fail to produce the hormone insulin, needed for the utilization of glucose by muscle cells. When deprived of their primary fuel, the tissues produce energy from fat which results in high blood levels of toxic ketone bodies (acetone). The diabetic has very high blood levels of glucose in the blood and urine. The patient consumes much fluid, produces much urine, and is always hungry and weak; yet, in spite of eating constantly, the patient loses weight. When ketone bodies accumulate in the blood, the brain ceases to function and the patient slips into a coma and dies.

In the Egyptian Papyrus Ebers (c. 1500 B.C.), a condition was referred to which is assumed to have been diabetes. The ancient Chinese, Japanese, and Hindu knew that the urine of people suffering from sugar disease was sweet tasting. The clinical signs of the disease, which received the name "diabetes" (Greek: to flow through or siphon) from the Greek physician Aretaeus of Cappadocia (A.D. 30-90), were described by the Roman physician Aulus Cornelius Celsus (c. 25 B.C. to c. A.D. 50). The Persian physician Avicenna (980-1037) gave a complete description of the disorder and also of its complications. He noted the presence of a honeylike substance in the urine ("mellitus," Latin for honey), which Michel-Eugène Chevreul identified in 1815 as grape sugar (glucose). The French physiologist Claude Bernard (1813-1878), who propounded the theory that blood sugar was derived from the breakdown of liver glycogen, found that diabetics had high levels of blood glucose. Adolf Kussmaul (1874) detected acetone in the urine and blood of diabetics for which Bernard Naunyn (1895) introduced the term acidosis (ketosis).

In addition to the acinary cells producing pancreatic digestive juice, described by the seventeenth century Dutch anatomist Regnier de Graaf, the German histologist Paul Langerhans had discovered, in 1869, some peculiar cell aggregations in the pancreas which were later named "islets of Langerhans" in honor of their discoverer. Johann Conrad Brunner, in 1682, showed that if he removed the pancreas, the experimental animals began to drink and urinate continuously. This finding and Cawley's (1788) and Étienne Lancereaux's (1877) realization that there was a connection between the clinical signs of the disease and pancreatic lesions, were the beginning of a new era: the study of the pancreas as the causative factor of diabetes. Thus, Hedon (1892) and Baron Joseph von Mering and Oscar Minkowski (1889) were able to produce diabetes in experimental animals by surgical removal of the pancreas. This led to the demonstration that the pancreatic islets of Langerhans are the source of an internal secretion necessary for the metabolism of glucose. Researchers reported that when they tied the pancreatic duct which takes the digestive juice to the intestine, the acinary cells atrophied but the islets of Langerhans remained intact and the animals did not become diabetic. Nevertheless, from 1910 to 1920, attempts by Minkowski and others to extract the active ingredient from the islets of Langerhans were unsatisfactory.

This was the situation when a young Canadian surgeon had an inspiration that would become the turning point in the search for the elusive pancreatic hormone. Sir Frederick Grant Banting was born November 14, 1891, on a farm in Alliston, Ontario, Canada. When he was graduated from the faculty of Medicine at the University of Toronto, he joined the army during World War I. After his return from Europe, he began a surgical practice in London, Ontario, Canada. On October 31, 1920, Banting was preparing a lecture on the pancreas for his medical class. While reading an article by Moses Barron entitled "The Relation of the Islets of Langerhans to Diabetes with Special Reference to Cases of Pancreatic Lithiasis" in the journal *Surgery, Gynecology and Obstetrics*, which reported that the blockage of the pancreatic duct caused the pancreas to shrivel leaving the islets of Langerhans untouched, Banting immediately wrote: "Ligate pancreatic ducts of dogs. Keep dogs alive till acini degenerate leaving Islets. Try to isolate the internal secretion of these to relieve glycosuria [sugar in urine]." He realized that when one tried to extract the active hormone from the islets of Langerhans, the pancreatic digestive juice destroyed the protein hormone before it could be isolated. By letting the acinary cells shrivel first, there would be no digestive juice left and the hormone could be isolated intact. He presented his idea to John James Rickard Macleod, head of the Department of Physiology of the University of Toronto, and requested permission to conduct the necessary experimental work in his laboratory. Although Macleod did not believe in the existence of an islet hormone or that Banting would be able to prove otherwise, after long deliberations he gave permission to Banting to use the facilities and provided him with a graduate student assistant, Charles Herbert Best.

Banting and Best began their experiments on dogs on May 17, 1921. On August 3, the two researchers had the first conclusive result showing that their pancreas extract lowered the blood sugar of dogs who became diabetic by surgical removal of the pancreas. At first, Macleod was skeptical about Banting's report on the successful isolation of the antidiabetic hormone, and he made the two researchers repeat their experiments several times. After he was satisfied that the results were valid, he invited James Bertram Collip to join the group. On December 12, Collip began working on the purification of the extract to make it injectable into humans. On January 23, 1922, it was tested on Leonard Thompson, a fourteen-year-old boy dying of diabetes. The injection of the extract lowered his blood sugar and cleared his urine of ketone bodies and sugar. The first official paper on the discovery, entitled "Internal Secretion of the Pancreas," was published in February, 1922, in the *Journal of Laboratory and Clinical Medicine* by Banting and Best. On October 26, 1923, the Swedish Nobel Committee awarded the Nobel Prize in Physiology or Medicine to Banting and Macleod for the discovery of insulin. The two winners, accompanied by Best and Collip, traveled to Stockholm two years later. On September 15, 1925, at the ceremonial presentation of the award, Banting shared his half of the prize with Best and Macleod followed suit by sharing his prize with Collip.

It is interesting to note that Banting's original idea proved to be flawed, because the digestive factor in the acinary cells of the pancreas is present in an inactive form which is activated only in the intestine. As Banting and Best later discovered, they could extract insulin even from intact beef pancreas. In the end, it appears that what gave Banting and Best priority over their predecessors was the availability of a faster and more sensitive technique for the testing of blood sugar levels, thereby allowing them to recognize the effectiveness of their extract.

Impact of Event

The importance of the discovery of insulin can be appreciated only when one considers the plight of the millions of diabetics in the pre-insulin era. In particular, one has to realize the tragic fate of diabetic children who, shortly after the onset of the disease, changed from healthy, active children into weak, drowsy skeletons who soon became comatose and died. One cannot describe the despair of parents when they were told the dreaded diagnosis of their child's disease, knowing quite well that it was the equivalent of a death sentence. Only by keeping the child on a starvation diet could its life be prolonged by a short time span, a life devoid of the simplest pleasures of childhood. Then, after long years of disappointment when physicians were powerless as their patients wasted away, insulin promised new health, new vigor, and new life to these juvenile diabetics.

The discovery of insulin at the University of Toronto was one of the most revolutionary events in the history of medicine. Its impact was so great because of the miraculous effect insulin had on diabetic patients. The most dramatic example of its spectacular power was its ability to conquer the diabetic coma. The discovery of insulin has had significant social consequences for diabetics. It not only restores good health and grants additional years of life but also enables diabetics to have a career and a family. It also assures effective medical care for diabetics who are of advanced age. The leap from despair and death to hope and health was so sudden that it gripped the public imagination. It is estimated that there are more than 15 million diabetics living today who without insulin would die at an early age. Because of insulin, they are active, useful members of society. For example, George Minot, a juvenile diabetic who was saved by insulin, discovered a treatment for pernicious anemia, another disease which in the past was always lethal.

The work of the Toronto team represented a great step forward toward the elucidation of the physiology and pathology of sugar metabolism in the human body. It paved the way to subsequent improvements in the treatment of diabetes mellitus, such as the present clinical trials with computerized insulin pumps and with transplantation of islets of Langerhans in order to avoid the necessity for daily injections. It is hoped that it will also lead to a cure instead of a treatment of diabetes.

Bibliography

Best, Charles H. "A Canadian Trail of Medical Research." In *Selected Papers of Charles H. Best*. Toronto: University of Toronto Press, 1963. This chapter provides information about Best's life and his collaboration with Banting in the discovery of insulin. The book has a foreword by the Nobel laureate Sir Henry Dale and an introduction by the world-renowned diabetes specialist, Eliot P. Joslin. The rest of the book is technical but understandable to a layperson with some science education.

Bliss, Michael. *Banting: A Biography.* Toronto: McClelland and Stewart, 1984. A good biography of the main discoverer of insulin, with a few illustrations, a good index, and extensive end notes. It is written in a clear, nontechnical style. It deals with some controversial issues and some negative angles of Banting's character. In this sense, it complements Stevenson's biography of Banting.

_____. *The Discovery of Insulin.* Toronto: McClelland and Stewart, 1982. An attempt to give an objective account of the discovery of insulin by the University of Toronto research team. It claims to set the record straight about the roles played by the different protagonists of the story. The work contains illustrations, a good index, a very exhaustive bibliography, and extensive (33 pages) end notes. The style is clear, interesting, and easy to understand.

De Kruif, Paul. "Banting Who Found Insulin." In *Men Against Death*. New York: Harcourt, Brace, 1932.

_____. "Minot Against Death." In *Men Against Death*. New York: Harcourt, Brace, 1932. These two chapters, written by a renowned science writer, tell the story of how Banting and Best discovered insulin and Minot and William P.

Murphy, the treatment of another fatal disease, pernicious anemia. It is obligatory reading for people interested in the history of the battle waged by medical science for the prolongation of life. The work contains a short index and photographs of the scientists whose lives and work de Kruif so vividly described.

Stevenson, Lloyd. *Sir Frederick Banting.* Toronto: Ryerson Press, 1946. This was the first complete biography of Banting based on primary sources. It emphasizes mainly the positive sides of Banting. As it was written twenty-eight years before Bliss's biography and only five years after Banting's tragic death, it is understandable that Stevenson deemphasized the controversial aspects of Banting's life and work. Nevertheless, it is a very valuable source of information for any student of the history of medicine in general and the history of diabetes in particular. The book is very long (435 pages), has a good index, and a good bibliography.

Wrenshall, G. A., G. Hetenyi, and W. R. Feasby. *The Story of Insulin: Forty Years of Success Against Diabetes.* London: The Bodley Head, 1962. A good account of the historical development of the knowledge of the sugar disease from the earliest times to 1962. The work has a short but adequate index and relevant illustrations. In addition to the historical aspect, the authors discuss the role of insulin in the body and the causes and consequences of diabetes. The foreword was written by R. D. Lawrence, a diabetic who, because of insulin, survived to lead a productive life as a renowned clinical researcher. The book is written for the general reader in an easily understood style.

René R. Roth

Cross-References

Bayliss and Startling Discover Secretin and Establish the Role of Hormones (1902), p. 179; Sanger Wins the Nobel Prize for the Discovery of the Structure of Insulin (1958), p. 1567; The First Commercial Genetic Engineering Product, Humulin, Is Marketed by Eli Lilly (1982), p. 2221.

McCOLLUM NAMES VITAMIN D AND PIONEERS ITS USE AGAINST RICKETS

Category of event: Medicine
Time: 1922
Locale: The Johns Hopkins University, Baltimore, Maryland

McCollum and collaborators established the existence of vitamin D, named it, and contributed to its use in the eradication of rickets

> *Principal personages:*
> ELMER VERNER MCCOLLUM (1879-1967), an American biochemist and nutritionist who carried out pioneering research on vitamin D, vitamin A, and the B vitamins
> THOMAS BURR OSBORNE (1859-1929), a nutritionist under whom McCollum worked at the Connecticut Agricultural Station
> JOHN HOWLAND (1873-1926), the physician-in-chief of pediatrics at The Johns Hopkins Hospital who collaborated with McCollum in several studies of rickets

Summary of Event

Rickets (or rachitis) is a disease that causes abnormal bone formation, particularly in the long bones and the ribs. First described in the second century A.D. by Galen of Pergamum and Soranus of Ephesus, rickets was a widespread health problem until discovery and dissemination of the antirachitic factor, vitamin D. Elmer Verner McCollum and coworkers pioneered this effort in 1922, showing that the antirachitic factor was a distinctive substance. They named this substance vitamin D because it was the fourth vitamin to be discovered. The occurrence of rachitis is now rare—except in underdeveloped countries—as a result of the vitamin D fortification of food (especially milk) in the industrialized nations of the world.

Rickets, which usually begins before age three, is caused by the improper and incomplete uptake of calcium into the fast-growing bones of children. The resultant insufficient calcification of these bones prevents them from hardening properly. Therefore, the bones of a rachitic child are so soft that they bend and twist into abnormal shapes. Furthermore, they will fracture easily. Fortunately, as afflicted children grow up, their bones harden, but the abnormal shapes are retained. Rickets is rarely fatal, but it produces several cosmetically unappealing conditions including curvature of the spine, bow legs, knock-knee, and chicken breast. Rickets sufferers are also unusually susceptible to the common cold, to bronchitis, and to pneumonia.

As may be expected, vitamin D is utilized in preventive chemotherapy, not in the correction of rickets. The two most common forms of the vitamin used in humans are calciferol (vitamin D_2) and cholecalciferol (vitamin D_3). These fatlike substances are derived from the steroids ergosterol and 7-dehydrocholesterol (7-DC), respectively. The human body converts 7-DC to cholecalciferol at the surface of the skin in a process that is energized by ultraviolet light from the sun. Exposure of adults to normal amounts of sunlight causes enough vitamin D_3 production in the skin to make it unnecessary to add any vitamin D to their diet.

Children, however, require about 0.020 milligram of vitamin D per day in the diet if rickets is to be avoided. One way to administer the vitamin is as the cholecalciferol in cod-liver oil, a rich natural source of the vitamin. Fortification of milk with vitamin D_2 is more widespread today. It is important to note that excess dietary vitamin D should be avoided because it is toxic.

McCollum, who first identified vitamin D and named it, carried out many of the early important studies on this vitamin. Reputedly, McCollum's interest in biochemistry and vitamins began when he worked at the the the Connecticut Agricultural Experiment Station under Thomas Burr Osborne. This employment occurred during McCollum's doctoral training in organic chemistry at Yale University, and ended when he was awarded the Ph.D. in 1906. In 1907, McCollum was employed by the Wisconsin College of Agriculture, where he was assigned to investigate the chemical makeup of the food and excrement of dairy cattle. It was here that McCollum's research began to bloom. This resulted from the fact that he developed the first white rat colony in the United States devoted to use in the study of nutrition. Utilization of rats as experimental subjects allowed McCollum and his coworkers the opportunity to circumvent the complicated and tedious methodology that was required to study cattle and other large animals. This revolutionary concept of nutritional research was so successful that other scientists all over the world soon began to emulate McCollum's efforts. In six years, McCollum passed through the academic ranks from instructor to full professor.

In 1913, McCollum reported that rats fed "certain fat deficient" diets exhibited a growth retardation that was reversed by feeding rats with "either extract of egg or of butter." By 1915, McCollum's research group had demonstrated that several trace substances, which McCollum called vitamins A and B, were necessary for normal health and growth in rats. Thus, McCollum helped to initiate the alphabetical names used in vitamin nomenclature. In 1917, McCollum became the chair of the department of chemistry, and professor of biochemistry, at the School of Hygiene and Public Health of The Johns Hopkins University in Baltimore. He continued his efforts to understand the vitamins and pioneered the study of vitamin D, for which he is best known, again using rats for his experiments.

McCollum's pioneering identification of the existence of vitamin D in 1922 was accompanied by development of the line test for its measurement in foods. The line test begins with removal of bone sections (pieces of bone) from rats fed either normal, vitamin D-deficient, or vitamin D-supplemented diets. These bone sections are soaked in dilute solutions of light-sensitive silver nitrate. This treatment causes a silver compound to become a bone component wherever recent bone calcification has occurred. Exposure to light converts the silver compound to black, metallic silver in a process similar to that seen in photography. With normal bone, a very distinct black line is produced at the bone ends. No such line is seen is severe rickets, and indistinct lines are observed in healing cases of the disease. The test is "expressed with a scale of one to four, using plus and minus signs." It is viewed as both sensitive and accurate.

McCollum made many other important contributions to the field of nutrition as noted in about two hundred publications. These valuable endeavors led to his membership in many national and international organizations involved in the maintenance and improvement of human health, including the National Advisory Health Council, the Food and Nutrition Board of the National Research Council, and the World Health Organization. McCollum was also elected to prestigious scientific societies exemplified by the United States National Academy of Sciences and the Royal Society of London. He was awarded honorary degrees from universities. McCollum's great influence on the field of nutrition was honored when The Johns Hopkins University founded the McCollum-Pratt Institute. This influence continued throughout McCollum's career and persisted long after his retirement in 1946. His research and writing efforts (such as his 1957 book *A History of Nutrition*) continued during a decade as emeritus professor of biochemistry at The Johns Hopkins University.

Impact of Event

In 1922, rickets was a worldwide disorder that affected many children. Today, it has essentially been eradicated. The successful treatment of the disease began when McCollum and coworkers produced evidence in 1922 that cod-liver oil contained a specific antirachitic chemical (vitamin D). As McCollum stated in *From Kansas Farm Boy to Scientist* (1964): "The demonstration of the existence of a vitamin which exerts a profound influence in directing the growth of bones proved to be of great public-health value."

McCollum demonstrated that this research stimulated great interest among many investigators. Furthermore, the discovery, coupled with the participation of prominent pediatricians in the effort, such as John Howland, led to rapid general acceptance by physicians of the efficacy of using cod-liver oil to prevent rickets. From that time on, the medical profession passed from haphazard use of the oil—in a skeptical fashion—to its routine use. As a result, rickets soon became rare.

Actualization of the existence of the antirachitic substance quickly led to isolation and characterization of vitamins D_2 and D_3. Subsequently, in the hands of other researchers, study of the pure vitamin began to show promise. First, it became possible to add vitamin D_2 to milk to ensure almost universal dissemination of the vitamin among the population of the industrialized countries. Next, it was shown that vitamin D_2 (or D_3) functioned after conversion as another chemical that was actually a hormone (hormone D).

The form of hormone D made by the body, from vitamin D_3, is called 1,25-dihydroxycholecalciferol. Hormone D acts by stimulating rapid intestinal reabsorption of calcium via a protein. This calcium resorption minimizes calcium loss in the feces and prevents the bone decalcification that results in rickets.

Additional examination of the action of vitamin D has led to better understanding of the processes of bone deposition and resorption as well as to explanation of the interrelationships between hormone D and other calcium-controlling substances (such as calcitonin and parathyroid hormone) made by the body. Such investigations have also led to the realization that bone is not simply a "dead," body-support matrix. Rather, bone is a vital, live tissue that can produce dissolved calcium in the blood to serve many purposes.

This realization has had further ramifications, and it is clear that calcium serves as a biological signal in life processes that include control of the blood pressure, blood clotting, nerve impulse transmission, and muscle contraction.

Therefore, the acorn of McCollum's efforts had produced a mighty oak tree of intertwined information about life. This information now promises eventual answers to many elusive but fundamental problems of life science that are clearly associated with calcium.

Bibliography

Becker, Stanley L. "Elmer Verner McCollum." In *Dictionary of Scientific Biography*, edited by Charles C. Gillispie. Vol. 9. New York: Charles Scribner's Sons, 1974. A brief biographical sketch and useful source of basic information on McCollum. Focuses on his career and provides additional sources of biographical information. Gives insight into McCollum's personality and wide impact on nutrition.

Funk, Casimir. *The Vitamins*. Baltimore: Williams & Wilkins, 1922. Covers many aspects of vitamin research of the time. An extensive source of developmental information on nutrition, containing about sixteen hundred references on basic research on the vitamins and vitamin deficiency diseases. The many references to McCollum's research indicate McCollum's influence and research versatility in nutrition.

McCollum, Elmer V. *From Kansas Farm Boy to Scientist*. Lawrence: University of Kansas Press, 1964. A charming autobiography that describes McCollum's life and his research efforts in the study of vitamins, trace minerals, and other aspects of nutrition. Reveals the inner thoughts of a brilliant, sensitive man who was a great scientist.

_____. *A History of Nutrition*. Boston: Houghton Mifflin, 1957. An interesting book on development of nutrition; covers the period from the mid-eighteenth century to 1940. Especially valuable to readers who wish to trace the evolution of the science and those who wish details on the development of the understanding of the nature and roles of vitamins and other essential foodstuffs.

_____. *The Newer Knowledge of Nutrition*. 2d ed. New York: Macmillan, 1922. Covers many aspects of nutrition around 1920. Deals with vitamins, foods, appropriate diets, analysis of foods, vitamin deficiency diseases, and many other topics. Contains many references to the contributions of McCollum's group, but also provides full, fair coverage of the efforts of others.

Smith, Emil L., et al. *Principles of Biochemistry.* 7th ed. New York: McGraw-Hill, 1983. An excellent biochemistry textbook; includes details on many aspects of the roles of calcium, vitamin D, and the other calcium-regulating substances on biological processes. Contains many references for those who wish more technical information.

Weckel, Kenneth G. "Vitamin D." In *McGraw-Hill Encyclopedia of Science and Technology,* edited by Sybil P. Parker. 6th ed. 20 vols. New York: McGraw-Hill, 1987. A brief and simple exposition of vitamin D, describing its forms and sources; its measurement in biological samples, and its biological actions, biochemistry, dietary requirements, and commercial preparation. Clear and useful information for the reader who wishes relatively nontechnical information.

Sanford S. Singer

Cross-References

Grijns Proposes That Beriberi Is Caused by a Nutritional Deficiency (1901), p. 103; Hopkins Suggests That Food Contains Vitamins Essential to Life (1906), p. 330; Steenbock Discovers That Sunlight Increases Vitamin D in Food (1924), p. 771; Szent-Györgyi Discovers Vitamin C (1928), p. 857; Krebs Describes the Citric Acid Cycle (1937), p. 1107.

CARTER DISCOVERS THE TOMB OF TUTANKHAMEN

Category of event: Archaeology
Time: November 4, 1922
Locale: The Valley of the Kings, Egypt

Carter's discovery of the relatively unspoiled tomb of a pharaoh provided an unprecedented glimpse into the splendor of ancient Egypt

Principal personages:
> HOWARD CARTER (1873-1939), an English archaeologist and draftsman who discovered the tomb of Tutankhamen and supervised the evacuation of its contents
> TUTANKHAMEN (c. 1371-1352 B.C.), a king of Egypt who reigned from the age of nine or ten until his death
> GEORGE EDWARD STANHOPE MOLYNEUX HERBERT, FIFTH EARL OF CARNARVON (1866-1923), an associate and patron of Carter

Summary of Event

Howard Carter began his Egyptological career as a draftsman for the Egypt Exploration Fund. In 1899, he was appointed inspector-in-chief of the monuments of Upper Egypt and Nubia by the Egyptian government. During his three-year tenure, Carter supervised a number of major restoration projects, including work in the Valley of the Kings, a rich but improperly explored area of royal tombs on the west bank of the Nile River, across from modern Luxor (ancient Thebes). Although there had been despoilers and treasure hunters in this valley in periods throughout its long history, Carter was among the first modern archaeologists to delve into its secrets. He cooperated with others in preparing several of the tombs for tourists, by installing electric lights and constructing a system of pathways inside the tombs.

In January, 1903, under the sponsorship of Theodore M. Davis, a retired American businessman, Carter discovered the royal tomb of Thutmose IV. Although forgotten now because of Carter's more spectacular success with Tutankhamen in later years, Carter's discovery and excavation of the royal tomb was sensational. Carter and his colleagues painstakingly cleared the tomb of its contents and published a lengthy, meticulous account of his work.

In February, 1903, Carter and his assistants found the longest and deepest tomb in Egypt. It belonged to Queen Hatshepsut, a unique woman in the history of ancient Egypt resulting from a twenty-year reign as sovereign. Her tomb has been called the most individual and extraordinary one in the Valley of the Kings. Also, Carter worked to clear and illuminate the previously discovered tombs of Merneptah (son of Ramses II and perhaps the pharaoh from whom the Israelites escaped) and Seti I. The latter tomb, with its famous ceiling painting of the constellations, is the one visited most often today.

Following a disagreement with his superior, Carter (by then recognized as one of the most prestigious Egyptologists in the world) resigned from his government post and spent five years selling his own paintings of the monuments and dealing in antiquities. From 1907 to 1923, however, he returned to archaeology under the sponsorship of the fifth Earl of Carnarvon, an English nobleman who was an amateur archaeologist in his own right, though often in poor health. Carter assisted Carnarvon in expanding his unusually fine private collection of Egyptian antiquities and directed his excavations.

In 1914, Carnarvon and Carter were granted a ten-year permit to excavate in the Valley of the Kings. Although it had been customary through much of the New Kingdom period in Egypt to bury pharaohs there, many of their tombs had never been located. Through an antiquities transaction, Carter not only acquired some relics of Amenhotep I but also was led eventually to the pharaoh's previously unknown tomb. Carter later found additional tombs while continuing to investigate and restore others.

Delayed by World War I, Carnarvon's valley excavations did not begin until December, 1917. (With so much excavation, the site began to look like a battlefield.) After several years of relatively unsuccessful effort, Carnarvon became less willing to fund the expensive work. Nevertheless, one promising area remained. Carter successfully persuaded his patron to invest the necessary monetary support. Luck was with them thereafter, because on November 4, 1922, Carter's workers exposed what appeared to be a rectangular pit cut out of a rock. By the next day, a stairway and sealed door proved to be yet another previously undiscovered tomb. Unlike other tombs, however, this door was still sealed, meaning, perhaps, that no one had entered it since ancient times.

Summoned by a telegram from Carter, Carnarvon hurried to Luxor. In Carnarvon's presence, the sealed doorway of the tomb was opened. Then, in one of archaeology's most dramatic moments, Carter looked through a small opening in the last door to see the interior of the tomb for the first time and was rendered speechless with amazement. As he later recalled, in one of the most famous passages in the literature of archaeology:

Slowly, . . . the remains of passage debris that encumbered the lower part of the doorway were removed, until at last we had the whole door clear before us. The decisive moment had arrived. With trembling hands I made a tiny breach in the upper left-hand corner. Darkness and blank space, as far as an iron testing-rod could reach, showed that whatever lay beyond was empty. . . . At first I could see nothing, the hot air escaping from the chamber causing the candle flame to flicker, but presently, as my eyes grew accustomed to the light, details of the room within emerged slowly from the mist, strange animals, statues, and gold—everywhere the glint of gold. For the moment— an eternity it must have seemed to the others standing by—I was struck dumb with amazement, and when Lord Carnarvon, unable to stand the suspense any longer, inquired anxiously, "Can you see anything?" it was all I could do to get out the words, "Yes, wonderful things."

Carter had, in the culmination of his career, glimpsed the greatest archaeological treasure-trove of modern times. The tomb consisted of six parts. The first two parts, both less than 2 meters wide, included a sixteen-step staircase entrance and a descending passage of 7.6 meters beyond. Both the staircase and the passage ended in sealed doors. On November 26, 1922, Carter looked through the second door into the tomb's largest room (8 by 3.6 meters), which he would call the antechamber. It was the first of the four rooms to be opened and the last to be sealed. A preliminary inspection of the antechamber by Carter and Carnarvon on November 27, 1922, confirmed that many of the objects within the tomb were inscribed with Tutankhamen's name, thus establishing the identity of the tomb. Carter and his staff spent seven weeks clearing, sorting, and preserving the more than six hundred artifacts found jumbled together in the antechamber. These objects ranged from still intact funerary bouquets, rush and papyrus sandals, royal robes covered with beads and sequins, and various alabaster cups and jars, to a masterfully painted wooden casket, two life-size wooden statues of Tutankhamen, three animal-sided couches, four disassembled chariots, and a spectacular golden throne.

On February 17, 1923, having completed his work in the antechamber, Carter opened another sealed door. Beyond it lay the smaller burial chamber (6.4 by 4 meters), which was almost entirely filled with four nested golden shrines (5 by 3.3 meters). After much effort, Carter removed each of the four shrines in turn, but in order to get them out, he had to demolish the partition wall between the antechamber and the burial chamber, which clearly had been constructed after the shrines were in place. On February 3, 1924, the magnificent quartzite sarcophagus of the king was exposed to view for the first time. Nine days later, and after some complicated operations, its granite lid was raised on pulleys, revealing the outermost of three finely decorated nested coffins. The innermost proved to be of solid gold. Within this golden coffin the royal mummy of Tutankhamen lay, with a spectacular gold mask covering its head and shoulders. Although badly damaged by funerary ointments, the mummy was sufficiently intact to determine that Tutankhamen was approximately eighteen years of age when he died.

The other two rooms, a storeroom adjacent to the burial chamber and an annex entered from the antechamber, were cleared from 1927 to 1929, after work in the burial chamber had been completed. Both rooms contained important collections of smaller artifacts, but except for a large canopied shrine in the storeroom, none of the more famous pieces was found there. Further laboratory work at the site was required before the last finds could be transported to the Egyptian Museum in Cairo, where they may now be seen.

Carter's years of work in the tomb concluded in 1932. His splendidly disciplined archaeological work set a new standard for others to follow.

Impact of Event

Carter's discovery of the tomb of Tutankhamen in the Valley of the Kings was not only the greatest event in the history of archaeological discovery there but also very nearly the last. Although some work in the Valley of Kings has continued, most of it has been concerned primarily with the preservation of previously discovered tombs. The Valley of Kings now appeared to be exhausted, so archaeologists moved elsewhere—concerned, for example, with the more humble tomb builders as much as with the illustrious dead.

As Carter soon realized, Tutankhamen's tomb was originally not royal. Atypical in both design and decoration, it was, by all indications, originally the tomb of a noble. Because the young king's death was unexpected, no royal tomb was ready for him, so this lesser one was converted hastily for his use. Moreover, some of the goods that stocked the grave were intended originally for other people as well. How so many fine objects of art, including the gold coffin and masks, were made ready in such a relatively short time is a subject of speculation and wonder to this day.

The discovery of the tomb made a great impact in the history of art. One has only to open any book dealing with ancient Egypt of the Eighteenth Dynasty to find numerous objects depicted from the grave of Tutankhamen. Although one may be attracted to the gold, as Carter was, the wooden objects found in the tomb are more precious, in some respects, because they are no less unique and even more perishable. More than one-half of all surviving ancient Egyptian furniture, for example, was found in this tomb. Other objects discovered in the tomb had previously been known, if at all, from paintings. Because of these fine museum pieces and the gripping drama of their discovery after years of effort, "King Tut," as the headline writers preferred to call him, is the best known of all Egyptian pharaohs. He is, Carter declared, "the king whose name the whole world knows."

Despite his youth and premature demise, Tutankhamen also had some historical importance. In particular, he discarded the solar religion of his predecessor (and perhaps father-in-law), Akhenaton, changing his name from Tutankhaten to Tutankhamen in the process, so as to reaffirm his loyalty to the traditional deity, Amon-Re. With similar intentions, he erected a row of sphinxes and a statue of himself within the great temple of Karnak, on the eastern side of the Nile. The intrigue that preceded and succeeded his reign are among the most written about in the history of ancient Egypt. Theories as to the cause of his death are numerous. The overall result of the discovery of Tutankhamen's tomb, then, was to place his era firmly within the modern mind by illustrating it with a breathtaking richness of art and undying historical enigma. Brief though it was, the reign of Tutankhamen seems a golden moment in the history of civilization that will never be forgotten.

Bibliography

Bierbrier, M. L. *The Tomb-Builders of the Pharaohs*. London: British Museum, 1982. A short, useful, and well-illustrated account of how the tombs were built and by whom.

Carter, Howard. *The Tomb of Tutankhamen*. New York: E. P. Dutton, 1972. An abridgment of the original edition in three volumes. This later edition includes a fine selection of photographs, many of them in color, by Harry Burton and others.

Carter's account of his work can be slow going, but despite some clumsy writing, is occasionally powerful.

David, Rosalie. *Cult of the Sun: Myth and Magic in Ancient Egypt.* London: J. M. Dent, 1980. A stimulating and somewhat controversial account of Egyptian solar religion, particularly as practiced by the radical reformer, Akhenaton. Several passages discuss the return to orthodoxy under Tutankhamen. See also David's later work, *The Ancient Egyptians: Religious Beliefs and Practices.* Boston: Routledge & Kegan Paul, 1982.

Mertz, Barbara. *Red Land, Black Land: Daily Life in Ancient Egypt.* New York: Dodd, Mead, 1978. This book makes the ancient Egyptians come alive. As part of her engrossing evocation of periods and customs long since passed, Mertz describes a number of well-illustrated archaeological objects, including several from the tomb of Tutankhamen.

Romer, John. *Valley of the Kings.* New York: William Morrow, 1981. A superb history of treasure hunting and responsible excavation in the Valley of the Kings by a historically minded archaeologist who also worked in the area. Carter's entire career is surveyed, the account of his work with Tutankhamen is readable and recommended for a wide audience.

Dennis R. Dean

Cross-References

Evans Discovers the Minoan Civilization on Crete (1900), p. 67; The French Expedition at Susa Discovers the Hammurabi Code (1902), p. 169; Bingham Discovers an Inca City in the Peruvian Jungle (1911), p. 491; Seventeen-Thousand-Year-Old Paintings Are Discovered in Lascaux Cave (1940), p. 1176.

ANDREWS DISCOVERS THE FIRST FOSSILIZED DINOSAUR EGGS

Categories of event: Archaeology and anthropology
Time: 1923
Locale: Flaming Cliffs, Shabarakh Usu, Gobi Desert, Outer Mongolia

The expeditions, which led to the discovery of the first fossilized dinosaur eggs, contributed to the progress of paleontology

Principal personages:

ROY CHAPMAN ANDREWS (1884-1960), a zoologist, explorer, expert on whales, and leader of the five expeditions in the Gobi Desert

WALTER WILLIS GRANGER (1872-1941), the chief paleontologist on the expedition who, with William K. Gregory, named *Protoceratops andrewsi*

HENRY FAIRFIELD OSBORN (1857-1935), a vertebrate paleontologist of the early 1900's

GEORGE OLSEN, a paleontologist who found the first eggs and discovered the first *Oviraptor* fossil

Summary of Event

The purpose of the series of expensive expeditions to the Gobi Desert from 1921 to 1930 was to investigate Henry Fairfield Osborn's theory that central Asia had been the site of the evolutionary origin of humans and other mammals. As president of the American Museum of Natural History in New York City, Osborn was in a position to promote the explorations. While he believed that supporting hominid fossil evidence would be found, Osborn was interested also in building the museum's collections. He especially promoted educational displays of taxidermy specimens, artifacts, and fossils found on expeditions.

To launch the Central Asiatic Expeditions into the Gobi (literally, the "sandy waste") was not a casual matter. Poor roads, great distances, few people, high winds, sandstorms, and severe climate were all factors to overcome. During the winter, the temperature was lower than −40 degrees Celsius. Because of these conditions, scientific work was limited to April through October. Conflicts were possible from both bandits, warlords, and local government officials. Food and gasoline had to be brought in by camel caravan. Fortunately, the water table is not deep, and occasional wells allowed caravan travel. Nevertheless, an expert who could thoroughly plan and wisely lead the expeditions was needed.

Roy Chapman Andrews, who had studied and collected whale specimens for the museum, was chosen to lead the expeditions. Andrews first thought of using airplanes, but the Chinese authorities would not give permission. Andrews then chose to use motor vehicles: two Fulton one-ton trucks and three Dodge cars, all unmodified, to travel into the wilderness of the Gobi Desert. He believed that the vehicles would save time and allow ten times as much exploration. The plan also included 150 camels to bring in advance supplies to depots, and a staff of forty men was hired to support about fifteen scientists. Andrews put together a staff of experts from various fields. When discoveries were made, all enjoyed the interaction of scientists who were experts in geology, paleontology, zoology, topography, and botany. Andrews included J. B. Shackleford to document discoveries with both photographs and movies. Shackleford did excellent work, but chance allowed him to play a larger role. During the first year in the field, an interesting fossil was discovered by him at a place they had named "Flaming Cliffs." Shackleford had wandered off to do some exploring while the group waited for word from a scout car. At an outcropping of upper Cretaceous rock, Shackleford found a skull 20 centimeters long. Walter Willis Granger, the chief paleontologist, recognized the skull as that of an unknown dinosaur. The skull and some ominous bits of egg shells found by Granger at the cliffs were sent to the museum.

When the specimens were returned to New York, William K. Gregory determined that the unknown dinosaur was a predecessor of the well-known three-horned American dinosaur *Triceratops*. This new Mongolian species, however, had yet to evolve its horns and was smaller. Gregory called it *Protoceratops andrewsi* and strongly suggested they find more specimens. The expedition returned to Flaming Cliffs in 1923, and two months were spent searching the area. Immediately on their arrival, more *Protoceratops* were found. The area was so rich that by the end of the first day, each worker was busy carefully applying glue and cloth to strengthen his own fragile specimen as it was removed.

On the second day, George Olsen reported that he was sure he had found fossil eggs. At first, the group was incredulous, and they teased him. Then, they tried seriously to account for the eggs. No birds were known from the lower Cretaceous. All the Jurassic and upper Cretaceous birds were much too small to have laid eggs of this size. Birds' eggs are usually ovate to prevent rolling out of a nest; reptile eggs, which are buried in the ground, are usually elongate. The specimens were ovate. The fact that they were found in beds where only dinosaur fossils were discovered implied dinosaur eggs. More than one type of dinosaur fossil was being found, but only one was large enough to lay the eggs. Therefore, *Protoceratops andrewsi* must have laid the eggs.

Three of the eggs were in a cluster and evidently had remained in the exact spot where they had been deposited by the dinosaur. The broken shells of several others were partially embedded in the rock. The eggs were about the size and shape of a large baked potato, about 22 centimeters long. The shells were hard but wrinkled. Several of the eggs had been broken in half. In these, the scientists were sure that they could detect the small bones of embryonic dinosaurs. Now, there was no doubt that the eggs were from a dinosaur. During the weeks of study at Flaming Cliffs, a complete developmental series of *Protoceratops* at all stages was collected. Specimens included eggs, just-hatched youngsters, and juveniles of various ages through

3-meter adults. Olsen found a different birdlike dinosaur among the fossils and suspected it of being a predator. Because of the circumstances, the dinosaur was named *Oviraptor philoceratops*: "thief with love for ceratopsian eggs."

Since the specimens were found at different levels, Andrews concluded that they were not all buried at the same time. That there should be so many fossils in one area of the same species indicated to him that the region must have been a feeding ground or perhaps a source of water. The area was a *Protoceratops* breeding ground. Andrews thought that perhaps the type of sand was the right type to provide the proper amounts of heat and air for incubation.

The expedition in the 1923 season sent back several skeletons, more than fifty skulls of *Protoceratops andrewsi*, and fifty eggs, some still in nests. Sixty cases of fossils packed in handy camel hair weighing 5 metric tons were shipped with the belief that the Flaming Cliffs were still not exhausted. In 1925, an even larger group of scientists returned to the cliffs to find additional fossils. Olsen continued to find most of the eggs. One of his nests, which had eggs fastened to the underside of a rock, can be found in the Field Museum of Natural History in Chicago. Eggs of two smaller dinosaurs were found also during later visits. Most of these specimens were sent to the museum in New York.

In 1925, one of the motor vehicle experts, Norman Lovell, happened upon the best *Protoceratops* nest. Interested in capturing a young eagle for a pet, he approached a cliff with a 60-meter drop. Reaching over from the top, he scratched his hand. The sharp object was a broken dinosaur eggshell, which was part of a nest. Granger removed the eggs while reaching over the cliff, braving high winds. A 0.5-metric-ton section of sandstone with the eggs was removed and sent to the museum. The nest held eighteen eggs standing on end in an irregular circle. Originally, more eggs might have been in the nest, but parts had crumbled away with erosion of the cliff.

Expeditions returned to the Gobi in 1928 and 1930 to make other discoveries. Popular articles and books by Andrews, Granger, and Osborn described their adventures.

Impact of Event

Roy Chapman Andrews' adventuresome spirit was evident in his writing. Steven Jay Gould, a gifted writer, has said that even today it is difficult to find a better adventure story than told by Andrews. People were just becoming accustomed to the idea of the dinosaurs. Fossils of the forgotten beasts had been found first in the nineteenth century. Restorations of the beasts were still rare. The large eggs made dinosaurs seem more real.

The amount of interest shown in the eggs surprised Andrews. He believed that the tiny skulls of the earliest known mammals that lived during the age of dinosaurs were far more important scientifically. Also, his 1925 discovery of artifacts from ancient "dune dwellers" at Flaming Cliffs was more in line with the goals of the expedition. Moreover, there was the finding of the bones of the giant *Baluchitherium*, a type of rhinoceros. The 95-million-year-old dinosaur egg discovery had been a fortunate accident, which he regarded as important, but not to the extent that the public perceived it.

Before the discovery, scientists had guessed that dinosaurs, like modern reptiles, must have laid eggs; but none had ever been found. An egg is a fragile structure; fossils were assumed to be unlikely. Fossils of eggs and juvenile dinosaurs have continued to be rare. John Horner (the paleontologist who discovered the eggs, nests, and fossils of babies of *Maiasaura* in 1981) called the discovery in the Gobi "spectacular" and called the absence of further eggs and juveniles "a major scientific puzzle." After Horner found dinosaur embryos in Montana, he carefully studied a *Protoceratops* egg from Flaming Cliffs and stated that the supposed bones were only calcite crystals in odd shapes. Expectations can affect observation. Andrews' staff had seen a bit more than what was there, but the eggs were still eggs.

The excitement and romance of the expeditions firmly established the reputation of the American Museum of Natural History. With the expeditions, the museum built and still boasts the largest collection of dinosaur fossils in the world. Furthermore, the museum was able to develop outstanding exhibits and also to function as a continuing resource of specimens for further scientific study.

Evidence to support Osborn's theory about Asia being the center of human evolution was not found. Not one early human bone was uncovered. Andrews, however, proposed that the relationship of *Protoceratops* to *Triceratops* supported the idea of a land bridge to North America by which life spread. He wrote in his journal that "the theory upon which we organized the expedition might be true; that Asia is the mother of the life of North America." Scientists believe that it certainly was a center of some sort, but not for humankind. Research on this issue is now centered on Africa. Science changes and is influenced by many ideas.

Scientists will continue to reinterpret the findings at Flaming Cliffs to fit new and better theories. Nevertheless, the expeditions will remain a landmark which has contributed much to the progress of paleontology. The science of dinosaurs is undergoing major changes, but the eggs and other fossils from the Flaming Cliffs continue to rank as outstanding discoveries in the effort to understand the past.

Bibliography

Andrews, Roy Chapman. "Explorations in the Gobi Desert." *National Geographic* 63 (June, 1933): 653-716. Reading this article and also sampling some of the others in this volume will provide a feeling for the time when the discovery was made. Many photographs by Shackleford are included. Some photographs have been colored by an early technique. A photograph on page 654 shows the cliff on which Lovell and Granger found the best nest. One of the motor vehicles at the site lends perspective and gives a feeling for the danger involved.

_____. *On the Trail of Ancient Man: A Narrative of the Field Work of the Central Asiatic Expeditions.* New York: G. P. Putnam's Sons, 1926. This book written in the first person for the lay reader still holds the excitement of the discoveries and the adventure of the exploration of the unknown. Andrews tells about the sandstorms, finding fossils, dealing with danger, and finding the dinosaur eggs. Andrews was an excellent writer who could draw vivid mental pictures of his experiences. One can sense the impact of reading the book in 1926.

Eldredge, Niles, Douglas Eldredge, and Gregory Eldredge. *The Fossil Factory: A Kid's Guide to Digging up Dinosaurs, Exploring Evolution, and Finding Fossils.* Reading, Mass.: Addison-Wesley, 1989. This paperback tells how to collect fossils. It is written for children by the curator of invertebrates at the American Museum of Natural History in New York and his sons. Parents and teachers will find this book useful. It tells how and where to look for fossils.

Gould, Steven Jay. *Wonderful Life: The Burgess Shale and the Nature of History.* New York: W. W. Norton, 1989. Gould writes about the nature of interpreting the fossil record. He skillfully uses the details of the Burgess Shale of British Columbia to reveal the human side of science. He tells of how the reinterpretation of evidence can tell a different story. Gould's style is elegant and witty.

Horner, John R., and James Gorman. *Digging Dinosaurs.* New York: Workman, 1988. Dinosaur eggs and baby dinosaur fossils are still being found. This exciting book tells of Horner and Robert Makela's discoveries and interpretations of hadrosaur nests in Montana. Horner is among those who hold that various dinosaurs were warm-blooded, more birdlike, active, and performed social behaviors such as protecting and feeding their young.

Johanson, Donald, and James Shreeve. "The Antiquity of Man." In *Lucy's Child: The Discovery of a Human Ancestor.* New York: William Morrow, 1989. This chapter gives the history of how the search for the site of the evolution of humans has shifted from Africa to Asia and back to Africa again. Cultural influences on the science of the times are mentioned. Asia was thought to be a more noble background for the evolution of humankind than Africa during Osborn's time.

Lambert, David. *The Dinosaur Data Book: The Definitive, Fully Illustrated Encyclopedia of Dinosaurs.* New York: Avon Books, 1990. Ideas about dinosaurs have changed considerably since the Andrews expedition. This book is a treasure of details about dinosaurs. Many illustrations include a *Protoceratops* laying eggs. The large paperback has drawings of the members of the suborder Ceratopsia, showing sizes relative to common animals. Major fossil sites are indicated.

Lessem, Don. "Secrets of the Gobi Desert." *Discover* 10 (June, 1989): 40-46. Fossil bones being found continue to indicate that the dinosaurs may have spread to one another's continents. *Protoceratops* appears to be an uncle of *Triceratops*, but Andrews was correct about a connection between the continents. Canadian and Chinese scientists tell about efforts to retrace the steps of Andrews, even finding a crushed tin flask with an outline of a 1920's Dodge convertible on it.

Paul R. Boehlke

Cross-References

Zdansky Discovers Peking Man (1923), p. 761; Dart Discovers the First Recognized Australopithecine Fossil (1924), p. 780; Barghoorn and Tyler Discover 2-Billion-Year-Old Microfossils (1954), p. 1481; Leakey Finds a 1.75-Million-Year-Old Fossil Hominid (1959), p. 1603; Barghoorn and Associates Find Amino Acids in 3-Billion-Year-Old Rocks (1967), p. 1851; Miller Discovers a Dinosaur Egg Containing the Oldest Known Embryo (1987), p. 2357.

DE BROGLIE INTRODUCES THE THEORY
OF WAVE-PARTICLE DUALITY

Category of event: Physics
Time: 1923
Locale: University of Paris, France

De Broglie provided a mechanical explanation for the wave-particle duality of light

Principal personages:
LOUIS DE BROGLIE (1892-1987), a French prince, historian, and physicist who was a winner of the 1929 Nobel Prize in Physics
NIELS BOHR (1885-1962), a Danish physicist and winner of the 1922 Nobel Prize in Physics
ERWIN SCHRÖDINGER (1887-1961), an Austrian physicist and winner of the 1933 Nobel Prize in Physics
WERNER HEISENBERG (1901-1976), a German physicist and winner of the 1932 Nobel Prize in Physics

Summary of Event

In the early twentieth century, scientists were having difficulty describing the nature of light. For a long time, the nature of light had been regarded as being like that of a particle. In the late nineteenth century, light was demonstrated to behave as waves. Early in the twentieth century, however, this belief was shifted again by experiments of a particle nature. The wave-particle duality of light was an experimental phenomenon in search of a theory.

At the beginning of the twentieth century, Max Planck had used the concept of the wave nature of light to explain blackbody radiation. As a wave, light has a wavelength (the distance between crests) and a corresponding frequency (the number of crests passing a point in a given amount of time). Planck had shown that the energy of light of a particular frequency had definite amounts of energy for that frequency, that is, energy is quantized. This seemed to favor the belief that light was wavelike in nature. Nevertheless, five years later, in 1905, when Albert Einstein explained the photoelectric effect, he reasoned that light behaved as particles. Einstein used Planck's theory of quantized light to explain why light striking the surface of certain metals resulted in the ejection of electrons from that metal, only by certain frequencies of light. He pictured the light striking the metal surface as particles of light, or photons, with sufficient energy to eject electrons.

The wave-particle nature of light was constantly debated and seemed dependent upon the experiment being performed. For example, the dispersion of white light into its component colors by a prism is a result of the wave nature of light. The photoelectric effect of light able to eject electrons as a result of a stream of photons points to the particle nature. Einstein had shown by his relativity theory that light could behave as both wave and particle and that the physical properties of each nature were related to each other. He showed that the momentum of the photon (a particle property) was related to the wavelength of the light (a wave property). Einstein's result demonstrated that light has wave and particle duality.

Louis de Broglie had been studying Planck's theories of quantized light and Einstein's wave-particle concept of light. He wrote several papers calling attention to the dual behavior of light. De Broglie wished to provide a mechanical explanation for the wave-particle duality. Thus, he needed to find a mechanical reason for a particle—the photon—to have an energy that was determined by a wave, or rather by the frequency of that wave. While thinking about light, the idea occurred to de Broglie that matter (a particle) might have a wave nature also. At about this same time, Niels Bohr had revealed a theory for the electronic structure of atoms. Bohr's theory was that the electrons in an atom were restricted to particular energy levels and positions, called orbitals. Only by exact additions of unit amounts of energy could the energy and orbital of an electron be changed. De Broglie was struck by the analogy of Bohr's orbital energies to standing waves. De Broglie had found an example of wave-particle duality in matter.

De Broglie's explanations of the wave-particle duality of matter were used as a thesis dissertation for his doctorate in physics. He presented it before the Faculty of Sciences at the University of Paris in 1923. His theory demonstrated that matter, as well as light, had a wavelike nature. De Broglie noticed that the momentum of the electron orbitals proposed by Bohr were whole number units of a fundamental quantity, Planck's constant. He knew that standing waves had unit changes in their momentum also. A standing wave can be thought of as a string, fixed at both ends, that is plucked. The string will oscillate back and forth, yet some points will remain at rest. The number of rest points will increase as the frequency of the vibration increases. De Broglie reasoned that the Bohr orbitals could be seen as a circular string, a snake swallowing its own tail. He discovered that the matter waves he had proposed fit Bohr's electron orbits exactly. He also found that the momentum and wavelength of his matter waves were related, similar to that of light. He had succeeded in explaining Bohr's orbits. Each orbit was a steady wave pattern. These orbits had determined and fixed sizes so that these distinct "quantized" wave patterns could exist.

When de Broglie somewhat reluctantly submitted his dissertation, the faculty at the University of Paris were unsure of the use of strings to explain Bohr's orbits. They asked Einstein to judge the acceptability of the dissertation. Einstein's reply was, "It may look crazy, but it is really sound!" The thesis was accepted, and later de Broglie was awarded a Nobel Prize.

De Broglie had discovered that light and matter had particle-wave duality. In the case of light, this was a confirmation of experimental observation. In the case of matter, this was an as-yet theoretical idea. Its importance, however, was at the subatomic level of matter, that of the electron surrounding a nucleus in the atom. This is the domain of quantized phenomena, infinitesimal sizes and speeds approaching that of light. Only under these conditions do these phenomena become observable. Bohr had shown that on the larger scale of observable phenomena, these quantum differences were so small as to be immeasurable. At the level of the fundamental properties, de Broglie had begun a new revolution.

Impact of Event

De Broglie had shown that light and matter must be considered as either waves or particles. This leads to an awkward result. If one wishes to locate an electron with a small distance, a wavelength of light at least that small must be used. When that photon and electron interact, however, the electron will acquire some of the momentum of the photon. The very act of locating the electron leads to a change of its momentum. For a more accurate determination of the electron location, a smaller wavelength photon is required. Thus, that photon will have more energy, and more momentum will be transferred to the electron. Werner Heisenberg carried out a careful analysis of this process in the mid-1920's. He showed that it is not possible to determine exactly how much momentum is transferred to the electron. This means that any attempt to locate an electron within a certain region causes an uncertainty in the momentum of the electron. This is called the Heisenberg uncertainty principle and is a fundamental principle of nature. The wave nature of a particle prohibits the simultaneous measurement of its position and momentum. The Heisenberg uncertainty principle is of no consequence for everyday, macroscopic objects. Yet, it has very important consequences in dealing with atomic and subatomic particles. Heisenberg's principle was a logical consequence of de Broglie's theory of the wave-particle duality of matter.

De Broglie's waves had offered a picture of what was occurring inside an atom. A way to visualize the shifting patterns of the wave was needed when it changed energy and produced light. Erwin Schrödinger, an Austrian physicist, found a mathematical equation that explained the changing wave patterns inside an atom. Schrödinger's equation provides a continuous mathematical description of the wave-particle duality of matter. He viewed the atom as analogous to de Broglie's vibrating string. The movement of the electron from one orbit to another was a simple change in the standing waves of the string. In a musical string, this occurs as the harmony of two wave patterns, the result being the differences in the frequency of the two waves.

Unfortunately, physicists were not altogether comfortable with Schrödinger's wave equation. These waves were difficult to imagine, being mathematical waves described by mathematical functions. Despite its unimaginability, however, Schrödinger's wave proved indisputable because it explained a great many physical phenomena to which the classical model could no longer be applied. It was a successful mathematical way to explain light from any atom, vibrations of molecules, and the ability of gases to absorb heat at low temperatures. Schrödinger's picture, although complicated and dependent upon a nearly unimaginable wave function, was reasonable. His equation and understanding of the wave-particle duality of nature have spawned modern physics, quantum physics.

The understanding of the wave-particle duality of matter, as modeled by Schrödinger's equation, has been instrumental in the founding of modern quantum physics. Quantum physics has been responsible for many of the technological advances in the twentieth century. These advances are traceable to de Broglie's pronouncement of the wave-particle duality of matter.

Bibliography

Guillemin, Victor. *The Story of Quantum Mechanics*. New York: Charles Scribner's Sons, 1968. A nontechnical book that conveys factual information and insight into the ways professional scientists think and work. In addition to presenting the historical background of quantum mechanics, the text continues into the theories and models of atomic and subatomic particles. The end of the book concludes by considering the philosophical implications of quantum physics.

Hoffmann, Banesh. *The Strange Story of the Quantum*. 2d ed. New York: Dover, 1959. A nontechnical book that serves as a guide to the development of quantum mechanics. Written for the general reader, this small book is a treasure of insight into the persons, places, and pitfalls encountered in the early history of quantum physics. A "must read" for the nontechnical reader interested in the development of quantum physics.

Jammer, Max. *The Philosophy of Quantum Mechanics*. New York: John Wiley & Sons, 1974. A guide to the analysis of the concepts, philosophy, and interrelation of the mechanics and ideas of the new physics. In addition, a guide to the literature of the subject, containing many general and technical references. Self-contained in its scope and material, it provides the reader with information about references in quantum mechanics.

McQuarrie, Donald A. *Quantum Chemistry*. Mill Valley, Calif.: University Science Books, 1983. A textbook that traces the beginnings of quantum mechanics and utilizes the results in the study of molecules. Excellent text for background and conclusions based upon the earliest works in quantum physics. Short biographies of the principal characters in the development of the field add to the interest. Excellent treatment of the historical beginnings of quantum mechanics on a technical level.

Wolf, Fred Alan. *Taking the Quantum Leap*. San Francisco: Harper & Row, 1981. An outstanding book for the nonscientist about quantum physics. Traces the earliest debates and experiments concerning the philosophy and practice of physics. Brings the reader up to date concerning the impact of the work of Planck into the present day. Presented in a humanized view of science that is accurate, historical, and conceptual, leading the reader to a solid, nontechnical grasp and beyond. Another "must read" for anyone interested in quantum physics.

Scott A. Davis

Cross-References

Einstein Develops His Theory of the Photoelectric Effect (1905), p. 260; Bohr Writes a Trilogy on Atomic and Molecular Structure (1912), p. 507; Heisenberg Articulates the Uncertainty Principle (1927), p. 835.

COMPTON DISCOVERS THE WAVELENGTH CHANGE OF SCATTERED X RAYS

Categories of event: Physics and chemistry
Time: 1923
Locale: St. Louis, Missouri

Compton's explanation for the change in wavelength of X rays scattered from matter provided an important confirmation of the quantum theory of radiation

Principal personages:

ARTHUR HOLLY COMPTON (1892-1962), an American physicist, educator, and philosopher who was the cowinner of the 1927 Nobel Prize in Physics

SIR JOSEPH JOHN THOMSON (1856-1940), an English physicist and discoverer of the electron who was the winner of the 1906 Nobel Prize in Physics

CHARLES THOMSON REES WILSON (1869-1959), an English physicist and inventor of the Wilson cloud chamber who was a cowinner of the 1927 Nobel Prize in Physics

CHARLES GLOVER BARKLA (1877-1944), an English physicist who was a winner of the 1917 Nobel Prize in Physics

ERNEST RUTHERFORD (1871-1937), an English physicist who proposed the theory of the planetary atom and won the 1908 Nobel Prize in Chemistry

Summary of Event

The importance of the Compton effect to the fields of chemistry and physics can be appreciated only when it is understood in the context of early twentieth century science. By the end of the nineteenth century, a general feeling of complacency was experienced by physical scientists.

All material substances were known to be composed of molecules, which were specific combinations of atoms of the ninety or so elemental substances found in nature. The research of Sir Joseph John Thomson indicated clearly that the negatively charged electron was a constituent of all atoms which, because they are all neutral, had to have some type of positive particle also. Ernest Rutherford's famous experiment in which alpha particles were scattered from a thin film of gold provided evidence for his theory of atomic structure. Rutherford's atom was composed of a tiny, but massive, positive nucleus surrounded by space occupied by tiny electrons. Chemists and atomic physicists believed that they had a fairly clear picture of the structure of the material world.

Physicists were enamored of the laws of motion of Sir Isaac Newton, which had explained successfully the motion of objects that varied in size from the near microscopic to the planets in the solar system. Equally well accepted were the laws of

James Clerk Maxwell, which described the behavior of electromagnetic radiation. Set in this theory, light was seen as a type of electromagnetic wave phenomenon. The attitude of physicists was that the basic laws of nature had been discovered and that it was necessary only to continue their application in explaining natural phenomena.

One of the clear distinctions made by scientists by the end of the nineteenth century was the classification of natural phenomena as either particle or wave phenomena. Particles were thought of as bundles of matter possessing mass, which determines the way in which the particles respond to applied force. In addition to mass, two fundamental properties were associated with particles because of their motion. These are momentum and kinetic energy, both of which are conserved in the absence of interaction with some outside force. A particle of mass m and velocity v has kinetic energy equal to $mv^2/2$ and momentum equal to mv. During a collision (any interaction in which the particles exert forces on one another) between two particles, momentum is always conserved. In some collisions, known as elastic collisions, kinetic energy is conserved also. Conservation of kinetic energy and momentum requires only that the total of each quantity is the same after the collision as before. The particles involved may exchange all or some of their momentum and kinetic energy with one another. Moving particles, then, may be seen as a means of transporting energy from one place to another.

Another means of transporting energy is the wave; familiar examples are water waves, sound waves, and electromagnetic waves such as light. All waves are characterized by wavelength lambda (distance between two identical points on adjacent waves) and frequency v (number of waves per unit time). Waves can be unambiguously identified by their ability to interfere with each other. Whenever two harmonic waves of equal amplitude intersect at some point in a medium, the net effect is the sum of the two waves. If the waves are always in phase at the intersection point, the net wave is twice that of either wave; but, if they are out of phase, they cancel. Two wave systems interfering in a medium give a pattern of amplitudes that is constant in time. Whenever a wave moves around some object or passes through a small opening, an interference pattern between waves coming from different points near the edge of the barrier is set up. This is known as a diffraction pattern. Observation of interference and diffraction patterns is regarded as a confirming test of the wave nature of a phenomenon. There was no doubt in the minds of early twentieth century physicists that light was a wave phenomenon. Diffraction and interference patterns had been observed and used in wavelength measurements.

X rays were discovered by Wilhelm Conrad Röntgen in the mid-1890's, and Max von Laue demonstrated the diffraction of X rays by crystals in 1912. It was determined quickly that X rays (electromagnetic waves of wavelength much shorter than that of light) provided a powerful new tool for the investigation of matter. Thomson studied the scattering of X rays by matter using the theory that the X rays interacted with bound electrons, causing them to oscillate at the same frequency as the incident radiation. The oscillating electrons, in turn, reradiated the energy at the same frequency as the incident radiation. Charles Glover Barkla investigated this phenomenon and found that the scattered X rays were of two kinds: One type had the same wavelength as the incident radiation and the second type had a longer wavelength.

It is at this point that Arthur Holly Compton investigated this secondary type of scattered radiation. His explanation helped to change the direction of physics. Compton's career as a research physicist began in 1919 when, as a Fellow of the National Research Council, he studied at Rutherford's laboratory in Cambridge. He studied the scattering and absorption of gamma rays and observed that the scattered radiation was more absorbable than the primary. This observation led eventually to his discovery of the Compton effect. He thought that the increased absorption indicated a change in the wavelength of the scattered rays and, if light could be described as having particle-like behavior, a decrease in its momentum. Compton did not think that the accuracy of the gamma ray data was enough to allow him to defend a photonic interpretation with confidence.

After his year at Cambridge, Compton moved to Washington University, where he intended to extend his gamma-scattering experiments into the X-ray region. Using a Bragg crystal spectrometer, he was able to analyze the scattered and primary radiation with great precision. Compton used monochromatic X rays from a molybdenum source, which were scattered from a target of graphite (a form of carbon), and found that the scattered rays contained radiation that had the same wavelength as the incident radiation as well as radiation of a longer wavelength. The wavelength of this second type of scattered radiation varied in a systematic way with the scattering angle.

This change in wavelength could not be explained in terms of the classical theories of electrodynamics. In 1922, after all attempts to use classical explanations had failed, Compton arrived at his revolutionary quantum theory for the interaction. He treated the process as a collision between a free electron and an X-ray quantum having kinetic energy and momentum. Applying the laws of conservation to the collision, Compton was able to derive the equations for the Compton effect in the form in which they are used today and found exact agreement with his data. The kinetic energy and the momentum of the scattered photon were decreased by an amount equal exactly to that acquired by the electron, which then recoiled. When Compton first proposed his explanation, there was no experimental evidence for the recoil electron, but this evidence was provided shortly afterward by Charles Thomson Rees Wilson, who observed tracks in the cloud chamber, which could be explained in terms of Compton's theory.

Impact of Event

The Compton effect holds a position of primary importance in the development of modern physics. From its first discovery and explanation, it has stimulated the development of quantum mechanics by providing experimental evidence that classical mechanics and electrodynamics were powerless to explain. During the entire early period of the quantum theory (from 1920 to 1930), the Compton effect was a central phenomenon against which the theory could be tested. It provided conclusive proof that Albert Einstein's concept of the photon (introduced early in the 1900's to explain the photoelectric emission of electrons), having both energy and momentum, was correct. Also, it indicated that material particles have a wave nature and show interference effects. This wave-particle duality found in both radiation and matter lies at the heart of modern quantum theory.

This remarkable discovery had consequences that went far beyond the photon concept; it became the basis for Werner Heisenberg's uncertainty principle, one of the most important developments in quantum theory. To locate an electron, it must be irradiated with photons of high energy, since errors in position are minimized by radiation of short wavelength. To be seen, the photon must enter the objective of the observing microscope, which gives a range of directions because of the finite width of the opening. Since only the approximate direction of the photon is known after the collision, the recoil of the electron may be known only approximately. Attempts to increase accuracy of the position measurement increase uncertainty in the recoil momentum, since even shorter wavelengths must be used. The net result of this is that the more information one gains about one of these variables, the less is known about the other variable. This forms the essence of the uncertainty principle.

The Compton effect has played an important role in many diverse areas of science, such as radiation shielding in nuclear physics. A beam of radiation is attenuated as it passes through matter as the photons are absorbed or scattered by the material. One of the experimental facts that Compton found was that the relative intensities of the primary and secondary radiation depended on the wavelength of the exciting radiation. The importance of the processes involved in attenuating the beam depends on the photon energies. Information of this type is important in designing radiation shielding.

The Compton effect has been used directly in the early diagnosis of osteoporosis. This disease is indicated by changes in bone density. The Compton scattering of gamma rays from bone has an intensity that depends on the number of scattering centers. This, in turn, is related to the density of the bone material. Similar techniques have been developed for the diagnosis of lung diseases which affect tissue density.

Information about the electronic structure of molecules and crystals has been obtained from the Compton effect. A Doppler shift resulting from the motion of the electrons toward or away from the photon either adds or subtracts from the Compton shift. Extensive study of the line broadening because of this Doppler shift has provided physicists and chemists information about the momenta of electrons in matter.

Bibliography

Boorse, Henry A., and Lloyd Motz. "The Compton Effect." In *The World of the Atom*. New York: Basic Books, 1966. This chapter contains a brief description of the Compton effect and its importance to the development of physics. Included are a reprint of a 1962 essay on Compton by S. K. Allison published in *Science* and two of Compton's early papers. The papers are technical, but the first part of the chapter is accessible to most readers.

Heathcote, Niels H. de V. *Nobel Prize Winners in Physics, 1901-1950*. New York: Henry Schuman, 1953. The chapter on Compton contains a clear, nonmathematical description of the Compton effect. Compton's Nobel lecture is quoted extensively. Suitable for a wide audience.

Hendry, John. *The Creation of Quantum Mechanics and the Bohr-Pauli Dialogue*. Boston: D. Reidel, 1984. This book is a history of quantum mechanics. Although the mathematics are kept to a minimum, the text requires at least an introduction to quantum mechanics at the beginning college level in chemistry or physics. Contains several references to the Compton effect and its importance to American physicists.

Massey, Sir Harrie. *The New Age in Physics*. New York: Harper, 1960. This book gives the story of the development of twentieth century physics. It provides a clear and very interesting picture of the development of modern physics. The wave-particle question is discussed in the first two chapters, as are other topics important to the understanding of the Compton effect.

Stuewer, Roger H. *The Compton Effect: Turning Point in Physics*. New York: Science History Publications, 1975. This book is a detailed analysis of the theoretical and experimental work in the field of radiation physics, relating to the background, discovery, and impact of the Compton effect. Although somewhat mathematical, it could be appreciated by readers with a general background in college physics.

Grace A. Banks

Cross-References

Röntgen Wins the Nobel Prize for the Discovery of X Rays (1901), p. 118; Barkla Discovers the Characteristic X Rays of the Elements (1906), p. 309; Thomson Wins the Nobel Prize for the Discovery of the Electron (1906), p. 356; Rutherford Presents His Theory of the Atom (1912), p. 527; Einstein Completes His Theory of General Relativity (1915), p. 625.

ZWORYKIN DEVELOPS AN EARLY TYPE OF TELEVISION

Category of event: Applied science
Time: 1923
Locale: Pittsburgh, Pennsylvania

Zworykin's concept of an all-electronic television receiver foreshadowed the development of modern television systems

Principal personages:

VLADIMIR ZWORYKIN (1889-1982), a Soviet electronic engineer, director of the medical electronics center of the Rockefeller Institute for Medical Research, and recipient of the National Medal of Science in 1967

PAUL GOTTLIEB NIPKOW (1860-1940), a German engineer and inventor

ALAN A. CAMPBELL SWINTON (1863-1930), a Scottish engineer and Fellow of the Royal Society

HEINRICH HERTZ (1857-1894), a German physicist who was a professor of physics at Karlsruhe Polytechnic and the University of Bonn

GUGLIELMO MARCONI (1874-1937), an Italian physicist who received the 1909 Nobel Prize in Physics

CHARLES F. JENKINS (1867-1934), an American physicist, engineer, and inventor

Summary of Event

Although Vladimir Zworykin is popularly known as the father of television, his work in the 1920's actually built upon the contributions of numerous scientists and electrical engineers who began theorizing about possible applications of electricity as early as the 1830's. Antecedents of all-electronic television can be found in several different, but related, areas in electrical engineering. The invention of the telegraph in the 1830's demonstrated the possibility of modulating an electrical current to transmit coded signals; the invention of the telephone in 1876 showed that sound waves could be converted into electrical impulses and back again. Heinrich Hertz's measurements of electromagnetic waves in the late 1880's provided empirical evidence of earlier theoretical speculations about the nature of electricity. Guglielmo Marconi's work with radio is reported by Orrin Dunlap as having been a direct response to Marconi's reading of Hertz's paper. In any event, engineers and scientists who had been working on the electrical transmission of images by wire responded to the challenge of achieving the wireless projection of visual images almost simultaneously with the development of radio.

In 1894, an American inventor, Charles F. Jenkins, described a scheme for electrically transmitting moving pictures. Jenkins' idea, however, was only one of an already long tradition in electrical engineering of theoretical television systems. Even before invention of the telephone or detection of electromagnetic waves, scientists had begun to consider how images might be transmitted with electricity. American and European scientists began attempting to transmit still images over telegraph wires in the 1840's. In 1842, for example, the English physicist Alexander Bain invented an automatic copying telegraph for sending still pictures. Although Bain's system scanned images line by line, many early attempts assumed the simultaneous transmission of every portion of an image was necessary, and so involved multiple wires—that is, a separate electrical current for each point on the image. By the 1870's, wide recognition of persistence of vision—retention of a visual image for a short period of time after removal of the stimulus that produced it—led to experiments with systems in which the image to be projected was scanned line by line but required one wire only. Rapid scanning of images became the underlying principle of all television systems, both electromechanical and all-electronic.

Although almost sixty years were to pass between the emergence of the concept of scanning and the development of working all-electronic systems, electromechanical systems began to appear in the 1880's. In 1884, a German inventor, Paul Gottlieb Nipkow, patented a complete television system that utilized a mechanical sequential scanning system and a photoelectric cell sensitized with selenium for transmission. The selenium photoelectric cell converted the light values of the image being scanned into electrical impulses to be transmitted to a receiver where the process would be reversed: The electrical impulses led to light of varying brightnesses being produced and projected on to a rotating disk that was scanned to reproduce the original image. If the system—that is, the transmitter and the receiver—were in perfect synchronization and if the disk rotated quickly enough, persistence of vision enabled the viewer to see a complete image rather than a series of moving points of light.

As attempts to refine mechanical systems progressed, it became clear all possessed a major handicap: Because the image to be projected was mechanically scanned, a barrier existed regarding potential improvements in sensitivity. Edward Constant, a historian of technology, has referred to such barriers or perceived theoretical limitations as "presumptive anomalies" which could lead to revolutionary changes within a technology.

For a television image to be projected onto a screen of reasonable size and retain good quality and high resolution, any system employing only thirty to one hundred lines, as early mechanical systems did, would clearly be inadequate. A few systems were developed which utilized two hundred or more lines, but the difficulties these presented made the possibility of an all-electronic system increasingly attractive. These difficulties were not generally recognized until the early 1930's, when television began to move out of the laboratory and into commercial production. John Swift has noted that although inventors such as John L. Baird in England, who had developed a mechanical system based upon the Nipkow principle, and Jenkins in the United States were aware of Zworykin's all-electronic work for Westinghouse Electric Corporation and RCA (Radio Corporation of America), they continued to refine mechanical systems until the government intervened.

Many Americans witnessed television for the first time in the 1930's during demonstrations of Jenkins' motor-driven mechanical scanners. The receivers had a large glass bull's-eyelike screen, while Baird's system had been adopted for initial television broadcasts by the British Broadcasting Corporation. It was not until the English government set broadcast standards mandating high definition television that Baird's development work on those mechanical systems ceased.

Interest in all-electronic television paralleled interest in mechanical systems, but solutions to technical problems proved harder to achieve. In 1908, a Scottish engineer, Alan A. Campbell Swinton, proposed what was essentially an all-electronic television system. Swinton theorized that the use of magnetically deflected cathode-ray tubes for both the transmitter and receiver in a system was possible. In 1911, Swinton formally presented his idea to the Röntgen Society in London, but the technology available did not allow for practical experiments.

In 1923, Zworykin filed a patent application for the iconoscope, or television transmission tube. His interest in all-electronic television dated back to his days in the Soviet Union as a student of Boris L. Rosing, in prerevolutionary St. Petersburg. Zworykin credited Rosing's work with cathode-ray tubes as a major influence on his own ideas. Zworykin's patent application for a camera tube differed from Swinton's 1911 plan, in that rather than disclosing a mosaic of rubidium cubes, Zworykin disclosed a layer of photoelectric material. On March 17, 1924, Zworykin applied for a patent for a two-way system. The first cathode-ray tube receiver had a cathode, modulating grid, an anode, and a fluorescent screen. Condenser plates produced electrostatic horizontal deflection, and coils produced magnetic vertical deflection.

According to Albert Abramson, Zworykin later admitted the results were very poor and the system, as shown, was still far removed from a practical television system. Zworykin's employers were so unimpressed that they admonished him to forget television and work on something more useful. Zworykin's interest in television was thereafter confined to his nonworking hours, as he spent the next year working on photographic sound recording. It was not until the late 1920's that he was able to devote his full attention to television. Ironically, Westinghouse had by then resumed research in television, but Zworykin was not part of the team. After he returned from a trip to France in 1928 where he had witnessed an exciting demonstration of an electrostatic tube, Westinghouse indicated it was not interested. This lack of corporate support in Pittsburgh led Zworykin to approach RCA. Zworykin reportedly demonstrated his system to the Institute of Radio Engineers at Rochester, New York, on November 18, 1929, claiming to have developed a working picture tube, a tube that would revolutionize television development; RCA recognized the potential.

Impact of Event

The picture tube, or kinescope, developed by Zworykin changed the history of television. Abramson noted that the kinescope made it possible to have a practical receiver in the home of the viewer, a device that the average person could operate, that required no technical knowledge to use, and that could be viewed under normal lighting conditions. Within a few years, mechanical systems disappeared and television technology began to utilize systems similar to Zworykin's by use of cathode-ray tubes at both ends of the system. At the transmitter, the image is focused upon a mosaic screen composed of light-sensitive cells. A stream of electrons sweeps the image and each cell sends off an electric current impulse as it is hit by the electrons, the light and shade of the focused image regulating the amount of current. This string of electrical impulses, after amplification and modification into ultrahigh-frequency wavelengths, is broadcast by antenna to be picked up by any attuned receiver, where it is retransformed into a moving picture in the cathode-tube receiver. The cathode-ray tubes contain no moving parts, as the electron stream is guided entirely by electric attraction. Although both the iconoscope and the kinescope were far from perfect when Zworykin initially demonstrated them, they set the stage for all future television development.

This television development has had an impact far beyond mere popular entertainment systems. Influential though television broadcasting may be upon everyday lives, cathode-ray tubes also have had many other important applications. Although Zworykin developed the cathode-ray tube to serve as part of a broadcasting system, and saw television as analogous to radio, it definitely has not been limited to this one use. Military radar systems, for example, display information on cathode-ray tubes, as do numerous other information display systems. Cathode-ray tubes have proved to be especially valuable in electronics applications, as the use of computers has become more widespread. Every computer terminal is now paired with a monitor— that is, a CRT or cathode-ray tube—so that the operator has immediate access to a visual display for both the input and output data.

Cathode-ray tubes have been used also in experimental communications systems similar to telephones, by including visual images along with sound, and in security systems in a variety of settings. What Zworykin may have envisioned as a simple entertainment device available for home use has spread far beyond its limited, originally intended, application. The cathode-ray tube has uses that range from supermarket cash registers to closed-circuit television security systems to large-screen color television sets, now equipped with the capability of providing sound in stereo. Zworykin's developments served as the beginning of modern television.

Bibliography

Abramson, Albert. *The History of Television, 1880-1941.* Jefferson, N.C.: McFarland, 1987. This book contains a comprehensive history of television in the United States, Europe, and the Soviet Union. The text includes endnotes, a bibliography, and a glossary.

Constant, Edward W., II. *Origins of the TurboJet Revolution.* Baltimore: The Johns Hopkins University Press, 1980. Constant utilizes a case study of the development of the turbojet to speculate about the origins of technological change. Although the work does not deal directly with television, it provides interesting insights into the processes of invention and innovation, which are applicable in any field.

De Forest, Lee. *Television: Today and Tomorrow.* New York: Dial Press, 1942. This book provides a thorough explanation of the technical principles of television. Written for the layperson by an electrical engineer who was responsible for many of the innovations that made television possible.

Dunlap, Orrin E., Jr. *Radio's 100 Men of Science.* New York: Harper & Brothers, 1944. This book provides brief biographies of one hundred scientists and engineers associated with the history of electricity, radio, and television, including Luigi Galvani, Oliver Heaviside, Nipkow, Zworykin, and Philo T. Farnsworth. Excellent reference work.

Hubbell, Richard W. *Four Thousand Years of Television: The Story of Seeing at a Distance.* New York: G. P. Putnam's Sons, 1942. Hubbell traces the history of television back to the invention of papyrus paper in ancient Egypt. Provides lucid explanations of the technical aspects of television and its ancestors.

McMahon, Morgan E. *A Flick of the Switch, 1930-1950.* Palos Verdes Peninsula, Calif.: Vintage Radio, 1975. Although this book primarily contains a pictorial history of radio and television, it also provides clear illustrations of the underlying concepts of both electromechanical and all-electronic television systems.

Shiers, George, ed. *Technical Development of Television.* New York: Arno Press, 1977. This book includes both histories of television and reprints of original articles by Zworykin, Jenkins, and others. The evaluations by observers of competing television systems in the 1920's and 1930's are particularly enlightening.

Swift, John. *Adventure in Vision: The First Twenty-five Years of Television.* London: John Lehmann, 1950. Details the history of television in England, the work of John L. Baird, and the demise of low-definition mechanical systems. Lavishly illustrated, with both line drawings and photographs.

Nancy Farm Mannikko

Cross-References

Fleming Files a Patent for the First Vacuum Tube (1904), p. 255; Edison Introduces the Kinetophone to Show the First Talking Pictures (1913), p. 537; Warner Bros. Introduces Talking Motion Pictures (1926), p. 820; The First Color Television Broadcast Takes Place (1940), p. 1166.

KAHN DEVELOPS A MODIFIED SYPHILIS TEST AND THE UNIVERSAL SEROLOGIC TEST

Category of event: Medicine
Time: 1923 and 1951
Locale: University of Michigan, Ann Arbor

Kahn developed a test for simplified detection of the venereal disease syphilis, which led to better syphilis control and to Kahn's universal serologic test, an advance in immunology

> *Principal personages:*
> REUBEN LEON KAHN (1887-1974), a Soviet-born American serologist and immunologist who developed an improved test for syphilis and pioneered the study of immunology, including the universal blood test
> AUGUST VON WASSERMANN (1866-1925), a German physician and bacteriologist who originated the Wassermann test for syphilis

Summary of Event

Syphilis is one of the chief venereal diseases, a group of diseases whose name derives from Venus, the Roman goddess of love. The term "venereal" arose from the idea that the diseases were transmitted solely by sexual contact with an infected individual. Although syphilis is almost always caught in this way, it occasionally arises after contact with objects used by syphilis-infected people in highly unhygienic surroundings, particularly in the underdeveloped countries of the world.

It is believed by many that syphilis was introduced to Europe by the members of Christopher Columbus' crew—supposedly after they were infected by sexual contact with West Indian women—during their voyages of exploration. Columbus is reported to have died of heart and brain problems very similar to symptoms produced by advanced syphilis. At that time, according to many historians, syphilis spread rapidly over sixteenth century Europe.

New diseases are always devastating, partly because of the lack of immunity, and early syphilis was no exception to the rule. Regrettably, the limited medicine of the time was of little help, and the early death rate from the disease was high. Every country blamed the high incidence of syphilis on some other nation (for example, the French called syphilis the Spanish disease, and vice versa). It was not until 1530 that the Italian physician Fracastor coined the name "syphilis" in an epic poem he wrote.

The origin of syphilis in the Western Hemisphere is supported by the reported paleontological evidence of its existence in pre-Columbian skeletons throughout North, South, and Central America. In contrast, no such evidence has been obtained—according to proponents of this theory—in the pre-Columbian remains found in

Europe or Asia. Another group of researchers propose that this theory of the origin of syphilis is not correct, and controversy over the issue still exists.

Modern syphilis is much milder than the original disease, and relatively uncommon. Yet, if it is not identified and treated appropriately, syphilis can be devastating and even fatal. It can also be passed from pregnant mothers to their unborn children. In those cases, the afflicted children (congenital syphilitics) will develop serious health problems that can include paralysis, insanity, and heart disease. Therefore, the understanding, detection, and cure of syphilis are important worldwide.

Syphilis is caused by a spiral-shaped germ, called a spirochete, *Treponema pallidum*. Spirochetes enter the body through breaks in the skin or through the mucous membranes, regardless of how they are transmitted. Once spirochetes enter the body, they rapidly spread. During the first four to six weeks after infection, syphilis—said to be in its primary phase—is very contagious. During this time, it is identified by the appearance of a sore, or chancre, at the entry site of the infecting spirochetes.

The chancre disappears quickly, and within six to twenty-four weeks, the disease shows itself as a skin rash, feelings of malaise, and other flulike symptoms (secondary syphilis). These problems also disappear quickly in most cases, and here is where the real trouble—latent syphilis—begins. In latent syphilis, now totally without symptoms (asymptomatic), spirochetes spread through the body and may localize in the brain or the heart. When this happens, they produce paralysis, mental derangement, and/or death.

Also, carriers of latent syphilis can infect husband, wife, or even babies in the uterus. For these reasons, it is very important that syphilis be identified and cured. The cure today is simple and only requires treatment with penicillin or other types of antibiotics. Very frequently, such treatment is carried out in venereal disease clinics or in the office of a family physician. Because one of the most serious results of syphilis is infection of unborn children to produce congenital syphilis, it is required that Americans wishing to marry are shown to be free of the disease before a marriage license is issued, and obstetricians often test their pregnant patients for the disease routinely. This syphilis detection is particularly important because no vaccine is yet available against the disease.

The first viable test for syphilis was originated by August von Wassermann in 1906. In this test, blood samples are taken and treated in a medical laboratory. The treatment of the samples is based on the fact that the blood of afflicted persons has formed antibodies to fight *Treponema pallidum*, and these antibodies can react with other substances (an extract of lipid—fatlike—body chemicals) that cause changes in the blood component called complement. When this reaction occurs, complement is said to be "fixed" and the test is positive. After syphilis is cured, the antibodies disappear and complement is no longer fixed, so the Wassermann test becomes negative. The Wassermann test is a very useful indicator of syphilis in 95 percent of all infected persons. The positive test is flocculation—or clumping—visible by use of a microscope or by visual inspection.

The Wassermann test was very time-consuming—requiring a two-day incubation period—complex, and somewhat lacking in sensitivity. In 1923, Reuben Leon Kahn developed a modified syphilis test, "the standard Kahn test," that was simpler, faster, and more sensitive. This test was complete after a few minutes, and it was based on the reaction of serum from syphilitics with an extract of certain lipid components of beef heart. By 1925, Kahn's test had become the standard syphilis test of the United States Navy and later became a worldwide test for the detection of the disease.

Kahn soon realized that his test was not perfect and that in some cases, related to other diseases, false positive reactions and false negative reactions occurred. This led him to a broader study of the immune reactions that produced the Kahn test. He investigated the role of various tissues in immunity, as differentiated from the role of blood antibodies and white blood cells. Kahn showed, for example, that different tissues of immunized or nonimmunized animals possessed differing immunologic capabilities. Furthermore, the immunologic capabilities of test animals varied with their age, being very limited in newborns and increasing as they matured.

This effort led, by 1951, to Kahn's "universal serological reaction," a precipitation reaction in which blood serum was tested against reagent composed of tissue lipids. Kahn viewed it as a "potential serologic indicator of various situations in health and in different diseases." This effort is viewed as an important landmark in the development of the science of immunology.

Impact of Event

At the time when Kahn developed his standard Kahn test for syphilis, the Wassermann test was used all over the world for the diagnosis of syphilis. As has been noted, one of the great advantages of the standard Kahn test was its speed, minutes versus days. For example, in October, 1923, Kahn is reported to have tested forty serum samples in fifteen minutes.

As pointed out by W. Montague Cobb, Kahn's scientific contribution represents three investigative careers: The first was the development of a practical, rapid precipitation test for syphilis and special procedures that helped to clarify reactions with lipid antigens (1920 to 1928). The second was a study of tissue immunity that identified differences of tissue localization of bacteria and foreign proteins in test animals of different ages and immune states (1930 to 1957). The third was a study of radiation effects on this tissue localization (1957 to 1973). These efforts resulted in more than 170 scientific publications. Kahn carried out his endeavors at the Michigan Department of Health, the University of Michigan, and Howard University.

Kahn is, however, most widely known for his efforts in the serological testing for syphilis. Recognition of his efforts there include honorary degrees and awards. In 1913, Kahn received an honorary M.D. from the University of Athens (Greece), followed by more degrees from Valparaiso University (Valparaiso, Indiana) and the Institutum Divi Thomae (Cincinatti, Ohio). His awards include the annual prize of the American Association for the Advancement of Science (1933) and medals from the Phi Lambda Kappa fraternity (1938 and 1957). Furthermore, the Michigan State Legislature passed a resolution in 1931 honoring Kahn's accomplishments and ideals, and he was elected to the Michigan Health Council Hall of Fame in 1965. In 1965, it was announced that a Reuben L. Kahn Laboratory of Immunology was to be established at Israel's Hebrew University Medical School.

Kahn also received memberships in many learned societies for his efforts. These include the Society for Experimental Biology and Medicine, the American Medical Association, the American Association of Immunologists, the Michigan Academy of Sciences, and the American Association of Pathologists and Bacteriologists.

Kahn's efforts have been important to immunology and to medicine. Among the consequences of his endeavors was the stimulation of other developments in the field, including the VDRL test (originated by the Venereal Disease Research Laboratory), which has replaced the Kahn test as one of the most often used screening tests for syphilis. Even more specific syphilis tests exist today, including a fluorescent antibody test for the antibody to *Treponema pallidum*.

Bibliography

Brown, William J. *Syphilis: Modern Diagnosis and Management*. Washington, D.C.: The Public Health Service, 1961. A short text designed as a primer for physicians by the Chief of the Venereal Disease Branch of the U.S. Centers for Disease Control. Explains the tools of diagnosis and management of syphilis, the course of the disease, problems associated with congenital syphilis, and other topics. Provides an annotated bibliography.

Cobb, W. Montague. "Reuben Leon Kahn, D.Sc., LL.D., M.D., Ph.D.—1887." *Journal of the National Medical Association* 63 (September, 1971): 388-394. An interesting article that describes Kahn as a scientist and as a person. One of the few available sources of biographical material. Gives Kahn's complete publication list and insight into his youth, education, and highlights of his life. Both pleasant and informative reading.

Davidson, Israel, and B. B. Wells. *Clinical Diagnosis by Laboratory Methods*. 13th ed. Philadelphia: W. B. Saunders, 1963. A compendium of clinical laboratory methodology. Chapters 17 and 18, on the serodiagnostic tests for syphilis and diseases other than syphilis, are particularly useful to the reader who wishes to compare and to understand the various methods used. Each chapter has copious references.

Kahn, Reuben L. *The Kahn Test: A Practical Guide*. Baltimore: Williams & Wilkins, 1928. Presents a summary of the precipitation phenomenon in syphilis and a detailed discussion of the technical use of the Kahn test. Meant as a guide for laboratory workers, including apparatus, reagents, standardization of the antigen, use of the test, procedure, and special aspects. Gives a useful overview of the area.

_____. "Rapid Precipitation Phase of the Kahn Test for Syphilis, with New Method for Indicating Results." *Journal of the American Medical Association* 81 (July 14, 1923): 88-92. The original report of the Kahn test. Details the methodology and equipment utilized; indicates the advantages of the test over older methods and over Kahn's own earlier efforts. Provides a useful overview.

_____. *Universal Serologic Reaction in Health and Disease*. New York: Commonwealth Fund, 1951. Presents data the author believes indicate that serologic reactions with lipid antigen are widely applicable in health and disease. Presented to "open the door to study of its value and its limitations as a serologic indicator in various situations in health and disease."

Parran, Thomas. *Shadow on the Land: Syphilis*. New York: Reynal and Hitchcock, 1937. Describes the contemporary impact of syphilis on the United States, on public health, and on other public problems. Includes a history of syphilis, its occurrence in America and other countries, and aspects of syphilis and its effects on society and individuals, including the congenital syphilis passed on to infants by infected mothers.

Stansfield, William D. *Serology and Immunology: A Clinical Approach*. New York: Macmillan, 1981. Contains a comprehensive chapter on the etiology and serology of syphilis. Although highly technical, also a rewarding information source for the reader who wishes methodologic details. Contains information on many other related aspects of serology and immunology.

Turner, Thomas B. "Syphilis." In *McGraw-Hill Encyclopedia of Science and Technology*, edited by Sybil P. Parker. 6th ed. 20 vols. New York: McGraw-Hill, 1987. A brief article on syphilis that touches many areas in a succinct manner. Explores the causative organism, development of the disease, and its identification, treatment, and prevention. Includes references for additional information on antibodies, complement-fixation, serology, and sexually transmitted diseases.

Sanford S. Singer

Cross-References

Ehrlich and Metchnikoff Conduct Pioneering Research in Immunology (1908), p. 422; Ehrlich Introduces Salvarsan as a Cure for Syphilis (1910), p. 476; Fleming Discovers Penicillin in Molds (1928), p. 873; Florey and Chain Develop Penicillin as an Antibiotic (1940), p. 1171; Hodgkin Solves the Structure of Penicillin (1944), p. 1240.

ZDANSKY DISCOVERS PEKING MAN

Category of event: Anthropology
Time: Summer, 1923
Locale: Chou-K'ou-tien, China

The tooth found by Zdansky was the first evidence that Homo erectus *had existed outside Java*

Principal personages:
OTTO ZDANSKY, an Austrian paleontologist who was sent to China by the Swedish Paleontological Institute of Uppsala and discovered Peking man

JOHAN GUNNAR ANDERSSON (1874-1960), a Swedish mining expert who was appointed to advise the Chinese government and the original excavator at Chou-K'ou-tien

DAVIDSON BLACK (1884-1934), a Canadian professor of anatomy who named *Sinanthropus pekinensis* and promoted major excavations at Chou-K'ou-tien

FRANZ WEIDENREICH (1873-1948), an anthropologist from the University of Chicago who directed excavations and described finds after Black's death

WENG CHUNG PEI (1904-   ), a Chinese paleontologist who discovered the first Peking man skull in 1929

Summary of Event

The story of the discovery (and subsequent loss) of Peking man is one of the most engrossing in the history of anthropology. It began in 1899 when K. A. Haberer, physician to the German legation at Peking, found his movements seriously restricted by the violent Boxer Rebellion and wisely restricted his avocation of fossil hunting to urban drugstores. (It had long been traditional in China to grind up vertebrate mammalian fossils and use them for medicine.) Haberer's soon-voluminous collection was then sent in several shipments to Munich, where his friend Max Schlosser described them in a monograph *Die fossilen Säugethiere Chinas*, 1903 (*Fossil Primates of China*, 1924). All the fossils in the collection were mammalian—no reptiles or birds—and one particularly distinctive tooth seemed to be either apelike or human. Eventually, it proved to be that of a prehistoric ape, but as a significant body of evidence from a hitherto little known locality the collection as a whole, and the enigmatic tooth especially, aroused interest throughout the West, in large part because Schlosser boldly predicted that some new form of prehistoric fossil would soon be found in China. Nothing further took place, however, until 1918, when Johan Gunnar Andersson turned to professional fossil collecting in China on behalf of Swedish institutions. When his discoveries proved to be not only abundant but also interesting, Otto Zdansky, a professionally trained paleontologist, was sent to China by the Swedish Paleontological Institute of Uppsala to improve the scientific quality of Andersson's work.

Arriving in the summer of 1921, Zdansky began operations of his own at an abandoned limestone quarry some 48 kilometers southwest of Peking (now Beijing), near a village called Chou-K'ou-tien (now Zhoukoudian). Andersson had already described the site two years before, and recommended it to Zdansky. The site was known locally as Chicken Bone Hill. After excavations began, however, Zdansky was told by his workmen of a richer site, Dragon Bone Hill, adjacent to another abandoned quarry on the other side of the village. On his first visit to the site, Zdansky was accompanied by Andersson, who immediately noticed a number of incongruous quartz fragments and identified them as chipped tools. Zdansky, however, did not agree that the fragments were tools.

Later, while excavating by himself in 1923, Zdansky found a single molar tooth at Dragon Bone Hill, the first fossil evidence of Peking man. Curiously enough, however, he did not inform Andersson of his find (relations between the two men were somewhat strained) and made no mention of it in his publications until 1926, when he had returned to Sweden. By this time, Zdansky's long-time patron (as chairman of the Swedish China Research Committee), Crown Prince Gustav Adolf, was scheduled to visit China. Asked to contribute finds, Zdansky informed Andersson of the two teeth he had earlier discovered (a second example having turned up before he left China). At a reception for the Crown Prince in Peking on October 22, 1926, Andersson, in turn, informed Gustav Adolf and the world. The news caused a sensation everywhere in the educated world, as Peking man (so named at this time) was regarded as the oldest form of humanity then known.

Among those present at the Peking meeting was Davidson Black, a professor of anatomy at Peking Union Medical College who had long been interested in the biological history of humankind. Without having seen Zdansky's actual specimens (which were still in Sweden), he wrote two short papers proclaiming that "the actual presence of early man in Eastern Asia is no longer a matter of conjecture" and concluding that the hypothesis of humans having originated in Asia was now considerably substantiated. (In a more cautious paper of his own, Zdansky pointedly failed to endorse either assertion, regarding the teeth as only probably human and the evidence as a whole too scant to support any far-reaching conclusions.) With support from the Crown Prince, the Geological Survey of China, and the Rockefeller Foundation, Black now undertook a further round of excavations at Chou-K'ou-tien. Having accepted an appointment at Cairo University, Zdansky declined to head the project and was replaced by Birger Bohlin, another Swedish paleontologist. Only three days before the end of the first season's work, on October 16, 1927, Bohlin found a beautifully preserved left lower molar tooth. On the basis of only three teeth, two of which he had never seen, Black was confident to propose a new hominid genus called *Sinanthropus pekinensis.*

Despite extensive efforts, further excavations yielded nothing of fundamental importance until December, 1929, when Black's Chinese assistant Weng Chung Pei found an almost complete skull of Peking man partially embedded in a cave. This skull, jawbone fragments found earlier, various teeth, and a large collection of non-human fossils from the site were described and summarized by Black (and several coauthors) in his best-known publication, *Fossil Man in China* (1933). After Black's premature death in 1934, however, a comparison of the skull that Pei had found, and fragments discovered by Eugène Dubois in Java (known as Java man), were seen to be so nearly identical that separate designations for the two finds seemed inappropriate. The name *Sinanthropus* was therefore discarded in favor of *Homo erectus*, which applied to both examples.

Between 1934 and 1937, when military conditions forced a halt, continuing excavations at Chou-K'ou-tien revealed a wonderful collection of further skulls, jaws, teeth, and even some limb bones. Franz Weidenreich then studied, described, and made casts of these specimens in a series of admirably competent monographs. In April, 1941, he brought the casts, photographs, and notes he had made of them with him to the United States. In December, 1941, an attempt was made to evacuate the precious fossils from Peking to a waiting American ship. Unfortunately, war between Japan and the United States broke out, forcing the interruption of the shipment, and the precious fossils disappeared.

Impact of Event

The most immediate consequence of the discovery of Peking man was to confirm—with fossil evidence now, for the first time—a long-prevalent belief that humankind had originated in Asia. Earlier work in archaeology (the discovery of the Sumerians by Sir Leonard Woolley in particular) had already established Asia as the home of human civilization. It was more logical, then, to assume it had been the original habitat for uncivilized humankind. It is believed today that humankind originated in Africa, as Charles Darwin had predicted. The first significant fossil evidence in support of Africa was the discovery of *Australopithecus* (the Taung child) by Raymond Arthur Dart in 1925. *Australopithecus* was still not fully human, and for some may never have been part of human ancestry at all. The more obviously human *Sinanthropus* distracted attention away from *Australopithecus* and the African origins hypothesis, thereby delaying its acceptance. It became somewhat more difficult for the early African discoverers, such as Robert Bloom and L. S. B. Leakey, to obtain a hearing for their beliefs.

Prior to its identification as *Homo erectus*, moreover, Peking man further complicated human genealogy by appearing to be a separate genus. Leakey cleverly utilized this perception in his book *Adam's Ancestors* (1934), in which he argued that the known diversity of prehistoric human types (Java man, Peking man, the since discredited Piltdown man, and the since redated Kanam man) were evidence of an extremely long period of prior evolution and therefore pushed human origins back into the Miocene epoch. Eventually, further (and more correctly interpreted) discoveries by the Leakeys and others would indeed put *Homo erectus* more toward the end of human evolution than at the beginning. The fact that *Homo erectus* had been found both in Java and China attested the migratory diversity of early man and tended to affirm his unity.

Finally, discoveries in the cave and quarry deposits of Chou-K'ou-tien were revolutionary in that they offered more information regarding the daily living of human ancestors than any previous fossil evidence had done. Peking man, for example, had used fire, but perhaps without knowing how to make it. He was, moreover, a cannibal and a primitive toolmaker. Many speculations followed as to what life in the caves must have been like. Whatever his merits, Peking man was the first opportunity given reputable scientists to study not only an early human but also the society that may have been created. Theorizing upon the evolution of human culture and the origins of present-day habits, beliefs, and institutions became popular. Public interest in the work of fossil anthropologists accordingly increased, as did a willingness to fund their efforts.

Bibliography

Black, Davidson, et al. *Fossil Man in China: The Choukoutien Cave Deposits, with a Synopsis of Our Present Knowledge of the Late Cenozoic in China.* Peiping: The Geological Survey of China, 1933. Though intended for specialists, Black's classic account is necessary to any serious consideration of his work. The synopsis is in three parts: The Chou-K'ou-tien Deposits and the Late Cenozoic of China; *Sinanthropus* Skeletal Remains, with a Note on Other North China Fossil Hominids; and *Sinanthropus* Cultural Remains, with a Summary of Other Ancient Cultures in North China. A useful bibliography of early papers is included.

Day, Michael H. *Guide to Fossil Man.* 4th ed. Chicago: University of Chicago Press, 1986. Day is unsurpassed as a source of current information regarding any type of fossil. The major problem with all books in this fast-moving field is that they quickly become out of date. Thus, other works should be compared to ensure that the latest finds, identifications, and interpretations have been taken into consideration.

Lewin, Roger. *Bones of Contention: Controversies in the Search for Human Origins.* New York: Simon & Schuster, 1987. A one-time close associate of the Leakeys, Lewin is primarily concerned with the history of discovery in Africa and how finds struggled for acceptance in the learned world. He has little to say about the discovery of Peking man, as such, but usually emphasizes its originally negative impact upon the African researchers.

Reader, John. *Missing Links: The Hunt for Earliest Man.* Boston: Little, Brown, 1981. Though also primarily concerned with Africa, Reader surveys the entire topic in chronological order, his first five chapters (of twelve) dealing with Neanderthal man, Java man, Piltdown man, *Australopithecus*, and Peking man. No other book so adequately reconstructs the context in which Peking man emerged, and no one retells the story of its discovery and loss more reliably. Excellent photographs and a very helpful bibliography are included.

Wendt, Herbert. *In Search of Adam: The Story of Man's Quest for the Truth About His Earliest Ancestors.* Translated by James Cleugh. Boston: Houghton Mifflin, 1955. Even though it is dated, this popular account is comprehensive and well illustrated; the section on Peking man remains adequate for a brief book.

Dennis R. Dean

Cross-References

Boule Reconstructs the First Neanderthal Skeleton (1908), p. 428; Dart Discovers the First Recognized Australopithecine Fossil (1924), p. 780; Weidenreich Reconstructs the Face of Peking Man (1937), p. 1096; Scientists Date a *Homo sapiens* Fossil at Ninety-two Thousand Years (1987), p. 2341.

HUBBLE DETERMINES THE DISTANCE
TO THE ANDROMEDA NEBULA

Category of event: Astronomy
Time: 1924
Locale: Mount Wilson Observatory, California

Hubble used the Cepheid variables to determine the distance to the Andromeda galaxy, which eventually led to the development of the big bang theory

Principal personages:

EDWIN POWELL HUBBLE (1889-1953), an American astronomer and Rhodes scholar who was well known for his studies on nebulas

HENRIETTA SWAN LEAVITT (1868-1921), an American astronomer who discovered that Cepheids are related to their absolute brightness

GEORGES LEMAÎTRE (1894-1966), a Belgian astronomer and civil engineer who formulated the big bang theory

HARLOW SHAPLEY (1885-1972), an American astronomer and director of Harvard Observatory

WILLEM DE SITTER (1872-1934), a Dutch astronomer who studied the expanding universe

Summary of Event

The question of how the cosmos began has always fascinated humanity. The Babylonians measured the positions of stars and the planets and concluded that those bodies affected human lives. Their answer was based on myths and therefore was not scientific. The ancient Greeks were the first to explain it in a scientific manner: The cosmos was a series of spheres with the stars attached to the outer sphere. They considered the entire universe to be a few million kilometers in diameter. This work culminated with Ptolemy and his theory of the geocentric cosmos. Everything—the moon, the planets, the sun—was moving around Earth. His theory accounted for all the known motions of the objects in the sky. His explanation was so successful that it was accepted as valid for almost fifteen hundred years, and the Catholic Church held it as dogma. Anyone challenging this idea was declared a heretic, put on trial, and sentenced to death or house arrest. The Inquisition placed Galileo on trial for his heresy of defending Nicolas Copernicus' heliocentric theory and placed him under house arrest for nine years until his death.

With the work of Copernicus, a new perspective was gained: Earth is not the center of the universe. It is merely another planet that moves around the sun. The edge of the universe was as far away as the planet Saturn. As technology improved, the importance of the universe has continued to diminish. In 1838, Friedrich Wilhelm Bessel measured the angular movement (stellar parallax) of star 61 Cygnus against its background stars and determined that it was 6 light-years away. The inability to measure this stellar parallax was one of the observations that led the ancients to conclude that the earth was not moving, and, therefore, the geocentric theory was correct. The stars were simply too far away for them to measure the parallax.

From 1915 to 1920, Harlow Shapley used the 254-centimeter Mount Wilson telescope to study globular clusters. These densely packed assemblies of gravitationally bound stars are, in turn, bound to the Milky Way. Shapley noted that the clusters were not evenly distributed in the sky. He knew also that certain stars, the Cepheid variables, have an interesting property: Their average luminosity correlates with the period of their variability. Luminosity is the amount of energy a star gives off per second and determines the star's absolute brightness. If there are two stars with the same luminosity, the one closer to Earth will appear brighter. The brightness of a star as viewed from Earth is its apparent brightness. A star's apparent brightness is dependent upon its absolute brightness and its distance from Earth; astronomers developed an equation to show that relationship.

For the Cepheids, the luminosity varies in a predictable manner and is in concert with the period of oscillation. Henrietta Swan Leavitt established this relationship in 1904, when she cataloged a large number of variable stars. She saw that for the Cepheids, the longer the period of light variation, the greater the average brightness of the star. If a variable's distance could be determined to calibrate the relationship, this would establish the star's absolute brightness. Astronomers could then reverse the process and use the period-luminosity relationship to measure the distances of other Cepheid variables and objects associated with them.

The method to determine the distance works in this manner: An astronomer measures a Cepheid's apparent brightness and period. The period-luminosity curve yields the star's absolute brightness, and the two brightnesses are entered into the distance-brightness equation. The calculation yields the Cepheid's distance from Earth. Since globular clusters contain Cepheids, Shapley was able to measure the distance to the clusters. Knowing the distances and the direction of the clusters, Shapley plotted their location relative to the location of Earth in the Milky Way. Since the number of clusters increased toward the portion of the Milky Way in the constellation Sagittarius, Shapley concluded that Earth's location is about two-thirds the distance from the center of the galaxy in Sagittarius and that the Milky Way is a disk about 100,000 light-years in diameter.

With the realization that the Milky Way is a grouping of billions of stars, one wonders if there are more of these groupings. Up to this point, astronomers did not have telescopes powerful enough to find out, but in 1919, Edwin Powell Hubble gained access to the world's most powerful telescope to date: the Mount Wilson 254-centimeter telescope. By 1924, he was able to resolve the fuzzy patches of light that Charles Messier had cataloged into individual stars a century and a half before. These "nebulas" were not clouds of glowing gas like those found within our galaxy, but they were galaxies similar to the Milky Way. Hubble was able to detect Cepheid variables in the Andromeda nebula. After determining the apparent brightness and period of oscillation for several Cepheids, he was able to calculate the distance to the Andromeda nebula at roughly 800,000 light-years. This is more than eight times the distance to the most distant stars in our galaxy. This proved that the light patches are separate, gravitationally bound groups of stars and independent of our own galaxy. Hubble went on to measure the distances to other nearby galaxies.

Two decades later, Walter Baade determined that the distance was off by more than two and that the Andromeda nebula is actually 2 million light-years from Earth. He discovered that there are two types of Cepheid variables: the classic variety and another set with a different brightness/period relationship. These other Cepheids are brighter for a given period of oscillation than the classic Cepheids. Hubble assumed that his Cepheids were fainter than they were, and therefore closer than they were.

Once Hubble determined that there were other galaxies, he gathered information about them. This led to their classification and the plotting of their possible evolution. With improvement in photography and other techniques, the light spectrum of a galaxy could be analyzed. The spectrum of a galaxy is like a rainbow with dark lines through it and is the total of all frequencies of light coming from the galaxy. The lines are caused by the absorption of certain light frequencies by cooler gases in the galaxy. If there is relative motion between the light's source and the detector, the spectrum is shifted; this is known as the Doppler effect. If the galaxy is moving toward Earth, the entire spectrum shifts toward the blue end of the spectrum. If the galaxy is moving away, the shift is toward the red end of the spectrum. The amount of shift is proportional to the velocity of the galaxy. With this method, Hubble determined that the farther the galaxy is from Earth, the faster it is receding. This suggests that the galaxies are moving away from one another and leads to the conclusion that the universe is expanding, as maintained by Willem de Sitter. The view of the cosmos has changed as new information has become available, but the discoveries of Hubble and others have left a portrait of a universe that is stranger than anything previously imagined.

Impact of Event

In order to answer the question of the origin of the cosmos, one must determine its characteristics. The universe could be small or large. It may have a boundary or it may continue forever, and it may be static or dynamic. Therefore, astronomers devote much of their time to the determination of the distances of various objects, such as planets, stars, nebulas, and galaxies, and how that distance changes over time. That distance obviously cannot be measured directly. Ingenuity, however, permits one to develop methods of indirect measurement, such as the use of trigonometry to find the distance to the moon and to the sun. As larger telescopes are built, new methods are developed that utilize the data coming from these instruments. This is seen in Hubble's use of the Mount Wilson 254-centimeter telescope to locate the Cepheid variables in the Andromeda nebula and thereby ascertain its distance.

The continuation of Hubble's work established the distances and the velocities of nearby galaxies. This permitted the measurement of the more distant galaxies by such methods as in the comparison of image sizes of galaxies. If a galaxy's image is similar to but smaller than the Andromeda nebula, then it is farther away in proportion to its image size than Andromeda. Linked with the galaxies' velocities found using the Doppler effect, it has been determined that the universe is from 13 to 18 billion years old and is expanding.

It is not known which theory can explain the old, expanding universe. There were two contenders: the big bang theory of Georges Lemaître and George Gamow, and the steady state theory of Thomas Gold and Fred Hoyle. The steady state theory proposed that the universe is expanding, but remains the same since new matter is created to take the place of the galaxies that are moving away from Earth. Astronomers are uncomfortable with the fact that the matter appears from nowhere, since it is very difficult to verify. Most astronomers now accept the big bang theory as the best explanation of how the universe began. Somewhere between 13 and 18 billion years ago, a very hot, very dense "object" exploded. As the temperature dropped, matter as it is now known came into existence: electrons, protons, neutrons, and other particles. As the universe cooled, hydrogen formed, along with a small amount of helium. The matter formed into the first stars and galaxies. There were no planets, since the elements, such as silicon, oxygen, or iron—which are necessary for a planet's formation—did not exist. Before planets could form, stars had to undergo supernova explosions for these elements and others to form.

The fate of the universe remains unknown. It may continue to expand forever. It would "die" as its stars use up their hydrogen fuel and become white dwarfs, neutron stars, or black holes. Or, if the universe has enough mass, its expansion will stop because of the gravitational attraction of that mass, and it will cause the universe to collapse into its original condition. It may start to expand again to produce another universe, one that may be completely different from our present universe with physical laws one cannot even imagine. The fate of the universe will be known as astronomers gather more information.

Bibliography

Baade, Walter. *Evolution of Stars and Galaxies*. Cambridge, Mass.: Harvard University Press, 1963. Baade's work on stellar populations led to the discovery that there are two varieties of Cepheid variables and resulted in the doubling of the estimated distance to the Andromeda nebula to 2 million light-years. Compiled from a series of lectures Baade gave in the fall of 1958.

Ferris, Timothy. *Galaxies*. San Francisco: Sierra Club Books, 1980. The book, written for a popular audience, deals with the Milky Way galaxy, the local cluster of galaxies, and the universe. It shows how and where the research of Hubble has led astronomers in their quest for answers about the cosmos. It contains many black-and-white and color photographs of stars and galaxies.

Friedman, Herbert. *The Amazing Universe*. Washington, D.C.: National Geographic Society, 1975. This is an excellent book about the Sun, the stars, black holes, and galaxies. Contains many spectacular photographs; also includes figures and diagrams.

Kaufmann, William J., III. *Galaxies and Quasars*. San Francisco: W. H. Freeman, 1979. A slim paperback with many figures and photographs, this book explains in nontechnical language the implications of Hubble's discoveries. It discusses the Cepheid variable luminosity-period relationship, the Doppler effect, and the geometry of the universe.

Murdin, Paul, and David Allen. *Catalogue of the Universe*. New York: Crown, 1979. This text features in-depth articles on various astronomical subjects from the solar system to the universe. Among these is the star that lends its name to the Cepheid variables: Delta Cephei. Good reference for discussions of specific objects.

Stephen J. Shulik

Cross-References

Hale Establishes Mount Wilson Observatory (1903), p. 194; Leavitt's Study of Variable Stars Unlocks Galactic Distances (1912), p. 496; Slipher Obtains the Spectrum of a Distant Galaxy (1912), p. 502; Hertzsprung Uses Cepheid Variables to Calculate the Distances to Stars (1913), p. 557; Hubble Confirms the Expanding Universe (1929), p. 878; Gamow and Associates Develop the Big Bang Theory (1948), p. 1309.

STEENBOCK DISCOVERS THAT SUNLIGHT INCREASES VITAMIN D IN FOOD

Category of event: Biology
Time: 1924
Locale: Madison, Wisconsin

With the discovery that the ultraviolet component of sunlight increased vitamin D in food, Steenbock stimulated extensive research on vitamins

Principal personages:
CHRISTIAAN EIJKMAN (1858-1930), a Dutch physician who identified beriberi as the first dietary deficiency disease and found that it was treatable

SIR FREDERICK GOWLAND HOPKINS (1861-1947), a British biochemist who discovered one of the essential amino acids and, with Casimir Funk, named vitamins as trace compounds necessary for life

ELMER VERNER MCCOLLUM (1879-1967), an American biochemist who, while working on nutrition and dietary problems, discovered fat-soluble vitamin A and D

HARRY STEENBOCK (1886-1967), an American biochemist who was a pioneer in the study of several vitamins, including the effect of sunlight to increase vitamin D in food

ADOLF WINDAUS (1876-1959), a German chemist who isolated the molecular structure of sterol and the related compound vitamin D

Summary of Event

The discovery of the effect of sunlight on food, which results in increased amounts of vitamin D, arose from two separate areas of research involving biochemistry and medicine. The first part of the investigation involved sterol and specifically cholesterol. In 1901, the importance of this substance was not yet known, and a number of able chemists had attempted to unravel the components of this substance without success. Cholesterol was one of a large group of related compounds called sterols that were found in animal and vegetable cells. In Germany, Adolf Windaus began by comparing this group of substances and found that they shared a common feature in a tetracyclic carbon skeleton. He was convinced that other natural products would share in this basic skeleton. By 1919, he had demonstrated that cholesterol could be transformed into cholanic acid. By 1932, the work of Heinrich Wieland and Windaus had paid off, and the correct structure of the sterol ring was discovered.

The story of vitamins began earlier in 1906, when Christiaan Eijkman sought a cure for the tropical disease beriberi. He observed that chickens that fed on polished rice exhibited symptoms similar to the disease in humans. When the chickens were fed rice with the hulls intact, however, the disease disappeared. Consequently, Eijkman demonstrated that the disease was caused by a dietary deficiency, which was later found to be a substance called thiamine, or vitamin B. In the same year, Sir Frederick Gowland Hopkins proposed that several substances were essential for the maintenance of health and with his colleague, Casimir Funk, named the term "vitamin."

In 1907, Elmer Verner McCollum was on the faculty of the University of Wisconsin at a time when Harry Steenbock was an undergraduate student. McCollum was involved in dietary and nutritional research and learned of Eijkman's work. He became convinced that a small quantity of a substance called vitamin was as essential to life as all the nutritional value of food. In 1913, he discovered a substance similar to vitamin B, except that it was found in fats, and this turned out to be vitamin A. Nine years later, he contributed to the identification of vitamin D.

By the 1920's, vitamin research was pursued in a number of laboratories in England, Germany, and the United States. One area of research involved the disease rickets, and it was known that fish liver oil could prevent its occurrence. By the early 1920's, it was discovered that the active agent in the fish liver oil was vitamin D. Although vitamin D could effect a cure for rickets, exposure to sunlight also proved to be effective. Hence, the problems of whether there were several paths toward a cure or if these paths were all part of a single therapeutic process remained to be solved.

Steenbock brought together the two strands of medical and biochemical research. He concentrated on the chemical analysis of livestock nutrition. He had participated in an experiment where components of a plant were mixed in such a way that they were chemically identical, but produced different nutritional results. The influence of McCollum's experimental methods, in which he used white mice, and the livestock experiment led to the beginning of the inclusion of live animal subjects in nutritional studies. Meanwhile, Steenbock continued his research activities in nutrition via the field of vitamin studies. In 1920, he isolated a compound called carotene, which was associated with yellow foods and contained vitamin A. By 1924, Alfred F. Hess and Steenbock independently exposed certain foods to sunlight and found that these were also effective in the cure of rickets. Somehow, light converted chemicals in food into vitamin D. The precise mechanism for this conversion was not resolved for some time.

In 1925, Hess invited Windaus to take part in the work on vitamin D. Windaus began a collaborative effort on the study of vitamin D and continued his work on the photochemical nature of sterol. Over the years, he identified a number of other compounds with similar characteristics. Windaus believed that cholesterol was the source of vitamin D since cholesterol exhibited similar properties when exposed to ultraviolet light. Working at Göttingen, Robert Pohl had identified an impurity in cholesterol, called ergosterol, which Hess and Windaus later proved could convert to vitamin D. Thus, by 1927, the major features of both the chemistry and structure of sterol and vitamin D had become clear.

Windaus found several variations of vitamin D from further research and eventually isolated one form that was identical to the one purified from tuna fish liver oil; this was confirmed by Hans Brockman in Windaus' laboratory. After the 1928 Nobel Prize in Chemistry was awarded to Windaus, *The Scientific Monthly* (April, 1929) devoted an article to the reasons why several noteworthy American and English scientists were overlooked. It came as a surprise that only Windaus should have received the credit for this work, since many other American scientists were involved in the research of rickets. The article expressed an opinion that Hess and Steenbock should have been given greater credit for identifying the process of exposing either food or living animals to ultraviolet light in order to activate vitamin D.

Impact of Event

Long before the discovery of vitamins, scientists had observed the effects of restricted diets on both human and animal populations. Diseases that had resulted from dietary deficiencies had been described in detail. For example, the lack of fresh fruits and vegetables during long sea voyages produced scurvy because of the absence of vitamin C. Although the remedy of fruits and vegetables was well known, little was known about their nature and cause. Metabolic changes, lesions, and structural alterations occur if the intake of vitamins falls below a certain level. Steenbock's discovery of the effects of ultraviolet light in the production of vitamin D coincides with an extensive period of research on vitamins.

The culmination of Eijkman's initial identification of vitamin B came in 1926 with the further refinement of the vitamin. The work of B. C. P. Jansen and W. F. Donath resulted in the isolation of a component called vitamin B_1 (thiamine). They began with more than 300 kilograms of rice polishing (the husks that cover rice grains) and produced less than 100 milligrams of thiamine crystal. Another resolution of an existing vitamin problem involved the initial observation by Steenbock of a relationship between vitamin D and carotene, which was later solved by Thomas Moore and Hans von Euler-Chelpin. In 1928, the final piece in the vitamin alphabet was provided by Albert Szent-Györgyi when he isolated vitamin C from oranges and cabbage.

The next stage in vitamin research was to discover the function of these substances. It had been demonstrated already that vitamins served to cure diseases and were used as a growth factor. Research suggested that vitamins acted on enzyme systems to regulate the respiration of cells and metabolism. In a series of experiments involving pigeons and thiamine, it was demonstrated that pigeons lacking this vitamin suffered from spasms. Thiamine was essential in the process of glucose metabolism, and without this vitamin, the mechanism for the breakdown of glucose was impaired. It became clear that thiamine directly influences five metabolic reactions which, in turn, regulate the energy flow necessary for the maintenance of the cells. Hence, these experiments showed the relationship between vitamin B and beriberi disease.

Subsequent explorations on more than twenty vitamins provided a complex picture of the role of these substances as regulators of various mechanisms at the cellular level. Vitamins, in very small amounts, are an indispensable component of food and organic life.

Bibliography

Bailey, Herbert. *The Vitamin Pioneers*. Emmaus, Pa.: Rodale Books, 1968. Covers the medical and biochemical historical development of vitamins. The sections on vitamins B and D are comprehensive and suitable for the general reader.

Farber, Eduard. *Nobel Prize Winners in Chemistry, 1901-1961*. Rev. ed. London: Abelard-Schuman, 1963. Useful source for general information on major twentieth century chemists. Contains a section on Windaus, which includes a biographical sketch and extracted sections from his Nobel Prize lecture.

Florkin, Marcel. *A History of Biochemistry*. New York: Elsevier, 1972. Volumes 30 to 36 are part of a multivolume set that covers the history of biochemistry. Volume 30 contains the history of enzymes and sterol. Highly technical for the general reader. Those with high school biology and chemistry, however, could read portions and still gain worthwhile information.

Ihde, Aaron J. *The Development of Modern Chemistry*. New York: Harper & Row, 1964. A lengthy, comprehensive history of the different areas of chemistry. Chapter 24 covers the developments in biochemistry that led directly to Steenbock's research. Topics discussed are nutrition, the search for vitamins, and metabolism.

Leicester, Henry M. *Developments of Biochemical Concepts from Ancient to Modern Times*. Cambridge, Mass.: Harvard University Press, 1974. Several good chapters provide the reader with a valuable overview of biochemical concepts. Chapters 15 to 17 cover enzymes and cell constituents, energy production and biological oxidation, and intermediary metabolism.

Victor W. Chen

Cross-References

Grijns Proposes That Beriberi Is Caused by a Nutritional Deficiency (1901), p. 103; Hopkins Suggests That Food Contains Vitamins Essential to Life (1906), p. 330; McCollum Names Vitamin D and Pioneers Its Use Against Rickets (1922), p. 725; Szent-Györgyi Discovers Vitamin C (1928), p. 857.

SVEDBERG DEVELOPS THE ULTRACENTRIFUGE

Categories of event: Chemistry and biology
Time: 1924
Locale: Uppsala, Sweden

Svedberg developed the ultracentrifuge, the machine that separated colloidal particles, including proteins, carbohydrates, cell organelles, and viruses, in a centrifugal field

Principal personages:

THEODOR SVEDBERG (1884-1971), a famous Swedish physical chemist and winner of 1926 Nobel Prize in Chemistry who invented the ultracentrifuge

JOHN B. NICHOLS, a colleague of Svedberg, with whom he developed an ultracentrifuge in 1923; it was not entirely successful because of problems resulting from convection

HERMAN RINDE, a colleague of Svedberg at the University of Uppsala whose efforts helped Svedberg to develop an ultracentrifuge that could carry out convection-free sedimentation

Summary of Event

Many essential aspects of modern chemical, biochemical, and biological knowledge arose, at least in part, because Theodor Svedberg developed the machine he called the ultracentrifuge. By definition, an ultracentrifuge is a fast centrifuge which produces a convection-free centrifugal field that is useful for the study of the properties of dissolved solutes, including the measurement of their molecular weights via sedimentation velocity and sedimentation equilibrium techniques, the identification of both their molecular sizes and their shapes, and the characterization of synthetic and natural macromolecules on the basis of the property called buoyant density. A centrifuge is a machine in which a compartment (rotor) is spun around a central axis to develop centrifugal force, which is measured in gravities and can be used to separate colloid particles and materials of different densities.

Svedberg was an important Swedish physical chemist who possessed a great interest in biology. Part of Svedberg's decision to become a physical chemist is reported to be because of the belief that numerous unsolved biological problems could be explained as chemical phenomena that could be studied best with the techniques of physical chemistry. He received B.S. and Ph.D. degrees in 1905 and 1907, respectively, from the University of Uppsala. In 1912, the university appointed him to the first Swedish chair of physical chemistry. One of his main lifelong interests was understanding the chemistry of colloids. It was this interest that led him to develop the ultracentrifuge.

A colloid is a mixture in which tiny particles of one or several substances are dispersed in another substance (very often water). The colloid particles are much larger than the crystalloidal molecules (for example, sugar) or the crystalloidal ions (for example, sodium and chloride ions). They are usually too small to settle out under the force of gravity or to be seen with light microscopes. The size of colloid particles ranges from 5 to 200 nanometers. Examples of very important biological colloid particles are proteins, deoxyribonucleic acid (DNA), and the viruses.

Svedberg's thesis described an electrical method for producing very pure colloidal suspensions of metals. His continued efforts identified many other important aspects of the physical chemistry of colloids. A particularly frustrating aspect of carrying out these studies resulted from the fact that it was very important to identify the exact size of colloid particles. This was difficult to do because the available methodology involved examination of the rate of their settling out (sedimentation) and only the very largest colloid particles sedimented at useful rates. Svedberg believed that sedimentation of colloid particles could be hastened to a point where their study became practical by subjecting them to the increased gravitational fields that could be produced in high-speed centrifuges. He proposed to design such a centrifuge in a fashion where sedimentation of the particles could be followed photographically. Svedberg began his work on an "optical" centrifuge while he was a visiting professor at the University of Wisconsin, Madison, in 1923. The centrifuge he developed (in collaboration with John B. Nichols) was not entirely useful. This resulted from the fact that, although sedimentation of colloid particles could now be followed, convection problems prevented the unequivocal identification of their sizes.

After returning to Sweden, Svedberg continued his efforts and aimed to develop convection-free centrifugal sedimentation. In 1924, he and a colleague (Herman Rinde) succeeded in doing so. At first, they studied inorganic colloids. They soon discovered, however, that the very important, poorly understood biological macromolecules, called proteins, would also sediment in their centrifugal fields. Svedberg and his coworkers then quickly made important discoveries in fundamental protein chemistry. First, they demonstrated that all the molecules of any particular protein were of one size (monodisperse particles). These data contrasted greatly with those obtained with metal colloids, which are polydisperse (composed of particles of many sizes), and flew in the face of the established belief that proteins were also polydisperse. The use of the Svedberg centrifuge, which he named the "ultracentrifuge," allowed scientists to measure the sizes and the shapes of proteins. This made the ultracentrifuge a very important research tool for biology, biochemistry, and medicine.

Svedberg received the 1926 Nobel Prize in Chemistry for his work on disperse systems. The Nobel committee stated that these endeavors "proved the real existence of molecules and atoms." In his Nobel acceptance lecture, Svedberg described the great potential he foresaw for use of the ultracentrifuge in chemistry, medicine, physics, and biology. Over the next sixteen years, he improved its design and function.

By 1936, Svedberg had produced an ultracentrifuge capable of spinning a centrifuge rotor at 120,000 revolutions per minute and of producing a centrifugal force of 525,000 times the force of gravity. Using this centrifuge, Svedberg and his coworkers examined hundreds of proteins from many different kinds of plants and animals. They found that the molecular weights of different proteins varied greatly. They also learned that proteins were round, monodisperse molecules possessed of high molecular weights; the same protein from different species had similar or identical molecular weights. Svedberg and his coworkers also studied the properties of carbohydrates (for example, cellulose and starch) in the ultracentrifuge. They discovered that these biomolecules were very long, thin, polydisperse molecules. Much of his work is described in *The Ultracentrifuge*, published in 1940; it was essential to the development of modern life science.

Svedberg's work with the ultracentrifuge helped to bring together many important aspects of physics, chemistry, and biology. He also made many other important scientific contributions, including a seminal study of radioactivity and important participation in the development of the Swedish synthetic rubber industry. Svedberg's scientific endeavors were reported in 240 publications. He received many honors and awards for these efforts, including the Nobel Prize, the Berzelius Medal of the Royal Swedish Academy of Sciences; the Franklin Medal of the Franklin Institute, and honorary doctorates from Harvard University, the University of Oxford, the Sorbonne, and the University of Delaware. Svedberg was also a member of more than thirty of the most highly prestigious professional societies, including the Royal Swedish Academy of Sciences, the Royal Society of London, and both the American and the Soviet Academies of Sciences.

Impact of Event

The development of the ultracentrifuge by Svedberg is of importance to many aspects of chemistry and physics. Nowhere has it been more generally valuable than in life science research. In fact, general availability of ultracentrifuges is viewed by most life scientists as being one of the outstanding technological events in the field. This sentiment, and the great credit given to Svedberg, are emphasized by the fact that the sizes of many biological particles, determined by ultracentrifugation, are denoted in "svedberg" units (s units), named in his honor.

The biological impact of ultracentrifugation is made very evident in use of such "s-values" to describe many important components of living cells that mediate or participate in life processes. For example, bacterial ribosomes (which mediate the synthesis of proteins) are described as being composed of 30 and 50 s subunits. Other examples of such usage abound throughout the literature of life science.

Furthermore, use of ultracentrifuges enabled biologists, biochemists, physicians, and other life scientists to shift the focus of their endeavors from taxonomic and morphologic study of whole organisms to examination of smaller and smaller parts of such organisms. Examples of such research include the isolation of viruses and identification of the basis for their method of attacking cells, the separation of the subcellular organelles (for example, cell nuclei) and the elucidation of their biological functions, the development of understanding of the molecular basis for storage and utilization of hereditary information, the visualization and description of individual protein and nucleic acid molecules, and the discovery of the methodology for carrying out genetic engineering. Truly, the ultracentrifuge hastened the development of life science into molecular biology.

As pointed out in *Ultracentrifugation in Biochemistry* (1959) and later treatises on the subject, the utilization of ultracentrifuges as research tools has evolved continually and led to changes "almost as dramatic as the era beginning in 1923 when Svedberg and his collaborators first began to exploit centrifugal fields for the study of macromolecules and colloid particles." For example, in 1947, there were less than twenty ultracentrifuges in operation worldwide. By 1959, three hundred sophisticated ultracentrifuges were being utilized by the world scientific community. By 1990, there were thousands of these instruments in service, and they have become routine tools—viewed as necessities—for most life science endeavors.

In recent times, it has become possible to make measurements that were not even conceptualized by the most advanced early researchers in the field of ultracentrifugation. Many new techniques have been added to supplement the classical methodology, and many new aspects of ultracentrifugation have developed. One outstanding example is the design of zonal rotors that allow large-scale use of ultracentrifugal technique suitable for industrial application.

Bibliography

Bloomfield, Victor A. "Ultracentrifuge." *McGraw-Hill Encyclopedia of Science and Technology.* 6th ed. New York: McGraw-Hill, 1987. This brief summary of the ultracentrifuge and its uses presents a diagram of an ultracentrifuge, an explanation of instrument design, diagrams of common rotors, and an explanation of usage in molecular weight determination by sedimentation equilibrium or sedimentation velocity. Also discussed is buoyant density. Presentation is simple and erudite, with many references providing more detail, if desired.

Chervenka, C. H., and L. H. Elrod. *A Manual of Methods for Large Scale Zonal Centrifugation.* Palo Alto, Calif.: Spinco Division of Beckman Instruments, 1972. This practical text describes operating principles, equipment needed, and procedures used in large-scale zonal centrifugation. It also contains methods used for the industrial scale isolation of viruses, subcellular organelles, proteins, and nucleic acids. References and useful diagrams abound.

Claesson, Stig, and Kai O. Pederson. "The (Theodor) Svedberg." In *The Dictionary of Scientific Biography*, edited by Charles Coulston Gillispie. New York: Charles Scribner's Sons, 1970. This brief, but complete, biographical article gives the reader an excellent picture of Svedberg and his contributions to science. The authors discuss his early study of colloid chemistry, development of the ultracentrifuge, contributions to radiation chemistry, and the like. A clear picture of Svedberg's personality is developed. Many references are included, both on Svedberg's work and about Svedberg's life.

Schachman, Howard K. *The Ultracentrifugation in Biochemistry.* New York: Academic Press, 1959. This highly technical book is the classical treatise on ultracentrifugation. It is recommended to readers who wish in-depth coverage. It describes many aspects of the construction and biochemical use of ultracentrifuges. Thoroughly covers sedimentation velocity, sedimentation equilibrium, and data interpretation. Several hundred references are included.

Svedberg, Theodor, and Kai O. Pederson. *The Ultracentrifuge.* Oxford, England: Clarendon Press, 1940. This book describes development of the ultracentrifuge by the Svedberg group. It covers most of the theory and methodology of ultracentrifuges of the time and describes the ultracentrifugation of natural and synthetic colloids. The reader gets a vivid picture of Svedberg and his work.

Tiselius, Arne, and Stig Claesson. "The Svedberg and Fifty Years of Physical Chemistry in Sweden." *Annual Review of Physical Chemistry* 18 (1967): 1-8. This article discusses the impact of Svedberg on physical chemistry in Sweden. It concisely covers many aspects of his contributions to the chemistry of colloids from the development of the ultracentrifuge to his overall role in academic science and technology. Some aspects of Svedberg's personality are also divulged.

Sanford S. Singer

Cross-References

Watson and Crick Develop the Double-Helix Model for DNA (1951), p. 1406; Nirenberg Invents an Experimental Technique That Cracks the Genetic Code (1961), p. 1687; Cohen and Boyer Develop Recombinant DNA Technology (1973), p. 1987; Berg, Gilbert, and Sanger Develop Techniques for Genetic Engineering (1980), p. 2115; A Human Growth Hormone Gene Transferred to a Mouse Creates Giant Mice (1981), p. 2154.

DART DISCOVERS THE FIRST RECOGNIZED AUSTRALOPITHECINE FOSSIL

Category of event: Anthropology
Time: Summer, 1924
Locale: Medical School, University of Witwatersrand, Johannesburg, South Africa

Dart discovered the first Australopithecine, or the link between ape and man, cast in limestone recovered from a quarry in Taung, South Africa

Principal personages:
RAYMOND ARTHUR DART (1893-1988), an anatomist who astounded the paleontological and scientific communities by discovering the first "missing link" between ape and humankind, *Australopithecus africanus*; he thus provided evidence for Charles Darwin's suggestion that Africa was the cradle of humankind

ROBERT BROOM (1866-1951), a Scottish physician with an admirable reputation for his many paleontological discoveries in South Africa who became Dart's most ardent supporter during the controversy following the discovery of *Australopithecus africanus*; discovered additional South African hominids: *Paranthropus*, *Plesianthropus*, and *Telanthropus*

Summary of Event

In 1871, Charles Darwin suggested in *The Descent of Man and Selection in Relation to Sex* that because living mammals in various regions of the world exhibit similarities to the extinct ones of the same region, it was quite likely that Africa would prove to be the continent where humankind first appeared. This notion was based on the idea that the gorilla and chimpanzee of Africa were humankind's closest living relatives. Darwin's suggestion was to become the center of a debate that greatly influenced the field of paleoanthropology. It was made knowing that the only fossils discovered by 1871 were found in Europe; for example, the first paleontological human remains were those of Neanderthal man, found in Germany in 1856. Indeed, the first hominid remains recovered outside Europe were those from Java, found in 1891 by Eugène Dubois.

Dubois, a Dutch anatomist and physician, had set out in 1887 from Holland to search for early man in the Dutch East Indies. Like Darwin, he believed that human ancestors would be found where the living mammals most closely resembled humans. Unlike Darwin, however, Dubois believed that the gibbon and orangutan of southeast Asia were the primates most closely resembling humans. In Java, during 1891, Dubois discovered the *Pithecanthropus erectus*, "the erect ape man." While his discovery became the center of a controversy, it prompted Western scientists to believe that humans first appeared in Asia, not Africa. Dubois' find, better known as

"Java man," has been reclassified into the genus and species *Homo erectus*, an intermediate stage in human evolution between modern *Homo sapiens* and the more primitive australopithecines.

In 1907, a fossil known as the "Heidelberg man" was discovered in Germany. Yet, the next hominid remains believed to be of major significance were those found by Charles Dawson in 1911 in Sussex in southern England. This fossil was taxonomically placed into a new genus and species known as *Eoanthropus dawsoni*, meaning "Dawson's dawn man." The fossil is perhaps best known as Piltdown man. While each fossil discovered and given a new taxonomic name frequently created controversy, this was not true of Dawson's discovery, because it complied with prevailing popular beliefs about what a human ancestor ought to resemble. Specifically, the Piltdown remains possessed a large, modern-looking cranium and a primitive face, namely, a large lower jaw with apelike dentition. At the time, it was widely believed that humans were distinguished from other animals by their superior intellect and that an intermediate form between man and apes would necessarily possess a large cranium. Additionally, those that accepted evolution believed that since a human ancestor would need to possess some primitive traits, such traits might be found in the face and lower jaw. *Eoanthropus* fulfilled such expectations.

It was into this atmosphere that Dart introduced a fossil recovered from a limestone quarry just outside Taung ("the place of the lion" in Bantu) in South Africa. In 1924, Dart was a young professor of anatomy in his second year of teaching in the Medical School at the University of Witwatersrand in Johannesburg, South Africa. Early during that summer, a fossil was brought to him from the Taung quarry by a student, Josephine Salmons. While Dart determined that the fossil was that of a previously documented extinct form of baboon, it prompted his interest in the limestone quarry at Taung. Thus, he made arrangements to receive further fossils from the quarry should any be encountered by workers. Later that summer, Dart received some boxes from Taung which contained more fossils. In one box was an unusual endocast, or fossilized cast, representing the interior of a cranium. The endocast was notable for its size and unique structure. Dart recognized the suggested anatomy as that of a higher primate, but unlike that of any living ape by virtue of its increased size. Further examination revealed a single large fragment of a fossilized facial skeleton. The endocast and face were portions of the same animal. To Dart, the remains revealed a never-before-seen combination of traits, suggesting an anthropoid halfway between man and ape.

In February, 1925, Dart introduced his find to the scientific community with a brief article in the British journal *Nature*. He described the fossil as a juvenile member of a new genus, *Australopithecus*, and species, *africanus*. Except for Robert Broom, a Scottish physician who had become a well-known paleontologist for his South African discoveries of transitional forms, bridging the gap between reptiles and mammals, the paleontological and scientific communities immediately opposed the acceptance of Dart's discovery. A major criticism was related to Dart's introduction of the new taxon based on a juvenile specimen. There was no question that the

fossil was that of a juvenile, a conclusion justified by the degree of dental development reflected in the fossil. Specifically, the specimen retained some of its decid-
uous, or baby, teeth. As a result, Dart's discovery has frequently been called the
"Taung Baby" or the "Taung Child." Some critics seized this issue and argued that,
by convention, juveniles should not serve as the basis for the creation of a new taxon
because dramatic differences in appearance could exist between juveniles and adults
of the same species. Others argued that Dart may have simply found a juvenile
member of an already documented fossil primate. Criticisms also were based on the
fact that the discovery was made in South Africa and not Asia, where the world's
attention had become focused since Dubois' discovery in 1891. Additionally, unlike
the previous perceptions of a human ancestor, and as reflected by Dawson's Piltdown
man, Dart's discovery possessed a small brain and a relatively modern-looking face
and dentition. The most petty criticism was with Dart's choice of a name. Because
some said he had employed a combination of Greek and Latin terms in the name
Australopithecus, he was ridiculed for his lack of adherence to taxonomic protocol.
Australo is of Latin derivation and means "of the Southern Hemisphere." *Pithecus*
is of Greek derivation, but as Dart later pointed out the term was also used by the
Romans, and means "simian" or "apelike." *Africanus* means "of Africa." Thus,
Australopithecus africanus literally means "the South African ape."

By the mid-1950's, many of Dart's critics were compelled to accept the significance of his 1924 discovery. Broom, who was unwavering in his support of Dart,
began his search for human ancestors after he was appointed curator of paleontology
at the Transvaal Museum in Pretoria in 1934. From 1936 through 1949, Broom and
his colleagues discovered various fossil hominids in South Africa and placed them
into three distinct genera: *Plesianthropus*, *Paranthropus*, and *Telanthropus*. Like Dubois' discovery, it was later determined that *Telanthropus* should be recognized as a
member of the genus and species *Homo erectus*. While different in various ways
from *Australopithecus africanus*, Broom's *Plesianthropus* and *Paranthropus* forms
represented members of a very similar animal. More important, they were adults,
and as Dart had suggested, they were unlike any animal yet documented. Except for
Telanthropus, Broom's finds were considered members of the same subfamily as
Dart's fossil (subfamily: *Australopithecinae*).

While some critics were dissuaded by Broom's discovery of adults, Dart also
found an adult in 1947. Other critics were converted to Dart's ideas as a result of the
1947 Pan-African Congress of Prehistory held in Nairobi, Kenya. The Congress was
organized by L. S. B. Leakey and allowed several widely respected physical anthropologists an opportunity to examine some of the early African hominids firsthand.
As a result, some previous critics of Dart's discovery became convinced that the australopithecine fossil was more closely related to humankind and far removed from
the apes.

The last bastion of critics was addressed in the early 1950's. In 1953, Kenneth
Page Oakley and others began a reexamination of *Eoanthropus dawsoni* in the light
of growing skepticism that the fossil did not conform in morphology with the discov-

eries from South Africa. Specifically, Oakley and others tested a new dating technique, fluorine dating, which revealed that the cranium and mandible from Piltdown were of different ages. Thus, it was proved that the Piltdown remains were fabricated and designed to appear as something they were not. The cranium was concluded to be one from the late Pleistocene epoch, while the mandible belonged to a modern orangutan. Both portions had been modified and stained in order to appear as though they were from the same animal. The Piltdown hoax remains a mystery. Who perpetrated the fraud and why is not known; but, certainly, once the hoax was revealed, the Piltdown remains could no longer be used to hinder the acceptance of the South African australopithecines as the link between modern *Homo sapiens* and the living apes.

Impact of Event

Dart's 1924 discovery of *Australopithecus africanus* has had various impacts. Certainly, one was the support it offered to Darwin's theory that Africa was the continent where humans first appeared. The acceptance of this notion led to the further search of Africa for human ancestors, a search that has continued to produce numerous important early hominid fossils. While the limestone and sedimentary contexts from which the South African fossils were recovered did not lend themselves to accurate geological dating, one could suggest that the fossils were from the lower Pleistocene epoch, or were approximately 1 million years old. Moreover, the South African discoveries led paleoanthropologists to conclude that early hominids first appeared in a grassland or savannah environment, as opposed to the tropical forests others were suggesting as a result of Dubois' *Pithecanthropus erectus* discovery. In addition, *Australopithecus africanus* and the remaining australopithecines provided clear evidence that habitual erect bipedal locomotion preceded the expansion of the brain. This idea contradicted the previous notions about the significance of increased cranial capacity during human evolution. Furthermore, the South African australopithecines suggested that the origin of a more-or-less modern dentition also preceded cranial development.

Some have called Dart's discovery of the first *Australopithecus* one of the most significant scientific events of the twentieth century. Though such claims are debatable, there can be little question that the discovery ranks near the top of important events in the fields of anthropology, paleontology, and prehistory.

Bibliography

Dart, Raymond A. *Adventures with the Missing Link*. New York: Harper and Brothers, 1959. A firsthand retrospective view of the discovery of *Australopithecus africanus* and the controversies that followed and surrounded the introduction of this taxon.

_____. "*Australopithecus Africanus*: The Man-Ape of South Africa." *Nature* 115 (February, 1925): 195-199. This is the publication that announced the discovery of the first australopithecine ever recovered. The circumstances of its discovery, the limestone quarry site at Taung, South Africa, and the fossil cranium and accompanying endocast are described. The remains are concluded to be those of a juvenile member of a new genus and species, *Australopithecus africanus.*

Johanson, Donald C., and Maitland A. Edey. *Lucy: The Beginnings of Humankind.* New York: Simon & Schuster, 1981. A book coauthored by another prominent figure in the field of paleoanthropology. This volume offers a popular account of other hominid discoveries from the Pleistocene of East Africa. It addresses the financial problems encountered in such research as well as various strong personalities and controversies that have influenced attempts to document the human fossil record.

Leakey, Richard E., and Roger Lewin. *Origins.* New York: E. P. Dutton, 1977. Draws, in part, upon the work of his parents, but Richard Leakey also discusses his own paleontological discoveries at Lake Turkana in northern Kenya. This popular volume suggests that there may have been three or more species of hominids existing as contemporaries in East Africa approximately 2 million years ago. Central to the text's theme is the question of why the lineage of *Homo* survived and the others did not.

Pfeiffer, John E. *The Emergence of Humankind.* 4th ed. New York: Harper & Row, 1985. Although not written in the style of most textbooks, this volume is used frequently as a textbook in introductory physical anthropology courses. It addresses the various lines of research often employed by paleoanthropologists in their attempt to learn about the hominid fossil record.

Turhon A. Murad

Cross-References

Boule Reconstructs the First Neanderthal Skeleton (1908), p. 428; Zdansky Discovers Peking Man (1923), p. 761; Weidenreich Reconstructs the Face of Peking Man (1937), p. 1096; Leakey Finds a 1.75-Million-Year-Old Fossil Hominid (1959), p. 1603; Ardrey's *The Territorial Imperative* Argues That Humans Are Naturally Territorial (1966), p. 1808; Simons Identifies a 30-Million-Year-Old Primate Skull (1966), p. 1814; Anthropologists Discover "Lucy," an Early Hominid Skeleton (1974), p. 2037; Sibley and Ahlquist Discover a Close Human and Chimpanzee Genetic Relationship (1984), p. 2267; Hominid Fossils Are Gathered in the Same Place for Concentrated Study (1984), p. 2279; Scientists Date a *Homo sapiens* Fossil at Ninety-two Thousand Years (1987), p. 2341.

EDDINGTON FORMULATES THE
MASS-LUMINOSITY LAW FOR STARS

Category of event: Astronomy
Time: March, 1924
Locale: Cambridge, England

Eddington demonstrated the relationship between a star's mass and its luminosity, which led to an understanding of how stars evolve

Principal personages:

SIR ARTHUR STANLEY EDDINGTON (1882-1944), an English astronomer, mathematician, and physicist whose work on the interior structure and evolution of stars led to important advances in astrophysics

JACOB KARL ERNST HALM (1866-1944), a German astronomer who suggested a possible relationship between a star's brightness and its mass

WILLIAM WALLACE CAMPBELL (1862-1938), an American astronomer and educator who worked with spectroscopic double stars to determine stellar masses

EJNAR HERTZSPRUNG (1873-1967), a Danish astronomer who first demonstrated the relationship between a star's color and its luminosity and who constructed the first Hertzsprung-Russell diagram

HENRY NORRIS RUSSELL (1877-1957), an American astronomer and astrophysicist who worked on calculating the masses of double stars, the relationship between a star's color and its luminosity, and who used the Hertzsprung-Russell diagram to illustrate his theory of stellar evolution

Summary of Event

In the early twentieth century, astronomy was changing. Until this time, astronomers had concerned themselves chiefly with the motions of heavenly objects and the laws and forces that described those motions. With the advent of the analysis of starlight (spectrography) and the use of photography, the science of astrophysics began to take shape. Scientists could now learn more about the properties of stars other than their motions and could begin the task of understanding what stars are like internally, how they form, and what fuels their existence. New data were becoming available which could be used to discover patterns or relationships among different properties of stars, as revealed by their light. The interpretation of these patterns and relationships was to be one of the first tasks of the science of astrophysics.

One type of new data was on the luminosities (brightnesses) and spectral types of stars. A star's spectral type was a classification assigned to it after a study of its light, as spread out by a prism or a grating (its spectrum). A program at Harvard College Observatory and other research provided astronomers with catalogs of spectral type and luminosity for many stars. In 1905, Ejnar Hertzsprung, a Danish astronomer, would reveal a relationship between a star's brightness and its type. This relationship was demonstrated in the Hertzsprung-Russell diagram, developed by Hertzsprung and Henry Norris Russell in the United States. Its discovery raised the questions of what this relationship meant and what implications it had for why stars are of differing colors and brightnesses.

Another type of new data was on the masses of stars. When studying double star systems, one of the laws formulated by Johannes Kepler in the seventeenth century can be used to determine the sum of the masses of the two stars in the system. In some cases, a ratio of the masses of the two stars can also be obtained, and this information can be used to determine the mass of each individual star. This could be done with either stars that are visibly pairs of stars (visual doubles) or with stars that look like a single star to the eye but that have spectra which reveal that there are really two stars present.

Jacob Karl Ernst Halm, at the Cape Observatory in South Africa, reviewed research conducted by William Wallace Campbell and by Russell with these double star masses and postulated a relationship between a star's mass and its spectral class. Halm then combined these two relationships in 1911 (spectral type-brightness and mass-spectral type) and suggested that there is a relationship between a star's mass and its brightness. This possible relationship was also discussed by Russell in 1913 and by Hertzsprung in 1918.

In 1924, Sir Arthur Stanley Eddington was a professor of astronomy at the University of Cambridge in England and director of the Royal Observatory in Greenwich. He analyzed mass and luminosity data for many stars and plotted a diagram of mass versus luminosity. The diagram showed a relationship between the two which generally indicated that the brighter a star was, the more massive it was. Stars range from dim low-mass stars to bright high-mass stars along a diagonal line stretching across the plot. Eddington not only demonstrated this relationship but also began the discussion of what its cause and implications were.

Eddington's theoretical explanation for the mass-luminosity relationship was based on the law of perfect gases. This law describes the relationship between the pressure, volume, and temperature of a gas. The temperature of a star is related to its luminosity, which is actually a measure of the amount of energy radiated away from the star in a given amount of time ("brightness" is commonly used as an equivalent term for luminosity, since energy is seen in the form of visible light). At the time, Hertzsprung-Russell diagrams of spectral type versus luminosity for groups of stars showed that there are two types of stars: those recognized by Hertzsprung as being larger (the giants) and the dwarf, or main sequence stars. The giant stars occupy one place on the diagram, with fairly constant luminosity and varying spectral types. The dwarf stars demonstrate Hertzsprung's color-luminosity relationship: Blue stars are brighter than yellow stars which, in turn, are brighter than red stars. At the time that Eddington formulated this explanation, it was thought that only giant stars were composed of gases which would follow the perfect gas laws (which only applied under certain conditions). Thus, the mass-luminosity relationship should apply only to giant stars. Eddington tested the idea that only giants should exhibit the relationship between their masses and their luminosities and was surprised to discover that the relationship held for stars on the main sequence too. This was in conflict with the prevailing assumption that main sequence stars were too dense for the perfect gas laws to apply to them and their relatively low luminosities (relative to the giants) were accounted for by their high densities. Eddington's discovery indicated that their low luminosities could be accounted for simply by their low masses. He explained that the perfect gas laws applied at higher densities than expected for stars, because the material of which the stars were composed was highly ionized; that is, the individual atoms were missing some of their electrons because of the presence of high temperatures. This ionization reduced the bulk of the atoms, and the net result was that the perfect gas laws "worked" for much higher densities than could otherwise have been expected.

An interesting feature of the mass-luminosity diagram is the relatively broad range of luminosities and much smaller range of masses. The most massive star then known was estimated to be about one hundred times the mass of the sun, and the least massive, about one-sixth the mass of the sun. Eddington had also considered the problem of radiation pressure in a star, and he used radiation pressure to explain the relatively small range of stellar masses. He showed that there is a condition of equilibrium in a star, with gravitational pressure inward balanced by gas pressure and radiation pressure outward. Beyond a certain mass, the radiation pressure becomes so great that a star would be blown apart by it; therefore, mass is the upper limit to stellar masses. (Today, the most massive star known has been estimated to be only about sixty-five times the mass of the sun.) Eddington developed an equation to describe equilibrium in a star that is still used today. This equation involved the assumption of perfect gas conditions and therefore at first he thought it should apply only to giant stars. The discovery that perfect gas conditions are also maintained in dwarf or main sequence stars extended the applicability of this equation and the model of a star's interior that resulted.

The demonstration of the mass-luminosity relationship for stars gave astronomers new areas to investigate and revealed something about the conditions in main sequence stars that had not been known before. It was an important step in the development of the current understanding of what makes stars shine and how they change over time.

Impact of Event

After documenting the mass-luminosity relationship, Eddington began sorting out problems of the structure of stars and their energy sources. The fact that the perfect gas law can be applied to both main sequence and giant stars was a great help to scientists studying stellar structure. The basic problem of stellar structure is that of producing a model star, that is, a description of the physical properties of a star at various depths below the star's surface, such as the temperature and density. In order to know these properties, one must know the degree to which the gas prevents the free outward flow of radiation. The perfect gas law gives astronomers a tool for calculating this quantity, calculating the temperature and density at various depths in the star, and producing stellar models which are compared with actual stars. Eddington's calculations assumed an average particle mass (for the particles of gas in stars), which today is known to be too high. This resulted from the fact that at the time the proportions of the various gases composing the stars were not known. It was not until Russell's discovery that the sun is almost entirely hydrogen that astronomers could use a particle weight more closely corresponding to reality.

The discovery of the mass-luminosity relation was important to theories of how stars change with time. In 1913, Russell had presented a scheme of stellar evolution in which all the stars on the main sequence were of different ages. The main sequence represented the path a star took throughout its lifetime, beginning as a bright blue star and cooling down to a dim red star as its energy source (heat from contraction under gravitational force) ran out. With Eddington's discovery, however, astronomers realized that stars on the main sequence had differing masses (since mass and luminosity are related and they have different luminosities): The stars on the dim red end of the main sequence were less massive than stars at the bright blue end. If the main sequence is an evolutionary path that stars follow, then mass loss must occur as stars age. This was difficult to explain; it was not until later discoveries on stellar evolution that astronomers realized that the main sequence is not an evolutionary path. The questions of how stars evolved and what their energy source was were solved in the 1930's, with the discovery of atomic fusion and the realization that fusion is occurring in stars. When two atoms fuse in the interior of a star, energy is released, and it is this energy that is seen as starlight and other types of radiation. Scientists now know that the mass of a star determines how quickly the fusion reactions take place inside it (how long it lives) and its place on the main sequence. A more massive star is brighter, hotter, and bluer, and when it comes to the end of its fuel supply, it has a more spectacular ending to its life than less massive, cooler stars.

Bibliography

Abell, George O. *Realm of the Universe*. 3d ed. Philadelphia: Saunders College Publishing, 1984. An introductory college textbook, this book explains various stellar properties and introduces the mass-luminosity relation and the diagram of this relation in the chapter on properties of stars. Explains how data are gathered on masses of binary stars and discusses the Hertzsprung-Russell diagram and its relevance to stellar masses and evolutions. Includes annotated bibliography, glossary, diagrams, and pictures, as well as exercises for the student.

Degani, Meir H. *Astronomy Made Simple*. New rev. ed. Garden City, N.Y.: Doubleday, 1976. Designed for self-motivated study, this book discusses the mass-luminosity law in the context of the sequences of stars on the Hertzsprung-Russell diagram. The discussion of stellar evolution emphasizes the importance of a star's mass in determining how it will change with time. Includes line diagrams and exercises for the reader and a glossary.

Eddington, A. S. *Stars and Atoms*. New Haven, Conn.: Yale University Press, 1927. The text of a series of lectures given in 1926 and adapted for publication. Eddington's description of the then-current knowledge of stellar structure is intended for the amateur willing to apply new ideas. The first section concerns stellar interiors and the mass-luminosity relation. Dated, but valuable for Eddington's own view of the work he performed and for his clear, engaging style.

Pannekoek, A. *A History of Astronomy*. New York: Interscience Publishers, 1961. The mass-luminosity relation is discussed in the chapter "Common Stars" in the context of the development of astrophysics in the early twentieth century, the development of the Hertzsprung-Russell diagram, and theories of stellar evolution. Some line drawings and black-and-white photographs. A scholarly classic in the history of astronomy.

Struve, Otto, and Velta Zebergs. *Astronomy of the Twentieth Century*. New York: Macmillan, 1962. Cowritten by an astronomer who participated in some of the astronomical history he describes, this book describes the work on stellar properties which culminated in Eddington's discovery of the mass-luminosity law, including mass determination for binary stars. Also gives background on stellar evolution and Hertzsprung-Russell diagrams. Some drawings, diagrams, and black-and-white photographs, plus glossary and bibliography.

Mary Hrovat

Cross-References

Hertzsprung Notes the Relationship Between Color and Luminosity of Stars (1905), p. 265; Hertzsprung Describes Giant and Dwarf Stellar Divisions (1907), p. 370; Russell Announces His Theory of Stellar Evolution (1913), p. 585; Eddington Publishes *The Internal Constitution of the Stars* (1926), p. 815.

HUBBLE DEMONSTRATES THAT
OTHER GALAXIES ARE INDEPENDENT SYSTEMS

Category of event: Astronomy
Time: December, 1924
Locale: Mount Wilson Observatory, Pasadena, California

Hubble demonstrated that the Milky Way galaxy is only one of many in the universe and founded the astronomical study of galaxies external to the Milky Way

Principal personages:
EDWIN POWELL HUBBLE (1889-1953), an American astronomer who determined that galaxies exist external to the Milky Way, began the task of classifying these external galaxies, and determined that the universe is expanding
HEBER DOUST CURTIS (1872-1942), an American astronomer who debated with Harlow Shapley on the nature of "spiral nebulas" (what are now known as external galaxies); he took the position that these nebulas are external to the Milky Way
HARLOW SHAPLEY (1885-1972), an American astronomer who worked on establishing the size and shape of the Milky Way and took the position that the spiral nebulas are parts of the Milky Way system
ADRIAAN VAN MAANEN (1884-1946), a Dutch astronomer who worked with measurements of photographic plates to determine motions of astronomical objects; some of his work was thought to show rotation in spiral nebulas

Summary of Event

In addition to stars and planets, the night sky contains fuzzy patches of light, or nebulas. People have wondered what these nebulas were for as long as people have observed them. William Parsons, the third Earl of Rosse, with his 72-inch telescope completed in 1845, was able to determine that some nebulas have a spiral structure; it required the astronomical tools of the twentieth century to determine the nature of these "spiral nebulas."

At the beginning of the twentieth century, there were two theories of spiral nebulas. One held that they were groups of stars that were part of the Milky Way galaxy. The other held that they were "island universes," large, distant, independent systems. An important question was the distances of these nebulas. The island universe theory held that the nebulas were remote from the Milky Way; the other theory held that they were closer. If distances for these objects could be determined, astronomers could determine which theory was correct.

Vesto Melvin Slipher, working at Percival Lowell's observatory in Flagstaff, Arizona, announced in 1914 that the spiral nebulas had large radial velocities, that is, large velocities along the line of sight to them, and that these velocities were all in the direction away from the Milky Way. This was taken as evidence that these nebulas, since they were all moving rapidly away, could not possibly be part of the Milky Way. Slipher had not conclusively solved the problem, however, since he had not determined the distances of these nebulas.

Distance has always been a difficult question for astronomers. By the early twentieth century, astronomers had used the technique of parallax to measure distances to some nearby stars. A star's parallax is the amount by which its position shifts relative to more distant background stars because of Earth's motion in its orbit throughout the year. Parallax is useful only for close objects; therefore, in the spiral nebula debate, other methods of measuring motion had to be used. Photography, which was applied to astronomical research in the second half of the nineteenth century, was important in measurements of the motions of astronomical objects, since photographic plates taken at different times could be compared and motions spotted.

Adriaan van Maanen, working at Mount Wilson Observatory, applied photographic techniques to the study of internal motions of spiral nebulas. He compared the positions of bright spots within spirals in pairs of photographs taken at different times in order to observe any motion of the points in the time interval between the plates. He published his results in 1916, which suggested that the spirals were rotating and that the rotation was rapid. In fact, if large distances and large sizes were assumed for the nebulas, and the proper corrections applied, the nebulas were calculated to be rotating at immensely fast speeds, in some cases exceeding the speed of light. This was known to be impossible; van Maanen's results were taken as evidence that the spiral nebulas must be nearby parts of the Milky Way.

In April, 1920, Harlow Shapley and Heber Doust Curtis presented their ideas to the National Academy of Sciences on the size of the Milky Way and the nature of the spiral nebulas. Based on his results obtained with a new distance determination method, Shapley had arrived at a much larger size for our galaxy than had been previously deduced. Curtis agreed with previous studies that indicated a smaller Milky Way. Curtis also believed in the island universe theory—that the spiral nebulas are other galaxies similar to the Milky Way. If Shapley was correct, then these spirals must be huge, and they must be at immense distances in order to appear as small as they do from Earth. Van Maanen's work indicated that these large distances were impossible. Shapley, thus, argued for a large Milky Way and for spirals that were close to it and part of it; Curtis argued for a smaller Milky Way and for the island universe theory of spirals.

Curtis' evidence for the island universe theory consisted of the radial velocities, as measured by Slipher, and his comparisons of the brightnesses of novas (stars that suddenly brighten) in spirals and in our own galaxy. That indicated that if the intrinsic brightnesses were about the same, then the spirals must be very distant for the novas to appear as faint as they do. Shapley's evidence for the closeness of the spirals consisted of van Maanen's measurements of the rotational velocities of the spirals. Today it is recognized that Shapley's results for the size and shape of the galaxy were substantially correct. Yet, the island universe hypothesis was strongly supported by evidence presented by Edwin Hubble to the American Association for the Advancement of Science in December, 1924.

In 1923, Hubble was working at Mount Wilson Observatory, studying plates taken with the 100-inch Hooker telescope. There he was the first to recognize the presence of Cepheid variables in spiral nebulas, the Andromeda nebula and its companion. Cepheid variables are stars whose brightness varies periodically and whose period of variation is related to their intrinsic brightness. Once a star's intrinsic brightness is known, and its apparent brightness as seen from Earth is measured, one can determine its distance (in the same way that one can estimate the distance of a light bulb based on its apparent brightness and the fact that it is a 60-watt bulb). Cepheid variables are, thus, immensely useful to astronomers in distance determinations (the new distance method used by Shapley). Shapley's recognition of these variables enabled Hubble to calculate that the nebulas were, in fact, at great distances and must be independent systems. Also, since size is related to distance as described above, they must be huge. Hubble found for the Andromeda nebula that the distance was about 930,000 light-years and the diameter almost 33,000 light-years (a light-year is approximately 6 trillion miles). These results were based on Hubble's assumptions that the relation between period and brightness holds for all Cepheids, that the Cepheids are physically connected with the spirals, and that there is no intervening material in the spirals that is absorbing part of the Cepheids' light. Although the first assumption turned out to be incorrect (there are actually two different types of Cepheid, and the ones Hubble studied were of the second type with a different period-luminosity relationship), the error in distance turned out to be on the small side; the distances are even greater than Hubble calculated. Hubble's results changed scientists' idea of the scale of the universe and of Earth's place in it.

Hubble was at first reluctant to publish his result, since he had no explanation of why van Maanen's results were incorrect. Although many influential astronomers were immediately convinced by Hubble's results, controversy lingered for some years after these results were presented. No one ever discovered the source of van Maanen's errors; it can only be noted here that he was working at the limits of the technique at the time. His results could not be duplicated by others, and all other evidence indicated that the galaxies were distant and separate from the Milky Way; van Maanen's work was gradually forgotten.

Impact of Event

Hubble's discovery of the distance of other galaxies and their independence from our own galaxy settled an important debate in astronomy at the time. The philosophical consequences of this debate and Hubble's resolution of it were immense. The great sizes and distances of the spirals meant that not only was Earth's sun only one of many in a huge galaxy but also that the Milky Way was merely one of many independent systems. This realization shifted humankind's place in the cosmos, a shift that could be said to be equal to that Nicolaus Copernicus made when he suggested that the sun, not the earth, was the center of the solar system.

Hubble's work led to the beginning of classification and study of galaxies external to the Milky Way; thus, Hubble has been called the founder of extragalactic astronomy. Once galaxies were identified as separate units of the cosmos, their shapes and sizes, their distances, and their distribution in space were studied. During the 1920's, Hubble presented a classification scheme for galaxies; this scheme is still in use for most galaxies. Classification and identification of different types of galaxies were important first steps in understanding the formation and evolution of galaxies. Extragalactic astronomy is a fascinating study of the universe; it began when Hubble proved that the spiral nebulas are external galaxies.

There were important cosmological follow-ups to Hubble's work. Once Cepheids were found in other spirals, and distances were known, Hubble was able to work out a plot of distance versus velocity for these spirals using radial velocities, as measured by Slipher and others. From this plot, he was able to see that the farther away a galaxy was, the faster it was moving away from Earth; therefore, he deduced that the universe was expanding. This was an important piece of evidence in the foundation of the big bang theory of cosmology. This plot could also be used to extrapolate backward in time to the big bang, when all the galaxies were compressed together and could be used to determine the age of the universe. Studies are still being conducted to determine the exact age. This work created a drastically different picture of the universe: a universe in motion, rushing away from an energetic beginning, rather than the static and stable universe that scientists previously postulated. The idea of an expanding universe, in conjunction with the ideas of Einstein's general relativity, gave cosmologists many new avenues to explore in their attempts to determine how the universe began and what it is doing now.

Bibliography

Berendzen, Richard, Richard Hart, and Daniel Seeley. *Man Discovers the Galaxies.* New York: Science History Publications, 1976. Excellent history of early twentieth century work in studying the Milky Way and external galaxies, including much information on the process by which these galaxies were determined to be independent systems. Accessible to the nonscientist and written in an enjoyable style. Makes much use of archival material, including correspondence, and contains many photographs, some charts, and graphs.

Gribbin, John. *In Search of the Big Bang.* New York: Bantam Books, 1986. This history of modern cosmology presents, in chapters 2 and 3 in particular, the story of the discovery of the nature of external galaxies. Gribbin puts Hubble's work into its context of the development of cosmological thought. Intended for the general reader; contains drawings and an annotated bibliography.

Hetherington, Norriss S. "The Purported Rotation of Spiral Nebulas." In *Science and Objectivity: Episodes in the History of Astronomy.* Ames: Iowa State University Press, 1988. This chapter investigates the possible sources of van Maanen's error when he measured rapid rotation in the spiral nebulas, with emphasis on how preconceptions and subjective ideas may have influenced the gathering of data. Discusses influence of van Maanen's work on Hubble. Well documented by quotations from contemporary letters.

Hubble, Edwin. *The Realm of the Nebulas.* New Haven, Conn.: Yale University Press, 1936. Text of lectures given by Hubble at Yale in 1935 on spiral nebulas. Chapters 1 and 4 deal with the discovery of the nebulas's distances; remainder of book describes then-current knowledge on types of galaxies, their distribution, and the overall view of the universe. Dated, but valuable for Hubble's view of his studies.

Shapley, Harlow. *Through Rugged Ways to the Stars.* New York: Charles Scribner's Sons, 1969. Shapley's autobiography contains a chapter on the Shapley-Curtis debate (chapter 6) and one that contains descriptions of Hubble and van Maanen (chapter 4). Written in a conversational style, this book gives insight into some of the events covered in this article as seen by a key participant. Includes photographs.

Struve, Otto, and Velta Zebergs. "Galaxies." In *Astronomy of the Twentieth Century.* New York: Macmillan, 1962. Cowritten by an astronomer, Otto Struve, who lived through some of the twentieth century astronomy described in the book. Tells the story of the discovery of galaxies as independent systems and of the resulting work in classifying and understanding galaxies. Contains photographs and drawings; endpapers of book contain a timeline of twentieth century astronomy.

Whitney, Charles A. *The Discovery of Our Galaxy.* New York: Alfred A. Knopf, 1971. Presents history of cosmological thought; in part 3, the discovery and study of external galaxies is discussed as well as the study of our own galaxy. Discusses actual observations and telescopes used to make discoveries. Includes photographs, drawings, glossary, and bibliography.

Mary Hrovat

Cross-References

Leavitt's Study of Variable Stars Unlocks Galactic Distances (1912), p. 496; Slipher Obtains the Spectrum of a Distant Galaxy (1912), p. 502; Shapley Proves the Sun Is Distant from the Center of Our Galaxy (1918), p. 655; Lemaître Proposes the Big Bang Theory (1927), p. 825; Hubble Confirms the Expanding Universe (1929), p. 878; De Vaucouleurs Identifies the Local Supercluster of Galaxies (1953), p. 1454.

WHIPPLE FINDS IRON TO BE AN IMPORTANT CONSTITUENT OF RED BLOOD CELLS

Category of event: Biology
Time: 1925
Locale: School of Medicine and Dentistry, University of Rochester, New York

Whipple discovered that liver/meat diets were effective treatments for anemia and that iron was an essential dietary ingredient

Principal personages:
GEORGE HOYT WHIPPLE (1878-1976), an American surgeon and pathologist who shared the 1934 Nobel Prize in Physiology or Medicine for his discovery of a treatment for pernicious anemia
FRIEDA S. ROBSCHEIT-ROBBINS (1895-), an American pathologist who worked with Whipple at the Universities of California and Rochester
GEORGE RICHARDS MINOT (1885-1950), an American physician who shared the 1934 Nobel Prize in Physiology or Medicine for his treatment of human anemia patients with Whipple's liver/meat extract
WILLIAM PARRY MURPHY (1892-), an American physician and colleague of Minot who shared the 1934 Nobel Prize in Physiology or Medicine for his treatment of human anemia patients

Summary of Event

Pernicious anemia is one of several forms of anemia in which there is a severe reduction in the number of red blood cells (erythrocytes) in the affected individual's bloodstream. Accompanying this severe reduction of red blood cells is a decreased level of blood hemoglobin, the most important protein found in blood cells and blood plasma. Hemoglobin is a tetrameric (that is, four-subunit) protein that transports oxygen from an individual's lungs throughout the bloodstream to every cell in the body, where it is used to drive the production of energy molecules (that is, adenosine triphosphate—ATP) via the Krebs cycle. Hemoglobin carries waste carbon dioxide back to the lungs via the bloodstream for exhalation. If a person has a low red blood cell count (anemia), then that person will not be producing enough hemoglobin to transport oxygen to all the cells in the person's body. Consequently, these cells will be incapable of producing enough energy for the chemical reactions needed to survive. Many cells will die, and often the affected individual will die as well.

In 1905, George Hoyt Whipple received his medical degree from The Johns Hopkins Medical School in Baltimore, Maryland, and continued researching blood and liver disorders. He and a colleague, John H. King, studied liver necrosis (decay) in dogs exposed to chloroform, discovering that the dog livers regenerated rapidly after being damaged by this chemical. Whipple became very interested in the inter-relationship between the liver and the bloodstream. He and King subsequently concentrated on the disease obstructive jaundice (icterus), where liver damage results in the release of yellowish bile pigments that concentrate in the victim's skin. They demonstrated that obstructive jaundice was caused by the escape of bile pigments into the bloodstream and not into the lymphatic system.

The liver, the largest organ in the body, has numerous functions essential for survival, including bile production, hemoglobin recycling, sugar storage (as the carbohydrate glycogen), protein and carbohydrate metabolism, blood filtering and detoxification, and storage of essential vitamins and minerals. All these functions are closely interrelated, and the liver's storage of vitamins and minerals is of special importance. Many of the body's enzymes—proteins that control the rate of cellular chemical reactions—require the assistance of minerals (for example, iron, copper, molybdenum) and vitamins (for example, vitamins A, B_{12}, C, D, niacin). For example, hemoglobin requires iron in order to transport oxygen.

In 1914, Whipple continued his studies of icterus with Charles W. Hooper at the University of California in San Francisco. After they discovered that the liver filtered hemoglobin from the blood and recycled the protein as a bile pigment called bilirubin, they considered the possibility that the liver may be involved in certain types of anemia, including pernicious anemia. Their experiments were performed on dogs obtained from local pounds and involved changing diets as well as periodic bleeding to induce anemia. The goal of their experiments was to determine how the dogs' bodies responded to conditions of artificially induced anemia. Despite the fact that these experiments were performed humanely and that the dogs usually survived, Whipple and his colleagues were criticized heavily by the general public, politicians, and animal rights groups. They were forced to battle these groups legislatively for several years to defend their research. Whipple and Hooper periodically bled dogs to maintain artificially induced anemia. These dogs had low red blood cell and hemoglobin counts as a result. Whipple and Hooper attempted several techniques at rapidly increasing hemoglobin production in these animals—rates faster than the body would normally recover on its own. They varied the dogs' diets and found different degrees of success. A diet composed of carbohydrates (for example, bread and milk) was ineffective, requiring one to five months for hemoglobin regeneration. A rice-potato diet was somewhat more effective; meat-rich diets were very effective. Diets composed of liver, lean scrap meat, and beef heart stimulated complete hemoglobin regeneration within two to four weeks.

Whipple and Hooper developed liver and meat extracts that produced the same dramatic results in artificially anemic dogs. In 1918, Hooper was the first physician to administer a liver extract to human victims of pernicious anemia. The three anemic patients' conditions improved considerably. Nevertheless, various clinical doctors ridiculed Hooper and his treatment. As a result, Hooper discontinued his research. Seven years would pass before the Harvard University physicians George Richards Minot and William Parry Murphy would use virtually the same treatment, save many lives, and subsequently receive a Nobel Prize.

Whipple continued the liver extract work with Frieda S. Robscheit-Robbins at the new School of Medicine and Dentistry at Rochester University in New York. From 1923 to 1929, they performed an extensively elaborate series of dietary administration experiments on artificially anemic dogs. During these years, Whipple and Robscheit-Robbins defined the necessary dietary constraints for treating pernicious anemia. They tested various substances isolated from liver and muscle extracts of cow, pig, and chicken. They developed new extracts which, in conjunction with Minot's group at Harvard University and the Eli Lilly Pharmaceutical Company of Indianapolis, Indiana, became effective treatments for human patients suffering from pernicious anemia. Thousands of lives were saved by these extracts.

In 1925, Whipple and Robscheit-Robbins discovered that the most effective mineral found in beef and liver extract that would stimulate hemoglobin regeneration was iron. They reported their results in an article entitled "Blood Regeneration in Severe Anemia: III. Iron Reaction Favorable—Arsenic and Germanium Dioxide Almost Inert," which appeared with three additional articles in volume 72 of the *American Journal of Physiology*. Iron by itself is a very effective hemoglobin regenerator, which is not surprising since iron is the central active portion of each hemoglobin protein subunit. They also discovered that beef liver was the most effective dietary treatment, causing hemoglobin and red blood cell regeneration from one-third of normal to normal in as little time as two weeks. Other effective dietary supplements included chicken gizzard smooth muscle, pig kidney, and beef kidney. They also discovered that the liver recycles hemoglobin into bile pigments (for example, bilirubin) and bile pigments into hemoglobin. They continued this research into the 1930's and 1940's.

While iron is an essential component of the pernicious anemia meat/liver extracts, vitamin B-12 was later shown to be equally as important in 1949. Vitamin B_{12} was isolated from liver extracts by the American biochemist Karl Folkers and the English biochemist Alexander Todd. Diets of iron and vitamin B_{12} are modern treatments for individuals suffering from pernicious anemia.

Whipple shared the 1934 Nobel Prize in Physiology or Medicine with Minot and Murphy. Minot and Murphy had applied Whipple's beef/liver extracts to treating human pernicious anemia patients beginning in 1925.

Impact of Event

George Whipple's contributions to medicine and to biology are multifold: First, he discovered a treatment for pernicious anemia, thereby saving countless thousands of lives. Second, he discovered that the mineral iron, stored in the liver, is essential for hemoglobin regeneration. Third, he unraveled several basic recycling enzymatic pathways within the mammalian body, including the recycling of hemoglobin and bile pigments. Finally, he improved the understanding of human liver and blood physiology, paving new ground in the study of blood disorders. The 1934 Nobel Prize in Physiology or Medicine, along with other awards, demonstrated the importance of his lifesaving work.

The use of liver extracts to treat human victims of pernicious anemia saved many lives from a disease that many scientists had thought to be untreatable. It was regrettable that Whipple and Hooper's 1918 treatment of patients had been ridiculed; many lives might have been spared during the seven-year interval between this event and its ultimate acceptance by the medical community. The liver extracts led eventually to the isolation of the important active ingredients for hemoglobin regeneration, including the mineral iron and vitamin B_{12}.

Iron is one of many minerals stored by the liver for later use in the body's cells. Iron serves as a cofactor, or helper substance, in the active centers of protein enzymes—the cellular molecules that control essential life chemical reactions in cells. Iron is essential for proper functioning of the protein hemoglobin, a molecule that is mass produced by red blood cells for the transport of oxygen to the cells of the body to drive cellular energy production reactions. Hemoglobin is nonfunctional without iron. The phrase "iron-poor blood" indicates a semianemic physical state. Whipple showed that iron can regenerate hemoglobin rapidly in only a few weeks. Hemoglobin is regenerated in the liver, one of the few body tissues capable of regeneration when it is not too severely damaged. This regenerative capacity of liver could be caused somehow by the fact that the liver is a storage center for virtually every type of material needed by the body. The liver controls the buildup and breakdown of the body's food reserves according to the body's needs. The liver can split hemoglobin into two sections: a heme component, which is iron, and the precursor of a bile pigment, bilirubin. The second section is a globin component, which is protein. The globin is recycled back into the body's protein metabolism; the heme is used to construct bile, a substance released from the liver into the small intestine to emulsify fat, thereby allowing the body to absorb the essential fat-soluble vitamins A, D, E, and K. Bile pigments can be reabsorbed back into the blood, returned to the liver, and used to construct the heme component of hemoglobin or more bile.

Whipple's achievements greatly improved the understanding of organisms as intricately interconnected organ systems. His work demonstrated the interplay between the liver, blood, and digestive systems. His studies would pioneer later research into other types of anemia, including the inherited thalassemia and sickle-cell anemia.

Bibliography

Alberts, Bruce, et al. *Molecular Biology of the Cell*. New York: Garland, 1983. This lengthy introductory molecular biology textbook for undergraduate biology majors is a comprehensive, theoretical survey of cell biology by several leading scientists. It contains excellent photographs, diagrams, and reference lists. Chapter 16, "Differentiated Cells and the Maintenance of Tissues," includes a good discussion of liver function and its regenerative capacity.

Corner, George W. *George Hoyt Whipple and His Friends: The Life of a Nobel Prize Pathologist*. Philadelphia: J. B. Lippincott, 1963. Corner, a very close friend and colleague of George Whipple, presents a touching portrait of not only a great scientist and physician but also a very wonderful man. This biography provides a detailed, but enjoyable, summary of Whipple's life, both scientific and private.

Garrison, Fielding H. *An Introduction to the History of Medicine.* 4th ed. Philadelphia: W. B. Saunders, 1963. This massive book is an extensive history of medical research from ancient times up to 1928. It is extensively referenced and includes a year-by-year chronology. The works of Whipple, Minot, Murphy, and other twentieth century pathologists are cited.

Nobelstiftelsen. *Nobel: The Man and His Prizes.* 2d ed. New York: Elsevier, 1962. This book is an excellent history of the Nobel Prize, beginning with Alfred Nobel and including the Nobel laureates in all fields up through the 1950's. Each laureate's work is discussed within the context of the history of his/her own field.

Spence, Alexander P., and Elliott B. Mason. *Human Anatomy and Physiology.* Menlo Park, Calif.: Benjamin/Cummings, 1979. This introductory anatomy and physiology textbook for undergraduate biology and premedical students is a detailed survey of the human body. It is well written and illustrated. Chapter 18, "The Blood," includes a discussion of various types of human anemias.

Whipple, George H. "Autobiographical Sketch." *Perspectives in Biology and Medicine* 2 (Spring, 1959): 253-289. Whipple's autobiography is a personal summary of his life that discusses his thoughts about science, academia, and his colleagues. He emphasizes his undergraduate and medical school days, as well as his experiences in supervising two medical schools. His love for teaching and research surfaces repeatedly.

Wyngaarden, James B., and Lloyd H. Smith. *CECIL Textbook of Medicine.* 16th ed. Philadelphia: W. B. Saunders, 1982. This enormous medical reference work is a tremendously informative source on anatomy, physiology, pathology, hematology, and the like. It contains detailed graphs, tables, and diagrams, plus an extensive reference list. Sections 99-103 provide considerable information on all types of anemia.

David Wason Hollar, Jr.

Cross-References

Hopkins Discovers Tryptophan, an Essential Amino Acid (1900), p. 46; Hopkins Suggests That Food Contains Vitamins Essential to Life (1906), p. 330; Steenbock Discovers That Sunlight Increases Vitamin D in Food (1924), p. 771; Szent-Györgyi Discovers Vitamin C (1928), p. 857.

PAULI FORMULATES THE EXCLUSION PRINCIPLE

Category of event: Physics
Time: Spring, 1925
Locale: Hamburg, Germany

Pauli significantly advanced the understanding of the electron-shell structure of the atom by establishing the principle that electrons are elementary particles of the "antisocial" type

Principal personages:

WOLFGANG PAULI (1900-1958), an Austrian theoretical physicist who discovered the exclusion principle (for which he was awarded the 1945 Nobel Prize in Physics), predicted the neutrino, and studied symmetry principles in quantum field theories

PIETER ZEEMAN (1865-1943), a Dutch physicist who discovered the magnetic splitting of the spectral lines, known as the Zeeman effect

ARNOLD SOMMERFELD (1868-1951), a German theoretical physicist who built the quantum-theoretic model of the atom and who had a direct influence on Pauli

NIELS BOHR (1885-1962), a Danish theoretical physicist who founded the modern theory of atomic structure and was awarded the 1922 Nobel Prize in Physics

JOHANNES ROBERT RYDBERG (1854-1919), a Swedish physicist who summarized spectral data into mathematically ordered forms and realized the significance of the atomic number

FRIEDRICH PASCHEN (1865-1947), a German physicist who discovered the "Paschen series" in the spectrum of the hydrogen atom and, together with Ernst Back, discovered the "Paschen-Back effect"

ALFRED LANDÉ (1888-1975), a German-American physicist who analyzed the anomalous Zeeman effect by introducing half-integers as magnetic quantum numbers

EDMUND C. STONER (1899-1968), an English physicist who published an important paper that prompted Pauli to formulate the exclusion principle

Summary of Event

Niels Bohr's pioneering quantum model of the atom explained the spectral systems of the hydrogen atom. Logically, physicists, including Bohr, directed their efforts toward extending the theoretical success to more complex atoms. From chemical study, it was concluded that every chemical element corresponds to one type of atom, and all the elements display their chemical properties regularly in the periodic table, beginning with the lightest and simplest: the hydrogen atom. Therefore, one task of atomic physicists of the 1910's and 1920's was to explain the periodic table of elements—the orderly array and the increasing complexity of the atoms. Another task was to explain the phenomena of atomic spectra. Bohr's quantum postulates were found inadequate for more complex atoms or for atoms in an external force field, for example, a magnetic field. Between about 1915 and 1925, European physicists searched intensely for new principles and guidelines for the construction of atomic models that would consistently account for chemical phenomena: the periodic table, physical phenomena, and spectral data.

That these phenomena would come together to reveal the structure of the atom became increasingly clear for a number of scientists, although it also became clear that the phenomena would be difficult to solve. In this regard, Wolfgang Pauli stated that it was the famous Swedish spectroscopist Johannes Robert Rydberg who noticed that the lengths of the periods in the periodic table, 2, 8, 18, 32, and so on, can be expressed simply as "two times n square" if n takes on all integer values. Atomic physicists were fascinated by these integers and incorporated them into their atomic models. When Pauli began his serious study of atomic structure, Bohr had already published his explanation of the periodic table with the *Aufbauprinzip*, which included two important ideas: The state of an electron in an atom is specified by three quantum numbers (the principal, the angular, and the magnetic); and atomic electrons form "shells," which would be filled up and closed with specific numbers of electrons. In a sense, the idea of electron shells and their closing anticipated the Pauli exclusion principle. Bohr was applying a basic axiom without much awareness about it. In doing so, among other things, he left behind a fundamental physical problem unanswered: why all electrons of an atom in its ground state were not bound in the innermost shell. (A physical principle believed to be universally true is: A stable physical system tends to stay in the state of minimum potential energy.) Bohr wrote in his paper: "Going from Neon to Sodium, we must expect that the eleventh electron goes into the third shell. . . ." Pauli, however, was very conscious of the necessity of logic and evidence. He wrote on the margin of Bohr's above-quoted passage: "How do you know this? You only get it from the very spectra you want to explain!" Pauli was on the verge of explaining the difficult spectral phenomena, especially the so-called anomalous Zeeman effect, which was the magnetic splitting of the spectral lines discovered by Pieter Zeeman.

Alfred Landé had already succeeded in summarizing the spectroscopic data of the anomalous Zeeman effect into simple laws. His true innovation was the introduction of half-integers as quantum numbers to explain the doublet spectra of the alkali metals. Although Pauli generalized Landé's result to account for the so-called Paschen-Back effect—a special case of the anomalous Zeeman effect discovered by Ernst Back and Friedrich Paschen—Pauli was still very puzzled by the "problem of the closing of the electronic shells."

In order to explain the doublet structure of the alkali spectra, Bohr and others hypothesized that the atomic core had an "angular momentum," that is, it rotated. Now, after much hard thinking, Pauli realized that he had to eliminate this hypothesis and attribute a new quantum theoretic property to the electron. At that time, he called it a "two-valuedness not describable classically." This would be the electron's fourth degree of freedom, requiring a fourth quantum number to specify it. This question of the physical meaning of this "two-valuedness" was answered in 1925 by George Eugene Uhlenbeck and Samuel A. Goudsmit, who realized the idea of the spin of the electron. According to them, the electron has an intrinsic angular momentum, which can assume two values that are of the same magnitude but opposite directions.

In October, 1924, an English physicist, Edmund C. Stoner, published "The Distribution of Electrons Among Atomic Levels." Whenever Pauli talked about the history of the exclusion principle, he would state that it was Stoner's paper that finally helped him to solve the problem of the closing of the electronic shells. He particularly liked to quote an essential remark made by Stoner: "[T]he number of energy levels of a single electron in the alkali metal spectra for a given value of the principle quantum number in an external magnetic field is the same as the number of electrons in the closed shells of the rare gases which corresponds to this principal quantum number." In the periodic table, the alkali metals are neighbors of the rare gases. The former are chemically active, whereas the latter completely inactive. Essentially, Stoner was solving this causal problem: The rare gases have their electron shells closed, whereas each of the alkalis has one electron in an otherwise empty shell; thus, this electron is "chemically active."

Finally showing true loyalty to physical phenomena, Pauli made a trip to Tübingen to use the spectroscopic data assembled there. He was obliged to verify some conclusions of the exclusion principle concerning the anomalous Zeeman effect of more complicated atoms. In the spring of 1925, Pauli published the exclusion principle, which can be formulated as follows: The state of every electron in an atom is specified by four quantum numbers; no two or more electrons in an atom can be at the same time in the same state; in other words, they can never assume simultaneously identical sets of the values of the four quantum numbers.

The formulation of the exclusion principle was made at the same time when other fundamental principles of quantum mechanics were established: Louis de Broglie's paper was published in 1925, Werner Heisenberg's in 1925, and Erwin Schrödinger's in 1926. In pursuing the structure of the atom, like his mentor Arnold Sommerfeld, Pauli adhered to physical phenomena closely. De Broglie, Heisenberg, and Schrödinger were more fascinated by classic quantum correspondence in terms of mathematical formalism. It was an inexplicable historical irony that they became the true founders of quantum mechanics, whereas Pauli, then a "true" physicist, was not.

Impact of Event

With the foundation of quantum mechanics laid, it was concluded that quantum mechanics implies a statistical (probabilistic or indeterministic) nature for microcosmic configurations and processes. Combining such understanding with the Pauli exclusion principle, Heisenberg, in 1926, pointed out that in comparison with classical physics, quantum mechanics leads to qualitatively different conclusions for particles of the same kind (for example, for electrons, protons, neutrons, or others) than for particles of different kinds (for example, mixed systems of electrons and other particles). In fact, to reflect the fundamental distinction, quantum mechanics needs an independent principle, which can be called "the principle of absolute identity."

In both classical and quantum physics, particles of the same kind are supposed to be physically indistinguishable. Yet the two—classical and quantum physics—differ in that the principle of absolute identity does not apply to the former. In classical physics, one can always assume that each of the particles of the same kind is given a (nonphysical) sign—a number or a name—and from then on, these particles are distinguishable by their signs. Quantum particles of the same kind, however, are absolutely indistinguishable from one another; they cannot even be assigned numbers, or any other nonphysical signs. Assigning numbers to particles of the same kind is a meaningful act in "classical" physics because the trajectory of every particle is traceable, at least in principle. Assigning numbers to particles of the same kind is a meaningless act in "quantum" physics because particles are not exactly particles; they do not follow trajectories. The numbers assigned to particles at any moment automatically "drop" at any subsequent moment.

From this principle, it was easily derived that quantum systems of the same kind of particles are either "symmetrical" or "antisymmetrical." The antisymmetrical particles, called fermions, obey the Pauli exclusion principle. Like electrons, these particles are "antisocial"; they can never stay in the same quantum state described by the same set of quantum numbers. On the contrary, the symmetrical particles, called bosons, are "sociable." In fact, these particles tend to gather in the same quantum state. The behavior of a system of the same fermions is decided by the so-called Fermi-Dirac statistics; the behavior of a system of the same bosons is decided by the so-called Bose-Einstein statistics.

After the discovery of the exclusion principle, Pauli was still dissatisfied with its theoretical understanding. In 1940, Pauli succeeded in developing a relativistic quantum theory, with which he could prove a necessary connection between spin and statistics: Particles with half-integer spin must be fermions (or fulfill the exclusion principle); those with integer spin must be bosons.

When Paul Adrien Maurice Dirac pioneered in developing "quantum electrodynamics," he applied the exclusion principle to predict the existence of the positrons. Later, in 1932, Dirac's prediction was verified by Carl David Anderson, who found positrons, the first particles of antimatter. Because the inside of metals is actually an electron gas, and the inside of the atomic nuclei is an assembly of the fermionic nucleons, the Pauli exclusion principle plays an important role in both solid-state physics and nuclear physics.

Bibliography

Boorse, Henry A., and Lloyd Motz, eds. *The World of the Atom*. Vol. 2. New York: Basic Books, 1966. Chapter 59, "The Exclusion Principle," includes three parts:

the editors' introductory commentary; Edward Uhler Condon and J. E. Mack's paper, published in 1930, "An Interpretation of Pauli's Exclusion Principle"; and Pauli's "Nobel Lecture." Clear and informative essays.

Born, Max. "Quantum Mechanics." In *My Life: Recollections of a Nobel Laureate.* New York: Charles Scribner's Sons, 1975. In the founding of quantum mechanics, Pauli's contribution was great, but not vital. In this chapter, Pauli's early, somehow misguided attitude toward the physical interpretation and mathematical formalisms of quantum mechanics is described.

Fierz, M., and V. F. Weisskopf, eds. *Theoretical Physics in the Twentieth Century: A Memorial Volume to Wolfgang Pauli.* New York: Interscience Publishers, 1960. Other than extensive mathematics, quotations in French, and articles in German, there is much history for a serious reader. Pauli differed from most theoretical physicists of his generation in that he continued to be an active leader in the study of elementary particles until his death.

Gamow, George. *Biography of Physics.* New York: Harper & Row, 1961. This title is a good, interesting history of mostly modern physics. In this volume, in addition to the Pauli exclusion principle, the so-called second Pauli principle is introduced in the context of Dirac's developing relativistic quantum mechanics. Both principles are included in the chapter "The Law of Quantum."

_____. *Matter, Earth, and Sky.* 2d ed. Englewood Cliffs, N.J.: Prentice-Hall, 1965. Excellent popular science. In chapter 13, electron shells and period systems are explained as well as Pauli's exclusion principle.

_____. *Mr. Tompkins Explores the Atom.* Cambridge, England: Cambridge University Press, 1945. In the chapter "Inside the Atom," the exclusion principle is clearly explained.

Heathcote, Niels Hugh de Vaudrey. *Nobel Prize Winners in Physics, 1901-1950.* New York: Henry Schuman, 1953. Because of the universal character of the exclusion principle, many chapters in this book are directly related.

Pauli, Wolfgang. "Exclusion Principle and Quantum Mechanics (Nobel Lecture)." In *Collected Scientific Papers*, edited by R. Kronig and V. F. Weisskopf. Vol. 2. New York: Interscience Publishers, 1964. Definitive narrative of the discovery and development of the principle by the discoverer himself. Sufficiently detailed and completely documented. Also contained are remarks on the history of the exclusion principle, which were delivered one year before Pauli's Nobel lecture.

Wen-yuan Qian

Cross-References

Barkla Discovers the Characteristic X Rays of the Elements (1906), p. 309; Thomson Wins the Nobel Prize for the Discovery of the Electron (1906), p. 356; Bohr Writes a Trilogy on Atomic and Molecular Structure (1912), p. 507; Rutherford Presents His Theory of the Atom (1912), p. 527; Lamb and Retherford Discover the Lambshift (1947), p. 1293.

THE GERMAN *METEOR* EXPEDITION
DISCOVERS THE MIDATLANTIC RIDGE

Category of event: Earth science
Time: April, 1925-May, 1927
Locale: South and Equatorial Atlantic Ocean

Using a newly developed echo sounder, the Meteor, *a refitted German gunboat, made the first transoceanic crossing with closely spaced soundings, leading to the discovery of the Midatlantic Ridge*

Principal personages:
ALFRED MERZ (1880-1925), a German geographer who was the scientific leader of the *Meteor* expedition and was responsible for planning and organizing the oceanographic research
FRITZ HABER (1868-1934), a German chemist who proposed the *Meteor* expedition for quantifying the commercially exploitable gold in seawater
HERMANN WATTENBERG (1901-1944), a German oceanographer who was the chemist on the expedition and later director of the Institut für Meereskund at Kiel
GEORG WÜST (1890-1977), a German oceanographer and student of Merz who took over the leadership of the oceanographic data collection and study after Merz's death

Summary of Event

The first large-scale expedition organized primarily to study the scientific aspects of the oceans was that of HMS *Challenger*, which circumnavigated the globe from 1872 to 1876. A principal part of the expedition was to increase the knowledge of the distribution of life in the ocean. In 1871, the Royal Society recommended that funds be raised from the English government for an expedition to investigate physical conditions of the deep sea in the ocean basins; chemical composition of seawater at all depths in the ocean; physical and chemical characteristics of the seafloor and the nature of the deposits of the seafloor and their origin; and the distribution of organic life at all depths in the sea, as well as the seafloor. The expedition included a staff of six scientists under the direction of C. Wyville Thompson. HMS *Challenger*, a refitted corvette, left England in December, 1872, and returned in May, 1876. During the expedition, approximately 127,500 kilometers of the Atlantic and Pacific were traversed; accomplishments included a total of 492 deep soundings, 133 bottom dredges, 151 open water trawls, and 263 serial water temperature observations. One of the significant accomplishments was the measurement of the ocean's depth to 8,815 kilometers in the Mariana trench.

There was an interval of approximately fifty years before the German *Meteor* expedition began its large-scale program to gather physical oceanographic data of the Equatorial and South Atlantic Ocean. Initially, the expedition was for the purpose of pursuing economic objectives. In 1872, E. Sonstadt reported gold concentration of 65 milligrams per metric ton of seawater. Since the Treaty of Versailles required that Germany repay its enormous World War I debt in gold, Fritz Haber, a German chemist, proposed that gold extracted from the international seas might solve the problem. Improved methods of chemical analysis in the 1920's showed that the gold content of seawater is extremely low; however, the German government had a two-fold purpose for the expedition: one being to "show the flag" in foreign ports and the other for a systematic and scientifically based study of the oceans. As planned originally, the expedition was to go around the world with a second option in the Pacific Ocean; however, a lack of funds restricted the study to the Atlantic Ocean.

This expedition marked the first use of echo sounders in the deep seafloor to map the physiography of the seafloor. With the exception of the *Meteor*, no detailed profiles of the deep seafloor were available prior to World War II. The profiles were closely spaced echo soundings taken by extremely diligent workers. Continuous recording echo soundings were developed in the 1920's, but none of these early instruments was suitable for use in the deep sea.

The Treaty of Versailles prohibited the German Navy from sending ships to foreign ports; however, in 1919, a member of the German Admiralty, Captain Nippe, proposed that a German vessel be outfitted and sent on a major oceanographic expedition. The *Meteor*, a class C gunboat, was selected for the study. The *Meteor* had a displacement of 1,300 tons, a length of 75 meters, and a keel depth of 4 meters, which made the gunboat ideal for the mission. Captain F. Spiess, head of the German Hydrographic Department, was responsible for the future of the *Meteor*. Alfred Merz, who was named the chief scientist, was an adviser to the German Navy in World War I. His first assistant was Dr. Schumacher from the Naval Observatory. The remaining staff consisted of Dr. Boehnecke from the Berlin Institut für Meereskund; Georg Wüst, who took over leadership of the oceanographic data and study after Merz's death; and Dr. Hentschel, a biologist from the Zoological Museum in Hamburg. The geologist for the first half of the expedition was Dr. Pratje, who was replaced by Dr. Correns; Hermann Wattenberg was the chemist; and completing the staff were meteorologists from Lindenberg and Hamburg.

One important scientific component, the acoustic depth (echo) sounder, was the complete responsibility of the Navy and thus the ship's crew. The *Meteor* was equipped with two different newly developed sounding devices manufactured by unrelated companies. One was similar to the American-made Fathometer and was manufactured by Atlaswerke; the other was manufactured by Signal Gesellschaft of Kiel. The "Atlas" sounder could record graphically down to 815 meters, while the "Signal" sounder required the operator to listen for the return signal and was best suited for deep soundings. Simultaneous shallow soundings agreed to within 10 and 20 meters. The ship's crew made soundings every 3.2 to 4.8 nautical kilometers, which provided new resolution to the picture of the ocean's floor. As part of the ship's equipment, a new anchor system had been developed that would make it possible to anchor in deep ocean.

On April 26, 1925, the *Meteor* left for Buenos Aires, Argentina, to start work on the planned sections in the South Atlantic. Actual surveys began on June 3, 1925, along 42 degrees south latitude. Merz was in charge in spite of his illness; however, by the time the vessel arrived at the fifth hydrographic station, his condition worsened to the point that Captain Spiess returned to Buenos Aires so that Merz could receive medical attention. Merz turned the leadership of the scientific part of the expedition over to Spiess. In reviewing the work along the first section, Spiess found that the acoustic depth sounder had revealed that much of the bottom had been incorrectly charted.

After completing the thirteenth traverse in the Equatorial Atlantic Ocean, the *Meteor* sailed for Germany, arriving home on May 29, 1927. In two years and one month, the *Meteor* had traveled more than 67,500 kilometers, collected data at 310 hydrographic stations, anchored ten times in deep ocean, and made approximately seventy thousand soundings of ocean depths and, as a result, was the first to reveal the true ruggedness of the ocean floor. With the exception of the *Meteor*, no detailed profiles of the deep seafloor were available prior to World War II. It was not until World War II that continuously recording deep-sea echo sounders were developed. The significant discovery of the *Meteor* was that a continuous ridge runs in a southwesterly direction from the vicinity of Walvis Bay, Southwest Africa. The discovery influenced the German investigators Theodor Stocks and Wüst to postulate in 1935 the now familiar herringbone pattern of ridges in the Atlantic. The Walvis Ridge strikes out from the continent seaward of the Angola uplift. It is strongly asymmetrical, narrow and steep-sided on the south. The main ridge typically has two crests separated by a central asymmetrical depression and a smaller frontal scarp.

Impact of Event

The *Meteor* expedition of 1925 to 1927, which discovered the Midatlantic Ridge, was a significant event. Unfortunately, it was not recognized widely at the time in presenting plausible evidence supporting Alfred Lothar Wegener's proposed theory of continental drift. It was not until the 1950's that a new generation of equipment and instruments was introduced that led to an explosion of data supporting continental drift, or plate tectonics as it is now called. Continuously recording echo sounders, magnetometers, temperature probes, explosion seismometers, piston corers, dredges, and deep-sea submersibles were used to discover worldwide magnetic anomalies, the great fracture zones that offset them, and the median rift where the seafloor is born.

In September of 1963, Frederick John Vine and Drummond Hoyle Matthews, American geologists, published in *Nature* a work entitled "Magnetic Anomalies over Oceanic Ridges." The paper hypothesized that the seafloor is spreading at ridge crests, the seismic second layer is basalt rather than consolidated sediment and has a high-remnant magnetism, and the earth's magnetic field reverses itself. In only two years, the hypothesis of seafloor spreading was confirmed by the Deep Sea Drilling Program, revealing that every matching pair of anomalies on the flanks of the Mid-atlantic Ridge was the equivalent of the matching continental slope of Africa and South America. In 1966, Peter Vogt and Ned Ostenso published one of the first detailed geophysical surveys of the Midatlantic Ridge that would lead ultimately to highly detailed maps of the entire North Atlantic.

In January, 1967, Henry William Menard published in *Science* an item which presented the results of sounding programs of the Scripps Institution of Oceanography at La Jolla, California. The expedition in the central Pacific traced the great fracture zones from the eastern Pacific westward past the Hawaiian and Line Islands, but they splayed out at a point Menard termed the "branching line."

During the mid- to late-1950's, Maurice Ewing, an American oceanographer, and Bruce Charles Heezen, an American geologist, found a globe-girdling rift, which they concluded was a continuous midoceanic ridge, even though soundings were lacking or even suggested otherwise. Also, they concluded there was a median valley along the crest of the ridge. Later, in the 1950's, Vic Vacquier, an American geologist, measured offsets on fracture zones associated with a midoceanic ridge in the Pacific Ocean using a towed, flux gate magnetometer that he had invented in the late 1940's. This discovery supported seafloor spreading. Harry Hammond Hess, an American geologist, was inspired by these findings to reinspect a collection of soundings he had made across an asymmetrical ridge with a trough at the base in the 1930's on the U.S. submarine *Barracuda*. It was determined later that his early soundings indicated a typical fracture zone in the Midatlantic Ridge. He noted that the Romanche Trench was a fracture zone.

The *Meteor*'s discovery was a midpoint during the development of the proposed theory of continental drift in 1912 and the concept of plate tectonics that became widely accepted in 1968. Earth scientists realize now that the positions of landmasses are not fixed. The splitting of continental blocks has resulted in the formation of new ocean basins, while older segments of the seafloor are being recycled continually in areas were deep-ocean trenches are found. This profound reversal of scientific opinion has been described as a scientific revolution, and the *Meteor* expedition played a pioneer role.

Bibliography

Hill, M. N., ed. *The Sea: Ideas and Observations on Progress in the Study of the Seas*. Vol. 3. New York: Interscience, 1963. This book is geared toward the researcher and is well illustrated. It is an excellent overview with sections on geophysical exploration, topography and structure, and sedimentation. There are reference sources at the end of each chapter.

Idyll, C. P. *Exploring the Ocean World: A History of Oceanography*. New York: Thomas Y. Crowell, 1969. An excellent overview for high school and college students. It is illustrated, with photographs, graphs, and charts. Includes a chronology of oceanographic developments. Each chapter contains a bibliography.

Menard, H. W. *The Ocean of Truth: A Personal History of Global Tectonics*. Princeton, N.J.: Princeton University Press, 1986. This book is easy to read and most entertaining. It is ideally suited for the high school and college reader who would like an overall view without technical language. Menard's writing style is very informative and brief enough to hold the interested reader.

Pickard, George L. *Descriptive Physical Oceanography: An Introduction*. 3d ed. Elmsford, N.Y.: Pergamon Press, 1979. This is a nontechnical introduction for undergraduates in the sciences and advanced high school students who wish to learn something of the aims and achievements of this field of scientific study.

Sears, M., and D. Merriman, eds. *Oceanography: The Past*. New York: Springer-Verlag, 1980. This book is a collection of papers from the Third International Congress on the history of oceanography. It is more suited for the graduate student and researcher in the science of oceanography. Although there are few illustrations, most chapters contain numerous notes and references. An excellent reference source.

Thurman, Harold V. *Introductory Oceanography*. 4th ed. Westerville, Ohio: Charles E. Merrill, 1985. This college introductory text is a very good general survey and is extensively illustrated. It contains a glossary and references after each chapter.

Earl G. Hoover

Cross-References

Anschütz-Kaempfe Installs a Gyrocompass onto a German Battleship (1906), p. 303; Wegener Proposes the Theory of Continental Drift (1912), p. 522; Langevin Develops Active Sonar for Submarine Detection and Fathometry (1915), p. 620; Richter Develops a Scale for Measuring Earthquake Strength (1935), p. 1050; Heezen and Ewing Discover the Midoceanic Ridge (1956), p. 1508; Hess Concludes the Debate on Continental Drift (1960), p. 1650.

GODDARD LAUNCHES THE FIRST
LIQUID FUEL PROPELLED ROCKET

Categories of event: Space and aviation
Time: March 16, 1926
Locale: Auburn, Massachusetts

Using liquid oxygen and gasoline as fuels, Goddard pioneered the first practical liquid fuel rocket, setting the stage for future developments in modern rocketry

Principal personage:
ROBERT H. GODDARD (1882-1945), a physics professor who is considered a pioneer in modern astronautics and was the first to develop a liquid fuel rocket motor

Summary of Event

Just as the conquest of the air had its twentieth century origins with the rather inauspicious trials in 1903 of the Wright brothers at Kittyhawk, North Carolina, so too the seemingly insurmountable obstacle of space flight had its humble beginnings with the initial test of Robert H. Goddard's liquid-fueled rocket in an Auburn, Massachusetts, cabbage patch on March 16, 1926. On that clear and cold day, with snow still on the ground, Goddard successfully launched a 3-meter-long rocket using liquid oxygen and gasoline as propellants; the projectile's flight lasted only two and one-half seconds, during which it rose a mere 12 meters and landed approximately 56 meters away from its fabricated pipe launching frame.

Although successful, the rocket's design was unwieldy and inefficient. Initially, Goddard had maintained that greater stability would be achieved by placing the motor and nozzles ahead of the fuel tanks, layout analogous to a horse and buggy. Subsequently, this arrangement was changed when it became obvious that the motor needed to be positioned at the rear of the rocket's body. Although Goddard had been working on various pumps for several years to control the flow of the reactants to the combustion chamber, neither pumps nor an electrical system were incorporated in the first liquid-fueled rocket prototype. By turning a valve and placing an alcohol stove beneath the motor, Clark University machinist Henry Sacks ignited the propellants before dashing for safety, while Goddard and colleague Percy Roope, standing behind an iron barrier, cautiously watched the experiment.

Yet, despite the improvised apparatus and rustic scene, this pivotal episode in the history of technology changed the future course of history. Not only did it firmly establish Goddard as the leading rocket theoretician and experimentalist between World Wars I and II, but also the success of a liquid-fueled rocket laid the groundwork for enhanced financial support from both the Smithsonian Institution and the Guggenheim Foundation.

Astute observers aware of Goddard's accomplishment now recognized that the liquid fuel rocket had enormous potential for the investigation of high-altitude phenomena, for possible travel in space, and as a weapon in modern warfare. While Goddard shunned publicity and continued to refine his designs for the next fifteen years, innovating in areas of guidance systems, motors, flight controls, and instrumentation, other workers in the United States, Russia, and Germany quickly followed in Goddard's footsteps. This activity was clearly reflected and demonstrated in Nazi Germany, for the V-2 rocket contained many of Goddard's designs and ideas.

Goddard's achievement of March, 1926, was not the result of amateurish dilettantism, but rather the culmination of a lifelong interest in rockets and the possibilities of space travel that was grounded in theoretical and experimental science. Growing up in New England, Goddard first speculated about rockets and space travel at age seventeen. Undoubtedly stimulated by reading H. G. Wells's *The War of the Worlds* (1898) and Garrett P. Serviss' *Edison's Conquest of Mars* (1898), he submitted a manuscript outlining his ideas on the possibilities of traveling through a near vacuum in 1907 to several scientific journals. Undeterred by the essay's subsequent rejection, Goddard began to formulate ideas concerning the use of liquid fuels in 1909, and after completing his Ph.D. in physics at Clark University and a postdoctoral fellowship at Princeton University, he began to pursue experimental work. Convinced that Sir Isaac Newton's third law was the basis of motion in space, he demonstrated that a gun recoiled in a vacuum when fired. At first, Goddard worked with solid fuel rocket designs. During World War I, he pursued investigations at the Mount Wilson Observatory in California, where he evaluated both black powder and smokeless powder as propellants. His practical efforts led to the development of the bazooka—a weapon that was used extensively during World War II—as well as bombardment and antiaircraft rockets. Nevertheless, these inventions were never used in the battlefield during World War I, as American involvement in the conflict ended in November, 1918. Goddard's extensive World War I weapons development experience convinced him that high nozzle velocities of combustible reactants were central to the design of a successful interplanetary rocket and, therefore, that solid materials were intrinsically limited in this crucial chemical characteristic when compared to the enormous potential of combustible liquids.

After World War I, Goddard returned to Clark University and formulated a coherent research program. By 1920, he had concluded that a liquid-fuel rocket motor, with its inherently smooth thrust, had the potential and was perhaps the most effective means of reaching the upper atmosphere and ultimately the reaches of space. In part, the development of his idea required further theorizing, yet experimental studies were also necessary. Central to Goddard's success was an uncanny ability to combine or hybridize knowledge from chemistry, physics, and the engineering sciences, with the express purpose of designing a workable rocket design. As no other contemporary, he had the ability to combine theory with practice.

Clearly, the most efficient fuel from a thermodynamic standpoint was hydrogen; acting as an oxidizer, oxygen possessed distinct advantages. Although difficulties in handling hydrogen forced Goddard to consider such alternatives as propane, ether, kerosene, and gasoline, he remained wedded to the notion of using liquid oxygen, even though it was hard to obtain locally and was extremely dangerous, since it boiled at −148 degrees Celsius and exploded upon contact with oils, greases, and flames. Within a short time, Goddard found a source for liquid oxygen at a local plant, and he pursued a number of static tests at the laboratory bench to measure the thrust produced by the expansion of reactant fuels during combustion. Self-contained pressure pumps also needed to be constructed; for several years prior to the momentous March, 1926, test flight, Goddard and assistant Nils Riffolt were occupied with this difficult problem. Pump design became so vexing, and external pressures to demonstrate the potential of his work to the Smithsonian Institution and other patrons so great, that at the end of 1925, Goddard, despite the inefficiency of this arrangement, resorted to the use of inert gas back pressure to feed the reactants.

Goddard's efforts between 1920 and 1925 involved "string and sealing wax" equipment and little financial assistance. Riffolt provided valuable technical expertise in the design of various pumps and motors, and Goddard's wife Esther assisted in numerous ways, including photographing various trials. Clark University had granted Goddard research funds at a critical juncture in 1923; but by 1925, internal funding was in short supply, and requests for money from the Smithsonian Institution were typically denied. Given the circumstances, Goddard was determined to test his ideas in early 1926, and his unqualified success in Auburn, Massachusetts, not only changed his career but also set the stage for an intense phase of experimental rocketry both in the United States and in Europe.

Impact of Event

Described as secretive and a loner, Goddard avoided attention despite the newsworthiness of the 1926 event. Always content to work within the scientific community's "invisible college" rather than act as a self-serving promoter, Goddard refused to cash in on his work by cultivating broader constituencies. Further small-scale tests incorporating technical refinements continued during the next three years. On July 17, 1929, Goddard launched a rocket with an instrument payload that included an aneroid barometer, thermometer, and recording camera. The noisy crash of this missile, uproar on the part of local officials concerning public safety, and Goddard's own pronouncements about the possibilities of such a liquid-fueled rocket striking the moon made *The New York Times*, thereby generating considerable public reaction. Aviation hero Charles A. Lindbergh learned of Goddard's work, and Lindbergh's considerable influence enabled Goddard to receive grants from both the Carnegie Institution and the Guggenheim Foundation.

By mid-1930, Goddard and a small group of assistants had organized a more sophisticated, full-time research program at a site near Roswell, New Mexico. Drawing on his newfound financial resources, Goddard made significant advances in almost every aspect of astronautics between 1930 and 1941. His work culminated with the 1941 launching of a rocket to an altitude of 2,700 meters. Gyrocontrol improvements, including linking a gyroscope to small movable vanes located directly in the exhaust blast, greatly enhanced flight stability. Further advances in the design of clustered engines, gimbal mounted tail sections, and turbine-driven propellant pumps were also worked out at this time.

Concurrently, interest in rocketry intensified both in the United States and abroad. By the late 1920's and early 1930's, members of the American Rocket Society and the German Society for Space Travel sustained a technical momentum that Goddard had initiated in the period before World War I. With the onset of World War II, investigations in rocket technology became high priorities within emerging American and German military-industrial complexes.

Germany's success with its V-2 rocket was a direct consequence of Goddard's scientific and technical achievements, and the V-2 program seemingly called into question Goddard's ability to organize a large-scale effort and fully exploit his ideas. Goddard's ideas were not brought to complete fruition in the United States during his lifetime. Nevertheless, Goddard remains as modern rocketry's foremost pioneer, a scientist who had vision, theoretical understanding, and the gift to translate these ideas into a viable technology.

Bibliography

Goddard, Robert H. *The Papers of Robert H. Goddard*. Edited by Esther C. Goddard. 3 vols. New York: McGraw-Hill, 1970. A most important resource for any serious student of Goddard and the history of rocketry, these edited papers contain summaries of Goddard's diary entries, reprints of noteworthy technical papers, and relevant correspondence among important members within the scientific community. As primary source material, this collection provides the reader with an intimate glimpse into the world of the distinguished Clark University professor and scientist, clearly and chronologically outlining the evolution of Goddard's ideas and techniques.

Hacker, Barton C. "Robert H. Goddard and the Origins of Space Flight." In *Technology in America: A History of Individuals and Ideas*, edited by Carroll W. Pursell, Jr. Cambridge, Mass.: MIT Press, 1981. In this brief essay, Hacker not only traces Goddard's career but also characterizes the institutional context surrounding his achievements. Despite popular notions concerning Goddard as a solitary, persevering scientific figure, the Smithsonian Institution, the Guggenheim Foundation, and the military played crucial roles in Goddard's ultimate success.

Lehman, Milton. *This High Man: The Life of Robert H. Goddard*. New York: Farrar, Straus and Co., 1963. A readable biography, Lehman exhaustively covers Goddard's life from youth to World War II technical investigations. While the author includes many details, Goddard's personality and social relationships remain somewhat unexplored and a mystery in this rather uncritical examination of the "rocket man."

Pendray, G. Edward. "Pioneer Rocket Development in the United States." In *The History of Rocket Technology: Essays on Research, Development, and Utility*, edited by Eugene M. Emme. Detroit: Wayne State University Press, 1964. Written by a pioneer in the development of rockets in America and an individual intimately knowledgeable of Goddard's scientific and technical work, this essay briefly and succinctly sketches Goddard's major accomplishments in astronautics.

Von Braun, Wernher, and Frederick I. Ordway III. *Space Travel: A History.* 4th ed. New York: Harper & Row, 1985. Perhaps the best single-volume history on human's conquest of space, von Braun and Ordway thoroughly discuss the scientific and technical contributions of Konstantin Tsiolkovsky, Hermann Oberth, and Goddard in a chapter entitled "The Pioneers of Space Travel." Containing a large number of remarkable photographs and an excellent bibliography, the book concisely summarizes Goddard's work both in Massachusetts and New Mexico by using an extensive chronological timeline that describes Goddard's static and in-flight investigations.

Williams, Beryl, and Samuel Epstein. *The Rocket Pioneers: On the Road to Space.* New York: Julian Messner, 1958. This easy-to-read historical study includes chapters on Sir William Congreve, Konstantin Tsiolkovsky, Herman Oberth, and Goddard. Well researched and written, the authors clearly describe Goddard's key technological innovations within the context of his lengthy scientific career.

John A. Heitmann

Cross-References

Tsiolkovsky Proposes That Liquid Oxygen Be Used for Space Travel (1903), p. 189; The Germans Use the V-1 Flying Bomb and the V-2 Goes into Production (1944), p. 1235.

EDDINGTON PUBLISHES
THE INTERNAL CONSTITUTION OF THE STARS

Category of event: Astronomy
Time: July, 1926
Locale: Cambridge, England

Eddington's pioneering contribution to astronomy and astrophysics, set forth in
The Internal Constitution of the Stars, *spanned the most important aspects of stellar*
structure constitution and evolution

Principal personages:

SIR ARTHUR STANLEY EDDINGTON (1882-1944), an English astronomer famous for studies on evolution of stars, cosmology, and internal constitution

WALTER SYDNEY ADAMS (1876-1956), an American astronomer

RALPH HOWARD FOWLER (1889-1944), an English physicist who developed the theory of "degenerate matter" in superdense stars

FRANCIS GLADHELM PEASE (1881-1938) and J. A. ANDERSON, the American astronomers who verified Eddington's computations of the diameters of several red giants

HENDRIK ANTHONY KRAMERS (1894-1952), a Dutch physicist whose theory of absorption coefficient was adopted by Eddington to obtain mass-luminosity relation

OTTO STRUVE (1897-1963) and JOHN STANLEY PLASKETT (1865-1941), the American astronomers who verified the distance measurement of stars

HANS ALBRECHT BETHE (1906-   ), a Nobel Prize-winning physicist and astrophysicist who formulated the theory of thermonuclear fusion of protons via the carbon-nitrogen-carbon cycle

Summary of Event

Astrophysical knowledge at the beginning of the twentieth century can be described only as rudimentary. The source of stellar energy was not yet discovered. Although proper motions of the stars—that is, the sum of radial and transverse velocities—were known, William Herschel's assumption of their randomness relative to the sun had been abandoned by Jacobus Cornelis Kapteyn on the basis of his pioneering study of the subject. At this stage, Karl Schwarzschild attempted to represent the radial velocity vectors of the stars as forming an ellipsoid. Kapteyn, however, noted that they formed, instead, a double-lobed curve.

In 1906, Sir Arthur Stanley Eddington, investigating proper motions of stars, was able to isolate two star streamers, or drifts. The above-mentioned facts were confirmed by his statistical analysis of the proper motion data. During these early years,

Eddington studied problems associated with the distribution of stars of different spectral class, planetary nebulas, open clusters, and the dynamics of globular clusters.

Eddington's pioneering work in astrophysics began in 1916. A decade earlier, Ralph Allen Sampson had pointed out the importance of radiation pressure in physics of stars, and Schwarzschild later developed a theory of radiative equilibrium for the stellar atmospheres. Eddington, realizing the important role the radiation pressure played in maintaining the equilibrium in massive stars, extended Schwarzschild's theory all the way to stellar core. Utilizing Robert Emden's differential equation for a polytropic sphere with index n = 3, assuming that the materials of a giant star behave like a perfect gas, and accounting for gravitational force, gas pressure, and radiation pressure, he developed the well-known equation of radiative equilibrium. Known as Eddington's model of a star, it was found to be applicable to white dwarfs as well.

It was known that matter inside a star would be highly ionized because of extreme temperature. Incorporating this fact into his theory of stellar equilibrium, Eddington showed that high ionization reduced the molecular weight of a gas by two for all elements except hydrogen. Radiation pressure was found to increase rapidly with rising stellar mass, resulting in instabilities; hence, Eddington concluded that the number of stars in excess of 10 solar masses would be rare.

The derivation of mass-luminosity relation of a star requires knowledge of fundamental processes contributing to stellar opacity. After the photoelectric absorption process, regarded as dominant, met with criticism, Eddington, employing Hendrik Anthony Kramers' theory of absorption coefficients and introducing his so-called guillotine factor, obtained the important mass-luminosity relation. Moreover, having realized that electron scattering is the major source of stellar opacity, he was able to derive an upper limit to luminosity for a given mass—"Eddington's limit"—which plays an important role in the investigation of X-ray sources and accretion discs around black holes. Based on the fact that the observed luminosity data fit well with his theoretical computation, Eddington concluded that both giant and dwarf stars were gaseous, even though the latter had exceedingly high density.

Eddington's computation on the basis of his theory of stellar constitution of angular diameters of several giant stars—including Betelgeuse, Antares, and Aldebaran—was confirmed observationally by Francis Gladhelm Pease and J. A. Anderson at Mount Wilson. Applying his theory to the dwarf star Sirius B, Eddington noted to his astonishment that the mass density of the star was 50,000,000 kilograms per cubic meter. He realized that such a dense star should exhibit measurable gravitational redshift in accordance with Einstein's relativity theory and had Walter Sydney Adams at Mount Wilson successfully verify this effect. Having established the diameter of Sirius B to be 38,000,000 meters, comparable to that of Earth, Eddington found its density to be 53,000,000 kilograms per cubic meter. Ralph Howard Fowler, employing Erwin Schrödinger's wave mechanics, formulated the theory of degenerate dense matter found in stars such as Sirius B.

A problem of great complexity that resulted in Eddington's interest in the internal constitution of stars and occupied his attention for a long time is associated with the Cepheid variable. Luminosities of these bright F and G stars vary with a periodicity ranging from a day to several weeks. After generalizing Johann Wilhelm Ritter's analysis of the adiabatic pulsation of a gaseous star in convective equilibrium to the case of a star in radiative equilibrium, Eddington was able to combine the result with the mass-luminosity formulism, so as generally to obtain period-luminosity relations of Cepheids. Although these earlier attempts did not agree with correct phase relations among the observed variables such as brightness and temperature, Eddington realized that one had to examine the problem of energy transfer more thoroughly and returned to it several times. He was able to establish that the longer the periodicity of a star, the lower its surface temperature. With his pulsation theory, Eddington laid the foundation for future work on the Cepheids.

In addition to covering his research for a time span of ten years, beginning in 1916, Eddington's *The Internal Constitution of the Stars* also contains chapters devoted to stellar surface, chromosphere, atmosphere, and abundance of elements. His speculative prediction about the source of stellar energy appears in one of his papers. Twenty years later, Hans Albrecht Bethe showed that within the dense, hot core of a star, four protons would combine to form a helium atom via the carbon-nitrogen-carbon cycle so that a small fraction of the mass would be converted into radiant energy. This is one of the possible sources of stellar energy. Eddington was keenly aware that the source of the star's energy must be deep within the core.

While involved with the major projects, Eddington investigated the problem of cosmic abundance of hydrogen and central temperature and density of stars. His theory of absorption lines of stellar atmosphere made it possible to interpret many observed spectral line intensities. His theory concerning the temperature, density, and composition of interstellar matter and its emission and absorption properties of light provided an independent rough measurement of distances.

Impact of Event

Eddington wrote more than 150 scientific articles and more than 13 books. His profound knowledge of mathematics, deep intuitive insight into natural problems, and unrelenting drive enabled him to delve into a wide range of topics. His pioneering contributions to astronomy and astrophysics are distilled in the classic masterpiece *The Internal Constitution of the Stars*. It would not be an overstatement to say that the publication of his work opened up a new and exciting vista of astronomy and astrophysics. Even while Eddington's research work was being published, the stimulus it provided was evident from the immediate and long-lived controversy it generated among leading people in the field of astrophysics, such as James Hopwood Jeans and Edward Arthur Milne.

The publication of *The Internal Constitution of the Stars* established Eddington firmly as the founder of modern theoretical astrophysics and provided pathways to the study of structure, constitution, and evolution of stars. Several aspects of investigations of stellar structure—pioneered by Eddington and treated in his book—were pursued by others, leading to successful conclusions. His search for a theory to explain the periodicity of Cepheid variables, one of his earliest research interests, was to occupy him during a substantial period of his life. The problem of the Cepheids was ultimately solved by Martin Schwarzschild, Paul Ledoux, and Robert Frederick Christy. His speculations and predictions in regard to stellar energy turned out to be an important initial step, leading Bethe and others to elegant solutions. Eddington's study of the effects of reflection in binaries for determining their masses served later as a prototype solution to problems of diffuse reflection and transmission of light.

His investigation of interstellar absorption of lines led to dual results: determination of relative abundance of elements by the method of the "curve of growth" developed by Albrecht Otto, Johannes Unsold, and Marcel Gilles Minnaert, as well as prediction of radial velocities and, hence, approximation of distances, confirmed by Otto Struve and John Stanley Plaskett. Eddington's deduction of the size and ultrahigh density of dwarf stars, followed by Fowler's theory of degenerate matter, later led Subrahmanyan Chandrasekhar to deduce an upper limit to masses of such stars, which is known as the Chandrasekhar limit. Thus, Eddington's contribution to astrophysics spanned the most important aspects of stellar structure. In Milne's words of 1945, he "brought it all to life, infusing it with his sense of real physics and endowing it with aspects of splendid beauty. . . . Eddington will always be our incomparable pioneer."

Bibliography

Chandrasekhar, S. *Eddington: The Most Distinguished Astrophysicist of His Time*. Cambridge, England: Cambridge University Press, 1983. These are the Centenary Lectures in memory of Eddington, delivered by Chandrasekhar at Trinity College, the University of Cambridge, in late 1982. This little book, a valuable source of information, offers a cameo view of the life and achievements of Eddington and is presented by a great astrophysicist of modern time.

Douglas, A. Vibert. *The Life of Arthur Stanley Eddington*. London: Thomas Nelson & Sons, 1957. This biography includes a complete list of Eddington's scientific papers and books, in addition to a genealogical table. The volume reads like a novel and is comprehensive in every respect, embodying all aspects of Eddington's life and scientific achievements. The text may serve even as an excellent primer for stellar structure, relativity, and the philosophy of science.

Eddington, Arthur Stanley. *The Internal Constitution of the Stars*. Cambridge, England: Cambridge University Press, 1926. The celebrated work of Eddington. One should not pass up an opportunity to read several chapters in this noteworthy book. Eddington's style is easy to read, and one can easily understand many of the arguments presented. The text, which contains a comprehensive list of references, can be absorbed in its entirety by a college-level junior.

_____. *Stellar Movements and the Structure of the Universe*. London: Macmillan, 1914. This book contains Eddington's statistical analysis of data on the proper motion of stars, distribution of stars based on their spectral class, planetary nebulas, and star clusters, published in about fifteen papers, in addition to the cosmological knowledge of the period. The volume is nonmathematical, with the exception of chapters 7 and 10. Aimed at the general reader of scientific literature. Provides a background for understanding Eddington's later work on stellar structure.

Struve, Otto, and Velta Zeberg. *Astronomy of the Twentieth Century.* New York: Macmillan, 1962. Discusses stellar properties and mass determination for binary stars. Contains drawings, black-and-white photographs, and diagrams, as well as a glossary and a bibliography. For a wide audience.

V. L. Madhyastha

Cross-References

Kapteyn Discovers Two Star Streams in the Galaxy (1904), p. 218; Hertzsprung Uses Cepheid Variables to Calculate the Distances to Stars (1913), p. 557; Schwarzschild Develops a Solution to the Equations of General Relativity (1916), p. 630; Eddington Formulates the Mass-Luminosity Law for Stars (1924), p. 785; Chandrasekhar Calculates the Upper Limit of a White Dwarf Star's Mass (1931), p. 948.

WARNER BROS. INTRODUCES
TALKING MOTION PICTURES

Category of event: Applied science
Time: August, 1926-September, 1928
Locale: United States

Warner Bros. innovated talkies, films with sound, giving rise to the Golden Age of the Hollywood film

Principal personages:

HARRY WARNER (1881-1958), the brother who used sound to fashion a major filmmaking company

ALBERT WARNER (1884-1967), the brother who handled the matters of getting the Warner films into theaters

SAMUEL WARNER (1887-1927), the technician who adapted the apparatus to filmmaking

JACK WARNER (1892-1978), the one who supervised the making of Warner's films

Summary of Event

Silent films had live sound accompaniment featuring music and sound effects. Five-hundred-seat neighborhood theaters made do with a piano and violin; four-thousand-seat picture palaces in New York and Chicago maintained resident orchestras of more than seventy members. What the silent cinema lacked was prerecorded, synchronized sound. During the late 1920's, Warner Bros. led the American film industry first to motion pictures with sounds recorded on synchronized records and added on the film beside the images.

The ideas that led to the coming of sound were the products of corporate-sponsored research by American Telephone and Telegraph Company (AT&T) and the Radio Corporation of America (RCA). Both improved sound recording and playback to help their design of long-distance telephone equipment and for better radio sets. Yet, neither company could nor would, enter filmmaking. It took Warner Bros. to prove to the predecessors of today's Paramount Pictures, Twentieth Century-Fox, Metro-Goldwyn-Mayer (MGM), Universal Pictures, and Columbia Pictures, that motion pictures with synchronized sound should be made standard in the film industry.

Warner Bros. pioneered with a plan, formulated by Harry and Samuel Warner. In 1924, Warner Bros. (the official spelling, to cut the cost of printing "Brothers") was a prosperous, albeit small, corporation that produced films needing finance. That year, Harry Warner approached the important Wall Street investment banking house of Goldman, Sachs and secured the help he needed. In 1925, Warner Bros. purchased Vitagraph, a pioneer film producer and distributor, an action that doubled Warner's production capacity and provided a worldwide network to market its films.

Thus, in 1925, before Warner Bros. even considered the new sound technology, astute film industry watchers began to notice the rise of the company.

As part of this initial wave of expansion, Warner Bros. acquired a Los Angeles radio station in order to publicize its films better. Through this deal, the four Warner brothers learned of the new technology that the radio and telephone industries had developed to record sound. During the spring of 1925, the brothers devised a plan by which to use the new recording technology to help with the corporate expansion. Warner Bros. could record the most popular musical artists on film and then offer these short subjects as added attractions to theaters that booked its features. (Albert Warner was instrumental in getting their films into theaters.) As a bonus, Warner Bros. could add recorded orchestral music to their feature films, and offer it to those theaters that relied on small musical ensembles. Brothers Samuel and Jack Warner would handle the actual filmmaking.

The innovation of sound did not come easily for Warner Bros. For example, it contracted for necessary equipment from AT&T. The telephone company would have rather dealt with a more important Hollywood corporation, but Paramount and the other major Hollywood companies of the day did not want to risk their sizable profit positions by junking silent films. The giants of the film industry were doing fine with what they had; they did not want to switch to something that had not been proved.

On August 6, 1926, Warner Bros. premiered its new technology, which it labeled "Vitaphone." The first package consisted of a traditional silent film (*Don Juan*) with a recorded musical accompaniment, plus six recordings of musical talent that were highlighted by the most famous opera tenor of the day, Giovanni Martineli, doing his specialty from *I Pagliacci*. These recordings were made in New York; after 1927, all filmmaking was done in Hollywood.

From the fall of 1926 through the spring of 1927, the prime moviegoing season in those days before air-conditioning of theaters, Warner Bros. developed several packages of a silent film with recorded orchestral music, plus six shorts of noted musical talent. As this policy evolved, the shorts became more "pop" and less classical. Al Jolson, for example, appeared before the Warner cameras and recorded two of his most famous hits. Warner Bros. concentrated on these so-called vaudeville shorts. By April, 1927, the company had recorded all the popular stars of the day.

Warner Bros. soon ran out of stars and, thus, had to devise something new. The company added Vitaphone segments to feature films. The reasoning was, if Jolson did so well in a short subject, imagine what could be done in a feature film designed and written especially for him. The film would be silent as the necessary narrative moved along, but as soon as the Jolson character was required to break into song, the sound technology would be utilized. This strategy represented a merger of the new with the old, designed not to offend dedicated silent filmgoers but to attract new patrons in theaters throughout the United States.

The first such Vitaphoned feature was *The Jazz Singer*, which premiered early in the fall of 1927. Over the summer months, Warner Bros. had convinced enough theaters to install the required sound equipment to make the investment in the part-talkie feature film a financial success. During the summer of 1927, Warner salespersons performed a masterful job of selling skeptical exhibitors, and the Vitaphone projection equipment began to appear in picture palaces throughout the United States.

The Jazz Singer premiered as scheduled in October, 1927. From the opening it was a hit. (Sadly, Samuel Warner did not live to see and hear it; he died shortly before the premiere.) *The Jazz Singer* package (including its accompanying shorts with sound) forced theaters in cities that rarely held over films for more than a single week to ask to have the package stay for two, three, and sometimes four straight weeks. (One week was considered normal in the 1920's; two weeks' duration usually set a house record.)

The Jazz Singer did well at the box office, but failed to better records set by such silent film blockbusters as *Four Horsemen of the Apocalypse* (1921), *Ben Hur* (1926), and *The Big Parade* (1925). Skeptics questioned the staying power of talkies. If sound was so great, they wondered why *The Jazz Singer* did not move to the top of the all-time box-office list. That would come a year later with *The Singing Fool*, also starring Al Jolson. From opening day (September 20, 1928) on, reviewers from *The New York Times*, to the cynics writing for *Variety*, tracked the greatest movie hit of its day. *The Singing Fool* cost an estimated $200,000, but drew $5 million. By Thanksgiving Day of 1928, the Warner brothers knew that *The Singing Fool* was inexorably climbing to become the new Hollywood box-office champion. In New York City, *The Singing Fool* registered the heaviest business in Broadway history, with an advance sale that exceeded more than $100,000 (more than half a million dollars in present currency).

Warner Bros. pioneered the use of sound and thus functioned as the innovator of that important new film technique. The Fox Film Corporation (predecessor of the present Twentieth Century-Fox) came second. Then, once it was shown that talkies could make money, the other major Hollywood movie corporations soon followed. Thus began the third phase of any technical change in the industrial United States. Many factors convinced Paramount, MGM, and Universal to follow the lead of Warner Bros.

Impact of Event

The coming of sound transformed filmmaking in its day as would the coming of color, wide-screen images, stereo sound, and other new technologies later in the history of film. Indeed, film history is segmented by this monumental change. Films are cataloged as silent or sound, and to fans at the end of the twentieth century, silent films seem to be something from ancient history. This technical change led to major shifts in the economic, aesthetic, and social power of films.

Warner Bros. changed the American film industry in a fundamental manner. Hollywood was transformed from a competitive environment to a tight oligopoly (industrial control by a few) of eight companies. Those eight companies (except for Radio Keith Orpheum—RKO—which dropped out in the 1950's, and MGM and United

Artists, which merged) remained the dominant companies. RKO came into existence only to provide RCA with an outlet for its sound equipment. As a single company, Warner Bros. was the sole small competitor of the early 1920's to succeed in the Hollywood elite, producing films for consumption throughout the world and for presentation in more than eight hundred picture theaters owned by Warner Bros. throughout the midatlantic region of the United States in the 1930's and 1940's.

This transformation led to what is known as the Golden Age of Hollywood during the 1930's and 1940's. Hollywood, with its images of multimillion dollar deals, film stars, and press agents, became a symbol of the film as a popular cultural force throughout the world. By 1930, for example, there were more reporters stationed in the filmmaking capital of the world reporting on the images and sounds of the new talkies than in any capital of Europe or Asia.

In particular, through *The Singing Fool*, Warner Bros. taught the film industry how to spill over into other popular entertainment markets through what are today called "spin-offs." Warner Bros. created the first talkies sequel: *Say It with Songs*, released at the beginning of the 1929 to 1930 movie season. (Like many a future sequel, *Say It with Songs* failed to match the box-office take of its predecessor.) Two tunes from the film, "Sonny Boy" and "There's a Rainbow 'Round My Shoulder," went on to make up the first million-selling phonograph record of the talkie era. Thereafter, popular films would prove to be a gold mine for creating new hit tunes.

Filmmakers had a new standard by which to fashion future classics of the cinematic art. No longer were films presented with different sounds in theater after theater. After the innovation of Warner Bros., the sound track became one of the features that filmmakers controlled when making a film. Indeed, sound became a vital part of the filmmaker's art. Film music, in particular, could make or break a film. For example, many forget the precise story in *Jaws*, but few forget its haunting rhythms, especially when the shark is about to attack.

Finally, the coming of sound made films the dominant medium of mass culture in the United States and throughout the world. Fashions, expressions, designs, and slang were created by filmmakers. Many had not viewed the silent cinema as important; with the coming of the talkies, there was no longer a question of the power of films. The talkies gave birth to a powerful means of expression that affected all aspects of society. In particular, soon after the coming of sound, the notorious Hays Code of prior restraint on film content went into effect. Talking films were simply too powerful to let filmmakers present realistic images and sounds. Films with sound later became important in mass communication through newsreels and documentaries.

Bibliography

Bordwell, David, Janet Staiger, and Kristin Thompson. *The Classic Hollywood Cinema: Film Style and Mode of Production to 1960.* New York: Columbia University Press, 1985. A massive tome that analyzes the implications of the coming of sound for the making of films and the Hollywood production process. Surprisingly, authors argue that the coming of sound changed little in the look and style of the Hollywood film.

Geduld, Harry M. *The Birth of the Talkies: From Edison to Jolson.* Bloomington: Indiana University Press, 1975. A pioneering study that details how the necessary inventions were created that made talkies technologically possible. Includes substantial material on the relations with the phonograph and radio industries.

Gomery, Douglas. "The Coming of Sound: Technological Change in the American Film Industry." In *The American Film Industry: A History Anthology of Readings,* edited by Tino Balio. Rev. ed. Madison: University of Wisconsin Press, 1985. A survey of the coming of sound and the important role this technological change played in the transformation and development of the American film industry.

_____. "Warner Bros. Innovates Sound: A Business History." In *The Movies in Our Midst,* edited by Gerald Mast. Chicago: University of Chicago Press, 1982. A history, based on corporate files, of the rise of a major movie company through its success in innovating sound films. Argues that the innovation was based on business, not artistic factors.

_____. "The Warner-Vitaphone Peril: The American Film Industry Reacts to the Innovation of Sound." In *American Film Industry: A Case Study Approach,* edited by Gorham A. Kindem. Carbondale: Southern Illinois University Press, 1982. Previous film historians argued that the film industry happened into sound in a chaotic manner. Gomery argues, based on company records, that Warner Bros. slowly and systematically innovated talkies.

Higham, Charles. *Warner Brothers.* New York: Charles Scribner's Sons, 1975. Examines the history of the family and company that pioneered the coming of sound and operated a major studio into the 1950's.

Walker, Alexander. *The Shattered Silents: How the Talkies Came to Stay.* New York: William Morrow, 1979. A history of the innovation of sound, by the Warner brothers and others, based solely on a close reading of the trade paper *Variety.* A useful but limited history.

Douglas Gomery

Cross-References

Johnson Perfects the Process to Mass-Produce Disc Recordings (1902), p. 138; Fessenden Perfects Radio by Transmitting Music and Voice (1906), p. 361; Louis and Auguste Lumière Develop Color Photography (1907), p. 375; Edison Introduces the Kinetophone to Show the First Talking Pictures (1913), p. 537; The First Color Television Broadcast Takes Place (1940), p. 1166; Land Invents a Camera/Film System That Develops Instant Pictures (1948), p. 1331.

LEMAÎTRE PROPOSES THE BIG BANG THEORY

Category of event: Astronomy
Time: 1927
Locale: United States

Lemaître proposed that the universe was once a giant atom that exploded and is continuing to expand

> *Principal personage:*
> GEORGES LEMAÎTRE (1894-1966), a Belgian cleric who was an astronomy and math hobbyist

Summary of Event

In the early twentieth century, astronomers and physicists were eager for new discoveries about the macrocosm of universal life. Although these sciences often worked together, it was not necessary to have a full understanding of one in order to contribute successfully to research or theory in that field. Often, astronomers would observe the physical world and puzzle about an unknown or unexplained phenomenon, which the physicists would resolve in terms of their theories and equations. On the other hand, a physicist might develop a new theory about the nature of the universe without having any observational data. In this event, astronomers would proceed to seek out the projected physical reality the physicist proposed from the equations. The big bang theory is an example of this equation first, observation second, discovery method.

Georges Lemaître's formal training was theological and clerical, leading him to a career in the Catholic church as a monsignor. Similar to other religious men who pursued interests in science as a hobby (such as Gregor Mendel in genetics), Lemaître's interests included theoretical mathematics and astronomy. In 1923, Lemaître left Belgium for an extended time of study and travel in the United States. During this visit, Lemaître pursued his own interest in science and math instead of formal Church-related matters. Lemaître stayed in Cambridge, Massachusetts, at Harvard University, where he studied astronomy as a research student. Albert Einstein's theory of gravitation, now accepted over Sir Isaac Newton's, had been confirmed four years prior to Lemaître's visit to Harvard. Edwin Powell Hubble's discovery of independent galaxies was still a year away. The following year, 1924, Lemaître, on an official trip for Harvard, went to Mount Wilson, California, to observe the work in which Hubble and others were engaged. During that year, Hubble would confirm that independent galaxies did indeed exist; however, the full ramifications of that discovery and the accompanying data were not fully developed at the time of Lemaître's visit. Lemaître was therefore unable to call upon this data when he first proposed the big bang theory.

During his visit to the United States, Lemaître began exploring Einstein's equations of gravitation. When Lemaître solved these equations in the simplest manner, he discovered that they described an expanding universe. The long-held belief prior to Lemaître's discovery described a homogeneous, isotropic, and static universe. While Lemaître still believed the universe to be homogeneous and isotropic, he now discarded the static view of the universe for the expanding universe. In 1927, Lemaître's first paper on the homogeneous but expanding universe was published. He affirmed his belief in a universe which is the same in all directions in terms of its physical makeup and the physical laws by which it is governed; however, he denied that it is a fixed universe. He argued that the simplest solution to Einstein's theory of gravitation demanded that the universe be expanding. At that time, there was no observational data to support Lemaître's claim. Einstein was reluctant to endorse the proposed theory until he had investigated Lemaître's solutions to the gravity equations. Unknown to most of the scientific community of the Western world, a Soviet meteorologist, Aleksandr Friedmann, had discovered the same solutions to the gravity equations and proposed the same view of an expanding universe in 1922. Both men came to the same conclusion independently and without any experimental data.

At Mount Wilson Observatory in 1929, Hubble discovered that the galaxies he was observing were moving away from the earth at incredible speeds; furthermore, those galaxies farther out in the universe were moving more rapidly than those galaxies that were closer. Hubble made his discovery unaware of Lemaître's theory of an expanding universe and rejection of the traditional static view. There now existed observational data to support Lemaître's view of expansion. In papers published in 1931 and 1933, Lemaître used Hubble's discovery to support his theory. Lemaître's argument was simple: Hubble had discovered that the galaxies in the universe were hurling themselves away from some central point at incredible speeds; therefore, if one reversed the film, these galaxies would be seen rushing into themselves at some central point. Furthermore, the well-established law of entropy (an organized unit that becomes more disordered as time passes) suggested that the universe, which was becoming more disorderly, must at some point have been very orderly. These two arguments led Lemaître to suggest the existence in history of some primordial atom, which contained all the matter of the universe in a singular large atom. Lemaître's view of the universe is well described if one imagines a deflated balloon covered in spots. As the balloon inflates, the spots move away from one another but continue to be the same relative distance apart. Dots far apart, such as two dots on opposite sides, would be moving away from each other at a greater speed during inflating than two dots that were adjacent. When the balloon is deflated, the film running backward, the dots rush back to a central point.

Hubble's research provided Lemaître with the observational data to support his theory, and Einstein agreed that Lemaître's solutions were indeed the best solutions to the gravitational equations. As a result of this support, scientists began to investigate Lemaître's theory, which the scientific community would label the big bang theory. For a short time, Lemaître continued to develop his ideas about the theory and its effects. He made some predictions about the effects of the big bang, which should be evident if indeed it was the beginning of the universe. These proposals suggested areas that could be investigated in an effort to confirm the theory. The idea suggested by Lemaître that was most pursued was the existence of some type of background radiation that must have been given off by the primordial atom when it exploded. Lemaître was confident that some type of background radiation would be discovered. After the theory became the property of the scientific community and several research projects were undertaken to examine it, Lemaître faded from the field to pursue other studies and problems of science which intrigued him. Until his death in 1966, he was still lecturing on the theory of the origins of the universe, although he did not actively engage in the current investigations.

Impact of Event

Lemaître's bold new insight into an expanding universe sent astronomers and physicists delving into their observations and calculations, hoping to unravel the mysteries of the origin of the universe. The big bang theory brought physics and astronomy together, creating a joint science known as astrophysics, which investigated the credibility of the theory and sought an explanation of the first few minutes of universal history. While Lemaître explained how the universe started, his theory and calculations told little about the nature of that early universe, aside from the idea of the primordial atom. The nature of that atom, the particles that constituted the atom, and the reaction of those particles in the first few minutes after the explosion were questions unanswered by Lemaître or his theory. Also unanswered were the cause and nature of the explosion that sent matter hurling through space.

The big bang theory required the examination of both the macrocosm and the microcosm. Astronomers and many physicists, focusing on the macrocosm, began to study the present universe in the light of the big bang in an effort to gather data about the first few minutes of history. Using Lemaître's idea of running the film backward from where the universe presently is to where it was, these scientists searched for clues. This search included scanning the heavens for the background radiation; such discoveries as cosmic rays and other forms of radiation resulted. In the microcosm particle, physicists began to explore the inside of the atom hoping to discover clues there that might lead back to the first few minutes of history. Their search required the building of particle accelerators in an effort to duplicate the energy of the initial explosion, which brought the scientific community into the subatomic world full of unknown particles. Lemaître's theory required scientists to fit antimatter, quarks, and other new forms of matter being discovered into the picture of early universal history.

While Lemaître's theory is a theory of science, it had many philosophical ramifications. If it was possible to run the film backward and understand the cause and effect beginning of the universe, would it then be possible to project forward with certainty where the universe would be in any number of years? Did this theory then support a deterministic view of reality? How did creatures with free will fit into the picture? Another philosophical and scientific question centers upon the cause of the explosion and time. Einstein proved that time was relative to space and speed. Yet, if the universe was once contained in one large atom taking up nothing defined as space and traveling at no speed, what was the cause of the explosion? The explosion could not be the result of changing circumstances over time, because time did not exist. The search for all the answers of the early history of the universe has been successful back to the first few thousandths of a second after the explosion. What nature was like in those fractions of a second and before requires a grand theory that unifies all of physics.

Bibliography

Abell, G. O., and G. Chincarini, eds. *Early Evolution of the Universe and Its Present Structure*. Boston: D. Reidel, 1983. Papers presented at the 1983 symposium of the International Astronomical Union in Kolymbari, Crete. Discussions of cosmology, early history of the universe, and conjecture as to where it could be heading. A detailed discussion of the present structure of the universe and how this informs science of the past is also presented. Includes bibliographies and indexes.

Berger, A., ed. *Big Bang and Georges Lemaître*. Boston: D. Reidel, 1984. This work is a compilation of papers presented at the International Symposium on Georges Lemaître. An excellent source of biographical information, the development of Lemaître's theory, and an overview of the work in cosmology up to 1984. Many equations, illustrations, bibliography, and a bibliography of Lemaître's writings.

Contopoulos, G., and D. Kotsakis. *Cosmology: The Structure and Evolution of the Universe*. 2d ed. Translated by M. Petrou and P. L. Palmer. New York: Springer-Verlag, 1987. Various explanations of the big bang theory and the implications of the differing interpretations of the theory are presented. While the book contains some equations and diagrams, it is written for the beginning student of cosmology and provides excellent explanations of some complicated issues.

Silk, Joseph. *The Big Bang*. San Francisco: W. H. Freeman, 1980. An excellent historical account of the big bang theory from Lemaître and Friedmann, through Hubble's discoveries to 1980. The book explains how the discoveries were made, their implications, and the reaction of the scientific community. Also traces the history of the universe using the big bang model. A glossary helps the novice understand and define new terminology. Includes an index.

Trefil, James S. *The Moment of Creation*. New York: Charles Scribner's Sons, 1983. This book is written on the premise that the big bang theory is correct, therefore it does not mention Lemaître or attempt to defend the theory. Instead, this book explains how science has come to an understanding of the first few minutes of history, using examples of discovery such as Hubble's work at Mount Wilson. Trefil then proposes what the universe might have looked like in the first few milliseconds after the explosion.

Charles Murphy

Cross-References

Einstein's Theory of Gravitation Is Confirmed over Newton's Theory (1919), p. 684; Hubble Confirms the Expanding Universe (1929), p. 878; Gamow and Associates Develop the Big Bang Theory (1948), p. 1309; The Inflationary Theory Solves Long-Standing Problems with the Big Bang (1980), p. 2125.

OORT PROVES THE SPIRAL STRUCTURE
OF THE MILKY WAY

Category of event: Astronomy
Time: 1927
Locale: Leiden, The Netherlands

Oort provided convincing evidence of the correctness of Lindblad's proposal that the Milky Way was a rotating spiral like many of the exterior galaxies

Principal personages:
> JAN HENDRIK OORT (1900-   ), a Dutch astronomer most noted for his theoretical work on the structure of the galaxy, as a radio astronomer, and as a theorist on comets
> BERTIL LINDBLAD (1895-1965), an astronomer who proposed in the mid-1920's that the Milky Way was a rotating spiral galaxy
> JOHN STANLEY PLASKETT (1865-1941), a Canadian astronomer whose extensive work with bright stars provided support for Oort's methods and conclusions

Summary of Event

In 1927, Jan Hendrik Oort published data that provided dynamical proof of the proper motion of the stars near the earth. This evidence established that the observed effects were the result of differential velocities that could best be explained as the result of movement in the spiral arm of a large galaxy. He found the galactic center in the direction of Sagittarius in opposition to the direction Jacobus Cornelis Kapteyn had found, but in accord with the findings of Harlow Shapley. Oort came to this study quite naturally since he had been a student of Kapteyn, the famous Dutch astronomer who was active in the study of the structure of the Milky Way. At the age of seventeen, Oort went to the University of Gröningen to study with Kapteyn. In his elementary lectures, Kapteyn emphasized deriving interpretation from observation rather than hypotheses or conjectures; in many ways, Oort's career followed this dictum.

After earning a degree at Gröningen, Oort studied at Yale University in the United States. He began work in 1924 at the Leiden Observatory, becoming a professor in 1935 and director of the observatory in 1945. Oort was always fascinated by the conflict between Kapteyn's star counts and Shapley's studies of the globular clusters. Oort hoped to resolve this conflict and applauded Bertil Lindblad's rather bold proposal of the solution to the problem. Lindblad was a Swedish astronomer who had suggested that a rotating model of the galaxy could explain most of the observed phenomena. Oort was aware that no globular clusters appeared near the galactic plane and surmised that gas and dust were obscuring them. It did not occur to him until 1925 that the same obscuration was causing Kapteyn to propose a much too small stellar system as well, because his assumption of uniform luminosity was not valid. This was the key to unraveling the conflict between the two systems.

Prior to Lindblad and Oort's work with the motion of the galaxy, dynamical astronomy was almost solely the province of the solar system specialists. Oort recognized from Kapteyn's discovery of the star streams, and Karl Schwarzschild's interpretation of them as an ellipsoidal distribution of stellar motions, that there was potential for the dynamical study of the galaxy. He was also influenced by Sir Arthur Stanley Eddington and Sir James Jeans. This interest in dynamics led to his 1927 presentation and was a consistent theme throughout his varied career, extending to the dynamics of star clusters, stellar systems, galactic clusters, and finally superclusters. Oort has consistently emphasized the lack of homogeneity in the distribution of galaxies, whereas Edwin Powell Hubble and others emphasized the large-scale homogeneity of the distribution of galaxies.

Oort began his research in the middle of the 1920's with a study of high-velocity stars. Other astronomers had already found a strange phenomenon, namely, that stars with radial velocities of 150 kilometers per second or higher tended toward one direction in galactic longitude. Oort studied somewhat lower-velocity stars and found a surprisingly sharp limit at 65 kilometers per second, above which all the stars were on the same side of the earth, and below which the stars were uniformly distributed over all longitudes. Oort's 1926 doctoral dissertation contained a full description of the effect but an inadequate explanation, for he was still attempting to explain the phenomenon on the basis of the dynamics of a local system within Kapteyn's perception of the shape and size of the galaxy. He noted, however, the concentration of globular clusters in the galactic plane and in only one direction. He further noted other objects with the same kind of concentration. He stated that the globular clusters had the same type of motion as the high-velocity stars and that their average velocity was about 92 kilometers per second, well above the 65-kilometer-per-second limit. The data pointed toward the strength of Shapley's contention that the universe was larger than Kapteyn perceived and that the earth was far from the center.

Within a year, however, rather than proposing a collection of swarms drifting in the large system of globular clusters—which had been Kapteyn's compromise with Shapley's evidence—Lindblad suggested that the galaxy consisted of concentric subsystems at various velocities, with the high velocities the consequence of the faster rotation of inner stars around the galactic center far from the sun in that direction. Oort then provided the evidence from his studies of the differential rotation of the galaxy, which conformed to Lindblad's model. He demonstrated that Kapteyn's streaming effect was caused by the inner stars catching up with the sun while the outer stars lagged behind. This initial research could have implied concentric rings of a circular or elliptical galaxy, and his research continued seeking firmer evidence for the spiral nature of the Milky Way. He established in 1930 (allowing for Robert Julius Trumpler's discovery of dust clouds which absorbed light and made distant star clouds appear fainter and more distant than they were) that Earth's orbit of rotation was

30,000 light-years from the center of the galaxy, which was a reduction of Shapley's 50,000 light-year estimate. He found the sun to be following a fairly circular orbit at a rate of approximately 220 kilometers per second, a velocity that would lead to orbiting the galactic center in approximately 230 million years.

Next, Oort investigated the relationship between his previous velocity distribution studies and the decrease in density of star numbers with increasing distance from the galactic center and increasing distance from the galactic plane. He determined the density of matter in the vicinity of the sun and made estimates of density at other points toward the center for the purpose of computing the gravitational forces and reaching a comprehensive dynamical model of the distribution of the mass. He noted that the high-velocity globular clusters could not be held by a system unless it was at least two hundred times more massive than Kapteyn's universe.

By 1932, Oort had established that only about two-thirds of the mass of the galaxy could be accounted for from the known stars and gas; thus, he implied a considerable unseen mass in the galactic plane which was hidden by gas and dust. The distribution of the mass also implied the spiral nature of the galaxy.

The desire to penetrate the unseen core led Oort into radio astronomy. During World War II, while The Netherlands was occupied and observation was denied, Oort turned to theoretical work on the structure of the Milky Way and encouraged his student Hendrik Christoffell van de Hulst to study the hydrogen atom emission in radio wavelengths. In 1944, van de Hulst announced that hydrogen ought to emit at the 21-centimeter wavelength. After the war, Oort and C. A. Muller built a 21-centimeter receiver and hooked it to an 8-meter antenna owned by the Dutch Post and Telegraph Service. An unfortunate fire destroyed their experiment and before they could rebuild, Edward Mills Purcell and Harold Ewen announced observations of hydrogen emissions. Oort duplicated their effort six weeks later. Oort and Muller then mapped a halo of hydrogen around the galaxy; in the following years, they went on to study the galactic structure in the optically obscured center, mapping the distribution of gas in the galactic disk. This gas distribution, as well as the earlier research on mass distribution, supported the spiral nature of the galaxy. These studies verified rotation rates near the center and found a concentrated mass.

The variety of Oort's career interests led him to propose the existence of a comet cloud outside the planetary orbits as an explanation for the origin of comets and to conclude that the Crab nebula was the supernova of A.D. 1054 recorded by Chinese astronomers. He studied the origin and evaporation of solid particles in interstellar space with van de Hulst. His variety of interests aided in extending his remarkably long, active career in astronomy.

Impact of Event

Jan Hendrik Oort's work in seeking to resolve the issue of size, shape, and motion of the Milky Way was a natural consequence of his studies under Kapteyn. His primary concern was to resolve the conflict between the view of the "universe" of Kapteyn and that of Shapley, which was several times larger. Significantly, he was able to blend physics, mathematics, and astronomy into a dynamical interpretation of the observed phenomena that took into account gaseous absorption of light in the galactic plane and toward the center of the galaxy. He was able to provide evidence for a rotating spiral galaxy that resolved many issues and made Shapley's view with modifications more acceptable than in its previous form.

Oort's published observational confirmation of differential galactic rotation, built upon the mathematical theoretical work of Lindblad, encouraged other astronomers to search for further evidence and to continue efforts to resolve the remaining problems of scale, which were not finally completed until Walter Baade's work on the two stellar populations appeared in 1952. Oort had a great effect on John Stanley Plaskett, who spent much time studying hot blue stars (types O and B) at the Dominion Astrophysical Observatory in Victoria, British Columbia. Plaskett applied Oort's analysis to the radial velocities of faint B type stars, which because they are extremely bright, can be detected at great distances. His analysis reduced the relative error of their radial velocities. His independent method produced results close to Oort's value for distance and direction of the galactic center.

Oort established that Kapteyn's galaxy was too small and Shapley's too large. Plaskett's verification of Oort's results focused renewed efforts to resolve the problem of the distance scale. The problem of identifying the nature and magnitude of absorption of light by gas and dust continued into the 1930's. Trumpler's work provided the first definitive proof of an absorbing medium that Oort had insisted was present. Those who followed Trumpler were able to use the absorption he found to resolve the issues among Kapteyn's, Oort's, and Shapley's models of the galaxy and the conflict between Oort's and Shapley's distances. Oort's extremely long career allowed him to follow up his own work by moving into radio astronomy in the late 1940's and 1950's, resulting in more complete confirmation of the spiral structure of the galaxy. Later studies have demonstrated that Trumpler's uniform absorbing medium is really small clouds with irregular patterns of absorption in different parts of the sky.

Oort's early work stimulated the development of better photography, faster films, shorter focal lengths, and the use of radio astronomy. Oort's many honors were well deserved and the fertility of his astronomical efforts can only be admired. His long career spans the full development of a comprehensive view of the nature, structure, and size of our galaxy.

Bibliography

Berendzen, Richard, Richard Hart, and Daniel Seeley. *Man Discovers the Galaxies.* New York: Science History Publications, 1976. Pages 63 to 69 of this excellent cosmological history contain a description that is readable, although somewhat technical, of Lindblad's and Oort's efforts to comprehend the dynamics of the galaxy. This work recognizes the importance of Oort's evidence for later cosmological studies.

Oort, Jan Hendrik. "The Development of Our Insight into the Structure of the Galaxy Between 1920 and 1940." In *Education in and History of Modern Astronomy*, edited by Richard Berendzen. New York: New York Academy of Sciences, 1972. This was a historical lecture delivered at the New York Academy in September, 1971, in which Oort discussed his work and its relation to that of several others active in this field.

_____. "Some Notes on My Life as an Astronomer." *Annual Review of Astronomy and Astrophysics* 19 (1981): 1-5. A brief survey of some of his early accomplishments which specially focused on his galactic studies. It indicates those influences that led him into galactic studies.

Stromgren, Bengt. "An Appreciation of Jan Hendrik Oort." In *Galaxies and the Universe*, edited by Lodewijk Woltjer. New York: Columbia University Press, 1968. The Vetlesen tribute to Oort by the eminent Danish astronomer is an excellent commentary on Oort's career to that point.

Whitney, Charles A. *The Discovery of Our Galaxy*. New York: Alfred A. Knopf, 1971. Pages 268 to 272 contain a compact, but clear exposition of Oort's work. Continues with a discussion of the issue of whether the spiral arms lead or trail as they rotate, which was an issue between Lindblad and Hubble, with Hubble eventually able to demonstrate that they trailed.

Ivan L. Zabilka

Cross-References

Kapteyn Discovers Two Star Streams in the Galaxy (1904), p. 218; Shapley Proves the Sun Is Distant from the Center of Our Galaxy (1918), p. 655; Hubble Demonstrates That Other Galaxies Are Independent Systems (1924), p. 790; Oort and Associates Construct a Map of the Milky Way (1951), p. 1414.

HEISENBERG ARTICULATES
THE UNCERTAINTY PRINCIPLE

Category of event: Physics
Time: February-March, 1927
Locale: Copenhagen, Denmark

With his uncertainty principle, Heisenberg asserted that there are definite limits to precise knowledge of atomic processes, a theory that has become a cornerstone of modern physics

Principal personages:
WERNER HEISENBERG (1901-1976), a German physicist who won the 1932 Nobel Prize in Physics for his seminal contributions to quantum mechanics
NIELS BOHR (1885-1962), a Danish physicist who received the 1922 Nobel Prize in Physics for his model of the atom
ALBERT EINSTEIN (1879-1955), a German-American physicist who received the 1921 Nobel Prize in Physics for work that helped to establish quantum theory

Summary of Event

At the beginning of the nineteenth century, Sir Isaac Newton's laws of physics, first published in 1687, were enjoying such enormous success, particularly regarding their power to predict the movements of heavenly bodies, that thinkers such as the French mathematician and astronomer Pierre-Simon Laplace began to extend these laws to the universe as a whole. Laplace argued that complete knowledge of the locations and speeds of the sun and planets at one point in time would allow scientists, using Newton's laws, to determine the state of the solar system at any other time. Therefore, if a superhuman intelligence could once know fully the state of every bit of matter and the forces acting on them, such an intelligence could determine precisely the state of the universe at any past or future time. The universe and everything in it was thought to function with the precision and regularity of clockwork—the state of the mechanism at one moment determining completely the future course of events.

The notion of universal determinism—the idea that the present and future are totally bound by the past—was the guiding spirit of much scientific inquiry throughout the nineteenth century. Many scientists rejected the idea, saying that it left no room for the elements of chance, choice, or creativity. Certain philosophers, such as Charles Sanders Peirce, argued that strict determinism cannot account for the phenomena of growth and evolution. Nevertheless, determinism continued to reign supreme within the scientific community, particularly in physics, which was considered the most basic example of a precise, predictable science.

It is against this background of classical physics that the significance of Werner Heisenberg's principle of uncertainty, or indeterminacy, is most easily seen. In attempting to predict the exact future state of any sort of physical system—from solar to subatomic—it is necessary that one be able to measure precisely the qualities and coordinates of the parts of the system at a given point in time. The belief in universal determinism and absolute predictability held by many nineteenth century physicists was based largely on the assumption that such precision of measurement is theoretically unlimited. Heisenberg's uncertainty principle dealt a fatal blow to this assumption and shook the supremacy of strict causality, or determinism. Heisenberg stated simply that it is impossible to measure simultaneously both the exact position and the exact momentum of a subatomic particle.

Heisenberg used the example of the gamma-ray microscope to demonstrate the validity of the uncertainty principle, proposing that concepts like position and momentum can have meaning only if one specifies how they are to be measured. In this hypothetical experiment, the location and speed of a particle such as an electron are measured by shining a tiny ray of light, as little as one photon, on the particle. This light will be scattered by the particle and will then enter the microscope and make a mark on a photographic plate; the particle's position and momentum can be calculated from this mark. The accuracy of these calculations, however, depends on the distance between the crests in the light waves used to make the observation. To obtain an exact measurement of the particle's position, one would need to use light of very short wavelength. Such high-frequency light, however, contains much energy, and when it is directed toward the particle, it will alter its momentum. By using light of longer wavelength and lower energy, on the other hand, one could obtain a precise measure of the particle's speed, but uncertainty would then creep in with regard to its location. Therefore, the more one closes in on the position, the less accurately one can know the momentum, and vice versa. In the realm of microphysics, since the exact state of an atomic system can apparently never be fully open to view, physical processes at this level cannot be precisely predicted.

Heisenberg formulated his uncertainty principle early in 1927, the year after he became an assistant to Niels Bohr at Bohr's research institute in Copenhagen. They engaged in almost daily dialogue on the foundations of quantum theory and the nature of physical reality. Near the end of February, 1927, there was a brief, but rather deliberate break when Bohr left to take a skiing vacation in Norway. During this time, Heisenberg conceptualized the gamma-ray microscope experiment and decided that the indeterminacy evident in the measurement of subatomic particles had to be considered a fundamental principle of quantum theory. When Bohr returned to Copenhagen, he realized that Heisenberg's thinking was at variance with the ideas he had been pursuing. Bohr, who was also searching for basic principles, had been trying to understand the fact, established in part by Albert Einstein's study of the photoelectric effect, that light, as well as matter, displays wavelike properties under some conditions and particle-like properties under other conditions. Physicists had been trying to understand the nature of the wave-particle duality for years.

Bohr realized that, since the property that appears depends on the type of experiment or observing apparatus one is using, one simply cannot describe microphysical phenomena as either particle-like or wavelike without also referring to the method of observation. The observer does not merely observe these properties, they are evoked. Bohr formulated the principle of complementarity as a way of understanding the wave-particle paradox: that the wave aspect and the particle aspect are mutually exclusive but complementary, and emphasizing that both aspects must be included in any complete picture of microphysical phenomena.

Bohr was convinced that the principle of complementarity revealed a basic fact about the possibilities and limitations of the knowledge of microphysics. Heisenberg believed that the principle of uncertainty expressed a similarly fundamental fact. The apparent disparity between these two principles was the focus of long and sometimes heated discussions between Bohr and Heisenberg. In the end, however, they were able to agree that uncertainty and complementarity were compatible, with Heisenberg's principle understood as a particular mathematical formulation of the more general principle of complementarity. These two principles, together with Max Born's probabilistic interpretation of electron waves, combined to form what has become known as the Copenhagen interpretation of quantum theory.

The basic issue at stake in the interface between the different but related principles of Heisenberg and Bohr concerns the appropriateness of using concepts familiar to classical physics and everyday life in understanding the realm of the atom. Heisenberg believed that concepts such as position and momentum, or particle and wave, are of limited applicability in this domain because of the limitations involved in their measurement. He thought that a clear and consistent theory could be expressed only in abstract mathematical terms. Bohr, on the other hand, maintained his strong conviction that concepts rooted in the everyday world of objects and events can, and indeed must, be used to describe microphysical phenomena, but that only one aspect of a complementary pair of concepts will be appropriate in a given experimental situation. Heisenberg recognized the great philosophical importance of Bohr's approach and added to his famous 1927 paper enunciating the uncertainty principle a postscript in which he said that Bohr would present a related principle that would deepen and extend the meaning of the uncertainty principle. Bohr introduced the principle of complementarity in September of 1927, likewise acknowledging Heisenberg's groundbreaking work.

Impact of Event

In the new brand of physics ushered in by Heisenberg, abstract mathematics played a much greater role than in any previous form of physics. Quantum physics thus became a very powerful and influential mathematical tool that has been used to forge new theoretical developments in other fields of science such as chemistry and biology and to fashion a variety of technological innovations such as transistors, lasers, and microchips. All of this scientific and technological activity can be carried out with little concern for the profound philosophical questions posed by the uncertainty principle. Many scientists, such as Einstein, who have been deeply concerned with the meaning of science for human life as a whole, have given much thought to these issues.

Soon after Heisenberg and Bohr presented their principles of uncertainty and complementarity in 1927, the Copenhagen interpretation became established as the generally accepted foundation for quantum theory. A number of major physicists, including Einstein, challenged the conceptual cornerstones upon which this version of the theory was built. The debate centered around the questions of objectivity and indeterminism. If the principle of uncertainty is taken as truly fundamental, then the state of a particle when it is not being observed should be considered. One would have to conclude that an unobserved particle has no definite characteristics. Actually, it could not be called a particle, or a wave, nor does it have any real position or momentum. As Heisenberg stated: "[W]hat we observe is not nature in itself but nature exposed to our method of questioning."

Einstein believed that any theory of physics that does not include physical reality cannot be considered a complete theory of nature. From 1927 to 1935, Einstein formulated a number of hypothetical experiments designed to discredit the uncertainty principle, but Bohr was able to refute each of these arguments. The Copenhagen interpretation maintained its sovereignty in the theoretical and practical work of the majority of physicists.

The controversy sparked by the uncertainty principle did not diminish. During the 1980's, it emerged again as a lively topic of discussion, partially as a result of new experimental findings. Certain physicists and philosophers, notably David Bohm, continue in the spirit of Einstein to explore the possibility of formulating an expanded interpretation of quantum theory.

It is important to understand that while the uncertainty principle revolutionized microphysics and led indirectly to numerous technological developments, it has had little impact on the physics of familiar objects. In the realm of everyday, easily perceived and measured objects and events, the determinism of classical physics still provides quite satisfactory predictions and explanations. Heisenberg's uncertainty principle has been quite effective in shaking the assumptions and assurances of universal determinism that had guided the thinking of many people—scientists and nonscientists alike—since Laplace proposed the idea in the early nineteenth century.

Something that both advocates and opponents of the Copenhagen interpretation would certainly agree upon is that the uncertainty principle has helped to reveal the perhaps unsuspected richness of reality, a wealth of patterns and potentialities too great to be grasped in a single observation or to be exhausted by a given experimental or conceptual structure. Heisenberg helped to push the search for an understanding of nature to a new level, to the point where matter meets mind and physics meets philosophy.

Bibliography

Bohm, David. *Causality and Chance in Modern Physics.* London: Routledge & Kegan Paul, 1984. Originally published in 1957, this edition has a new preface that refers to developments in Bohm's sustained efforts to formulate an interpretation of quantum theory capable of encompassing both classical determinism and the indeterminism of the Copenhagen interpretation in a broader understanding of the laws of nature. A clearly articulated, searching, and sophisticated philosophical inquiry by a contemporary physicist.

Bohr, Niels. *Atomic Physics and Human Knowledge.* New York: John Wiley & Sons, 1958. A collection of mostly short essays exploring the implications of research in atomic physics for various other fields such as biology, anthropology, and philosophy.

Cline, Barbara Lovett. *Men Who Made a New Physics.* New York: New American Library, 1965. An interesting and popularly written narrative of the lives, theories, and interrelationships of the physicists, primarily Einstein, Bohr, and Heisenberg, but also the earlier Ernest Rutherford and Max Planck, who between 1900 and 1930 created quantum theory. Illustrated, with an index and bibliography.

Guillemin, Victor. *The Story of Quantum Mechanics.* New York: Charles Scribner's Sons, 1968. Somewhat more advanced than Cline's book (cited above), this book places quantum theory in the context of the history of physics. Discusses philosophical and religious implications of the new physics. Contains a glossary of scientific terms, an annotated bibliography of suggestions for further reading, and an index.

Heisenberg, Werner. *Physics and Beyond.* Translated by Arnold J. Pomerans. New York: Harper & Row, 1971. Writing for a wide audience, Heisenberg demonstrates his belief that "science is rooted in conversations." Gives a first-hand account of some of the conversations that have shaped modern physics and, in important ways, the modern world. Chapter 6 details the events surrounding the creation of the uncertainty principle.

_____. *Physics and Philosophy.* New York: Harper & Row, 1958. Heisenberg discusses in largely nontechnical terms a variety of topics, including the history of quantum theory, the Copenhagen interpretation and some of its critics, and the role of modern physics.

Pagels, Heinz R. *The Cosmic Code.* New York: Simon & Schuster, 1982. A theoretical physicist's popular, readable, and reliable account of the development of relativity and quantum theory, of research into elementary particles, and of the nature of the scientific investigation of the physical world. Provides interesting insights into the personalities involved and includes many illuminating examples and illustrations of the major issues. Includes a bibliography and a detailed index.

Gordon L. Miller

Cross-References

Einstein States His Theory of Special Relativity: $E = mc^2$ (1905), p. 297; Thomson Wins the Nobel Prize for the Discovery of the Electron (1906), p. 356; Bohr Writes a Trilogy on Atomic and Molecular Structure (1912), p. 507; Rutherford Presents His Theory of the Atom (1912), p. 527; Einstein Completes His Theory of General Relativity (1915), p. 625; Lawrence Develops the Cyclotron (1931), p. 953; Cockcroft and Walton Split the Atom with a Particle Accelerator (1932), p. 978.

LINDBERGH MAKES THE FIRST NONSTOP SOLO FLIGHT ACROSS THE ATLANTIC OCEAN

Category of event: Space and aviation
Time: May 20-21, 1927
Locale: New York to Paris

In his high-wing monoplane, The Spirit of St. Louis, *Lindbergh became the first aviator to fly solo across the Atlantic Ocean, making the trip from New York to Paris in 33.5 hours*

Principal personage:

CHARLES A. LINDBERGH (1902-1974), an American aviator who emerged an instant hero because of his epoch-making flight from New York to Paris in May of 1927

Summary of Event

Early on the misty and somewhat foggy morning of May 20, 1927, a small group of assistants began rolling Charles A. Lindbergh's sleek high-wing monoplane, *The Spirit of St. Louis* out of its hangar to a special runway located at Roosevelt Field, Long Island. The airstrip, soggy and soft from rainfall, had been extended by Commander Richard E. Byrd for the express purpose of attempting to fly nonstop from New York to Europe, and because of a minor crash, Byrd's plans had been delayed. Graciously, Byrd had offered his competitor the facility, despite the fact that both were eager to earn the $25,000 Orteig prize. Lindbergh's careful planning, his choice of an aircraft of utmost simplicity in design yet incorporating the latest in technical sophistication, and his courage all contributed to a flight that would capture the public's attention and revolutionize commercial aviation.

With the backing of several St. Louis investors and two thousand dollars of his own money, Lindbergh had commissioned the Ryan Aircraft Company of San Diego to design *The Spirit of St. Louis* from his specifications and to construct the plane in sixty days during the winter of 1926-1927. Lindbergh had a lifelong interest in mechanical things, beginning with the driving of his father's Model T Ford in 1913. A failure as an engineering student at the University of Wisconsin, he subsequently received pilot training at a private aviation school in Lincoln, Nebraska, and from the U.S. Army Air Corps in Texas during the early 1920's. After performing in aerial circuses and as a barnstormer, Lindbergh served as an airmail pilot on the storm-plagued St. Louis to Chicago route in 1926; it was during one of those trying flights that he decided to fly the Atlantic alone.

The Ryan-built *Spirit of St. Louis* reflected the elegant simplicity of Lindbergh's thinking, but it was this very simplicity, coupled with the installation of Curtis-Wright Aircraft Company's newly designed and highly reliable "Whirlwind" nine-cylinder air-cooled engine that proved pivotal to his ultimate success. With no radiator to leak or clog, a backup magneto ignition system, and a double carburetor, the aircraft possessed the best powerplant available at the time. While *The Spirit of St. Louis* was equipped with neither a radio nor a parachute, its sensitive control mechanisms, sturdy construction, and incorporation of the latest instrumentation— including an earth inductor compass—made it a prototype for aircraft that would follow in the wake of its success.

Upon returning home a hero from Paris, Lindbergh, never eager to garner all the praise, recognized that his achievement of May, 1927, was far more the consequence of engine and airframe design rather than individual courage; this point was succinctly made by the title of his first book, *We* (1927). Lindbergh asserted in 1928 that it was the skill of many anonymous engineers, mechanics, and artisans that ultimately had led to the triumph of *The Spirit of St. Louis*.

As *The Spirit of St. Louis* was prepared for takeoff, a weary Lindbergh, unable to sleep in the early hours of May 20, began to assemble necessary supplies and equipment before taking off. Seated in a slightly reclined wicker seat in the cockpit and with a window on either side, Lindbergh was unable to see directly forward without peering through a movable periscope. Initially disturbed at the sound and vibration of his engine at start-up, Lindbergh's life was on the line, for he was piloting nothing more than a flying bomb, since the aircraft was loaded with more than a ton of fuel in tanks located within the wings and fuselage. The plane's weight, its untested landing wheels, and adverse runway conditions caused concern among the many onlookers who watched the silver *Spirit of St. Louis* skid and hop to its final takeoff, clearing trees and telephone wires at 7:52 A.M. On viewing the hair-raising event, one reporter commented that Lindbergh had left the ground by "his indomitable will alone."

Once airborne, Lindbergh began to follow the so-called Great Circle route from New England to France, thereby flying far from the most frequently used shipping lanes. Navigating by dead reckoning and taking readings about every 160 kilometers after which heading corrections were made, Lindbergh followed a path that took him over Brockton, Massachusetts; Mainadieu, Nova Scotia; St. Johns, Newfoundland; Dingle Bay, Ireland; Bayeux, France; and finally Le Bourget Field, Paris, where he arrived at 5:21 P.M. (eastern standard time), Saturday, May 21, 1927.

During the long voyage, Lindbergh had to confront two major challenges—ice formation on the wings and exhaustion. Well versed in piloting aircraft in adverse weather, Lindbergh steered his tiny plane above and around storm formations over the North Atlantic, but the weight of ice on the wings nearly terminated the flight. Yet, it was his constant battle to stay awake, an event he had planned for in California by staying awake for forty hours at a time, that proved most dangerous. As night descended after the first day, Lindbergh's sheer exhilaration with flying, an experience in which he as the pilot and his machine seemed to merge as one, gave way to fatigue during which his mind began to lose touch with reality. Mirages suddenly began to appear in the middle of the ocean, and he witnessed phantoms or ghosts move in and out of the fuselage. With the sighting of fishing trawlers off the coast of

Ireland, Lindbergh returned to his senses, and by reaching landfall near Dingle Bay, his navigation had proved to be nearly perfect. The remainder of the trip was uneventful, although ironically after traveling more than 4,800 kilometers, he had difficulty finding the Le Bourget airfield shrouded in darkness and obscured by the many city lights. Expecting to be greeted by only a handful of aviation enthusiasts, Lindbergh was shocked by the massive crowds pushing down barriers and pressing toward him, eager to touch the humble and unassuming pilot who was to be the hero of the decade and the instigator of a popular wave of enthusiasm centered on the seemingly limitless potential of aviation technology. With little financial support and no corporate backing, flying a plane that was built by a little-known aircraft company recognized only for its construction of mail planes used on west coast routes, an unknown outsider had set the future course for commercial aviation. In succeeding in what was considered a foolhardy stunt, Lindbergh was now a public figure— a hero in an age that was desperately looking for such an individual.

Impact of Event

When Lindbergh landed at the Le Bourget airport in Paris on May 21, 1927, the spirit of America was suddenly reborn. In a fashion not unlike that of the landing of the first space shuttle in 1980, a distracted and disillusioned America found new hope and pride. The roaring 1920's, despite all of its prosperity, were years of anxiety, uncertainty, and disappointment, in part the consequence of a post-World War I societal self-examination and in part a response to a new culture where seemingly the machine dominated the individual. For a time, Lindbergh's flight would erase all fears and doubts and Americans could simultaneously celebrate the somewhat paradoxical triumph of both the individual and an organized technological society.

In becoming the hero to a generation, Lindbergh's private life came to an end. Now under constant scrutiny by the press, Lindbergh became the symbol and inspiration of what Americans wanted to be. Since he had no copilot and limited financial support, his feat was emotionally rooted in the American past, an individual pioneer like those who developed the West during the nineteenth century. Further, his innate qualities were not the result of university education, for he had dropped out of the University of Wisconsin before completing his second year, never happy with formal learning. Rather, Lindbergh had acquired his values in the Minnesota woods, like pioneer stock who had settled the land two generations before him.

Upon returning from France, Lindbergh would embark on a forty-eight-state tour that inaugurated a new enthusiasm for commercial aviation. During 1928, almost every major community in the United States embarked on an airport construction program, and private flying schools as well as aeronautics within universities flourished. Thus, a powerful technological momentum developed that would radically catalyze the development of new engines, air frames, and the science of aerodynamics. Indeed, Lindbergh's courage, coupled with his ability to design fundamentally *The Spirit of St. Louis*, resulted in the golden age of aviation that followed during the 1930's.

Bibliography

Fife, George Buchanan. *Lindbergh, the Lone Eagle: His Life and Achievements.* New York: World Syndicate, 1927. Representative of a literary genre on Lindbergh that appeared within a year of his successful New York to Paris flight, Fife's book is useful. The book not only captures the phenomenal public response to the achievement but also describes with excellent detail the layout and instrumentation aboard *The Spirit of St. Louis.*

Gill, Brendan. *Lindbergh Alone.* New York: Harcourt Brace Jovanovich, 1977. In an extremely well-written short biography of Lindbergh that concludes with the years immediately after the 1927 transoceanic flight, Gill traces the "lone eagle's" life, his development as a pilot during the early 1920's, and the events that led to his May 21, 1927, achievement. The author's style is penetrating, and the work is especially of interest for its analyses of Lindbergh and the phantoms or ghosts that he claims to have experienced during the flight.

Lindbergh, Charles A. *Autobiography of Values.* New York: Harcourt Brace Jovanovich, 1977. Written near the end of his life and published posthumously, this autobiography provides a second look at Lindbergh's 1927 flight, thus supplementing his award-winning 1953 *The Spirit of St. Louis.* The book is clearly useful if one is to gain additional perspective on Lindbergh's personality, including his concern with environmental issues and his perceptions of the dynamic relationships between science, technology, and society.

_____. *The Spirit of St. Louis.* New York: Charles Scribner's Sons, 1953. A beautifully written account of Lindbergh's New York to Paris flight written some twenty-five years after the event, it remains the most important source for understanding the details of Lindbergh's momentous achievement. Using flashbacks and free association, Lindbergh discusses the exhilaration and hazards of the flight, the scenery observed, and navigational methods employed to maintain *The Spirit of St. Louis*'s course. He also reminisces on the many important events that helped shape his personality, values, and motives.

Mosley, Leonard. *Lindbergh: A Biography.* Garden City, N.Y.: Doubleday, 1976. In a work that clearly demolishes a number of hagiographic notions concerning Lindbergh, Mosley examines Lindbergh's long career, paying special attention to the aviator's late 1930's and early 1940's efforts to prevent the United States from entering World War II. Thus, the controversial aspects of Lindbergh's life, including his youth, are examined with a journalist flair, but also perhaps with a degree of simplicity in matters of scholarship that fails to deal with the subject adequately and with total fairness.

Parfit, Michael. "Retracing Lindy's Victorious Trip Across the Country." *Smithsonian* 18 (October, 1987): 200-220. In an informative article describing Lindbergh's 35,000-kilometer, forty-eight-state tour of 1927, Parfit asserts that Lindbergh not only kept the excitement of his achievement alive among the public but also did more in a short time to promote civil aeronautics than previous federal government attempts. Indeed, Lindbergh's transatlantic flight and his subsequent tour convinced the public that flying was no longer a sport for daredevils, but that it was safe, reliable, and could be used to move precious cargo.

Ward, John William. "Charles A. Lindbergh: His Flight and the American Ideal." In *Technology in America: A History of Individuals and Ideas*, edited by Carroll W. Pursell, Jr. Cambridge, Mass.: MIT Press, 1981. Perhaps the most insightful and interpretive article written on the consequences of Lindbergh's flight. Ward argues that the hero worship directed at Lindbergh was the result of Americans being able to celebrate simultaneously the triumph of both the individual in an increasingly bureaucratic age and paradoxically modern mechanical technology that made *The Spirit of St. Louis* possible. In the wake of post-World War I disillusionment, and in a decade during which assembly-line production dominated the economic scene, Lindbergh was a representative figure of the individual pioneer, rooted in the past and untainted by the modern institutions of a new industrial order that emerged in early twentieth century America.

John A. Heitmann

Cross-References

The Wright Brothers Launch the First Successful Airplane (1903), p. 203; Blériot Makes the First Airplane Flight Across the English Channel (1909), p. 448; The First Jet Plane Using Whittle's Engine Is Flown (1941), p. 1187.

BUSH BUILDS THE FIRST DIFFERENTIAL ANALYZER

Category of event: Applied science
Time: 1928
Locale: Cambridge, Massachusetts

The differential analyzer developed by Bush and his colleagues at the Massachusetts Institute of Technology was the first modern analog computer

> *Principal personages:*
> VANNEVAR BUSH (1890-1974), an American electrical engineer and a professor at Massachusetts Institute of Technology
> SIR WILLIAM THOMSON, LORD KELVIN (1824-1907), an English physicist and engineer
> CHARLES BABBAGE (1791-1871), an English mathematician and inventor

Summary of Event

Calculating equipment has developed along two distinct lines: one is digital computation and the other is analog computation. Analog machines, of which the mechanical differential analyzer is an example, operate on quantities that are capable of continuous variation. These quantities—shaft rotation, electrical voltage, and so on—are physical analogs of the problem under consideration, and the use of analog machines to simulate the behavior of actual equipment can be an important engineering tool. In addition to serving as simulators of actual physical situations such as electrical power networks, analog machines are used as equation solvers. One type of analog machine was both easily portable and in common use—the slide rule—but was replaced by electronic calculators in the 1970's. Another type, the differential analyzer, was developed to provide solutions for differential equations through a process of successive integration in a closed-loop configuration. Early mechanical differential analyzers were extremely large, composed of many different parts, and often weighed thousands of tons. In addition, these early analyzers required several days of setup before a problem or series of problems could be run.

Calculating devices are as old as humanity, but most have relied on treating variables as being counted as discrete entities. The abacus and its modern counterpart, the digital computer, both embody this assumption of counting discrete units; the analog computer does not. Instead, the analog computer measures variables along a continuous range of values in much the same way that a thermometer can measure temperature at any point or an odometer measures miles. Further, while digital calculators have an ancestry reaching back to antiquity, analog computers are a comparatively recent development. Because digital computers are based on counting, simple machines to aid humanity in establishing the presence or absence of discrete units were developed in a variety of places and cultures. The abacus dates from at least five thousand years ago and is still used in many countries. In 1642, Blaise

Pascal, the noted French philosopher-scientist, constructed a calculating machine to assist him in computing business accounts. A few years later, a German mathematician, Gottfried Wilhelm Leibniz, built a machine that he called a "stepped reckoner."

Not until 1820, however, did a reliable calculating machine capable of addition, subtraction, multiplication, and division become commercially available. It was not until 1835, when Charles Babbage designed his "analytical engine," that a computer in the modern sense appeared, at least on paper. Had it been built, it would have been the first digital computer to incorporate the principles of sequential control.

The first mechanical analog computers also appeared in the nineteenth century. Sir William Thomson, Lord Kelvin, an English physicist, attempted to build one of the earliest known analog computers in 1872 to serve as a tide predictor. The first modern working analog computer, however, was designed and built by a team headed by Vannevar Bush at the Massachusetts Institute of Technology (MIT) in the late 1920's. The machine was a forerunner of the specialized type of analog computers known as differential analyzers and was designed to solve a specific form of differential equation. When completed in 1928, the device could perform eighteen different functions.

When Bush joined the MIT faculty in 1919, his research focused on electrical power transmission. Calculating precisely the distribution of power within a network entailed solving large problems of simultaneous linear equations. This was a difficult and time-consuming procedure because the calculations frequently involved differential equations that were particularly intractable. Lord Kelvin had attempted to build a machine to solve such equations almost fifty years earlier but had been unsuccessful in going beyond second-order differential equations. Lord Kelvin showed that coupling together two of the integrators described by James Clerk Maxwell in an 1873 paper, "Treatise on Electricity and Magnetism," would work to solve for second-order derivatives. In principle, Lord Kelvin also contended that combining Maxwell's integrators in various configurations also should allow solutions for higher-order differential equations to be found. Simple integrators, such as the one described by Maxwell, have become common in a variety of settings. Perhaps the most familiar example is household electrical meters, which measure current and voltage and integrate their product, power or kilowatts, with respect to time.

When Bush began working on a differential analyzer, he used an electrical meter as the core of the machine. Working under Bush's supervision, a graduate student completed the first simple computer, a continuous integraph, in 1926. It was constructed to evaluate integrals that contained a product but was limited to the solution of first-order differentials. Having obtained both accurate and useful results from the continuous integraph, Bush and his students added a second integrating unit to the first computer. They discovered, however, that they could not use another electrical meter. Bush turned to the Kelvin device as a possible solution, as the rotation of the meter appeared ideally suited to rotate the disk of a mechanical integrator. Unfortunately, as soon as a load was placed on the moving parts of the machine, its accuracy dropped. Connecting the two integrators with a servomotor solved the problem, and a Kelvin device capable of solving for second-order derivatives became a reality. It still had limitations, however: It could not solve higher-order differential equations or systems of simultaneous differential equations. Bush decided to try to build a true differential analyzer, a machine that would connect integrator after integrator.

When he attempted to build the larger machine, Bush discovered that the servomotor provided only a partial solution. It proved difficult to set properly and oscillated wildly at times when transmitting large magnifications of turning force, or torque. In 1927, a new device appeared: the torque amplifier. Use of torque amplifiers meant there was no longer a limit to the number of integrators that could be interconnected and a true differential analyzer could be built. The first had six integrators and could be used to solve most of the differential equations engineers were likely to encounter, including systems of two or three simultaneous second-order equations.

The increase in scale and the addition of torque amplifiers required that a large room be used to house the differential analyzer with its complex mass of interconnected metal axles, gears, disks, handles, and electric motors. The six integrators consisted of glass disks on movable tables. Joel Shurkin reports that one set of measurements determined the movement of the table, another determined the rotation of the disk, and a metal wheel on the glass disk measured a third variable by its distance from the disk. The torque amplifiers controlled all of this by permitting the wheels and shafts running the differential analyzer to move easily without slippage. In an analog computer, the physical movement of parts performs the actual computation, so all parts must move precisely. A collection of shafts and straps connected to servomotors through the torque amplifiers moved the integrators, but the differential analyzer itself was purely mechanical. Electricity was used only for powering the amplifiers, the shafts, and the printers.

Impact of Event

The differential analyzer was the first serious attempt to build a computer for use by scientists. When Bush described the differential analyzer in a paper published in 1931, other scientists and engineers immediately began to build similar machines. The differential analyzer quickly found a variety of applications in civilian and military settings, as it could be used both to simulate complex systems, such as electrical power grids, and to solve the difficult equations posed by ballistics problems.

As political conditions in Europe and the Far East deteriorated during the 1930's, the U.S. War Department became involved increasingly in both computer research and usage. The Navy was particularly interested in applying the differential analyzer to solving ballistics problems and funded such research actively. This research support soon was extended to include work on digital computers, and mathematicians such as Grace Hopper, who later became known as the inventor of COBOL, were recruited to work as programmers on these projects. In addition to spin-offs such as an increased interest in digital computers, the successful development of an analog computer meant that scientists and engineers could perform simulations of complex technical systems at a considerable savings over the expense of actual tests of those systems. The analog computer proved to be an invaluable tool in the development of aircraft, guided missiles, automobiles, and the like. By using simulator studies, a large data base can be obtained before trial flights or test drives commence, and those studies also can suggest how a limited number of physical trials can be most efficiently utilized. The development of the analog computer corresponded to a number of other significant developments within the history of technology, such as research in nuclear power and the development of jet aircraft, and contributed significantly to them.

It would have been impossible to build actual working prototypes of some large technological systems, such as nuclear power plants, and to construct preliminary design models for jet aircraft, which would be prohibitively expensive if done for every proposed design change or modification. Analog computers have allowed engineers and scientists to progress in the development of new technological devices and systems more economically and more quickly.

Bush's successful work with the differential analyzer may have helped to shape future science policy in the United States. Although his own research interests moved away from analog computing in the 1930's, the interest the differential analyzer aroused in the scientific community contributed to Bush's personal influence and success. As chairman of the National Research Committee and director of the Office of Scientific Research and Development during World War II, Bush helped to forge the connections among the federal government, universities, and private industry, which determined the priorities for basic research in the physical sciences for generations. Bush's personal influence on the American scientific community will persist long after the mechanical differential analyzer has been relegated to the status of a historical curiosity.

Bibliography

Ashurst, F. Gareth. *Pioneers of Computing*. London: Frederick Muller, 1983. Explains differences between digital and analog computers, in addition to providing biographies of John Napier, Pascal, and others. Ashurst's style is rather awkward, but the wealth of information in this comparatively small book more than compensates for it.

Hartley, M. G. *An Introduction to Electronic Analogue Computers*. New York: John Wiley & Sons, 1962. Provides a brief history of computers as well as explaining the difference between analog and digital computers.

Heyn, Ernest V. *A Century of Wonders: One Hundred Years of Popular Science*. Garden City, N.Y.: Doubleday, 1972. Excellent illustrations, easy-to-understand (if brief) explanations of the evolution of a variety of technologies, including electronic computers.

Shurkin, Joel. *Engines of the Mind: A History of Computers*. New York: W. W. Norton, 1984. A general history of computers that attempts to resolve priority disputes without taking sides. Focuses more on the social history and personalities of the persons involved than on the technical.

Williams, Raymond Wilson. *Analogue Computation: Techniques and Components*. New York: Academic Press, 1961. Provides background in both history and theory of analog computers.

Nancy Farm Mannikko

Cross-References

Eckert and Mauchly Develop the ENIAC (1943), p. 1213; The First Electronic Stored-Program Computer (BINAC) Is Completed (1949), p. 1347; UNIVAC I Becomes the First Commercial Electronic Computer and the First to Use Magnetic Tape (1951), p. 1396; Backus' IBM Team Develops the FORTRAN Computer Language (1954), p. 1475; Hopper Invents the Computer Language COBOL (1959), p. 1593; Kemeny and Kurtz Develop the BASIC Computer Language (1964), p. 1772.

GAMOW EXPLAINS RADIOACTIVE
ALPHA-DECAY WITH QUANTUM TUNNELING

Category of event: Physics
Time: 1928
Locale: Leningrad, Soviet Union, and Göttingen, Germany

Gamow used the newly established quantum mechanics to explain the puzzling phenomenon of radioactive alpha-decay

Principal personages:

GEORGE GAMOW (1904-1968), a Soviet-American physicist who expounded original theories on a wide range of nuclear, cosmological, and genetic topics

EDWARD UHLER CONDON (1902-1974), an American physicist who was noted for the theory of tunneling

RONALD WILFRED GURNEY (1898-1953), a British-American physicist who published the quantum theory of radioactive alpha-decay in 1928

ERNEST RUTHERFORD (1871-1937), a British physicist who was the leading figure in pioneering radioactive and nuclear studies and was the winner of the 1908 Nobel Prize in Chemistry

LOUIS DE BROGLIE (1892-1987), a French physicist who made a contribution to the founding of quantum mechanics with the introduction of the idea of "matter wave"

WERNER HEISENBERG (1901-1976), a German physicist who introduced matrix mechanics and the uncertainty principle

ERWIN SCHRÖDINGER (1887-1961), an Austrian-British physicist who made a contribution to the founding of quantum mechanics with the introduction of the fundamental equation and cowinner of the 1933 Nobel Prize in Physics

MAX BORN (1882-1970), a German physicist who collaborated with Heisenberg in formulating the statistical interpretation of the wave function and cowinner of the 1954 Nobel Prize in Physics

HANS WILHELM GEIGER (1882-1945), a German physicist who was noted for the Geiger-Nuttall law, Geiger-Müller counter, the coincidence principle, and established the empirical law of alpha-decay

JOHN MITCHELL NUTTALL (1890-1958), a British physicist who was known as the codiscoverer of the Geiger-Nuttall law of alpha-radioactivity

Summary of Event

George Gamow's 1928 achievement was a theoretical explanation of the phenomenon of radioactive alpha-decay. The newly established quantum mechanics served as his theoretical basis. Beginning from 1898, Ernest Rutherford and his assistants studied radioactivity most successfully. They classified the phenomenon and clarified many important phenomenological regularities. The alpha-particles, the heaviest of all three types of radioactive emissions, are positively charged; in fact, they are the atomic nuclei of the inert gas helium. Yet, all atomic nuclei are not alpha-radioactive. Only the heavy ones can emit alpha-particles, which are usually of uniform kinetic energy characteristic of the parent species of nuclei. The kinetic energy of alpha-particles ranges from 4 to 9.5 MeV (millions of electronvolts).

Radioactivity is a probabilistic phenomenon. All radioactive nuclei change as a result of one or more of the three types of disintegration. Yet, when disintegration occurs to one particular nucleus, it is unpredictable. It may happen instantly or it may occur in the remote future. Some nuclei (isotopes) disintegrate rapidly, others disintegrate slowly. The probabilistic character of the phenomenon required physicists to use statistical concepts such as the "half-life" to describe and discuss them. The half-life of an isotope is the time for one-half of any given quantity of the nuclei to disintegrate. Half-lives vary vastly from one species of nuclei to another. Some isotopes are very radioactive; in one-trillionth of a second, a half of this type of atom could change its identity. Some isotopes are radioactively very stable; it may take one trillion years for half of this type of atom to change.

In 1911, two physicists in Rutherford's group, Hans Wilhelm Geiger and John Mitchell Nuttall, derived from experimental data a remarkable law that relates the half-life of a species of nuclei to the energy of the alpha-particles emitted from them: the parent nuclei. The Geiger-Nuttall law was, in fact, a set of succinct equations. The theoretical understanding of these empirical equations, however, had to wait for the establishment of quantum mechanics, a milestone to take place sixteen years later.

In 1927, Rutherford published his discovery of the phenomenon of alpha-decay. Gamow conceived his quantum theory of tunneling from this publication. From the standpoint of classical physics, the phenomena were simply paradoxical. First, the experiment of atomic scattering made it clear that every atom has a positively charged, small, and heavy nucleus. Since alpha-particles are also positively charged when they approach a nucleus, because of the mutual repulsion between electricity of the same sign, they are rejected and scattered by the nuclei. Thus, for positive charges, including alpha-particles, the atomic nucleus is surrounded with a barrier of potential energy. By shooting alpha-particles of different kinetic energy at various species of nuclei, Rutherford assessed the height of the potential barrier around a nucleus, which could be as high as 25 to 35 MeV, several times the kinetic energy of alpha-particles. For example, uranium 238 is a radioactive species that emits alpha-particles of 4.2 MeV. The scattering experiment showed that the potential barrier around the uranium 238 nucleus might be as high as 25 MeV, more than five times the kinetic energy of the alpha-particle that the same nucleus sometimes emits. It was not known how a 4.2 MeV alpha-particle could escape a 25 MeV barrier. Rutherford proposed an ingenious classical solution to the puzzle. He suggested that starting from the nucleus, each alpha-particle was accompanied by two electrons which neutralize its positive charge. For this neutralized alpha-particle, the potential barrier was no longer a barrier, and it would have no difficulty passing the barrier zone. After sending off the alpha-particle, the two electrons somehow separated from it and returned into the nucleus. Gamow, however, thought this theory was too ingenious; he believed that the phenomenon was another quantum event inexplicable to classical physics.

Louis de Broglie's first step made in 1925 toward the establishment of quantum mechanics was a startling suggestion. He argued, on the basis of analogy with classical physics, that every elementary particle is associated with a "matter wave." One year later, following de Broglie's lead, Erwin Schrödinger introduced a general "wave equation." He stated that his differential equation should solve microcosmic problems in general—such as Sir Isaac Newton's equation, the second law of motion, in classical mechanics. Werner Heisenberg formulated his version of microcosmic mechanics in 1925. Atomic spectra are sharp lines representing radiations with definite frequencies, intensities, and polarizations. One of Niels Bohr's basic ideas was that spectral lines were transitions between quantum states. As the easiest way to specify a quantum state is to assign an integer to it, the transition between two quantum states could be specified by a pair of integers. Heisenberg pursued this line of thinking and concluded that every microcosmic "observable" should be specified the same way: by a pair of integers. Consequently, Heisenberg's mechanics was formulated with matrices, that is, square arrays of numbers. This was the origin of matrix mechanics, accomplished by Heisenberg, Pascual Jordan, and Max Born. After introducing his basic equation, Schrödinger proved the mathematical equivalence between matrix mechanics and wave mechanics.

In 1927, Heisenberg and Born succeeded in arriving at important results that would clarify the physical meaning of the new quantum mechanics: Heisenberg formulated the "uncertainty principle" and Born propounded the statistical interpretation of the quantum wave function. According to Heisenberg, it is impossible, even in principle, to determine at the same time the exact position and exact velocity of a particle. Born understood that the square of the amplitude of the wave function—the solution of the Schrödinger equation—represented an opportunity of finding a microcosmic particle.

In the summer of 1928, Gamow applied these empirical and theoretical results to solve a long-standing paradox in the phenomenon of radioactivity. He followed de Broglie in using an analog from classical physics, the relation between geometrical and wave optics, especially with regard to the issue of total reflection, which is a logical consequence of geometrical optics. According to the wave optics, however, no total reflection is total. Gamow pointed out that, according to wave mechanics, penetration into a potential barrier of a microcosmic particle, though with insufficient kinetic energy, is not impossible. Gamow solved the Schrödinger equation of this problem and showed that the wave function beyond the barrier did not vanish. Thus, according to Born's statistical interpretation of the wave function, the probability for the particle to tunnel through the barrier is not nil. Probability should depend on how large the barrier is. The new quantum mechanics could calculate the exact dependence of the probability upon the height and the width of the barrier: The higher and wider the barrier is, the smaller the probability becomes. The theory also shows that, for an ordinary baseball or tennis ball, for example, the chance of penetration, let alone tunneling through, is practically zero.

Impact of Event

It soon became evident that the quantum effect of "tunneling" also could be derived directly from Heisenberg's uncertainty principle, more specifically, from its energy-time format. This was a satisfying step that further demonstrated the inherent consistency of quantum mechanics.

Following the initial theoretical success, Gamow discussed the tunneling of potential barrier with John Douglas Cockcroft and encouraged him to bombard light nuclei with moderately accelerated protons. (Their goal was to explore the possibility of inducing artificial nuclear transmutation. Before the theory of quantum tunneling was evinced, the suggestion of using protons with insufficient kinetic energy would be rejected offhandedly.) Cockcroft performed such experiments. In the early 1930's, this preliminary achievement commenced a new stage for particle acceleration as well as artificial transmutation.

The empirical equations of alpha-decay—the Geiger-Nuttall law—together with the conspicuous fact that radioactive "half-lives" vary in a vast range (from a trillionth of a second to trillions of years) were now given a unified quantum theoretical explanation. The great success of the new theory in a new realm of physical phenomena, and on the difficult issues of the probabilistic nature of the microcosm and the statistical character of its theory, left an immediate and dramatic impact in scientific circles.

The founding of quantum mechanics between 1925 and 1927 represented a denouement of prolonged and collective effort in explaining physical and chemical phenomena pertaining to the structure of the atom. To the practicing physicists of the time, the denouement was also a propitious beginning. The significant development showed that microcosmic phenomena needed a new type of mechanics, intrinsically different from the classical Newtonian mechanics so that it could be used to extend and refine the original crude theories of atomic and molecular structures.

The timely appearance of publications by Gamow, Ronald Wilfred Gurney, and Edward Uhler Condon signaled the beginning of the theoretical study of the atomic nucleus. More significant, their theory of quantum tunneling dramatically furthered the success of quantum mechanics and strengthened confidence in this new and strange theory. Quantum tunneling is not trajectory, but wavelike; it is not exact, but statistical; or, as physicists and philosophers believe, it is not deterministic, but indeterministic. The theory has to be statistical because microcosmic phenomena themselves are probabilistic.

Scientists such as Albert Einstein did not accept the statistical interpretation of the wave function. To a lesser extent, de Broglie and Schrödinger, cofounders of quantum mechanics, shared Einstein's viewpoint. The majority, however, disagreed with

Einstein, de Broglie, and Schrödinger. Most theoretical and experimental physicists were won over by the indeterminism of the new microcosmic mechanics. In this serious academic debate, the theoretical success achieved by Gamow, Gurney, and Condon played a significant role. Long before any theory was proposed, radioactive phenomena had been recognized as statistical. It is very satisfying for most physicists that such phenomena are explained by a theory that is intrinsically statistical.

Bibliography

Boorse, Henry A., and Lloyd Motz, eds. *The World of the Atom*. Vol. 2. New York: Basic Books, 1966. Chapter 67, "The Barrier Around the Nucleus," includes two parts: editors' explanatory comments and Gamow's "Quantum Theory of the Atomic Nucleus," the English translation of his original (German) paper published in 1928. The first part is a very readable essay.

Born, Max. *My Life: Recollection of a Nobel Laureate*. New York: Charles Scribner's Sons, 1978. A substantial volume valuable for historical scholarship. Attractive to general readers. Several chapters discuss the history of quantum mechanics. Careful readers will acquire a clear picture of Born's contribution to the founding of quantum mechanics.

_____. *Physics in My Generation*. 2d rev. ed. New York: Springer-Verlag, 1969. This book is a must for understanding the history of quantum mechanics. Suitable for the general reader.

Gamow, George. *Mr. Tompkins Explores the Atom*. Cambridge, England: Cambridge University Press, 1944. Popular science classic. The last chapter, "The World Inside the Nucleus," includes the phenomena and theory of radioactive alpha-decay, "atom-smasher," nuclear fission, and other interesting topics. In another chapter, "Reality of Atoms," Gamow discusses the uncertainty principle.

_____. *My World Line: An Informal Autobiography*. New York: Viking Press, 1970. A scholar of Soviet history may find this book interesting. Gamow explicitly states that he, Gurney, and Condon deserved a Nobel Prize for their 1928 contribution.

_____. *Thirty Years That Shook Physics*. Garden City, N.Y.: Doubleday, 1966. Very interesting anecdotal history of quantum mechanics. In chapter 2, Gamov discusses the evolution of the quantum theory of the nucleus.

Heisenberg, Werner. *Nuclear Physics*. New York: Methuen, 1953. Interested lay-readers can digest and enjoy this book. Radioactive phenomena are first introduced in chapter 3; chapter 6 clearly explains the tunneling theory.

Rutherford, Ernest. *The Newer Alchemy*. Cambridge, England: Cambridge University Press, 1937. An excellent book by a great authority. For the reading public, this is probably still the best introduction to radioactivity. Somewhat dated. The quantum theory of alpha-decay was not mentioned because Rutherford did not like any speculation that could not be explained.

Wen-yuan Qian

Cross-References

Becquerel Wins the Nobel Prize for the Discovery of Natural Radioactivity (1903), p. 199; Cockcroft and Walton Split the Atom with a Particle Accelerator (1932), p. 978; Frédéric Joliot and Irène Joliot-Curie Develop the First Artificial Radioactive Element (1933), p. 987; Esaki Demonstrates Electron Tunneling in Semiconductors (1957), p. 1551; Rohrer and Binnig Invent the Scanning Tunneling Microscope (1978), p. 2093.

SZENT-GYÖRGYI DISCOVERS VITAMIN C

Categories of event: Biology, chemistry, and medicine
Time: 1928-1932
Locale: Cambridge, England; Szeged, Hungary; Pittsburgh, Pennsylvania

Szent-Györgyi isolated "hexuronic acid" in England and four years later in Hungary, he and Svirbely proved that this substance was vitamin C

Principal personages:
ALBERT SZENT-GYÖRGYI (1893-1986), a Hungarian biochemist who was a recipient of the Nobel Prize in Physiology or Medicine in 1937
CHARLES GLEN KING (1896-1988), an American biochemist and nutritionist who obtained vitamin C from lemon juice at the University of Pittsburgh
JOSEPH L. SVIRBELY (1906-   ), an American chemist who did postdoctoral work in Hungary with Szent-Györgyi
SYLVESTER SOLOMON ZILVA (1885-1956), an English biochemist whose work on vitamin C influenced both Szent-Györgyi and King
SIR WALTER NORMAN HAWORTH (1883-1950), an English chemist whose work on carbohydrates and on the structure and synthesis of vitamin C led to his Nobel Prize in Chemistry in 1937

Summary of Event

Although the Nobel Committee as well as many scientists and scholars have given a lion's share of the credit for the discovery of vitamin C to Albert Szent-Györgyi, a historical analysis reveals that this great achievement resulted from work by numerous scientists. As Szent-Györgyi recognized, his discovery depended on basic advances in chemistry, biology, and medicine, because vitamin C is both a complex chemical substance and the physiological linchpin in the deficiency disease scurvy. Physicians in the Middle Ages had recognized some aspects of this disease, which was characterized by debility, swollen joints, a tendency to bruise easily, bleeding from the gums, and the loss of teeth; however, it was not until the eighteenth century that the Scottish physician James Lind recognized that these symptoms constituted a disorder caused by defective nutrition. His experiments on sailors during long ocean voyages showed that the ingestion of certain fruits and vegetables could cure the disease. Despite Lind's success, several decades passed before George Budd proposed clearly that scurvy could be alleviated by the presence, in Lind's fruits and vegetables, of an unknown organic substance necessary for the body's execution of certain vital functions. Yet, this idea of scurvy as a chemical disease had little influence on the rest of the nineteenth century, largely because physicians were accumulating evidence that diseases were caused by definite agents (the germ theory) rather than by the lack of particular substances in the diet. Even lime juice, which had proved so effective for Lind, was unable to cure scurvy consistently.

The most significant step toward the discovery of vitamin C was made in 1907, when Axel Holst, a bacteriologist, and Theodor Frölich, a pediatrician, published their discovery that, through dietary manipulations, a disease analogous to human scurvy could be generated in guinea pigs (like human beings and unlike most animals, guinea pigs do not manufacture their own vitamin C). When Holst and Frölich fed hay and oats (foods deficient in vitamin C) to guinea pigs, the animals developed scurvy, but when they were fed fresh fruits and vegetables, they remained healthy. In this way, Holst and Frölich were able to measure quantitatively a food's antiscorbutic property. Scientists could, therefore, use bioassays to determine how rich or poor in vitamin C a substance was. Although the path seemed clear to isolating the vitamin, researchers encountered great difficulties because of vitamin C's extreme sensitivity to destruction by oxygen. Nevertheless, in the decade after World War I, Sylvester Solomon Zilva at the Lister Institute in London obtained increasingly active preparations of the vitamin. He was able to determine some of its properties; for example, he found that it was a nitrogen-free compound containing carbon, oxygen, and hydrogen and that it was a strong reducing agent (that is, it readily gives up some of its hydrogen).

While Zilva and other scientists were trying to isolate vitamin C directly, Szent-Györgyi actually found the substance in the course of searching for something else. In the 1920's, his research centered on biological oxidation, that is, on how cells oxidize various foodstuffs. He was particularly entranced by the observation that some plants (apples and potatoes, for example) turn brown after being cut and exposed to air, whereas others (oranges and lemons, for example) experience no color change. He suspected that a certain substance was controlling these color-change reactions, and he looked for it not only in fruits and vegetables but also in the adrenal cortex of mammals. He believed that the color change to a bronzelike skin in patients with Addison's disease (a disorder of the adrenal gland) was associated somehow with the color changes in plants. He worked assiduously to isolate this substance, a powerful reducing agent, from adrenal glands. In this period when insulin's discovery was exciting scientists, he actually thought that he was about to discover a major new hormone.

Unfortunately, his research was plagued with problems, and it was not until 1926, when he met Frederick Gowland Hopkins at a conference in Sweden, that things changed. Hopkins, who was interested in vitamins and biological oxidation, invited Szent-Györgyi to the University of Cambridge, where he would support the Hungarian's efforts to isolate this potential hormone in the adrenal cortex. Using many glands from oxen, Szent-Györgyi was able to separate the reducing agent from all other substances present. With considerably more effort than with oxen adrenals, he also was able to obtain the same substance from orange juice and cabbage extracts, a result that his colleagues found most surprising.

Through chemical analysis, he determined that the substance contained six carbon atoms, eight hydrogen atoms, and six oxygen atoms, and that it was a carbohydrate related to the sugars. He initially wanted to name the substance "Ignose" (from the Latin *ignosco*, meaning "I don't know," and "ose," the designating suffix for sugars), but the editor of the *Biochemical Journal* thought that the name was too flippant, whereupon Szent-Györgyi suggested "Godnose," which was similarly rejected. Because the substance contained six carbon atoms and was acidic, he and his editor agreed on the name "hexuronic acid." For some, the publication of Szent-Györgyi's discovery of hexuronic acid in 1928 constitutes vitamin C's discovery, but others deny this because he had not proved the equivalence of hexuronic acid and vitamin C yet. In his paper, he made no claim of this equivalence, although he did note that the reducing properties of plant juice studied by such experts in vitamin C analysis as Zilva were probably caused by hexuronic acid. The possible identification of hexuronic acid and vitamin C had come up in discussions in Hopkins' laboratory. To Szent-Györgyi, the similarity in the properties of these two substances was striking. Szent-Györgyi and Hopkins were so impressed by these similarities that they sent Zilva some hexuronic acid to test for its antiscorbutic activity. Zilva came up with negative results and concluded—falsely, it turned out—that the evidence was against the identity of hexuronic acid and vitamin C.

In 1929, Szent-Györgyi prepared 25 grams of hexuronic-acid crystals from the adrenal glands of animals at the Mayo Clinic in Rochester, Minnesota. On returning to Europe, he gave one-half of the crystals to the English chemist Sir Walter Norman Haworth, an expert in determining the structures of carbohydrates, and he kept the other half to study the substance's role in plants and animals at a research center in Szeged, Hungary. When a young postdoctoral student, Joseph L. Svirbely, arrived at Szeged in the fall of 1931, Szent-Györgyi was given the opportunity to use his hexuronic acid for another, more consequential purpose.

Svirbely had done his doctoral studies on vitamin C under Charles Glen King at the University of Pittsburgh. Working with Henry Clapp Sherman, an expert on the chemistry of foods, King decided to try to isolate one of the vitamins. (Scientists then recognized, on the basis of their biological activity, five vitamins, but they had failed to identify any of them satisfactorily as a specific chemical compound.) King chose to attempt the isolation of vitamin C. In 1928, he learned of Szent-Györgyi's hexuronic acid, and in the spring of 1929, at an American Chemical Society meeting, King became aware of speculations that hexuronic acid might be vitamin C, an idea that was reinforced for him when he visited Hopkins' laboratory at the University of Cambridge in the fall. On his return to Pittsburgh, he and his associates, building on the work of Zilva, prepared concentrates of vitamin C from lemon juice and then tested their antiscorbutic properties through tedious and time-consuming bioassays. King eventually obtained relatively pure crystals of a substance that protected guinea pigs from scurvy. His first paper on the preparation and properties of vitamin C was published in 1929. After this initial paper, King continued to develop techniques for concentrating and characterizing the vitamin C obtained from lemon juice; Svirbely became part of this effort. According to King's associate, William A. Waugh, by 1931, he and King were aware that their crystals exhibited the properties of Szent-Györgyi's hexuronic acid, but they were not sure of the actual identity of these substances, and did not publish their observations.

Svirbely was the bridge between King's work and Szent-Györgyi's. It is doubtful that, without the stimulus that Svirbely provided, Szent-Györgyi would have tried to prove the identity of his hexuronic acid and vitamin C, because this identification would require bioassays and he did not enjoy working with animals. Furthermore, he was against vitamin research (he once said that vitamins were problems for the chef, not the scientist). Nevertheless, when Svirbely mentioned that he could tell if something contained vitamin C or not, Szent-Györgyi gave him his remaining hexuronic acid to determine if, as he expected, it was the same as vitamin C. In a fifty-six-day test using guinea pigs, Svirbely established, in the fall of 1931, that the animals without hexuronic acid in their diets died with symptoms of scurvy, while the animals receiving hexuronic acid were healthy and free from scurvy.

On the advice of Szent-Györgyi, Svirbely kept King informed of their work. King, for his part, continued his purification and analysis of lemon-juice concentrates of vitamin C, but he had a more difficult task than Svirbely, because his samples were impure, whereas Svirbely was working with pure vitamin C. Svirbely's repetition of his guinea pig experiments during the winter of 1931 to 1932 left no doubt that he and Szent-Györgyi had proved the identification of hexuronic acid and vitamin C. Svirbely informed King in March about this identification; however, King continued to vacillate about the similarity or identity of hexuronic acid and vitamin C. Svirbely's letter about his experiments ended King's doubts, and he sent a brief report that appeared in *Science* on April 1, 1932, announcing his discovery of vitamin C and its identity with Szent-Györgyi's hexuronic acid (unfortunately, he failed to mention his correspondence with Svirbely). *The New York Times* took up his claim in a headline that appeared on its front page: "Pittsburgh Professor Isolates Vitamin C." Two weeks later, Svirbely and Szent-Györgyi published a paper in *Nature* on their discovery of the vitamin. A bitter priority controversy ensued between Szent-Györgyi and King that continued throughout their lives. The Nobel Prize Committee, after considering both claims, decided to award an unshared prize to Szent-Györgyi for his discovery of vitamin C and his work on biological oxidation. Although King still has his defenders, most scientists now regard Szent-Györgyi as the person most responsible for the discovery of vitamin C.

Impact of Event

The isolation of vitamin C generated widespread comment and convinced most scientists that the long-sought vitamin had been found. Vitamin C's impact was deepened and extended by Szent-Györgyi's discovery in 1933 that Hungarian red peppers contained large amounts of the vitamin. Whereas previous biochemists could make only minuscule amounts of the material with great difficulty, Szent-Györgyi now could produce pounds of the substance. In his lectures about his work, he liked to hold up a bottle containing several kilograms of the vitamin. To scientists accustomed to thinking of vitamins solely in extremely minute amounts, this was a surprising and enlightening experience.

The discovery of vitamin C led quickly to the determination of its precise three-dimensional structure and to its synthesis from smaller molecules. Using material supplied by Szent-Györgyi, Haworth worked out the structural formula of vitamin C in 1933, and later in that year Tadeus Reichstein, a chemist, synthesized vitamin C in Zurich and showed that it had the same chemical and physiological properties as the natural substance. At about this time, Haworth and Szent-Györgyi suggested that the vitamin be given the name "ascorbic acid," after its property of combating scurvy.

During the 1930's, King continued his investigations of the vitamin by determining its distribution in plant, animal, and human tissues. He also found that much vitamin C was lost when milk was pasteurized, leading to ascorbic-acid supplements being added to infant formulas. In 1941, King and Waugh succeeded in obtaining a patent for their method of isolating vitamin C from lemon juice, but they failed to get a patent for the vitamin itself. Patent officials reasoned that ascorbic acid was a well-known substance and had been isolated by Szent-Györgyi from adrenal glands in 1928.

Vitamin C has continued to be of great interest to scientists and the public. Thousands of papers have been written about its activity in various living things. In the late 1930's, the League of Nations set up a committee to establish international standards for the vitamin, and the committee recommended that individuals ingest at least 30 milligrams each day to prevent scurvy. In the period during and after World War II, however, some scientists raised questions about whether this minimum daily requirement was the optimum amount to maintain humans in the best possible health. Many people, convinced that modern food processing was destroying vitamins, began to supplement their diets with vitamin pills, and some industries began to fortify their products with vitamins.

In the 1960's, Irwin Stone, an industrial chemist, popularized the idea that human beings need much more vitamin C than the minimum daily requirement for the best health (the megavitamin theory). In 1965, he interested Linus Pauling, a Nobel-Prize-winning chemist, in his ideas, and Pauling became an advocate of what he called "orthomolecular medicine," that is, the treatment of various disorders in the human body through adjustments of normally present substances. In 1968, Pauling suggested that schizophrenia could be treated effectively by supplementary vitamins, and in 1970 he wrote a book, *Vitamin C and the Common Cold*, that became a best seller and stimulated many people throughout the world to increase their daily intake of vitamin C. In 1979, he published, with the Scottish physician Ewan Cameron, a book on cancer and vitamin C, in which they argued that the incidence and severity of cancer could be reduced if the public and patients took large amounts of this vitamin. Pauling's books and articles created an ongoing controversy, guaranteeing that this fascinating substance, discovered through the efforts of Szent-Györgyi and others, will continue to provide subjects for rewarding scientific research well into the future.

Bibliography

Carpenter, Kenneth J. *The History of Scurvy and Vitamin C.* Cambridge, England: Cambridge University Press, 1986. The story of scurvy from 1498 to the present, told by a professor of nutrition at the University of California, Berkeley. Makes occasional use of chemical formulas, but most of the discussions are accessible to the general reader. Illustrated with many photographs, tables, and line drawings. Also contains an extensive list of references and a detailed index.

Friedrich, Wilhelm. *Vitamins.* New York: Walter de Gruyter, 1988. A systematic presentation of the historical, chemical, biological, and medical aspects of the most important vitamins; a valuable research tool for scientists as well as for students. Friedrich, a professor in the Institute for Physiological Chemistry at the University of Hamburg, has synthesized a gigantic mass of material, particularly evident in his chapter on vitamin C. Concludes with a literature supplement (which updates references to May, 1986) and an extensive index.

Goldblith, Samuel A., and Maynard A. Joslyn, eds. *Milestones in Nutrition.* Westport, Conn.: AVI, 1964. An anthology of important papers in nutrition (part of a series), intended to "inspire and encourage" students to learn the chief ideas of food science through the foundational classics of their discipline. An ample section on vitamin C includes the principal papers of Szent-Györgyi, King, Zilva, and others. Does not contain an index.

Leicester, Henry M. *Development of Biochemical Concepts from Ancient to Modern Times.* Cambridge, Mass.: Harvard University Press, 1974. A history of biochemistry written by a biochemist with a strong interest in the history of science. A chapter on vitamins discusses the history of ascorbic acid. A set of notes at the end of the book contains many bibliographical references. Contains an index of proper names and a subject index.

Moss, Ralph W. *Free Radical: Albert Szent-Györgyi and the Battle over Vitamin C.* New York: Paragon House, 1988. Depicts Szent-Györgyi as a romantic scientist, ruled by intuition in his personal, political, and scientific life. Takes Szent-Györgyi's side in the controversy with King over the discovery of vitamin C, and presents new information to bolster Szent-Györgyi's claim. Many bibliographical references in the set of notes at the end of the book. Indexed.

Pauling, Linus. *Vitamin C, the Common Cold, and the Flu.* San Francisco: W. H. Freeman, 1976. An updated version of *Vitamin C and the Common Cold* (1970), which was dedicated to Szent-Györgyi for his discovery of the vitamin. Argues that a proper understanding of previous research leads to the conclusion that most people would benefit from a larger amount of vitamin C in their diet. An award-winning book, aimed at a general audience; initiated a controversy about the effectiveness of megadoses of vitamin C in preventing colds and alleviating their symptoms. Includes a set of references and an index.

Waugh, William A. "Unlocking Another Door to Nature's Secrets—Vitamin C." *Journal of Chemical Education* 11 (February, 1934): 69-72. A review of the recent studies on the isolation and characterization of vitamin C by one of King's principal associates. Presents the story from King's point of view; objective rather than ironic in tone. Concludes with a list of the thirty-seven papers and books that Waugh used in his analysis.

Robert J. Paradowski

Cross-References

Hopkins Suggests That Food Contains Vitamins Essential to Life (1906), p. 330; McCollum Names Vitamin D and Pioneers Its Use Against Rickets (1922), p. 725; Steenbock Discovers That Sunlight Increases Vitamin D in Food (1924), p. 771; Krebs Describes the Citric Acid Cycle (1937), p. 1107.

PAPANICOLAOU DEVELOPS THE PAP TEST FOR DIAGNOSING UTERINE CANCER

Category of event: Medicine
Time: January, 1928
Locale: Cornell Medical College, New York

Papanicolaou developed a cytologic technique called the Papanicolaou smear (Pap test) for diagnosing uterine cancer, the second most common fatal cancer in American women

Principal personages:

GEORGE N. PAPANICOLAOU (1883-1962), a Greek-born, naturalized American physician and anatomist whose Pap test has been ranked with the efforts of Marie Curie in reducing the burden of cancer

CHARLES STOCKARD (1879-1939), an American anatomist and chairman of Cornell Medical School's anatomy department who launched Papanicolaou's efforts

HERBERT TRAUT (1894-1972), an American gynecologist who collaborated with Papanicolaou in aspects of Pap testing

Summary of Event

Cancer, first named by the Greek physician Hippocrates of Cos (460-377 B.C.), is one of the most painful and dreaded forms of human disease. It is known now to occur when body cells run wild and interfere with the normal activities of the body. The early diagnosis of cancer is extremely important because early detection often makes it possible to effect successful cures. The modern detection of cancer is usually done by the microscopic examination of the appearance of the cancer cells, via the techniques of the area of biology called cytology.

Development of cancer cytology began in 1867, after L. S. Beale reported tumor cells in the saliva from a patient who was afflicted with cancer of the pharynx. Beale recommended the use in cancer detection of microscopic examination of cells shed or removed (exfoliated) from organs including the digestive, the urinary, and the reproductive tracts. Soon, other scientists identified numerous striking differences between normal cells from various tissues and cancers of those tissues. These differences include cell size and shape, the size of cell nuclei, and the complexity of cell nuclei.

Modern cytologic detection of cancer evolved from the work of George N. Papanicolaou, a Greek physician who trained at the University of Athens Medical School. In 1913, he emigrated to the United States and began his American career as an assistant in the pathology department of New York Hospital. Papanicolaou entered the arena of cytologic examination of cells when he began working, in 1917, with Charles Stockard at New York's Cornell Medical College. Stockard, chairman of the anatomy department, allowed Papanicolaou to study sex determination in guinea pigs. Papanicolaou's efforts required him to obtain ova at a precise period in their maturation cycle, a process that required an indicator of the time at which the animals ovulated. In search of this indicator, Papanicolaou designed a method that involved microscopic examination of the vaginal discharges from female guinea pigs. Initially, he sought traces of blood, such as those seen in the menstrual discharges from both primates and humans. Papanicolaou found no blood in the guinea pig vaginal discharges. Instead, he saw temporal changes in the size and the shape of the uterine cells shed in these discharges. The changes Papanicolaou noted recurred in a fifteen- to sixteen-day cycle. This cycle correlated well with associated changes of uterus and ovaries during the fifteen- to sixteen-day guinea pig menstrual cycle. Papanicolaou's research, published in 1917 (in *The American Journal of Anatomy*), laid the basis for study of the sexual cycle in laboratory animals. It has become also a standard method for the identification of the effects of sex hormones in these animal species. Its use was instrumental also in the first isolation of sex hormones (estrogens) by Edgar Allen and E. A. Doisy in 1923.

Papanicolaou next extended his efforts to the study of humans. This endeavor was designed originally to identify whether comparable changes in the exfoliated cells of the human vagina occurred in women. Its end goal was to gain an understanding of the human menstrual cycle, similar to that which he had obtained in the animal studies. In the course of this work, Papanicolaou observed distinctive abnormal cells in the vaginal fluid from a woman afflicted with cancer of the cervix. This led him to begin to attempt to develop a cytologic method for the detection of uterine cancer, the second most common type of fatal cancer in American women of the time.

In 1928, Papanicolaou published his cytologic method of cancer detection in the *Proceedings of the Third Race Betterment Conference*, held in Battle Creek, Michigan. The work was received well by the news media (for example, the January 5, 1928, *New York World* credited him with a "new cancer detection method"). Nevertheless, the publication—and others he produced over the next ten years—were not very interesting to gynecologists of the time. Rather, they preferred use of the standard methodology of uterine cancer diagnosis (cervical biopsy and curettage). As Papanicolaou said, "I failed to convince my colleagues of the practicability of the procedure." Consequently, in 1932, Papanicolaou turned his energy toward studying human reproductive endocrinology problems related to the effects of hormones on cells of the reproductive system. One example of this work was published in *The American Journal of Anatomy* (1933), where he described "the sexual cycle in the human female." Other such efforts resulted in better understanding of reproductive problems that include amenorrhea and menopause.

It was not until Papanicolaou's collaboration with gynecologist Herbert Traut (beginning in 1939), which led to the publication of *Diagnosis of Uterine Cancer by the Vaginal Smear* (1943), that clinical acceptance of the method began to develop. Their monograph documented an impressive, irrefutable group of studies of both normal and disease states that included nearly two hundred cases of cancer of the uterus. Soon, many other researchers began to confirm their findings; by 1948, the newly named American Cancer Society noted that the "Pap" smear seemed to be a very valuable tool for detecting vaginal cancer. Wide acceptance of the Pap test followed and, beginning in 1947, hundreds of physicians from all over the world flocked to Papanicolaou's course on the subject. They learned his smear/diagnosis techniques and disseminated them around the world.

With widespread use of the pap test came many honors for Dr. Papanicolaou. Some of them included the Cross of a Grand Commander of the Greek Royal Order of the Phoenix, the Lasker Award of the American Public Health Association, the Honor Medal of the American Cancer Society, the Bordon Award of the American Association of Medical Colleges, and the Amory Award of the American Association of Arts and Sciences. In time, Papanicolaou became one of the best-known members of the American medical profession.

At the end of 1961, he became the director of the Papanicolaou Cancer Research Institute in Miami, Florida. Unfortunately, he died in 1962; however, he has not been forgotten: At the posthumous dedication of the Papanicolaou Cancer Research Institute, he was eulogized as "a giver of life—one of the elect men of earth who stand for eternity like solitary towers along the way to human betterment." This sentiment remains throughout the biomedical community.

Impact of Event

The Pap test has been cited by many physicians as being the most significant and useful modern discovery in the field of cancer research. One way of measuring its impact is the realization that the test allows the identification of uterine cancer in a presymptomatic stage, long before other methodology can be used. Moreover, because of resultant early diagnosis, the disease can be cured in more than 80 percent of all cases identified by Pap test. In addition, Pap testing allows the identification of cancer of the uterine cervix so early that its cure rate can be nearly 100 percent.

Another measure of the efficacy of the Pap test comes from actuarial examination of the consequences of its widespread utilization in routine cancer screening technique, beginning in the early 1950's. For example, several insurance companies reported that the 1951 death rate from uterine cancer of insured thirty-five- to forty-four-year-old women (160 per million) was halved by 1961 (80 per million). In contrast, the reduction in the death rate from cancer of all types was only about 11 percent in that time period.

Papanicolaou extended the use of the smear technique from examination of vaginal exudates to diagnosis of cancer in many other organs from which scrapings, washings, and exudates can be obtained. These tissues include the colon, the kidney, the bladder, the prostate, the lung, the breast, and the sinuses. In most cases, such examination of these tissues has made it possible to diagnose cancer much sooner than possible by other existing methods. Therefore, the smear method has become a keystone of cancer control in voluntary and required national health programs throughout the world.

The principal use of Pap testing has been traditionally in cancer screening. It is utilized successfully in evaluation of the effectiveness of both cancer radiotherapy and cancer chemotherapy, and in the early detection of recurrence of cancer after surgery. Papanicolaou's 1928 prediction has come to pass; namely, "A better understanding and more accurate analysis of the cancer problem is bound to result from use of this method. It is possible that analogous methods will be developed for the recognition of cancer in other organs."

Bibliography

Berkow, Samuel G. "After Office Hours—A Visit with Dr. George N. Papanicolaou." *Obstetrics and Gynecology* 16 (1960): 248-252. This personal interview with Papanicolaou describes him both as a man and as a medical scientist. Insight is given to Papanicolaou's great contributions to endocrinology, in general, and to cancer research. The overall value of the Pap test is described.

Carmichael, D. Erskine. *The Pap Smear: Life of George N. Papanicolaou.* Springfield, Ill.: Charles C Thomas, 1973. This brief, but complete biography describes the life and career of Papanicolaou and chronicles his development as a man and as a scientist. The book contains excellent documentation of his research efforts.

Papanicolaou, George N. "New Cancer Diagnosis." In *Proceedings of the Third Race Betterment Conference.* Battle Creek, Mich.: Race Betterment Foundation, 1928. Papanicolaou describes study of the existence of distinctive cells in the vaginal fluid of humans with cancer and states that a new diagnostic method for cancer of the genital tract is described. He proposes, correctly, that better understanding of the cancer problem will come from its use.

_____. "The Sexual Cycle in the Human Female as Revealed by Vaginal Smear." *American Journal of Anatomy* 52 (1933): 519-637. This long article is a compendium of normal cytological changes seen in human vaginal discharges. Papanicolaou describes the use of the smear test to identify normal cytological changes in the human reproductive cycle. The report established human cytology on a firm basis.

Papanicolaou, George N., and Charles Stockard. "The Existence of a Typical Estrus Cycle in the Guinea Pig: With a Study of Its Histological and Physiological Changes." *American Journal of Anatomy* 22 (1917): 225-283. The paper describes study of the vaginal fluid of guinea pigs and sets down the sequence of cytologic patterns of shed cells occurring in fifteen- to sixteen-day cycles correlatable with morphologic changes in the reproductive system of the guinea pig. Establishes the technique used for the study of the sexual cycle in laboratory rodents.

Papanicolaou, George N., and Herbert F. Traut. *Diagnosis of Uterine Cancer by Vaginal Smear.* New York: The Commonwealth Fund, 1943. This monograph describes the exfoliate cytology of many normal and disease states, including the menstrual cycle, abortion, ectopic pregnancy, menopause, several vaginal and cervical infections, and 179 cases of cancer of the uterus. It was instrumental in the clinical acceptance of the Pap test as a means for cancer diagnosis.

Sanford S. Singer

Cross-References

Bayliss and Starling Discover Secretin and Establish the Role of Hormones (1902), p. 179; Rous Discovers That Some Cancers Are Caused by Viruses (1910), p. 459; Li Isolates the Human Growth Hormone (1950's), p. 1358; Birth Control Pills Are Tested in Puerto Rico (1956), p. 1512; Baulieu Develops RU-486, a Pill That Induces Abortion (1982), p. 2185; A Gene That Can Suppress the Cancer Retinoblastoma Is Discovered (1986), p. 2331.

MEAD PUBLISHES *COMING OF AGE IN SAMOA*

Category of event: Anthropology
Time: August, 1928
Locale: New York, New York

With the publication of her very successful book, Mead popularized the field of cultural anthropology

> *Principal personages:*
> MARGARET MEAD (1901-1978), an American anthropologist whose studies of adolescent development among primitive peoples made her the most renowned anthropologist of her day
> FRANZ BOAS (1858-1942), a German-American anthropologist, often regarded as the "father of American anthropology"
> DEREK FREEMAN (1915-   ), a professor of anthropology and author of a polemical book critical of Mead's work
> LLOWELL D. HOLMES (1925-   ), an American anthropologist and author of a book that recounts his restudy of Samoa and is largely supportive of Mead's earlier work

Summary of Event

Franz Boas, Margaret Mead's mentor, published his landmark book, *The Mind of Primitive Man*, in 1911, which freed anthropology from the stigma of racism. Before that time, there were "higher" and "lower" races rated on a scale of intellectual capacity. Boas' book was the cornerstone of a new view of humans and led to the controversy between two schools of thought in anthropology, which is sometimes dubbed the "nature versus nurture" debate. Those on the side of "nature" contended that there were innate racial differences that accounted for differences in individual intellectual abilities, whereas those on the side of "nurture" (Boas' followers) argued that the abilities of members of the human species often differed because of cultural differences in their upbringing, as well as differences in their heredity. Boas believed that there was a need to study this problem so as to determine the relationship between the hereditary factors and the environmental factors.

Margaret Mead was only twenty-three years old when she set out on her great adventure to the South Seas, where she hoped to salvage what remained of primitive cultures before they disappeared forever. In her autobiography, *Blackberry Winter*, Mead described her thoughts as she left for Samoa—thoughts of urgency to study and record the ways of life in remote parts of the world. She had a sense that such ways of life were vanishing from the earth before the onslaught of modern civilization. She believed that she must be one of those to record these unknown ways before they were lost forever.

Mead had been married to Luther Cressman, a theological student, in September,

1923. She retained her maiden name for professional purposes all of her life, not as common a practice in those days as it is today. Two years later, however, she and Luther agreed to go off on separate paths of study—he to Europe and she to Samoa. She had many misgivings about what she was setting out to do, since she really did not know much about field work. Her course on methods with Boas was not about field work, but about theory, how to organize material so as to refute or support some theoretical point. She had consented to Boas' suggestion that she study the adolescent girl, but she persisted in her determination to do the study in the South Seas, against Boas' recommendation that the study be made in some safer location, among the American Indians, for example.

On arrival in Samoa, her first problem was to learn the language. She had been warned that the reports others had made were "contaminated by the ideas of European grammar," and even the recorded descriptions supposed to have been given by local chiefs were weighted by European notions about rank and status inserted by the researchers doing the recording. Therefore, she moved into the household of a "chief who enjoyed entertaining visitors." She slept with the chief's daughter on a pile of sleeping mats on a sleeping porch. Mead learned much from the family about Samoan habits and etiquette. She even had to bathe in public, in full view of crowds of children and passing adults, under the village shower. She learned to wear a saronglike garment, which she could slip off before a shower and exchange for a dry one afterward.

Mead learned enough of the Samoan language in her first six weeks to give her the confidence to look for a place to stay among the natives of the island of Tau, about 240 kilometers east of Pago Pago in American Samoa. The western half of the Samoan Islands, which contains by far the greater part of the land area, is a United Nations Trust Territory, administered by New Zealand. She moved into the household of the only American family on Tau, a pharmacist's mate in the U.S. Navy, Edward Holt, his wife, and children. From November, 1925, until June, 1926, Mead lived with the Holts; she interviewed a group of about fifty teenage girls and kept notes on her findings. She could entertain crowds of adolescent girls on her porch day after day, and thus gradually build up a census of the whole village, and work out a background for each of the girls she was studying.

In June, 1926, Mead ended her Samoan sojourn and boarded a small ship in Pago Pago bound for home by way of Sydney, Australia, Ceylon, Aden, Sicily, and Marseilles, where her husband met her. They traveled to New York, where she worked as Assistant Curator of Ethnology at the American Museum of Natural History, where she was to remain the rest of her professional life. Mead soon completed all but the last two chapters of *Coming of Age in Samoa*, which she subtitled *A Psychological Study of Primitive Youth for Western Civilization*. She asked Boas to write a foreword. He described the difficulties that beset the individual in civilization, difficulties likely to be ascribed to fundamental human traits. Boas doubted the correctness of this assumption, but said that hardly anyone had yet set out to identify himself with a primitive population in sufficient depth to obtain an insight into these problems. Mead had confirmed, he believed, the suspicion long held by anthropologists that "much of what we ascribe to human nature is no more than a reaction to the restraints put upon us by our civilisation."

Coming of Age in Samoa was published in 1928. When Mead returned from Samoa, she was asked to give lectures about her work. The audience would ask her what the meaning was of what she had found in Samoa. She then wrote the last two chapters, one comparing the lives of Samoan girls with their American counterparts, and the other which she called "Education for Choice." Mead soon left on a new study in the Admiralty Islands. It was months before she learned that her book had become a best seller. Mead would write many more books, but none brought her the phenomenal success of *Coming of Age in Samoa*. By 1968, the book had gone through a new edition and at least five more printings. Certainly, *Coming of Age in Samoa* has never been difficult to read, and more than sixty years after it was published, it is still one of the most sought after books in any library.

Impact of Event

The publication of *Coming of Age in Samoa* broke new ground in anthropology, and not only made Mead one of the most famous of American scientists but also brought to anthropology recognition as a science. Mead was honored with one of the most prestigious offices in American science, the presidency of the American Association for Advancement of Science in 1970. *The New York Times* was moved to editorialize on anthropology shortly after the book came out, in its June 4, 1929, issue, under the heading "American Race Types."

Although the book's reception was favorable for the most part, it chose sides in the "nature versus nurture" controversy in anthropology and came down resoundingly in favor of nurture. Therefore, in 1983, an emeritus professor of anthropology at the Australian National University, Derek Freeman, had the temerity to criticize Mead in an unabashedly polemical book, *Margaret Mead and Samoa: The Making and Unmaking of an Anthropological Myth*. The debate over Freeman's book began two months before its publication, when a copy of the text brought on an editorial in *The New York Times* in January, 1983, under the headline: "New Samoan Book Challenges Margaret Mead's Conclusions." The controversy even made the cover of *Time* magazine.

Mead did not lack her own champions. Professor Llowell D. Holmes of Wichita State University in Kansas had received inquiries from Freeman in 1966 asking about Holmes' and Mead's research in Samoa. Holmes soon realized that Freeman was seeking evidence that would prove damaging to Mead's studies. Thus, Franz Boas, who was in at the beginning by inspiring Margaret Mead to undertake the research that resulted in one of the most important books in anthropology in this century, *Coming of Age in Samoa*, was called upon again at the end. For Franz Boas, like another great twentieth century anthropologist, Bronisław Malinowski, was a student of physics before he ventured into anthropology, and hence laid the foundation for a new physical anthropology, for which Margaret Mead was an apt disciple.

Bibliography

Freeman, Derek. *Margaret Mead and Samoa: The Making and Unmaking of an Anthropological Myth*. Cambridge, Mass.: Harvard University Press, 1983. A highly controversial book, which sets out its purpose in the first paragraph, the refutation of Mead's Samoan work and her defense of cultural determinism. He brings Karl Popper into the book in its dedication, but there is little Popperian in the overall polemical tone of the writing.

Holmes, Llowell D. *The Quest for the Real Samoa. The Mead/Freeman Controversy and Beyond*. South Hadley, Mass.: Bergin and Garvey, 1987. "I owe nothing special to Margaret Mead," Holmes states in the preface. Yet, he did begin field work in Samoa in 1954. His conclusions, for the most part, corroborate Mead's own conclusions.

Howard, Jane. *Margaret Mead: A Life*. New York: Simon & Schuster, 1984. The definitive Mead biography, complimentary, for the most part, but bringing out some of the criticisms as well. Her private life, her three marriages—the first to an American clergyman, the second to a New Zealand psychologist, and the third to the father of her only daughter, Mary Catherine Bateson, an eminent English anthropologist—are discussed.

Mead, Margaret. *Blackberry Winter: My Earlier Years*. New York: William Morrow, 1972. Mead's autobiography, vividly describing her field trips to Samoa, New Guinea, and Bali, and the opposition she met and overcame as a young woman in a profession dominated by men. She describes herself as a child, student, wife, mother, and grandmother. Illustrated.

_____. *Coming of Age in Samoa*. New York: William Morrow, 1928; 2d ed., 1961; 5th printing, 1968. This is a book which "put anthropology on the map." It has a reputation down through the years, perhaps undeserved, for containing steamy prose describing the sexual life of young girls in the tropics. It is very popular in university libraries.

Joseph A. Schufle

Cross-References

Sutton States That Chromosomes Are Paired and Could Be Carriers of Hereditary Traits (1902), p. 153; Pavlov Develops the Concept of Reinforcement (1902), p. 163; Hardy and Weinberg Present a Model of Population Genetics (1908), p. 390; Morgan Develops the Gene-Chromosome Theory (1908), p. 407; Boas Publishes *The Mind of Primitive Man* (1911), p. 481; Benedict Publishes *Patterns of Culture* (1934), p. 997.

FLEMING DISCOVERS PENICILLIN IN MOLDS

Category of event: Medicine
Time: September, 1928
Locale: London, England

Fleming discovered penicillin, an antibiotic that later became a wonder drug that saved millions of lives

Principal personage:
> SIR ALEXANDER FLEMING (1881-1955), an English bacteriologist who discovered the antibiotic penicillin and shared the 1945 Nobel Prize in Physiology or Medicine with Baron Florey and Ernst Boris Chain

Summary of Event

During the early twentieth century, scientists were increasingly interested in bacteriology, or the study of infectious disease. This field has since been renamed microbiology and includes the study of viruses, protozoa, fungi, and bacteria. Bacteriologists were able to identify the source of diseases such as pneumonia, syphilis, meningitis, gas gangrene, and tonsillitis. Prior to the discovery of antibiotics, exposure to bacteria such as streptococci, staphylococci, pneumococci, and tubercle bacilli resulted in serious and often fatal illnesses. Penicillin was the first of a series of twentieth century "wonder drugs" used to treat bacterial infections. This powerful antibiotic altered the lives of millions of patients who would otherwise have fallen prey to diseases caused by bacteria.

Sir Alexander Fleming began his scientific career in 1901, when he inherited a small legacy that enabled him to enter St. Mary's Medical School in London. Fleming was a prizewinning student and a superb technician. He qualified as a doctor in 1906 and remained at St. Mary's as a junior assistant to Sir Almroth Edward Wright, a prominent pathologist and well-known proponent of inoculation. In 1909, Fleming was one of the first to use Paul Ehrlich's new arsenical compound (Salvarsan) for treatment of syphilis. He became renowned for his skilled administration of Salvarsan.

During World War I, Wright and Fleming joined the Royal Army Medical Corps and conducted wound research at a laboratory in Boulogne. Fleming was in charge of identifying the infecting bacteria by taking swabs from wounds before, during, and after surgery. His results showed that 90 percent of the samples contained *Clostridium welchii*, the anaerobic bacteria that cause gas gangrene. Although scientists could isolate the bacteria, they were uncertain as to the best method for combating diseases. Antiseptics were a known means for killing bacteria but were not always effective, especially when used in deep wounds. Wright and Fleming showed that white blood cells found in pus discharged from wounds had ingested bacteria. Fleming also demonstrated that contrary to popular opinion, when antiseptics were packed into a wound, bacteria survived in the crevasses. Antiseptics destroyed the body's own defenses (white blood cells), allowing the remaining bacteria to create serious infection unimpeded. The horrors of bacterial infection during World War I had a lasting impact on Fleming, who decided to focus his postwar research on antibiotic substances. Fleming was convinced that the ideal antiseptic or bacteria-fighting agent should be highly active against microorganisms but harmless to the body's own white blood cell defenses.

In 1921, Fleming observed the dissolving effect that a sample of his own nasal mucus had on bacteria growing in a petri dish. He isolated the antibiotic component of the mucus and named it "lysozyme." Further research showed that lysozyme was also present in human blood serum, tears, saliva, pus, and milk. Fleming had discovered a universal biological protective mechanism that kills and dissolves most of the airborne bacteria that invade exposed areas of the body. He also found that lysozyme does not interfere with the body's white blood cells. Surprisingly, the discovery of lysozyme, subsequently recognized as fundamentally important, received little attention from the scientific community. Ronald Hare, Fleming's associate and biographer, attributes the neglect of lysozyme to "Fleming's inability to express himself clearly and lucidly in either words or print." The significance of lysozyme continued to be overlooked until researchers discovered its presence in white blood cells. Despite the neglect of lysozyme, Fleming continued to focus his research on antibiotics.

In September, 1928, Fleming noticed that a mold was growing in a petri dish containing strains of staphylococci and that bacteria surrounding the mold were being destroyed. It is likely that the source of the mold spores was the laboratory below Fleming's, where mycologist C. J. La Touche was growing molds for research on allergies. Because of his interest in antibiotics, Fleming was conditioned to recognize immediately that an agent capable of dissolving staphylococci could be of great biological significance. He preserved the original culture plate and made a subculture of the mold in a tube of broth. Fleming's mold was later identified as *Penicillium notatum*. Further experiments showed that the "mould juice" could be produced by several strains of *Penicillium* but not by other molds. The substance was nontoxic and did not interfere with the action of white blood cells.

Fleming described his findings in a paper entitled "On the Antibacterial Action of Cultures of a Penicillium, with Special Reference to Their Use in the Isolation of B. Influenzae," which appeared in the *British Journal of Experimental Pathology* (volume 10, 1929). The unusual title refers to Fleming's use of penicillin to isolate B. Influenza, a bacteria that was not vulnerable to penicillin. His paper describes the mold extract and lists the sensitive bacteria. Most important, Fleming suggested that penicillin might be used in the treatment of infection. In addition to describing his experiments, Fleming also stated that the name "penicillin" would be used to describe the mold broth filtrate. His description of penicillin came to be regarded as one of the most important medical papers ever written.

Fleming's petri dish elicited little interest from colleagues at St. Mary's, who were familiar with his previous work and assumed that this was an example of lysozyme being produced by a mold. Fleming knew this to be untrue, as lysozyme was incapable of destroying a pathogenic organism such as staphylococcus. Once again, Fleming's limited ability as a writer and speaker left his audience content to shelve his latest discovery along with lysozyme. Even Ernst Boris Chain, who discovered Fleming's paper during a literature search in 1936, "thought that Fleming had discovered a sort of mould lysozyme which, in contrast to egg white lysozyme, acted on a wide range of . . . pathogenic bacteria."

During 1929, Fleming continued to investigate the antibiotic properties of penicillin, collecting data that clearly established the chemotherapeutic potential of penicillin. Fleming was unable to purify and concentrate penicillin adequately, and, hence, did not conduct clinical tests that could prove the effectiveness of the antibiotic in vivo. The significance of Fleming's discovery was not recognized until 1940, when Baron Florey and Chain discovered the enormous therapeutic power of penicillin.

Impact of Event

Fleming's discovery of penicillin had no immediate impact on twentieth century medicine. By 1931, he had discontinued work on the antibiotic and turned to the study of sulfa drugs. In 1940, Florey and Chain succeeded in concentrating and clinically testing penicillin, after which Fleming's discovery gained enormous notoriety and he was showered with accolades and honors. In 1943, he was elected to fellowship in the Royal Society; in 1944, he was knighted; and in 1945, he received the Nobel Prize in Physiology or Medicine jointly with Florey and Chain.

Penicillin achieved particular notoriety because of World War II and the demand for an antibiotic that could halt diseases such as gas gangrene, which infected the wounds of numerous soldiers during World War I. With the help of Florey and Chain's Oxford group, scientists at the United States Department of Agriculture's Northern Regional Research Laboratory developed a highly efficient method for producing penicillin using fermentation. An excellent corn starch medium was developed for both surface and submerged culture of penicillium molds. After an extended search, scientists also were able to isolate a more productive penicillium strain (*Penicillium chrysogenum*). By 1945, a strain was developed that produced five hundred times more penicillin than Fleming's original mold.

During World War II, the U.S. Office of Scientific Research and Development's Committee on Medical Research conducted large-scale clinical tests of penicillin on 10,838 patients. Their results provided doctors with effective methods and dosages for use of penicillin in treatment of many diseases.

American pharmaceutical companies were galvanized by the development of an efficient production technique and positive clinical tests. Corporations such as Merck, Pfizer, Squibb, and many other corporations built large factories, which mass-produced penicillin for use by the U.S. armed forces. The War Production Board increased production by allocating supplies and equipment to twenty-two U.S. chemical companies engaged in the production of the antibiotic. Penicillin prevented many of the horrendous casualties that Fleming witnessed during World War I. Penicillin is still the most powerful antibiotic and is widely used throughout the world.

Penicillin is regarded as among the greatest medical discoveries of the twentieth century. Almost every organ in the body is vulnerable to bacteria. Before penicillin, the only antimicrobial drugs available were quinine, arsenic, and sulfa drugs. Of these, only the sulfa drugs were useful for treatment of bacterial infection, but in many cases, high toxicity precluded their use. With this limited arsenal, doctors were helpless as thousands died in epidemics caused by bacteria.

Diseases such as pneumonia, meningitis, and syphilis are now treated with penicillin. Penicillin and other antibiotics also had a broad impact on medicine as major operations such as heart surgery, organ transplants, and management of severe burns became possible once the threat of bacterial infection was minimized. Fleming's discovery brought about a revolution in medical treatment by offering an extremely effective solution to the enormous problem of infectious disease.

Bibliography

Fleming, Alexander. "On the Antibacterial Action of Cultures of a Penicillium, with Special Reference to Their Use in the Isolation of B. Influenzae." *British Journal of Experimental Pathology* 10 (1929): 226-236. Fleming's first description of his discovery gives valuable insight into his experimental technique and understanding of the antibiotic potential of penicillin.

Hare, Ronald. *The Birth of Penicillin, and the Disarming of Microbes.* London: George Allen & Unwin, 1970. Hare's account is a firsthand description of Fleming's work. The author worked at St. Mary's at the time of Fleming's discovery and was among those who witnessed Fleming's early work with penicillin. Gives the reader an interesting perspective on penicillin research before 1940.

Hobby, Gladys L. *Penicillin: Meeting the Challenge.* New Haven, Conn.: Yale University Press, 1985. A good, overall description of the roles played by Fleming, Florey, Chain, and numerous other scientists in the discovery, development, and eventual mass production of penicillin. The author benefits from extensive personal work with penicillin as a scientist employed by the Pfizer Corporation. Includes extensive footnotes.

Macfarlane, Gwyn. *Alexander Fleming: The Man and the Myth.* Cambridge, Mass.: Harvard University Press, 1984. The most recent and complete biography of Fleming. Macfarlane expands on Hare's work (see Hare, cited above) by adding more detail and documentation. Macfarlane has also written a biography of Florey and takes care to dispel those parts of the "Fleming myth" that abound in early biographies.

Maurois, André. *The Life of Alexander Fleming.* New York: E. P. Dutton, 1959. Maurois' book is the authorized biography of Fleming and includes two chapters on his penicillin research.

Peter Neushul

Cross-References

Ehrlich Introduces Salvarsan as a Cure for Syphilis (1910), p. 476; Florey and Chain Develop Penicillin as an Antibiotic (1940), p. 1171; Waksman Discovers the Antibiotic Streptomycin (1943), 1224; Hodgkin Solves the Structure of Penicillin (1944), p. 1240; Duggar Discovers Aureomycin, the First of the Tetracyclines (1945), p. 1255.

HUBBLE CONFIRMS THE EXPANDING UNIVERSE

Category of event: Astronomy
Time: 1929
Locale: Mount Wilson, California

Hubble established the linear relationship between distance and velocity of recession (the amount of redshift of the spectrographs) for distant galaxies

> *Principal personages:*
> EDWIN POWELL HUBBLE (1889-1953), an American astronomer who engaged in extensive studies of the external galaxies, establishing them as island universes in the process of separating from one another
> VESTO MELVIN SLIPHER (1875-1969), an American astronomer, active in galactic astronomy at Lowell Observatory in Arizona, who obtained photographs of galactic spectra that Hubble used to establish his relationship
> HENRIETTA LEAVITT (1868-1921), an American astronomer who discovered the relationship between intrinsic brightness and period of variability for Cepheid variable stars, providing the primary means of distance measurement to nearby galaxies
> GEORGES LEMAÎTRE (1894-1966), a Belgian cosmologist who proposed an original condensation of matter in a super dense state (the cosmic egg) which developed into the present universe
> WALTER BAADE (1893-1960), a German-American astronomer who was able to resolve the stars, including the Cepheid variables, into two populations, thereby resolving the scale and age problem of the universe

Summary of Event

In 1929, Edwin Powell Hubble announced that there was a linear (proportional) relationship between the distance of a galaxy from the earth and its velocity of recession. The velocity of recession was defined in terms of how rapidly the galaxy appeared to be moving away from the earth based upon the amount of shift toward the red end of the spectrum for that galaxy, an application of the Doppler effect. This discovery was of major importance because it implied that the universe was expanding; the discovery, in turn, supported the cosmology of Georges Lemaître, proposed in 1927, as it was further developed into the big bang cosmology by George Gamow in 1948.

Hubble discovered the relationship because he combined the photographic spectra that Vesto Melvin Slipher had taken with an adequate means of measuring distance. The initial key in measuring the distance to the galaxies was the work of Henrietta Leavitt. In 1911 and 1912, Leavitt, working at the Arequipa, Peru, station of the

Harvard Observatory, analyzed Cepheid variables. Leavitt arranged the stars in order according to their period, the length of time over which they varied. She noticed that arrangement by period placed them in order of intrinsic (absolute) brightness, that is, their brightness based on their estimated distance from Earth. She discovered what became known as the period-luminosity scale, which meant that once the apparent brightness and period of a Cepheid was measured, the apparent brightness could be compared with intrinsic brightness and the distance calculated.

A second necessary component was the measurement of the amount of redshifting of the galaxies. Beginning in 1913, Slipher produced a series of photographs of the spectra of galaxies. Slipher noted that the fainter the galaxies, the greater their redshift, an indicator that the velocity of recession was greater for the more distant galaxies. Slipher had no firm measure of distances, however, and thus no means of establishing the apparent relationship. It was Hubble who put together the measurements of distance that established the distance recession relationship, which is now called Hubble's law.

Hubble began work in 1919 with the 1.52 meter diameter telescope on Mount Wilson, near Pasadena, California, when he returned from service in World War I; he then moved to the 2.54-meter Hooker telescope. He studied objects within the Milky Way, such as novas (exploding stars), stars associated with gaseous nebulas, and variable stars. By 1922, he published a paper noting the differences between the gaseous nebulas and those that were suspected of being more remote.

By 1928, using Leavitt's period-luminosity scale, he estimated that Andromeda was more than 900,000 light-years away (the distance light travels in a year at 299,000 kilometers per second). This figure was far beyond Jacobus Cornelis Kapteyn's 50,000 light-year diameter for the Milky Way and even beyond Harlow Shapley's estimates of 200,000 light-years, which proved too large. Hubble later adjusted this estimate to 750,000 light-years because of absorption of light by interstellar gas and dust. It is now known that Hubble's estimates were too small, for in 1952, Walter Baade was able to demonstrate that there were two types of Cepheid variables with different intrinsic brightnesses. As a consequence, modern estimates of the distance to the Andromeda nebula are more than 2 million light-years. Hubble, however, had established that Andromeda was extragalactic.

Later, Hubble was able to increase the number and distance of the galaxies that he could measure. Using the Hooker telescope, he was able to resolve some of the fringes of nebulas into stars. Statistical estimates based upon the brightest stars gave an independent measure of distance beyond where Cepheids were resolvable. By 1929, he had measured twenty-three galaxies out to a distance of about 20 million light-years. Hubble then compared their distance with the amount of redshift, or velocity, of recession. He found that the redshift displacements were proportional to distance and in 1929 made the announcement. Actually, his data barely demonstrated the linear relationship, because all the galaxies he measured were very close. Hubble was influenced by the cosmological model of Willem de Sitter, which appeared to be a classical static solution to Albert Einstein's gravitational field equations, but which predicted a redshift based upon distance.

In later years, Hubble and Milton L. Humason remeasured Slipher's amount of displacement of the spectra. By 1931, Hubble and Humason had measured some forty new velocities out to a distance of 100 million light-years. The major contribution to reliability was that twenty-six of these were in eight clusters which would give several redshifts at relatively the same distance as a check against the method.

Hubble found the velocity of recession directly proportional to distance by a factor that came to be called the Hubble constant, which he estimated to be 170 kilometers per second for each million light-years of distance. This rate was about eleven times the modern value of 15 kilometers per second per million light-years and resulted from his underestimation of the distances of his calibrating galaxies. His original value for the constant indicated an age for the universe of only 2 billion years, much less than the 3 or 4 billion years that geologists had derived for the age of the earth. His figure created an anomaly that persisted until Walter Baade's discovery of two stellar populations, which reduced the size of the constant and lengthened the age of the universe.

Hubble knew his discovery was significant as a means of distance measurement if the linear relationship would hold for more distant galaxies. As he searched for additional nearby galaxies to verify his initial results, he realized that it would take decades to photograph the entire sky and count galaxies, so he sampled 1,283 regions of the sky and counted more than forty-four thousand galaxies. He estimated that more than 100 million galaxies were within reach of the 2.54-meter Hooker telescope. Astronomers now know that more than a billion galaxies are within reach of the 5-meter Hale telescope on Mount Palomar.

While searching for additional close galaxies to strengthen the reliability of his law, Hubble was able to formulate additional methods of aiding distance measurement. On the basis of his samples, he reasoned that the galaxies were approximately uniformly distributed (homogeneous) in space, indicating that brightness as well as redshift was a distance indicator. Attempting to understand the structure of space was a natural outgrowth of reaching the limit of what he could measure. On the "small" scale, there were irregularities: pairs, groups, and clusters of galaxies. On the large scale, the uniformity persisted. Hubble's next step was to use the photographs of the forty-four thousand galaxies to classify them into types: globular, elliptical, spirals, barred spirals, and irregulars, with various subgroups within these large groups. Focusing upon the brightness of a single type, he presumed, would assist in distance measurements and allow extension of the distance/redshift relationship.

Impact of Event

The establishment of the expansion of the universe is regarded by many astronomers as the most significant achievement in twentieth century astronomy, for it made as great a change in conceptions of the universe as Copernicus had made four hundred years before. Hubble's ability to convince his astronomical colleagues that the relationship between distance and redshift was linear was the natural consequence of work completed in 1919. Establishing the scale of distance was a key to understanding the nature of the universe, which has led to Hubble's position as the founder of extragalactic astronomy.

Hubble was not the first to presume that there were objects of interest beyond our galaxy. Many astronomers had suspected that Sir William Herschel was correct in his opinion that the "nebulas," those faint patches of light scattered throughout space, were "island universes" of stars, located outside the bounds of our own galaxy. Proving this, however, was difficult. Significantly, in the mid-1920's, Lemaître theorized that the universe originated from an original superdense cosmic egg that had expanded into the present universe. He suggested that the spectra of galaxies shifting toward the red end of the spectrum would be an indicator of this expansion. Hubble demonstrated that theoretical cosmology could be related to the observed phenomena.

While the significance of Hubble's law was immediately recognized, there were difficulties. His work was in conflict with Adriaan van Maanen's measurements of the proper motions of spiral galaxies. Van Maanen found high velocities which implied they were close by. Confusion resulted until 1935, when Hubble was able to demonstrate that there were systematic errors in van Maanen's work that invalidated it.

A second implication of Hubble's work that caused consternation was the implication that all the other galaxies were smaller than the Milky Way, and that the globular clusters in Andromeda would have to be intrinsically dimmer than those in the Milky Way. These clusters pointed to the fact that his initial values for the constant were incorrect.

The most important implication of Hubble's law was that at some distant past time all the matter in the universe was gathered in one place at the same time. Hubble initially estimated that this event took place 2 billion years ago. Adjustments based on Baade's work and other modifications revised that estimate significantly; more recent estimates range near 20 billion years ago. Whatever the time span, the picture is of a superdense state that exploded into the present universe.

Specifically, Hubble's law resolved the issue of "island universes" that had been under debate since 1920. It supported Lemaître's concept and laid to rest Einstein's static solution to the field equations. It brought the work of Lemaître into direct contact with observational results and demonstrated again the validity of the theory of relativity. With Baade's resolution of the distance scale in 1952, it restored the perspective that there is no privileged position in the universe. The astronomical community properly regards Hubble's law as one of the most significant achievements of the century.

Bibliography

Adams, Walter S. "Obituary: Dr. Edwin P. Hubble." *The Observatory* 74 (February, 1954): 32-35. A short biographical sketch in which the main emphasis is the distance-redshift relationship. The chronology surrounding his doctoral degree and service in World War I is confusing, but the rest is a clear, reliable, and interesting account.

Gribbin, John. *In Search of the Big Bang*. New York: Bantam Books, 1986. A popular, accurate, and comprehensive statement of the currently accepted cosmology which contains an excellent summary of Hubble's contribution. One of the most readable books for a general audience.

Hetherington, N. "Edwin Hubble: Legal Eagle." *Nature* 39 (January 16, 1986): 189-190. A fascinating short analysis of the influence of Hubble's legal training upon the manner in which he presented his astronomical evidence. Also considers the way in which he conducted his conflicts with other scientists. Presents a perspective different from all the other sources, but does not decrease the significance of Hubble's work.

Hubble, Edwin. "The Exploration of Space." In *Theories of the Universe*, edited by Milton Karl Munitz. Glencoe, Ill.: Free Press, 1957. This short discussion is an excerpt from his book *The Realm of the Nebulae*, and from his article "Exploration in Space," *Proceedings of the American Philosophical Society*. An attractive summary and retrospect of his work that pays attention to the contributions of other astronomers working on related topics.

_____. *The Realm of the Nebulæ*. New Haven, Conn.: Yale University Press, 1936. A comprehensive summary of Hubble's work with the distant galaxies, chapters 4 and 5 of which contain a statement of his discovery of Hubble's law and the procedures used for determining Hubble's constant. It was published long before the resolution of the problems the law raised.

_____. "A Relation Between Distance and Radial Velocity Among Extra-Galactic Nebulae." In *Source Book in Astronomy, 1900-1950*, edited by Harlow Shapley. Cambridge, Mass.: Harvard University Press, 1960. An excerpt from an article in the *Proceedings of the National Academy of Science*. This is an understated historical piece that presented the proportional nature of the relationship based on the distance established for twenty-four galaxies from among forty-six for which the radial velocity was known. He drew few conclusions in this first paper, and there is little sense of the great drama that depended upon this discovery.

Jaffe, Bernard. "Edwin Powell Hubble." In *Men of Science in America*. New York: Simon & Schuster, 1946. A biography of Hubble that contains a popular account of his discovery and the importance of it. An old, dramatic, and dated account, but one that remains interesting reading.

Mayall, N. U. "Edwin Powell Hubble." *Biographical Memoirs of the National Academy of Sciences* 41 (1970): 175-214. An extensive laudatory biography that describes each of his major accomplishments. Contains some interesting anecdotal material not in other sources. An abbreviated version of the memoir appeared in *Sky and Telescope* in January, 1954.

Smith, Robert W. "The Origins of the Velocity-Distance Relation." *Journal for the History of Astronomy* 10 (October, 1979): 133-165. A comprehensive statement of Hubble's accomplishments that is readable, but does have some diagrams and a few mathematical equations. More skeptical of Hubble's data than other sources. Struve, Otto, and Velta Zebergs. *Astronomy of the Twentieth Century.* New York: Macmillan, 1962. Pages 444 to 455 contain an excellent nontechnical summary of Hubble's work. In this particular work, the significance of Hubble's law is less clear because it is embedded in later developments that clarified it, although the authors do call it the most significant discovery of the century.

Ivan L. Zabilka

Cross-References

Leavitt's Study of Variable Stars Unlocks Galactic Distances (1912), p. 496; Slipher Obtains the Spectrum of a Distant Galaxy (1912), p. 502; Hubble Demonstrates That Other Galaxies Are Independent Systems (1924), p. 790; Lemaître Proposes the Big Bang Theory (1927), p. 825; Gamow and Associates Develop the Big Bang Theory (1948), p. 1309.

SCHMIDT INVENTS THE CORRECTOR FOR THE SCHMIDT CAMERA AND TELESCOPE

Categories of event: Astronomy and applied science
Time: Winter, 1929-1930
Locale: Bergedorf, Germany

Schmidt extended both astronomy and astrophotography by designing a special lens to correct a fundamental defect in images formed by spherical mirrors

Principal personages:

BERNHARD VOLDEMAR SCHMIDT (1879-1935), an Estonian optical instrument maker who revolutionized astronomical instrumentation with a device called a corrector plate

RICHARD SCHORR (1867-1951), a German astronomer and director of the Hamburg Observatory at Bergedorf, who employed and encouraged Schmidt

WALTER BAADE (1893-1960), a German-born American astronomer whose many achievements included efforts to popularize the Schmidt camera in the international astronomical community

KARL SCHWARZSCHILD (1873-1916), a German astronomer and theoretical physicist who, as director of the Potsdam Astrophysical Observatory, was the first top-rank professional astronomer to encourage Schmidt's efforts

Summary of Event

The first telescope, invented by a Dutch spectacle maker in the early seventeenth century, was a simple combination of two lenses in a tube. Since it employed refraction, in which light obliquely entering glass from air undergoes a change in direction, such a telescope is often termed a refractor. Although Galileo did not invent the telescope, he pioneered its astronomical use, discovering sunspots, craters on Earth's moon, the phases of Venus, and the four large moons of Jupiter, now called the Galilean moons in his honor.

Even today, many amateur astronomers use refractors; however, inescapable technical difficulties with them became evident as astronomy progressed. A lens, for example, can be supported only about its rim without obscuring the light path; therefore, large lenses may sag under their own weight, distorting the image produced. Furthermore, a lens focuses red and blue lights at different places, a fault called chromatic aberration, causing colored rings around the images.

By 1897, when the Yerkes Observatory (the site of the world's largest refractor) was completed on the shores of Lake Geneva, Wisconsin, it was clear that the future of giant telescopes lay along a different path. This involved a completely new optical system called the reflector, in which the primary light-gatherer is a mirror rather than a lens. In 1668, Sir Isaac Newton constructed the first working reflector: a concave mirror, which was supported from behind and reflected all colors similarly, eliminating chromatic aberration. Although Newton's mirror was made from metal, subsequent telescope makers preferred to form the mirror from glass covered with a thin reflective layer of metal. Glass of high optical quality was not necessary, since light never entered it. In addition, lens makers needed to grind, or "figure," only one side of the glass, obviously saving time and cost over figuring the two sides of a lens of the same diameter.

Reflectors, on the other hand, are not without their own problems, and by the early twentieth century, one of the most troublesome of these problems was still unresolved: Would the optimum shape of the concave mirror be spherical or parabolic? A spherical one is easier to construct, but inherent in all such mirrors is a flaw called spherical aberration, in which light that does not strike the surface of the mirror along its axis of symmetry is not brought to an exact focus. Similarly, parabolic mirrors produce sharp images only for light entering from or nearly from the center of the telescope's field of view. The image formed by all other light suffers from "coma," in which fuzziness and cometlike tails appear. Stopping the aperture of either type of mirror to admit less light will sharpen the image but, unfortunately, prolongs photographic exposure times. In any case, the largest reflectors of the early twentieth century afforded a very narrow field of view, and a photographic survey of the entire sky with any of them would have required millions of separate pictures of small segments of the heavens.

The resolution to this impasse came from Bernhard Voldemar Schmidt, a highly skilled optical instrument maker. Born on the Estonian island of Naissaar in the Gulf of Finland, he was fascinated with scientific investigation in general and stars in particular. Despite the loss of much of his right arm to a boyhood experiment with gunpowder, Schmidt taught himself to grind lenses and mirrors. Hoping for better astronomical and astrophotographic equipment than he could afford, he wrote a letter in 1904 to Karl Schwarzschild, director of the Potsdam Astrophysical Observatory in Germany, offering to make a large mirror. Thus began ten years of successful cooperation in which Schmidt ground precise mirrors for Schwarzschild. The outbreak of World War I disrupted this collaboration; in addition, Schwarzschild's brilliant career was aborted in 1916 by his death from service in the war.

In 1916, Schmidt contacted Richard Schorr, director of the Hamburg Observatory in Bergedorf. Even though Schorr was impressed with Schmidt's photographs, postwar financial constraints unfortunately prevented Schorr from hiring Schmidt. Depressed with the state of his career, Schmidt wrote in 1925, "I'm ready to turn my whole stock into junk and sell it for old iron and charcoal, and then take up something new." The following year, Schorr was at last able to offer Schmidt a position at the Hamburg Observatory. Schorr supplied the reclusive Schmidt with housing, unfettered use of a basement workshop, and a salary; for once, Schmidt enjoyed financial stability, access to the facilities of a large observatory, and steady encouragement. In this fertile environment grew the idea for what subsequent generations now call the Schmidt telescope and the Schmidt camera.

At Hamburg Observatory, Schmidt met Walter Baade, a staff astronomer who reached prominence at Mount Wilson Observatory and Mount Palomar Observatory. In 1929, Schmidt confided to Baade that he was confident he could produce a telescope with both a wide field of view and a large aperture for increased light-collecting. From the details he gave Baade at the time, Schmidt apparently had been pondering this approach for some time, but he characteristically left no documentation of the process whereby he had attained the breakthrough.

Schmidt's great contribution to optics was a marriage of lenses and mirrors, the prototype of catadioptric telescope designs which include Schmidt-Cassegrain and Maksutov telescopes. In addition to a spherical mirror, Schmidt used a "corrector plate," a lens thickest in the center, not so thick near the edges, and thinnest in between. It succeeded at its primary purpose: to correct almost completely the mirror's spherical aberration by refracting the incoming light before it struck the mirror. (Strictly, the lens can exactly correct spherical aberration for only one wavelength of light.) The corrector also afforded several incidental benefits, one of which would be evident to anyone who has ever cleaned eyeglasses or contact lenses. Any optical surface open to the air will collect dust and require cleaning. Cleaning a large reflector, however, may jeopardize the thin metal coating on the mirror. By sealing the telescope tube, Schmidt's corrector plate extended vastly the operational lifetime of its associated mirror.

On the other hand, there were drawbacks to Schmidt's design. Although none has proved a serious obstacle to worldwide implementation of his idea, four might be mentioned. First, the corrector lens will introduce some small chromatic aberration. (Since the corrector plate is actually almost flat, this is relatively insignificant.) Second, optical considerations dictate that a Schmidt telescope be longer than a comparable simple reflector. Third, the corrector plate is difficult to grind properly. Fourth, a photograph made by film inside a Schmidt telescope, thus functioning as a Schmidt camera, will be distorted unless the film itself is spherical.

With the encouragement of Baade and Schorr, Schmidt built the original Schmidt telescope in 1930; the Hamburg Observatory placed the first Schmidt camera in operation the following year. Revolutionary photographs quickly followed, but the skepticism of prospective customers, combined with international politico-economic considerations—for example, Adolf Hitler's rise to power—prevented Schmidt from selling even one Schmidt camera outside of Hamburg before his death in 1935.

Impact of Event

The Schmidt telescope, as historian of science Barbara Land remarked, "sees far and wide at the same time." Furthermore, it sees quickly. To appreciate why in each case, the concepts of angular size and f-number must be recognized. The width of a fist at the end of an extended arm covers about 10 degrees of the observer's sky. In order to see faint objects, large telescopes are needed for their large light-gathering power. On the other hand, the field of view of the largest reflectors is minuscule. In Richard Learner's words, the 2.54-meter Mount Wilson telescope would take at least fifty plates to photograph the full moon, which is about half a degree across, but "covers an area that is only a few millionths of the whole sky. A complete survey with such a telescope would take about 10,000 years." In contrast, the first Schmidt telescope had a field of view more than 15 degrees wide.

The focal length of a lens or mirror is the distance from the component to the point where incoming parallel light is focused. Thus, a stronger component has a smaller focal length. The f-number of a lens or mirror is its focal length divided by its diameter; the smaller the f-number, the shorter the time required for a given amount of light to be collected, as for a photograph. Schmidt's work can be viewed as inventing a succession of lower and lower f-numbers, culminating in f/1.75 for the 1931 Schmidt telescope. The Schmidt telescope is therefore well suited for either visual or photographic sky surveys, since it produces a wide and sensitive view of the sky with minimal distortion even out to the edges of the image or photograph.

During his life, Schmidt had jealously guarded details of the corrector plate and the curved film. In 1936, the year after Schmidt's death, Schorr revealed these details to the world. In only six years, more than twenty Schmidt telescopes with mirror diameters of more than 24 centimeters were produced. A mere three years after Schmidt's death, Baade and others persuaded the Rockefeller Foundation to fund an instrument that became known as the "Big Schmidt." Delayed by World War II, this telescope with a 1.8-meter mirror and a 1.2-meter corrector plate was put into operation in 1948 as an indispensable companion for the giant 5-meter Hale telescope, located on Mount Palomar.

With a field of view of more than three hundred times that of the Hale telescope, the Big Schmidt has become the ultimate "spotter scope." Far more important, however, is its epochal survey of the northern two thirds of the sky during the 1950's, capturing objects down to one-half-millionth as bright as the dimmest naked-eye star. Each photographic plate covers an area approximately 6 degrees square and may show up to a million stars. Some two decades later, two Schmidt cameras (at the United Kingdom Siding Spring Observatory in Australia and the European Southern Observatory in Chile) cooperatively surveyed the southern third of the heavens.

Astronomical progress is ongoing, and better surveys are certain to follow as technology improves. With these pioneering surveys, however, Schmidt cameras have already provided invaluable information in recording conditions at the time of the survey, furnishing an inventory of objects surveyed, and allowing better identification of previously observed objects.

Bibliography

Asimov, Isaac. *Eyes on the Universe: A History of the Telescope.* Boston: Houghton Mifflin, 1975. Helpful informal background on observational astronomy, starting in prehistory and current through its publication date in the space age. Schmidt and his telescopes are discussed in several pages; as with most of Asimov's writing, the text is very interesting reading.

Capaccioli, Massimo, ed. *Astronomy with Schmidt-Type Telescopes.* Boston: D. Reidel, 1984. Proceedings of a colloquium of the International Astronomical Union held at Asiago, Italy. While highly technical in places, this 619-page volume is useful to the interested reader as an overview of the diversity of applications of Schmidt's work by major-league astronomers.

Hodges, Paul C. "Bernhard Schmidt and His Reflector Camera: An Astronomical Contribution to Radiology." *American Journal of Röntgenology and Radium Therapy* 15 (January, 1948): 122-131. At the time, Hodges said that radiology was in a race to see which would provide more enhanced imaging, electronics or Schmidt cameras. It is now known that electronics won. This absorbing article contains unique insights, photographs (courtesy of Professor Baade), and extensive references.

Land, Barbara. *The Telescope Makers: From Galileo to the Space Age.* New York: Thomas Y. Crowell, 1968. Chapter 8, on Schmidt, draws heavily from material provided by Dr. Wachmann. Especially helpful to the novice in simply but lucidly recounting the history of astrophotography up to Schmidt's time.

Learner, Richard. *Astronomy Through the Telescope.* New York: Van Nostrand Reinhold, 1981. Splendidly lives up to the photographic excitement implied by its title. Well worth a prolonged browse by the general reader wanting to see more about the theory and practice of astrophotography; however, it adds little in particular to the study of Schmidt and his work.

Miczaika, G. R., and William M. Sinton. *Tools of the Astronomer.* Cambridge, Mass.: Harvard University Press, 1961. A moderately technical discussion of telescope optics on pages 85 to 110 will be interesting to many readers. It serves as an excellent primer for most readers who are approaching the volume edited by Capaccioli from less than a serious amateur background in astronomy.

Silverman, Milton. "The Eye That Exposes Secrets." *Saturday Evening Post* 222 (April 22, 1950): 28-29. A delightful interview with Baade and tantalizing views of other applications of Schmidt's corrector plate highlight this article on the Big Schmidt at the outset of its sky survey. Schmidt's personality comes alive in this article, which, if it errs, does so in being too laudatory of Schmidt.

Wachmann, A. A. "From the Life of Bernhard Schmidt." *Sky and Telescope* 15 (November, 1955): 4-9. A primary source for any further study of Schmidt and his work, written by a colleague of Schmidt in Bergedorf on the occasion of the installation of a new Schmidt telescope at the Hamburg Observatory. Priceless glimpses of Schmidt, in both prose and photographs.

Clyde J. Smith

Cross-References

Hale Establishes Mount Wilson Observatory (1903), p. 194; Hale Oversees the

Installation of the Hooker Telescope on Mount Wilson (1917), p. 645; Hale Constructs the Largest Telescope of the Time (1948), p. 1325; De Vaucouleurs Identifies the Local Supercluster of Galaxies (1953), p. 1454; Construction of the World's Largest Telescope Begins in Hawaii (1985), p. 2291; NASA Launches the Hubble Space Telescope (1990), p. 2377.

BERGER DEVELOPS THE
ELECTROENCEPHALOGRAM (EEG)

Category of event: Medicine
Time: April 22, 1929
Locale: Psychiatric Clinic, University of Jena, Germany

Berger devised a system of electrodes, the electroencephalogram, to measure brain wave patterns in humans, thereby heralding an entirely new era of neurophysiology

Principal personages:

HANS BERGER (1873-1941), a German psychiatrist and research scientist who devised a method of investigating the electrical activity of the brain

RICHARD CATON (1842-1926), an English physiologist and surgeon who recorded the action currents of the brains of animals

EDGAR DOUGLAS ADRIAN (1889-1977), an English neurophysiologist who confirmed Berger's observations

SIR BRIAN HAROLD CABOT MATTHEWS (1906-   ), an English neurophysiologist who collaborated with Adrian in confirming Berger's observations

Summary of Event

In the latter part of the nineteenth century, the field of psychophysiology had fallen into disrepute among neurologists and psychiatrists. Two new approaches had become fashionable: the neoanatomical approach of Bernhard Friedrich A. Gudden, Theodor H. Meynert, Paul E. Flechsig, Auguste Henri Forel, and Constantin von Monakow; and the functional approach, as exemplified by the work of Emil Kraepelin, Eugen Bleuler, Sigmund Freud, Max Adler, and Carl Jung. Hans Berger, however, was not attracted by either of these two avenues of research. The former was not functional enough to satisfy his psychophysiological interests, and the latter, in his opinion, lacked a firm foundation in the natural sciences, which he had always regarded as indispensable to the understanding of brain function and its relation to mental processes. Thus, from the outset of his career, Berger chose the difficult position of being an outsider, a role in which he was to remain for the rest of his scientific career.

As a scientist, Berger's search for the human electroencephalograph (English physiologist Richard Caton described the electroencephalogram, or "brain wave," in rabbits and monkeys in 1875) was motivated by his desire to find a physiological method that might be applied successfully to the study of the long-standing problem of the relationship between the mind and the brain. His scientific career, therefore, was directed toward the elucidation of the psychophysical relationship in terms of principles that would be rooted firmly in the natural sciences and would not have to rely upon vague philosophical or mystical ideas.

During his early career, Berger attempted to study psychophysical relationships by plethysmographic measurements of changes in the brain circulation of patients with skull defects. In plethysmography, an instrument is used to indicate and record by tracings the variations in size of an organ or part of the body. Later, he investigated temperature changes occurring in the human brain during mental activity and the action of psychoactive drugs. He became disillusioned, however, by the lack of psychophysical understanding generated by these investigations.

Next, he turned to the study of the electrical activity of the brain and, in the 1920's, set out to search for the human electroencephalogram. He believed that the EEG would finally provide him with a physiological method capable of furnishing insight into mental functions and their disturbances. In 1920, Berger made his first unsuccessful attempt at recording the electrical activity of the brain from the scalp of a bald medical student. At that time, he modified his methods of research and attempted to stimulate the cortex of patients with skull defects by applying an electrical current to the skin covering the defect. The main purpose of these stimulation experiments was to elicit subjective sensations. Berger hoped that eliciting these sensations might give him some clue about the nature of the relationship between the physiochemical events produced by the electrical stimulus and the mental processes revealed by the patients' subjective experience. According to his diaries, the availability of many patients with skull defects—in whom the pulsating surface of the brain was separated from the stimulating electrodes by only a few millimeters of tissue—reactivated Berger's interest in recording the brain's electrical activity.

At the time of these experiments, Berger had very little electrophysiological experience, and his knowledge of physics and instrumentation was limited. In addition, the instruments available to him were not well suited to the research he was contemplating. Nevertheless, he conducted his first electrical recordings from skull defects in 1924 by using the large Edelmann string galvanometer, an instrument that had been designed to record electrocardiograms. In 1926, he acquired the new Siemens coil galvanometer, an apparatus that also was used in electrocardiography. Later, in 1932, the Siemens Company constructed an oscillograph with an amplifier for him. This instrument had adequate gain and, in contrast to the earlier galvanometers, was a voltage-measuring, rather than a current-measuring, device. All of these instruments were used in conjunction with an optical recording system in which electrical oscillations deflected a mirror upon which a light beam was projected. The deflections of the light beam were proportional to the magnitude of the electrical signals. The movement of the spot of the light beam was recorded on photographic paper moving at a speed of 3 centimeters per second; occasionally slower speeds were used. The paper width was 12 centimeters, and the lengths of the records varied between about 3 and 8 meters.

During his investigations, Berger remained faithful to his old recording instruments, even when better methods and equipment—such as cathode ray oscillography or Tönnies' ink-writing oscillograph—became available. In the 1930's, Berger hoped that Siemens would provide him with a multiple oscillograph system, but this hope remained unfulfilled. Thus, to the end of his career, whenever he wished to record with more than one channel at a time, he was forced to use simultaneously the Siemens oscillograph and the coil galvanometer. A major problem with this method, however, was that the gains of the two instruments were very different; thus, it was difficult to put the light spots of the two systems in precise vertical alignment. Therefore, many of his double recordings appear rather idiosyncratic and unsatisfactory from a technical point of view, a fact of which he was well aware.

In July, 1924, Berger observed small, tremulous movements of the galvanometer string while recording from the skin overlying a bone defect in a seventeen-year-old patient (who had been a subject for his earlier cortical stimulation experiments and who had been operated on earlier because he was suspected of having a brain tumor). In his first paper on the electroencephalogram, Berger described briefly this case as his first successful recording of an EEG. Nevertheless, from his experimental protocol, it is known that he did not trust fully this observation, although he was greatly encouraged by it. At the time of these early studies, Berger already had used the term "electroencephalogram" in his diary. Yet, for several years he had doubts about the cerebral origin of the electrical oscillations he recorded. As late as 1928, he almost abandoned his electrical recording studies.

The publication of Berger's first paper on the human encephalogram in 1929 "Über das Elektrenkephalogramm des Menschen" ("On the Electroencephalograph of Man," 1969), in the *Journal für Psychologie und Neurologie*, had little impact on the scientific world. It was either ignored or regarded with open disbelief. At this time, even when Berger himself was not completely free of doubts about the validity of his findings, he managed to continue his work. He published additional contributions to the study of the electroencephalogram in a series of fourteen papers. As his research progressed, Berger became increasingly confident and convinced of the significance of his discovery.

In his studies on the human encephalogram, Berger repeatedly touched on basic neurophysiological and neuropharmacological problems; he also commented on the characteristics and importance of EEG changes in a variety of pathological states. He approached these questions exclusively from the point of view of his own personal interest in psychophysiology, and it is clear that he was not interested primarily in the basic neurophysiology, neuropharmacology, or clinical pathology of the EEG. Nevertheless, he was the first to make many perceptive observations in these areas and to develop some theoretical concepts about the origin and the regulation of the EEG in normal and pathological states.

Impact of Event

The impact of Berger's discovery, unfortunately, was not immediate. There were many reasons for Berger's lack of recognition and the widespread skepticism regarding his work on the EEG of humans. One source of the resistance was to be found among the expert neurophysiologists. Those who conducted research on the axons and their action potentials simply could not believe that regular oscillations of quasi-sinusoidal form could represent the electrical activity of an organ as complex as the human brain and that such activity could be recorded from the scalp. Edgar Douglas Adrian and Sir Brian Harold Cabot Matthews, in their 1934 paper on the "Berger rhythm," admitted that, initially, they had been skeptical about the validity of Berger's work. This skepticism was reinforced by the common assumption that Berger, a psychiatrist, was an unlikely person to make such a striking discovery. Adrian, whose competence as a neurophysiologist could not be questioned, fully confirmed Berger's observations and thus put the seal of scientific respectability upon Berger's work. Soon, interest in the EEG spread throughout all the countries of the Western world—except for Germany. Ironically, soon after the international scientific community finally had accepted Berger into their ranks, he was removed from his post by the Nazis in 1937. Shortly thereafter, the laboratory was dismantled.

The long-range impact of Berger's work is, however, incontestable. When Berger published his last paper on the human encephalogram in 1938, the new approach to the study of brain function that he inaugurated in 1929 had gathered momentum in many centers, both in Europe and in the United States. As a result of his pioneering work, a new diagnostic method had been introduced into medicine. Physiology had acquired a new investigative tool. Clinical neurophysiology had been liberated from its exclusive dependence upon the functional anatomical approach, and electrophysiological exploration of complex functions of the central nervous system in the neurophysiological laboratories had received major impetus. Berger's work had finally received its well-deserved recognition.

Many of those who undertook the study of the electroencephalogram were able to bring a far greater technical knowledge of neurophysiology to bear upon the problems of the electrical activity of the brain than Berger had ever been able to. Yet, the community of neurological scientists has not ceased to look with respect to the founder of electroencephalography who, despite overwhelming odds and isolation, initiated a new era of neurophysiology.

Bibliography

Berger, Hans. "Hans Berger on the EEG of Man." Translated by Pierre Gloor. *Electroencephalography and Clinical Neurophysiology*, supp. 28 (1969). An excellent translation of Berger's fourteen reports (1929 to 1939) on the electroencephalograph of humans. The introduction is the most useful and thorough piece of writing on the history and development of Berger's work on the EEG. Places Berger's work in a historical context; provides firsthand documentation on the discovery from Berger's own diaries. Includes graphs, charts, extensive notes, and an index.
Cooper, R., et al. *EEG Technology*. 3d ed. Boston: Butterworths, 1980. In the first chapter, entitled "Origins of the Encephalogram," Berger's work is cited in its historical context. Although aimed at the EEG technician, the book gives a useful overview of the advances in EEG technology since its inception. Contains appendices; references follow each chapter.

Gale, Anthony, and John A. Edwards. *Physiological Correlates of Human Behavior.* Vol. 2 in *Attention and Performance.* New York: Academic Press, 1983. A section devoted to the EEG and human behavior describes the pioneers and popularizers of electrical brain-wave recording devices—Caton and Berger in particular. Describes advances in the understanding of brain function from these pioneers to the 1980's. Contains extensive references and an index.

Kooi, Kenneth A., et al. *Fundamentals of Electroencephalography.* 2d ed. New York: Harper & Row, 1978. A compact source of information about human electroencephalography aimed at both the student and technician. Discusses the basic concepts, principles, and clinical information necessary to evaluate EEGs; gives a brief history of the development of the phenomenon. Contains graphs, illustrations, and extensive references after each chapter.

Scott, Donald. *Understanding the EEG.* Philadelphia: J. B. Lippincott, 1975. Explains, in simple language, what an EEG is, what diagnostic information it can provide, and what deductions can be made from it. Appeals to those interested in brain activity and its significance—students and practitioners alike. Discusses Berger's work in a brief historical section. Contains a glossary of terms, bibliography, and an index.

Genevieve Slomski

Cross-References

Ramón y Cajal Establishes the Neuron as the Functional Unit of the Nervous System (1888), p. 1; Moniz Develops Prefrontal Lobotomy (1935), p. 1060; Cerletti and Bini Develop Electroconvulsive Therapy for Treating Schizophrenia (1937), p. 1086; Aserinsky Discovers Rapid Eye Movement (REM) in Sleep and Dreams (1952), p. 1424; Sperry Discovers That Each Side of the Brain Can Function Independently (1960's), p. 1635; Janowsky Publishes a Cholinergic-Adrenergic Hypothesis of Mania and Depression (1972), p. 1976.

DRINKER AND SHAW DEVELOP AN
IRON LUNG MECHANICAL RESPIRATOR

Category of event: Medicine
Time: July, 1929
Locale: Harvard University; Boston, Massachusetts

Drinker and Shaw developed the iron lung mechanical respirator, a life-saving device for victims of poliomyelitis that led to the invention of other life-saving respiratory care

Principal personages:

PHILIP DRINKER (1893-1977), an engineer who made many contributions to medicine, including the Drinker respirator (iron lung)

LOUIS SHAW (1886-1940), the respiratory physiologist who assisted Drinker in the development of the iron lung

CHARLES F. MCKHANN III (1898-   ), a pediatrician and founding member of the American Board of Pediatrics who participated in Drinker's work with the iron lung

Summary of Event

Poliomyelitis (polio, or infantile paralysis) is an infectious viral disease that damages the central nervous system, causing paralysis in many serious cases. Its effect results from the destruction of neurons (nerve cells) in the spinal cord. In many cases, the disease produces crippled limbs and the wasting away of muscles. In others, "anterior" polio results in the fatal paralysis of the respiratory muscles. It is fortunate that use of the Salk and Sabin vaccines, beginning in the 1950's, has virtually eradicated the disease.

In the 1920's, however, poliomyelitis was a terrifying disease. Its most feared, untreatable outcome was the paralysis of the respiratory muscles that caused rapid death by suffocation. Often, such death occurred only a few hours after the first signs of respiratory distress appeared. In 1929, Philip Drinker and Louis Shaw, both of Harvard University, reported the development of a mechanical respirator that would keep those afflicted with the disease alive for indefinite periods of time (see "An Apparatus for the Prolonged Administration of Artificial Respiration").

This device, soon nicknamed the "iron lung," provided essential life support for thousands of people who suffered from respiratory paralysis as a result of poliomyelitis or other diseases. It was used for many years. In 1990, according to John A. Meyer, a thoracic surgeon (see "A Practical Mechanical Respirator, 1929: The 'Iron Lung'"), iron lungs are "fascinating relics, reminders of high tech medicine of an earlier day." Meyer's comment is corroborated by Drinker and Charles F. McKhann III, who noted that a modern survey indicated that only three hundred iron lungs remained in use in the United States.

Development of the iron lung arose after Drinker, then an assistant professor in Harvard's Department of Industrial Hygiene, was appointed to a Rockefeller Institute commission formed to develop improved methods for resuscitating victims of electric shock and illuminating gas poisoning. The best-known use of the iron lung—treatment of poliomyelitis—was a result of numerous epidemics of the disease that occurred from 1898 until the 1920's, each leaving thousands of Americans paralyzed. The concept of the lung reportedly arose from Drinker's observation of physiological experiments carried out by Shaw and Drinker's brother, Cecil. Those experiments were components of an effort to design artificial respiration methods that would enhance a patient's survival after surgery.

The experiments involved the placement of a cat inside an airtight box—a body plethysmograph—with the cat's head protruding from an airtight collar. Shaw and Cecil Drinker then measured the volume changes in the plethysmograph to identify normal breathing parameters. Philip Drinker placed cats paralyzed by curare inside plethysmographs and showed that they could be kept breathing artificially by use of air from a hypodermic syringe connected to the device. Next, they proceeded to build a human-sized plethysmograph-like machine, with a five-hundred-dollar grant from the New York Consolidated Gas Company. Its construction was carried out by a tinsmith and the Harvard Medical School machine shop.

The prototype machine was tested on Drinker and Shaw, and after several modifications were made, a workable iron lung was available for clinical use. This machine consisted of a metal cylinder large enough to accommodate a patient. One end of the cylinder, which contained a rubber collar, slid out on casters along with a stretcher on which the patient was placed. Once the patient was in position, and the collar fitted around the patient's neck, the stretcher was pushed back into the cylinder and the iron lung was made airtight by securing louvers.

The iron lung then "breathed" for the patient by using an electric blower to remove and replace air alternatively. Careful examination of each patient was required to allow optimum adjustment of the rate of operation of the machine. A cooling system, and ports for drainage lines, intravenous lines, and the other apparatus needed to maintain a wide variety of patients, were included in the machine.

The first person treated in an iron lung was an eight-year-old girl afflicted with respiratory paralysis resulting from poliomyelitis. The iron lung kept her alive for five days. Unfortunately, she died from cardiac failure as a result of pneumonia. The next iron lung patient, a Harvard University student, was confined to the machine for several weeks and later recovered enough to resume a normal life. The iron lung thereafter rapidly entered hospital practice. As Meyer stated: "Treatment facilities tended to concentrate at University and city-county hospitals, each with its Respirator Center, where long lines of Drinker tank respirators were lined up side by side."

James H. Maxwell pointed out that one problem that limited maximum use of the iron lung came from fears of physicians that their patients would be "forever tethered to the lung." This, Maxwell said, led to inappropriate delays before patients were placed in the respirators. In contrast to this view, Maxwell showed evidence that only a small percentage of patients became chronically dependent on the machine.

In order to clarify how an iron lung works, it is useful to begin by building a model of the chest and lungs. The equipment needed consists of a 3.8-liter bottomless glass jar with a narrow neck, a one-hole rubber stopper that fits into the neck of the jar, a hollow tube shaped like the letter "y," two small balloons, a circular rubber sheet with a diameter about 5 centimeters larger than that of the bottom of the jar, and strong adhesive tape. The model is assembled as follows: The balloons, which simulate lungs, are attached to the two ends of the y-shaped tube. The tube is pushed through the stopper. The stopper is then pushed into the mouth of the jar (which represents the chest cavity), with the balloons positioned inside the jar. The end of the tube that protrudes from the jar is open to the atmosphere, like the trachea (airway) that leads from the mouth to the lungs. To complete the model, the rubber sheet (which represents the diaphragm that closes off the chest cavity) is taped tightly over the open bottom of the jar.

The rubber sheet can be pulled on to simulate breathing, thereby inflating the balloons. Alternatively, the sheet can be pushed upward, to simulate exhalation, and deflate the balloons. The basis for the inflation or deflation observed is the pressure difference produced when the rubber sheet is moved. When it is pulled on, the air pressure outside the jar becomes higher than that in the balloons and air rushes into them. As the sheet is pushed on, the pressure inside the jar increases, the balloons are compressed, and air is forced out of them.

In the human chest, inhalation occurs when the diaphragm contracts and powerful muscles, which are paralyzed in poliomyelitis sufferers, expand the rib cage. This lowers the air pressure in the lungs and allows inhalation to occur. In exhalation, the diaphragm and chest muscles relax, and air is expelled as the chest cavity returns to its normal size. In case of respiratory paralysis treated with an iron lung, intake or expulsion of air from the iron lung alternately compresses the patient's chest, producing artificial exhalation, and allows it to expand so that the chest can fill with air. In this way, iron lungs "breathe" for the patients using them.

Impact of Event

It is noted in "Philip Drinker" (1977) that the Drinker respirator, or iron lung, came into use in 1929 and "soon thereafter, iron lungs were considered indispensable, saving uncounted lives of poliomyelitis victims until the development of the Salk vaccine in the 1950's." Furthermore, the retrospective response to the iron lung by Meyer was that "no satisfactory mechanical respirator existed before" the iron lung. In addition, Meyer notes that for a quarter of a century it was the sole reliable machine of its kind and "a lifeline for thousands of patients afflicted with respiratory failure caused by poliomeyelitis."

The positive responses to Drinker's invention included his receipt of Philadelphia's John Scott Medal (shared with Louis Shaw, in 1931), the Charles Chapin Memorial Award (1948), and the Cummings Memorial Award of the American Industrial Hygiene Association in 1950. He was also awarded honorary degrees from Norwich University in 1940 and from Hahneman Medical College in 1942. Drinker's election to prestigious learned societies included honorary membership in England's Royal Society of Health and the Finnish Industrial Medical Society. Furthermore, he was elected president of the American Industrial Hygiene Association in 1942 and became chairman of Harvard's Department of Industrial Hygiene.

According to Maxwell, the iron lung played a critical role in the development of modern respiratory care. This, he said, resulted from the fact that "use of the iron lung proved that large numbers of patients could actually be kept alive with mechanical support." In addition, Maxwell noted that while the lung was not the only influence on the development of such care, "the iron lung and polio treatment helped to foster an entirely new era in treatment of respiratory conditions."

Not all experts in respiratory care agree with such an assessment of the iron lung. In fact, many anesthesiologists disagree heartily. For example, H. H. Bendixen, an anesthesiologist, notes that "the tank (iron lung) respirator must be called a technological detour, despite the fact that it has had life-saving clinical use." He also states that though the iron lung "became the mainstay of poliomeyelitis treatment" until the 1950's, "the mortality rate remained high and was not significantly reduced" until combined intermittent positive pressure breathing was combined with the use of the iron lung.

Bibliography

Bendixen H. H. "Respirators and Respiratory Care." *Acta Anaesthesia Scandinavica* 102 (1982): 279-286. This review article, written by an anesthesiologist, traces "intellectual and technical roots of respirators and respiratory care," identifies the role of polio in these developments, and explains Bendixen's point of view on the roles of respirators and anesthesiology in modern respiratory care.

Drinker, Philip, and Charles F. McKhann III. "The Iron Lung, First Practical Means of Respiratory Support." *Journal of the American Medical Association* 255 (1986): 1476-1480. This article, written by the sons of Philip Drinker and a major medical collaborator, summarizes Drinker's development of the machine, comments on earlier respiratory devices, describes use of the iron lung in polio epidemics, and identifies later evolution of respiratory care. Provides a useful insight into Philip Drinker's life. Pictures of activated iron lungs are included.

Drinker, Philip, and Louis Shaw. "An Apparatus for the Prolonged Administration of Artificial Respiration." *Journal of Clinical Investigation* 7 (1929): 229-247. The original development and first uses of the iron lung are described in depth. The theoretical and practical aspects of its design are enumerated, and the hopes of its developers for the future are indicated. Valuable aspects of the personalities of its developers also emerge.

Maxwell, James H. "The Iron Lung: Halfway Technology or Necessary Step?" *The Milbank Quarterly* 64 (1986): 3-28. This article describes the history and development of the iron lung, examines its clinical utility, cost, strengths and weaknesses of its use, and its role in the evolution of respirators and respiratory care. More than sixty references are provided.

Meyer, John A. "A Practical Mechanical Respirator, 1929: The 'Iron Lung.'" *Annals of Thoracic Surgery* 50 (1990): 490-493. This article describes the iron lung and discusses its development as a valuable therapeutic possibility and its use in polio epidemics. Meyer concludes that, although the iron lung was cumbersome, "it supported patients over the long term with fewer complications than do the respirators of today."

"Philip Drinker." *The National Cyclopedia of American Biography.* Vol. 57. Clifton, N.J.: James T. White, 1977. This brief biographical sketch is one of the only readily available references on Drinker's life and work. It contains aspects of his early life, his education, career, and accomplishments. Drinker is portrayed as a serious scientist and engineer. It is made clear that the iron lung was merely one of his many endeavors.

Sanford S. Singer

Cross-References

Gibbon Develops the Heart-Lung Machine (1934), p. 1024; Salk Develops a Polio Vaccine (1952), p. 1444; Sabin Develops an Oral Polio Vaccine (1957), p. 1522.

GÖDEL PROVES INCOMPLETENESS-INCONSISTENCY FOR FORMAL SYSTEMS, INCLUDING ARITHMETIC

Category of event: Mathematics
Time: July, 1929-July, 1931
Locale: University of Vienna, Austria

Gödel derived Incompleteness-Inconsistency theorems for any formal system strong enough to include the laws of arithmetic

Principal personage:
    KURT GÖDEL (1906-1978), an Austrian mathematician and logician

Summary of Event

Partly in response to the appearance of logical and set-theoretic contradictions following David Hilbert's *Grundlagen der Geometrie* (1899; *The Foundations of Geometry*, 1902), a number of redoubled efforts focused on extending or reducing mathematics and logic to remove or resolve these difficulties. First published in 1899, Georg Cantor's paradox states that if S is the set of all sets and T is the set of all subsets of S, then since T corresponds one-by-one to itself as a subset of S, it cannot have a greater cardinal than S; yet, by Cantor's theorem, it must. In addition to Cantor's paradox, and Bertrand Russell's proof that Gottlob Frege's system was contradictory, several other paradoxes impacting both mathematics and logic arose during this period. These include Burali-Forti's paradox of the greatest ordinal number, Berry's paradox of the least integer not nameable in less than nineteen syllables, Richard's paradox of the class of all decimal numbers definable in a finite number of words, and symbolic forms of the Cretan-Liar conundrum. The varying approaches of Russell and Hilbert called for the axiomatization, and then formalization, of a suitable portion of existing logic and/or mathematics, including "ideal" statements that did not have identifiable elementary intuitive meanings, to include the new system of (paradox-free) mathematics. In a formal system, all combinatory methods of constructing formulas to express mathematical propositions, and all mathematical assumptions and principles of logic used in proving theorems, are to be governed by a finite set of stated rules. An essential requirement of Hilbert's original (finitistic) program was that all demonstrations of the formal consistency of a mathematical system involve only procedures that make no reference to an infinite number of properties or operations with mathematical formulas. Second, these proofs were to be undertaken only by "safe" methods such that the resulting formal system of axioms be entirely consistent, interpreted by Hilbert to mean that no two configurations should exist that constitute proofs in the system of a formula A and its negation $-A$.

In his 1904 lecture on the foundations of logic and arithmetic at the University of Heidelberg, Hilbert for the first time observed that, while it is possible to prove the consistency of geometry by an arithmetic interpretation, for the consistency of arithmetic itself, the appeal to some other more fundamental discipline seems illegitimate. Hilbert, for example, required use of the principle of mathematical induction to justify his definitions of whole numbers, yet had no proof of the consistency of this principle or its resulting definitions. Hilbert, nevertheless, initially suggested building up logic and arithmetic simultaneously, as well as translating these proofs completely into the language of symbolic logic to turn the proof of consistency into a problem of elementary manipulations in arithmetic. Hilbert did not return to foundational studies until his 1917 Zurich lecture on axiomatic thinking, in which he praised the axiomatization of logic by Russell and Alfred North Whitehead as the crowning of all work in efforts at completely translating all of mathematics into a self-contained symbolic language. It was only after 1920 that Hilbert, in collaboration with Paul Bernays and in opposition to Hermann Weyl and L. E. J. Brouwer, began to focus explicitly on proof theory. In this approach, description of a formal axiomatic system must enable clear decision as to whether any given formula is an axiom and is a permissible inference from other axioms. This is considered a decision procedure for whether a given finite list of formulas constitutes a proof in any given system. Yet, a decision procedure is not provided as to whether a given formula is itself provable. The problem of finding a decision procedure has been called the decision problem for formal systems, first recognized as a problem for logic by Ernst Schröder in 1895, and in mathematics by Leopold Löwenheim in 1917 and Thoralf Skolem in 1922. A decision procedure for a formal system embracing a segment of mathematics such as arithmetic would, in principle, make automatic the solution to any problem in that segment. Because of historically intractable problems such as whether Pierre de Fermat's last theorem is true, pointed out by Brouwer and others, a decision procedure in this case would mean that the infinitely many arithmetical problems require only a finite number of solutions.

By 1928, it was widely believed that the consistency of number theory and arithmetic had finally been nearly achieved by the finitist method of Hilbert and Bernays. As reported in Hilbert's September, 1928, lecture "On the Problems of the Foundations of Mathematics" in Bologna, Italy, Hilbert announced that his students Wilhelm Ackermann and John von Neumann had completed consistency proofs for almost the entire field of arithmetic. Hilbert then listed four of twenty-eight as-yet unresolved problems: a finite consistency proof of mathematical analysis, an extension of this proof to higher-order analysis and functional calculus, the completeness of the axiom systems for number theory and analysis, and the completeness of the system of logical rules (first-order logic).

From the Austrian philosopher and logician Rudolf Carnap's diaries and letters to associates, it can be determined that Kurt Gödel was first stimulated to foundational problems by reading the text of Hilbert's lecture, as well as by attending Brouwer's Vienna lecture in March, 1928, on mathematics, science, and language. From Gödel's collected papers, it is clear that he was strongly impressed by the intuitionist claim that all of mathematics would never be completely formalizable or preplanned a priori. In 1928, Gödel read the first edition of Hilbert and Ackermann's *Grundzüge der theoretischen Logik* (foundations of theoretical logic), in which the completeness of the restricted form of Hilbert's operational level 1 predicate calculus was formulated and posed as an open problem for further study.

A major obstacle to the general solution of Hilbert's formal decision problem was the lack of a clear and accepted concept of decidability and computability. By decision procedure or decidability for a given formalized theory is meant a method permitting one to decide in any given case whether a specific proposition formulated in the theory's symbolism can be proven exclusively by means of the axioms and techniques available to the theory itself. Gödel decided to focus explicitly on this problem and wrote the results as his doctoral dissertation in September, 1929, proving the completeness of first-order logic. In the summer of 1930, however, Gödel began to study the problem of proving the consistency of formal analysis itself (including higher arithmetic, logical analysis, and set theory), doubting the feasibility of Hilbert's wish to prove consistency directly by finitist methods Gödel instead believed that the difficulties encountered by Ackermann and von Neumann could be lessened by dividing the total problem into different stages or levels. In this case, he sought to prove the consistency of number theory by finitist number theory and then to prove the consistency of analysis by number theory, assuming the latter's truth as well as consistency.

The technical details of Gödel's proofs are practically impossible to recapitulate in nontechnical nonmathematical language. In terms of mathematical technique, Gödel's proof employed what has since been known as the arithmetizing of a formalism, in terms of a one-to-one mapping between every proposition in a given theory and the natural numbers of arithmetic. Gödel then extended to general mathematical expressions, such as variables, formulas, propositions, and logical axioms and operations, a similar higher-order arithmetical representation using various recursive functions. (A set of relations is recursive if there is a mechanical method or algorithm permitting one to decide automatically in a particular set whether a given relation does or does not belong to that set.) Gödel ran into several of the paradoxes connected with truth and definability. He realized that "truth" in number theory cannot be defined within number theory itself and that, therefore, his original plan of proving the relative consistency of analysis could not work. Although Gödel realized that these paradoxes did not, strictly speaking, apply to the precisely specified formal analysis of axiomatic systems, he realized that analogous nonlogical analogs could be carried out by substituting the notion of provability for truth. Pursuing this approach, Gödel concluded that any formal system in which a certain amount of theoretical arithmetic can be developed (according to Giuseppe Peano's symbolic system) and that satisfies certain minimal consistency conditions is necessarily incomplete in Hilbert's sense. Gödel, therefore, proceeded to draw the conclusion that in suitably strong systems such as that of Russell and Whitehead's *Principia Mathematica* (1910-1913) and Ernst Zermelo's set theory, there are formally undecidable propositions. This means that for number and set theory, there can be no absolute consistency proof of any of these systems formalizable within these systems. Using Hilbert's own methods and formalism, Gödel showed that in any formal system with arithmetic, there exist elementary arithmetic propositions that are "intuitively" obvious, yet undeducible, within the system, and that any proof expressing the consistency of the formal system is not deducible within the system. Hence, Gödel had not only settled Hilbert's first three problems in the negative but also had refuted Hilbert's underlying general belief in there always being a finitist consistency proof. In Gödel's interpretation, this meant that the formal axiomatization of systems of formal mathematics cannot simplify only these systems through logical combinatorics, but introduce inescapable and insoluble problems. Gödel hinted further that the limits of mathematical formalization operate such that every concept in a mathematical theory is meaningful and legitimate, except for certain "singular" points or regions, beyond which the set- and logical-theory paradoxes appear, as something analogous to division by zero. In Weyl's view, Gödel established that what is provable by intuition and by deduction, respectively, overlap but are not mutually reducible or expressible.

Impact of Event

Whereas Brouwer's verbally expressed intuitionist convictions on the inexhaustibility and unprovability of mathematics were impressive predominantly to those of affine philosophic outlook, Gödel's precise formal arguments were more convincing (if less accessible) to mathematicians and logicians of all outlooks. Gödel's famous first paper was written as part one of a double publication; he planned to give full background and details of his second theorem's proof in his concluding paper. Unfortunately, this second exposition was never published because, as Gödel admitted, his introductory proof-sketch was generally accepted even by those antagonized by his results. As noted by several authors, although many reexaminations have been attempted, no simpler proofs other than Gödel's originals have, as yet, been developed.

Gödel continued to pursue what he saw as the underlying problems of mathematical evidence and intuition. In 1941, Gödel found an interpretation of Brouwer's intuitionist number theory using primitive recursive functions of his own origination. This result was jointly regarded as an extension of both Hilbert's formalism and Brouwer's intuitionism. The further development of recursive function theory by, for example, Alonzo Church and Alan Turing, in the context of other problems that could not be decided formally with axiomatic systems, made possible a large number of results about general decision procedures.

There are as many philosophical reactions to and interpretations of Gödel's recondite conclusions as philosophers, including those of Ludwig Wittgenstein, Russell, and Jean Cavaillès. Both Russell and Wittgenstein, using differing arguments like Brouwer, basically acknowledged the correctness of Gödel's result as part of formal axiomatic arithmetic, but denied any wider application of Gödel's theorems to cases of "uncertainty" and "incompleteness" in mathematics, science, and language at large. Diametrically opposed responses were published by Cavaillès *Sur la logique et la théorie de la science* (1947; on the theory of science). In his own essay on Russell's mathematical logic, Gödel wrote that he did not consider the incompletability of formal systems (such as Russell's *Principia*) as encompassing a final argument against a neoplatonistic conceptually realistic interpretation of mathematics, but rather as indicating an essential limitation on the expressive power of abstract formal symbolisms considered apart from their field of application. For Gödel, the unexceptional everyday agreements in accepting a mathematical proof reveals a kind of universality and objectivity in mathematics that goes beyond the intersubjective agreement envisioned by Brouwer. Conceptual realism, according to Gödel, requires not only objective concepts but also that to which mathematical concepts are applied, that is, mathematical objects. In his largely unpublished manuscripts, Gödel speaks in a unique idiom about the "perception" and "intuition" of mathematical objects as the common denominator in learning and applying mathematics within mathematics, as well as in the physical and engineering sciences. These are still areas of much continuing debate.

Bibliography

Bulloff, J. J., T. C. Holyoke, and S. W. Hahn. *Foundations of Mathematics: Symposium Papers Commemorating the Sixtieth Birthday of Kurt Gödel*. New York: Springer-Verlag, 1969. Several valuable essays underscore and examine the philosophical assumptions that Gödel held but never fully published, from the viewpoints of both mathematicians and philosophers.

Feferman, S., J. W. Dawson, and S. C. Kleene, eds. *Kurt Gödel: Collected Works*. 2 vols. New York: Oxford University Press, 1986-1990. Includes English translations of unpublished notes as well as technical journal and conference publications. Contains a complete bibliography on Gödel.

Nagel, Ernest, and James R. Newman. *Gödel's Proof*. New York: New York University Press, 1958. The most accessible and complete semitechnical account of the recursive functional symbolism and its motivations in a simplified reconstruction of Gödel's incompleteness proof.

Shanker, S. G., ed. *Gödel's Theorem in Focus*. New York: Croom Helm, 1978. A valuable collection on interpretations, principally by philosophers of mathematics, about the conceptual origins and implications of Gödel's theorems. Written in readable, if not always well-referenced, style.

Van Heijenoort, Jean, comp. *From Frege to Gödel*. Cambridge, Mass.: Harvard University Press, 1967. Underscores the historical progression of the "problem of mathematical foundations" from about 1885 through 1940.

Wang, Hao. *Reflections on Kurt Gödel*. Cambridge, Mass.: MIT Press, 1985. Offers very extensive and detailed biographical information and a painstakingly constructed detailed chronology of Gödel's readings, course work, lectures, and associations, from his diaries, collected and unpublished letters and manuscripts, and original and untranslated publications.

Gerardo G. Tango

Cross-References

Levi Recognizes the Axiom of Choice in Set Theory (1902), p. 143; Russell Discovers the "Great Paradox" Concerning the Set of All Sets (1902), p. 184; Brouwer Develops Intuitionist Foundations of Mathematics (1904), p. 228; Zermelo Undertakes the First Comprehensive Axiomatization of Set Theory (1904), p. 233; Russell and Whitehead's *Principia Mathematica* Develops the Logistic Movement in Mathematics (1910), p. 465; Turing Invents the Universal Turing Machine (1935), p. 1045; The Bourbaki Group Publishes *Éléments de mathématique* (1939), p. 1140; Cohen Shows That Cantor's Continuum Hypothesis Is Independent of the Axioms of Set Theory (1963), p. 1751.

CONSTRUCTION BEGINS ON
THE EMPIRE STATE BUILDING

Category of event: Applied science
Time: 1930
Locale: New York City

The Empire State Building, the tallest building in the world when it was completed in 1931 and for four decades after, stands as an engineering and architectural triumph

Principal personages:
>WILLIAM F. LAMB (1883-1952), the New York architect responsible for the design of the Empire State Building
>ALFRED E. SMITH (1873-1944), the former governor of New York who became president of the corporation that built and operated the Empire State Building
>LOUIS SULLIVAN (1856-1924), a Chicago architect who articulated the aesthetic principles of the skyscraper, in particular its verticality
>ELISHA GRAVES OTIS (1811-1861), an American inventor of the elevator, which made tall buildings practicable
>LEWIS W. HINE (1874-1940), an American photographer who recorded the construction of the Empire State Building

Summary of Event

Before the advent of the skyscraper, the tallest buildings in American cities were churches. Commercial buildings were usually four to five stories high, which was about as high as most people were willing to climb to conduct their business. In 1852, an American mechanic named Elisha Graves Otis invented the elevator, which provided a rapid and safe means of vertical transport. This and the development of the structural steel frame, which eliminated the need for immense foundations and thick walls, made tall buildings both possible and practical for the first time.

The term "skyscraper" was coined around 1890 to describe the new multistory office buildings being built in Chicago and New York City. These buildings fired the imagination of architects, builders, and the American public alike; the skyscraper became for many the symbol of American progress and prosperity. Early American skyscrapers were largely derivative in style, taking their form and design from the great architectural styles of the past, in particular, Gothic architecture. The skyscraper shared with Gothic architecture a dizzying verticality. The structural principles of the skyscraper and the Gothic cathedral had much in common. In the skyscraper, the interior steel frame permitted a nonweight-bearing skin. Similarly, in the cathedral, massive but relatively slender stone pillar framework allowed nonweight-bearing walls between them. In both cases, the structural framework created the possibility for large areas of glass windows.

By the late 1800's, progressive architects were calling for a new style of sky-scraper architecture based on the technological innovations that had made the tall building possible in the first place. Among these was Chicago architect Louis Sullivan, who became known as "The Father of the Skyscraper." In his 1896 essay, "The Tall Office Building Artistically Considered," Sullivan argued against the use of historical elements in the skyscraper and challenged his profession to develop a new kind of skyscraper that would express the nature of its construction, the spirit of a new industrial society, and above all the idea of sheer height: "It must be tall, every inch of it tall . . . a proud and soaring thing, rising in sheer exultation . . . from bottom to top . . . a unity without a single dissenting line."

New York City became the focus for much of the construction and the playing field in the competition to build the tallest building. The Woolworth Building, erected in 1913, often referred to as "The Cathedral of Commerce," was designed by New York architect Cass Gilbert in the Gothic style. At a height of 214 meters, it reigned for seventeen years as the world's tallest building. In 1930, the Chrysler Building, designed by William Van Alen, was completed. Seventy-seven stories high, rising 319 meters, it became the world's tallest building, taller even than the Eiffel Tower in Paris. Yet, even before the Chrysler Building was finished, construction had begun on another skyscraper that would overshadow it.

The Empire State Building, built on the site of the old Waldorf-Astoria Hotel on Fifth Avenue at 34th Street, was intended to put an end to the competition for tallest building. It was to tower an unbelievable 102 stories, 381 meters, above the streets of Manhattan. Its developers, John J. Raskob and Pierre Samuel Du Pont, along with the former New York Governor Alfred E. Smith, who acted as a sort of "front man" for the project, announced in August, 1929, their intention to build the tallest building in the world. They chose the construction firm of Starrett Brothers and Eken, and the architectural firm of Shreve, Lamb, and Harmon for the project. William F. Lamb, one of the principals of the firm, was named chief designer. He had designed a number of commercial buildings notable for their efficiency and simplicity. His design for the Empire State Building, dictated to a certain degree by the New York City zoning laws, is an exceptionally skillful piece of massing. The tower is set back from the street above the fifth floor, and then soars uninterrupted for more than 305 meters to the eighty-sixth floor. The exterior of the building is made of lime-stone and granite. Vertical columns of chrome-nickel-steel alloy that extend from the sixth floor to the top give the building a soaring and shimmering quality. The building contained sixty-seven elevators and sixty-five hundred glass windows, more than any previous building, and was topped with a 61-meter mooring mast for dirigibles.

Lamb properly considered it his masterpiece. Its handsome and dignified design was much admired and earned for the architect the acclaim and recognition of his peers. The great French architect Le Corbusier and the American architect Frank Lloyd Wright are both said to have praised the building. Lamb received the gold medal of the New York Architectural League and an award of honor from the New

York chapter of the American Institute of Architects.

The construction schedule for the Empire State Building was extremely ambitious—eighteen months from start to finish. Steel was brought in from Pittsburgh, cement from upstate New York, limestone from Indiana, marble from Germany and France, and lumber from the Pacific Coast. More than three thousand people worked on the project daily, a veritable army of carpenters, bricklayers, derrick operators, structural steel workers, elevator installers, electricians, plumbers, and heating and ventilation specialists.

The building's construction was recorded in a series of breathtaking photographs taken by Lewis W. Hine. Trained as a sociologist, Hine was a pioneer in the field of documentary photography. His first photographs had been of the thousands of immigrants then arriving at New York's Ellis Island from all over the world. His series on the construction of the Empire State Building shows the workmen, dubbed "sky boys" by the media, performing their various tasks at vertiginous heights. Perhaps the most famous of these photographs is of a worker ascending a cable, seemingly in defiance of the laws of gravity, with the Hudson River in the background.

The building was completed on April 11, 1931, twelve days ahead of schedule. It officially opened on May 31, 1931, in the midst of the Great Depression. At the time, only 28 percent of the building was rented. The press quickly dubbed it the "Empty State Building." It was the thousands of tourists who visited the observation deck on the eighty-sixth floor, each paying a dollar for admission, that kept the Empire State Building Corporation financially solvent in those years. Eventually, however, the magnificent building proved a financial as well as an aesthetic success, and today stands as a monument to American industriousness and ingenuity.

Impact of Event

In the public imagination, the Empire State Building quickly came to symbolize New York City, eclipsing even the Statue of Liberty. Officially opened by President Herbert Hoover, who turned on the lights in the Empire State Building from his office in Washington, D.C., the building drew a steady stream of visitors that included heads of state, politicians, and other celebrities. Winston Churchill made the trip up to the observation deck on the eighty-sixth floor, as did the King of Siam, Queen Elizabeth II and Prince Philip, Nikita S. Khrushchev, Fidel Castro, the Shah of Iran, Helen Keller, and George Bernard Shaw.

Merely two years after it opened, the Empire State Building even had a part in a Hollywood movie. In 1933, the building was immortalized in the classic *King Kong*, starring Fay Wray. In the climax of the picture, the giant love-sick ape makes its last stand atop the tower of the world's tallest building amidst gunfire from a squadron of army combat planes.

The Empire State Building took its place in the history of architecture not only as the most beautiful or technologically revolutionary building ever built but also as the tallest. It remained the tallest building for more than forty years. It was not until 1972, when the first of the 41-meter-tall twin towers of the World Trade Center was completed in lower Manhattan, that the Empire State Building was surpassed in height. The World Trade Center in turn was surpassed in 1974 by the Sears Tower in Chicago, which at 443 meters became the tallest building in the world. The World Trade Center, however, offers little to the Manhattan skyline besides sheer mass. It lacks the poetry and romance of the Empire State Building, which was a bold and challenging venture, an emblem of ultimate achievement. This historical significance of the Empire State Building endures and makes it a symbol of the city whose skyline it still dominates.

The Empire State Building has had critics as well as fans, and both because of its size. As early as 1915, doubters expressed concern over the size and scale of the tall buildings being built in America's cities. The Equitable Life Assurance Building, designed by Ernest Graham, was completed in that year. It was only thirty-nine stories high but massive in terms of bulk. Critics likened it to a "great file cabinet" and deplored its "utterly banal façade." It stimulated the City of New York to legislate restrictions on the shape and location of skyscrapers. Ironically, the design of the Empire State Building was determined to a large extent by just such restrictions, in particular, the zoning law setback requirements.

The size of the Empire State Building rekindled the debate over how big was too big, especially after an airplane crashed into its side, killing fourteen people. The debate continues today. Developers push for taller and bigger buildings to ensure maximum return for their investment. Many critics, city planners, and city dwellers, on the other hand, contend that skyscrapers have a dehumanizing effect, dwarfing the inhabitants of the cities they overshadow, turning the streets into deep canyons, and blocking out light and air.

Bibliography

Goldberger, Paul. *The Skyscraper.* New York: Alfred A. Knopf, 1981. History and commentary on the skyscraper by the architecture critic for *The New York Times.* The author approaches his subject from an aesthetic point of view. Goldberger traces the divergent styles of the Chicago and New York City schools, contrasting the theatrical, "purely visual impulse" of New York City skyscraper architecture with the more intellectually rigorous and austere style of the Chicago skyscraper.

Huxtable, Ada Louise. *The Tall Building Artistically Reconsidered: The Search for a Skyscraper Style.* New York: Pantheon Books, 1984. A treatise on the history, aesthetics, politics, and economics of the tall office building—what Pulitzer Prize winner Huxtable calls the "drama of the skyscraper." Huxtable, who was architecture critic for *The New York Times* from 1963 to 1982, chronicles the search for a skyscraper style, from the time when architects looked to the architectural styles of the past for inspiration to the newer varied styles of today.

James, Theodore, Jr. *The Empire State Building.* New York: Harper & Row, 1975. A loving and meticulously researched tribute to the Empire State Building. Includes fascinating information on the history of the site, the men responsible for the building, and the events surrounding its design, construction, and official opening.

James quotes extensively from newspapers, telegrams, and speeches of the day. Contains numerous photographs (including sixteen photographs from the Lewis Hine series), an appendix of interesting statistics, and an index.

Macaulay, David. *Unbuilding*. Boston: Houghton Mifflin, 1980. Master draftsman David Macaulay, author and illustrator of the award-winning book *Cathedral*, dismantles the Empire State Building, starting from the top down, in a series of brilliant pen-and-ink drawings. The text and illustrations provide a humorous as well as technically accurate explanation of the structural elements of the building.

Sabbagh, Karl. *Skyscraper*. London: Macmillan, 1989. This book was written in conjunction with the television filming of the construction of a 235-meter skyscraper in New York City. Sabbagh shows the human factors of such a vast undertaking as well as the physical and technological factors. The book tells the story of "the steel, the brick, the stone, and the roof" of the building, and also the people involved in the project, including the architects, engineers, real estate agents, bankers, dynamite experts, seismologists, welders, electricians, bricklayers, crane operators, and steel fabricators.

Nancy Schiller

Cross-References

Construction Begins on the Panama Canal (1904), p. 249; Hale Constructs the Largest Telescope of the Time (1948), p. 1325; The St. Lawrence Seaway Is Opened (1959), p. 1608; The Verrazano Bridge Opens (1964), p. 1782.

LYOT BUILDS THE CORONAGRAPH FOR TELESCOPICALLY OBSERVING THE SUN'S OUTER ATMOSPHERE

Category of event: Astronomy
Time: 1930
Locale: Meudon (Paris), France

Lyot's coronagraphic telescope permitted the first extended observations of the sun's outer (coronal) atmosphere, including prominences and solar flares, without the necessity of a natural solar eclipse

Principal personage:
BERNARD LYOT (1897-1952), a French astronomer

Summary of Event

Although the chromosphere and corona represent only a very small part of the sun's total atmosphere, they have long been astronomically interesting yet difficult to access. The subdivisions of the chromosphere and corona together encompass the sun's outer atmosphere as inferred from both visual and telescopic observation, photometrically showing only 0.5×10^{-6} the brightness of the total sun. During the total stage of a solar eclipse, the sun's corona appears as an asymmetric halo, the apparent brightness of which generally decreases from the sun's limb outward. With an overall increase in solar activity every eleven years, additional radial streamers, or rays, can appear outward from the corona. In a period of minimal solar activity, there is simply a diffuse distribution of visible radiation, with minimum intensity at the solar poles and a maximum intensity at the equator. The corona's shape also shows minimum ellipticity every three years prior to a sunspot cycle maximum. Normally, the much greater intensity of the halo, or aureole, of scattered light surrounding the sun's disk hides the corona. Observed visually at sea level, the average sky further scatters coronal light to about one thousandth of this amount. Only rare locations, such as high mountaintops, even during an eclipse offer the chance to observe the corona unaided.

The research question of the origins and behavior of the corona is important for stellar as well as solar astrophysics. From a planetary solar system perspective, the corona is effectively a transition zone between the solar surface and the interplanetary medium (for example, solar wind). From an astrophysical viewpoint, the conditions that exist in the solar corona are of great interest in determining the laws governing magnetohydrodynamic gases, spectral emissions from highly ionized atoms, and the like. Some of the important questions about the corona are what the temperature implications of the greatly increased spectral emissions above the solar limb are, and if the chromosphere and corona are wholly or partly a collection of turbulent gas streams or a more uniform atmosphere.

Until about 1930, the solar corona had been observed astronomically only during total eclipses of the sun, meaning only a few minutes per year of measurements, often under hurried and inoptimum conditions, with a total observation time from 1630 to 1930 of less than one hour. Spectroheliographs are special solar telescopes that can make observations at any wavelength, but are slow and unsuited to accurate observations of short-lived eclipse and flare phenomena. Various attempts by astronomers such as Alexander Hale to take spectroheliographs to mountaintops for coronal observation were failures. The first recorded spectrum of the corona was recorded by Georges Rayet in 1868. Since the late 1890's, many (unsuccessful) attempts were made at telescopically detecting the sun's corona outside of eclipse conditions, including George Ellery Hale's single absorption-line spectroscopy in 1900 and Henri-Alexandre Deslandres' use of infrared band radiation in 1904. In 1906, Karl Schwarzschild recorded the first simultaneous spectra from both the sun's center and inner corona, using a neutral diffusing filter and spectrophotometer. In 1931, W. Grotrian published results from the 1926 eclipse, recorded by modifying Schwarzschild's instrument.

As was realized eventually, ordinary reflector or refractor telescopes further scattered solar light from the already weakened and scattered visual appearance. The details of designing and building a special lens and some kind of shielding disk for noneclipse coronal observation required reduction of unwanted scattered light by a factor of more than 100,000. In response to these requirements, Bernard Lyot of the Meudon Observatory conceived, and in 1930 designed and constructed a new optical telescope, in which the diffusion of light inside the lens and telescope tube were minimized to these standards. In Lyot's original coronagraph, the sun's disk is eclipsed artificially, or occulted, by a polished metal cone. The direct image of the remaining (corona) sun is formed on a black screen slightly larger than the disk's image. The shiny cone also reflects back the sun's light to the side, preventing it from falling back on the main objective lens. Nevertheless, it was further necessary to prevent the solar light diffracted by the main objective from getting into the second middle objective lens. Lyot accomplished this by placing an aperture stop at the point where the light from the main lens is imaged by the final field lens. A further refinement was to place another opaque disk at the center of the second objective to catch any multiply reflected light from the primary lens and from the occulting cone.

In this chromatically aberrant design, the occulting disk is in focus only for single wavelengths. It is possible to compensate for the overcorrection of the secondary lens so that the final image is aberration-free. To minimize scattering from even microscopic defects of the tube and dust particles, all inner surfaces were smeared with thick oil, thus reducing thermal air currents. The coronagraph requires special care and environmental conditions. All lenses must be kept as clean as possible at all times from dust and aerosol particles. Atmospheric scattering as noted is a severe limit, but is reduced notably for altitudes above a few kilometers. Thus, most coronal observatories have been constructed at heights above 1,800 meters and generally above 3,000 meters if possible. Winter frequently provides the best observing times; Lyot discovered optimal conditions immediately after heavy snowfalls had cleared the air of atmospheric dust particles.

Impact of Event

Wider use of the coronagraph, from 1932 on, provided vastly increased opportunities for coronal observation. Because it is not limited by the brevity of a solar eclipse, Lyot's coronagraph permitted far more precise measurements of the comparative intensities of different spectral lines vital to astrophysical theories of stellar composition and dynamics. Observations using Lyot's coronagraph—supplementing observations made during eclipses between 1893 and 1936—showed that the maximum equatorial elongation of the corona occurs 0.7 year before the minimum of solar prominences at higher solar latitudes. Coronal "rays" were shown also to be gas bodies of higher temperature forming above solar faculae, analogous to auroral polar lights insofar as both take the shape of the prevailing magnetic lines of force. Coronagraphic measurements permitted the first rigorous estimates of the temperature, lifetime, luminosity, and characteristic length and height of solar prominences. On the basis of coronagraph and eclipse data, Bengt Edlén in 1939 first identified the coronal lines of highly ionized atoms associated with electron temperatures of 10^6 Kelvins. Lyot showed that corona emission lines are very wide, confirming hypotheses by Edlén and others that Doppler broadening because of extremely high kinematic temperature is a common solar feature.

Notwithstanding his success, Lyot was not satisfied with his coronagraph's performance, suspecting that there was a need to reduce further or compensate for residual thermal diffusion within the coronagraph itself. Continuing his experiments, Lyot combined his coronagraph with a spectroheliograph, minimizing the heat leak problem. With this combination, in 1937 he succeeded in photographing the two brightest spectral lines in the green and red regions of the corona's spectrum over the entire solar disk. Lyot and other solar astronomers wanted to be able to observe simultaneously solar prominences over the chromosphere as well as corona. Lyot's original dissertation research, from 1923 to 1930, concerned polarization of light reflected from planetary surfaces. In 1938, Lyot devised his quartz-polaroid monochromatic interference filter system. The principle of this filter is the passage of solar light through a series of polarizing layers having their planes of polarization parallel to one another. These filters are separated by thin plates of quartz glass whose thicknesses are calculated to produce optical interference fringes. The combination of the appropriate number and thickness of polarizers permitted a transmission band of only 1 angstrom width, allowing rapid observations over the entire sun using the well-known hydrogen alpha spectral line. In 1940, Lyot added to his filter another special optical arrangement, which permitted him to isolate different wavelengths and take 16-millimeter moving films of them.

Lyot's final innovation was the coronagraphic photometer, which enabled tracing of weak spectral lines even with ordinary refractor telescopes at sea level. Because of the technical difficulties in making the main lens and meeting all environmental conditions, coronagraphs typically are not large instruments. To date, the largest coronagraph is the 40-centimeter coronagraph of the Sacramento Peak Observatory in Sunspot, New Mexico, and at the High Altitude Observatory in Boulder, Colorado. Other coronagraphs are located at Pic du Midi, France; Mt. Norikura, Japan; Freiburg, Germany; and Capri, Italy. To avoid atmospheric scatter, brightness, and fluctuations, from May, 1973, to January, 1974, the Apollo Telescope on the Skylab Space Station included a special white light coronagraph. From the thermospheric altitudes of an orbiting spacecraft, the sky is completely black overhead, and coronagraphic observations nearly match those of a total eclipse. Skylab recorded more than one thousand hours of coronagraph data, discovering the new phenomenon of coronal transients: huge shock waves of ionized gas, following a flare or prominence, which propagate outward through the corona.

For many researchers, the period from 1930 to 1947 was considered the watershed between the era of fortuitous uncalibrated coronal observations of opportunity and detailed controlled observations. Bernard Lyot succeeded in accomplishing what many predecessors had tried but failed to do: observe coronal details without an eclipse.

Bibliography

Beer, Arthur, ed. *Vistas in Astronomy.* New York: Pergamon Press, 1955. Although technical, this accessible volume has valuable information on spectroheliograph and coronagraph technologies and results.

Dyson, Frank, and Richard vander Riet Wooley. *Eclipses of the Sun and Moon.* Oxford, England: Clarendon Press, 1937. Reports noncoronagraphic observing methods and results.

Evans, John W., ed. *The Solar Corona.* New York: Academic Press, 1963. An intermediate advanced-level text. Gives important summaries of empirical and theoretical understanding of the sun's corona.

King, Henry C. *The History of the Telescope.* Cambridge, Mass.: Sky Publishing, 1955. The best overall history of telescopes and attachments in general. Contains some coronagraph data.

Stix, Michael. *The Sun: An Introduction.* New York: Springer-Verlag, 1989. An introductory technical treatment of solar observations and structure.

Gerardo G. Tango

Cross-References

Hale Discovers Strong Magnetic Fields in Sunspots (1908), p. 417; Russell Announces His Theory of Stellar Evolution (1913), p. 585; Einstein Completes His Theory of General Relativity (1915), p. 625; Schwarzschild Develops a Solution to the Equations of General Relativity (1916), p. 630; Von Weizsäcker Finalizes His

Quantitative Theory of Planetary Formation (1943), p. 1208; Parker Predicts the Existence of the Solar Wind (1958), p. 1577; A Radio Astronomy Team Sends and Receives Radar Signals to the Sun (1959), p. 1598; Skylab Inaugurates a New Era of Space Research (1973), p. 1997.

MIDGLEY INTRODUCES DICHLORODIFLUOROMETHANE AS A REFRIGERANT GAS

Category of event: Chemistry
Time: 1930
Locale: Dayton, Ohio

Midgley introduced dichlorodifluoromethane as a safe refrigerant gas for domestic refrigerators, leading to a rapid growth in the acceptance of refrigerators in homes

Principal personages:
 THOMAS MIDGLEY, JR. (1889-1944), an American engineer and chemist who also introduced dichlorodifluoromethane and tetraethyl lead
 CHARLES F. KETTERING (1876-1958), an American engineer and inventor who was the head of research for General Motors
 ALBERT HENNE (1901-1967), an American chemist who was Midgley's chief assistant
 FRÉDÉRIC SWARTS (1866-1940), a Belgian chemist and professor who pioneered research in organic fluorine compounds

Summary of Event

The availability of reliable refrigerators, freezers, and air conditioners has made a major impact on the way people live and work in the twentieth century. People can live more comfortably in hot and humid areas. A great variety of perishable foods can be transported and stored for extended periods. As recently as the early nineteenth century, the foods most regularly available to most Americans were salted meats and bread. Items now considered as essential to a balanced diet such as vegetables, fruits, and dairy products were produced and consumed only in small amounts. Commercial refrigeration became a necessity and a reality during the nineteenth century, when the population became concentrated in towns and cities. Through the early part of the twentieth century, the pattern of food storage and distribution evolved to make perishable foods more available. Farmers shipped dairy products and frozen meats in mechanically refrigerated railroad cars or in refrigerated ships. Wholesalers had large mechanically refrigerated warehouses. Smaller stores and most American households used iceboxes to keep perishable foods fresh. The iceman was a familiar figure on the streets of American towns, delivering large blocks of ice regularly.

In 1930, domestic mechanical refrigerators were still relatively uncommon, although they were being produced in increasing numbers. Most of them were vapor compression machines, in which a gas was compressed in a closed system of pipes outside the refrigerator by a mechanical pump and condensed to a liquid. The liquid was pumped into a sealed chamber in the refrigerator and allowed to evaporate to a gas. This evaporation is what cools the interior of the refrigerator.

The major mechanical problems in designing an efficient home refrigerator had been solved by 1930; small and quite efficient electric motors to power the compression cycle had been developed, and compact and reliable automatic temperature controllers had become available. The remaining source of difficulty was the material constituting the working gas of the refrigerator. This gas had to have particular properties. It had to boil at a fairly low temperature, preferably between about −1.1 degrees Celsius and 4.4 degrees Celsius, and had to have an appropriate heat of vaporization—meaning that, in its evaporation from liquid to gas inside the sealed chamber of the refrigerator, it had to abstract a reasonable amount of heat energy from the inside of the refrigerator. The gases in use in domestic refrigerators in 1930 included ammonia, sulfur dioxide, and methyl chloride. These gases were acceptable if the refrigerator's gas pipes never sprang a leak. In actual operation of refrigerators, leaks sometimes occur; at such times, these refrigerant gases posed serious problems because all were toxic. Ammonia and sulfur dioxide both had unpleasant odors; if they leaked, at least they would be detected rapidly. Methyl chloride could form a dangerously explosive mixture with air, and it had only a very faint, and not unpleasant, odor. In a hospital in Cleveland during the 1920's, a refrigerator with methyl chloride leaked, and there was a disastrous explosion of the methyl chloride/air mixture. After that, methyl chloride for use in refrigerators was mixed with a small amount of a powerfully unpleasant-smelling compound to make leaks detectable. (The same principle is used nowadays with natural gas.)

General Motors, through its Frigidaire division, had a substantial interest in the domestic refrigerator market. Frigidaire refrigerators used sulfur dioxide as the refrigerant gas. Charles F. Kettering, Director of Research for General Motors, was an engineer and inventor with an impressive record of solving problems. Among his major successes had been his collaboration with Thomas Midgley, Jr., a mechanical engineer and self-taught chemist, in discovering that tetraethyl lead was an effective antiknocking agent for gasoline. Kettering decided that Frigidaire needed a new refrigerant gas for its household refrigerators, a material that would have the good thermal properties of methyl chloride or sulfur dioxide, but that would be nontoxic and nonexplosive. In early 1930, he sent Lester S. Keilholtz, chief engineer of General Motors' Frigidaire Division, to Midgley, who was working at Dayton, Ohio, with the challenge to develop such a new gas.

Midgley's chemical associates, Albert Henne and Robert McNary, researched what types of compounds might have been reported already that fitted Kettering's specifications. Apparently, an inaccuracy in a reference source made them think about compounds containing fluorine as possible refrigerants. The reference listed the boiling point of carbon tetrafluoride as −15 degrees Celsius, in the right range for a refrigerant. When they checked other research articles, they found that the reference was incorrect; the actual boiling point was 92.2 degrees Celsius, far too low for the compound to be useful. That library search suggested, however, that the right compound might be found among carbon compounds containing both fluorine and chlorine. Only a few such compounds had been reported; the Belgian chemist Frédéric

Swarts had done pioneering basic research on them in the late nineteenth and early twentieth centuries, but no applications had resulted. Midgley, Henne, and McNary worked with Swarts's data and concluded from their calculations that dichlorodifluoromethane, a compound whose molecules each contain one carbon atom, two chlorine atoms, and two fluorine atoms, should have ideal thermal properties and the right boiling point for a refrigerant gas. The great unknown was the toxicity of such a compound. They would have to prepare it in order to test the compound.

The preparation involved reaction between carbon tetrachloride (a common solvent used, at that time, in the dry-cleaning industry) and antimony trifluoride. The chemists prepared a few grams of dichlorodifluoromethane and put it, along with a guinea pig, into a closed chamber. They were delighted to see that the animal seemed to suffer no ill effects at all and was able to breathe and move normally. They were briefly puzzled when a second batch of the compound, made with another sample of antimony trifluoride, killed a second guinea pig almost instantly; soon, they discovered that an impurity in the antimony trifluoride had produced a potent poison in their refrigerant gas. A simple washing procedure completely removed the poisonous contaminant. Experiments confirmed their calculations; dichlorodifluoromethane was ideally suited to be a refrigerant gas, being nontoxic, nonflammable, and possessing excellent thermal properties. Its boiling point of −5.6 degrees Celsius was in the required range. This astonishingly successful research project was completed in three days. A few months later, Midgley announced the discovery at a meeting of the American Chemical Society held in Atlanta, Georgia, in April, 1930. When Midgley was awarded the Perkin Medal for industrial chemistry in 1937, he gave the audience a graphic demonstration of the properties of dichlorodifluoromethane. He inhaled deeply of its vapors and exhaled gently into a jar containing a burning candle. The candle flame promptly went out. This visual evidence proved that dichlorodifluoromethane was not poisonous and would not burn.

In order to produce the new refrigerant in commercial quantities, General Motors arranged to form a new company with du Pont, which was the established supplier of sulfur dioxide to Frigidaire. The new product, dichlorodifluoromethane, was given the shorter name of Freon. The du Pont laboratories undertook extensive toxicity testing, which confirmed the safety of Freon, and Kinetic Chemicals arranged with the Interstate Commerce Commission to allow interstate transport of Freon and anhydrous hydrogen fluoride, which was needed to make Freon in quantity. Within a year of the original discovery by Midgley and his associates, Freon was being manufactured and shipped not only to Frigidaire but also to most other major manufacturers of refrigeration and air-conditioning equipment.

Impact of Event

Because of its desirable properties, Freon quickly became the preferred refrigerant gas for refrigerators and air conditioners; it still retains that position. The availability of this safe refrigerant gas gave a major impetus to the production and sale of small and medium-sized refrigerators and freezers; it led to the patterns of food production, distribution, and consumption that are standard in the late twentieth century.

Air conditioning was developed early in the twentieth century for industries such as printing and pharmaceutical companies that needed climate control in factories. By 1930, a few theaters, motion picture houses, and hospitals were air-conditioned. Freon made small, safe air conditioners practical for houses and automobiles. By the late 1970's, most American cars and residences were equipped with air conditioning, and other countries with hot climates followed suit. Consequently, major relocations of populations and businesses have become possible. Since World War II, there have been steady migrations to the "Sun Belt," the states spanning the United States from southeast to southwest, because these areas have become much more livable with air conditioning.

Dichlorodifluoromethane was later called Freon 12 to distinguish it from other chlorofluorocarbons. During World War II, when United States servicemen were fighting in areas where diseases such as malaria are endemic, there was a need for an easy way to spray insecticides. The aerosol can was invented for this purpose, and the propellant chosen was a Freon, because of its volatility and inertness. After the war, aerosols became popular, and spray cans were used to deliver paints, shaving cream, and many other products. A new product developed at the same time was foamed plastic; styrofoam is a familiar example. Plastic foams are good insulators, especially when they are made with a Freon blowing agent; they are used in insulation for buildings, beverage cups, and other insulated containers. As a result of these novel applications, worldwide production of chlorofluorocarbons increased during the 1960's and 1970's. Production of Freon 12, for example, peaked at 473,000 tons in 1974.

In 1974, scientists began to ask whether there might be a serious effect on the environment from the release of chlorofluorocarbons into the air. They speculated that, because these compounds were so unreactive, they would persist and slowly migrate into the stratosphere, where they might be decomposed by the intense ultraviolet light from the sun, which does not reach the earth's surface because it is absorbed by a thin, but vital, layer of ozone in the stratosphere. The decomposition products of the chlorofluorocarbons would include reactive free chlorine atoms, which were known to have the capability of destroying large amounts of ozone. Thus, in the judgment of the scientists who raised these questions, continued release of chlorofluorocarbons into the air could reduce greatly the ozone layer, permitting more ultraviolet radiation from the sun to reach the earth's surface. In addition to possible adverse climatic effects, this would raise the incidence of skin cancers, which can be initiated by overexposure of the skin to ultraviolet radiation.

Impressed by the plausibility of these arguments, the Environmental Protection Agency banned the use of chlorofluorocarbons as aerosol propellants in the United States in 1978. They are being used still as refrigerant gases and as blowing agents for foamed plastics. International conferences on the environmental effects of chlorofluorocarbons have been held, and the major industrial nations have agreed to stop producing chlorofluorocarbons that are believed to affect the ozone layer. Chemical manufacturers are developing alternative refrigerant gases that will be slightly broken down by sunlight in the lower portions of the earth's atmosphere and will not survive to interfere with ozone in the stratosphere.

Bibliography

Anderson, Oscar Edward. *Refrigeration in America*. Princeton, N.J.: Princeton University Press, 1953. A valuable survey of the history of refrigeration in the United States, with eight chapters devoted to changes between the pre- and post-Freon eras.

Benarde, Melvin A. *Our Precarious Habitat: Fifteen Years Later*. New ed. New York: John Wiley & Sons, 1989. Assesses environmental risk factors, including chlorofluorocarbons, and their potential impact on human health. Nontechnical; reasonably balanced discussion.

Haynes, Williams. "Thomas Midgley, Jr." In *Great Chemists*, edited by Eduard Farber. New York: Interscience, 1961. A detailed biography of Midgley by a major contributor to the history of industrial chemistry in the United States. Contains accounts of Midgley's life and of his major discoveries.

Schufle, Joseph A. "Thomas Midgley, Jr." In *American Chemists and Chemical Engineers*, edited by Wyndham D. Miles. Washington, D.C.: American Chemical Society, 1976. A brief biography of Midgley, with particular stress on his chemical discoveries and training.

Smart, Bruce E. "Fluorine, Organic Compounds. Chlorofluorocarbons." In *Encyclopedia of Chemical Technology*. Vol. 10, *Ferroelectrics to Fluorine Compounds*, edited by Herman F. Mark et al. 3d ed. New York: John Wiley & Sons, 1978. A technical account of the production of chlorofluorocarbons, including production methods and statistics.

Spiro, Thomas G., and William M. Stigliani. *Environmental Issues in Chemical Perspective*. Albany: State University of New York Press, 1980. A moderately technical, balanced view of the chlorofluorocarbon problem.

Thevenot, Roger. *A History of Refrigeration Throughout the World*. Translated by J. C. Fidler. Paris: International Institute of Refrigeration, 1979. A broad view of refrigeration worldwide, with major sections on the changes brought about by the introduction of Freons. Does not discuss the ozone layer problem because the history was up to 1975.

Harold Goldwhite

Cross-References

Fabry Quantifies Ozone in the Upper Atmosphere (1913), p. 579; Birdseye Develops Freezing as a Way of Preserving Foods (1917), p. 635; Rowland and Molina Theorize That Ozone Depletion Is Caused by Freon (1973), p. 2009; The British Antarctic Survey Confirms the First Known Hole in the Ozone Layer (1985), p. 2285.

ZINSSER DEVELOPS AN IMMUNIZATION AGAINST TYPHUS

Categories of event: Biology and medicine
Time: 1930
Locale: Harvard University, Cambridge, Massachusetts

Zinsser demonstrated clinical differences in forms of typhus and developed an effective vaccine against the disease

Principal personages:

HANS ZINSSER (1878-1940), an American bacteriologist and immunologist who was a major contributor in the study of rickettsia disease and a pioneer in the application of immunology to the treatment of typhus

HOWARD T. RICKETTS (1871-1910), an American bacteriologist who discovered small bacteria-like organisms in the gut of the wood tick; the organism Rickettsia was named after him

JOHN FRANKLIN ENDERS (1897-1985), an American immunologist and colleague of Hans Zinsser who was awarded the 1954 Nobel Prize in Physiology or Medicine for his work in growing poliomyelitis viruses in large quantities using the tissue-culture technique developed by Zinsser

Summary of Event

As a bacteriologist and immunologist, Hans Zinsser was interested in the epidemiology of infectious diseases. During an outbreak of typhus in Serbia in 1915, he traveled with a Red Cross team in order to study the clinical and pathological aspects of the disease. He made subsequent trips to the Soviet Union in 1923, Mexico in 1931, and China in 1938. His observations supported the commonly held belief that typhus was caused by an organism, the rickettsia, isolated and named by Henrique da Rocha-Lima in 1916 for Howard T. Ricketts. The organism was known to be borne by a louse or a rat flea and transmitted to humans by way of a bite. The unsanitary living conditions resulting from poverty and overcrowding provided an atmosphere conducive for the spread of the disease.

The rickettsia are microorganisms whose shape ranges from rod to spherical. Within the carrier's body, the rickettsia stimulate the cells of endothelial tissue to use phagocytosis (eat up) so that the microorganism could enter and live in the cytoplasm of the endothelial cell, which line the gut of the insect. The rickettsia multiplies within the tissue and passes from the insect body with the feces. Since the internal cells of the insect are destroyed, the insect dies within three weeks of becoming infected with the microorganism.

As the flea or louse feeds on a human, it causes an itch which, when scratched, may result in a break in the skin. This, in turn, provides an opportunity for the rickettsia-laden feces to enter the body. Dried, air-borne feces can be inhaled. Once within the human host, the rickettsia invades endothelial cells associated with blood vessels and causes an inflammation of the blood vessels. The resulting cell death leads to tissue death. In a few days, the infected host exhibits symptoms such as a rash, a severe and sudden headache, a rise in temperature, photophobia (visual intolerance to light), vertigo, tinnitus (ringing in the ears), deafness, and an altered mental state, which gives the disease its name, typhus (from the Greek meaning cloudy or misty). Left untreated, the patient dies within nine to eighteen days.

Typhus was first described in Europe in the fifteenth century. It is among the oldest diseases known to be caused by the rickettsia. Medical science now recognizes three clinical forms: the epidemic louse-borne; the Brill-Zinsser; and the murine, or rodent-related, form. The epidemic louse-borne or classical form is the severest manifestation of the disease. *Rickettsia prowazekii* is the causative agent and is carried by the human body louse *Pediculus humanus*. The Brill-Zinsser form presents symptoms similar to but milder than the epidemic type. It involves the reactivation of the organism within the host cells, indicating that the host had encountered the epidemic form earlier. The murine form is caused by *Rickettsia typhi* (previously called *Rickettsia mooseri*), which is borne by a rat flea. This variety also presents symptoms which are milder than the epidemic type. The pathology of murine typhus closely resembles that of Rocky Mountain spotted fever, which is caused by *Rickettsia rickettsii*.

When Zinsser began his work on typhus, the information that existed concerning the disease was in a chaotic state. Zinsser sought to organize the information and bring order to the study of the disease. Zinsser and his colleagues, including John Franklin Enders, Hermann Mooser, M. Ruiz Castañeda, and others, sought to establish the relation of one form of typhus to the others. In 1898, an endemic form of typhus prevalent among immigrants in New York City had been described. The endemic form was called Brill's disease. Mooser, in the late 1920's, proved that the causative agent of Brill's disease was *Rickettsia mooseri* and that the organism was carried by the rat flea. The endemic form became known as the murine form and the causative agent was later renamed as *Rickettsia typhi*.

In the 1930's, Zinsser suggested that there were actually two forms of the disease being described by Brill. One that was rodent-associated (murine form) and another that had its own causative agent and was a reactivation of an organism picked up at an earlier time when the patient was exposed to the epidemic disease present in many European countries at that time. He demonstrated that *Rickettsia prowazekii* was the agent involved in both the European epidemic version and the reactivated version, which was known as Brill's disease. As a result of Zinsser's effort to distinguish the two types of typhus disease, it was renamed Brill-Zinsser disease.

As a result of analyzing the mechanism of the Weil-Feliz diagnostic test for rickettsial diseases, Zinsser was aware that the disease-causing organism had an antigenic component, most likely a polysaccharide. In 1932, Zinsser and Castañeda identified agglutinins, or antibodies, in the blood serum of typhus-infected patients with the murine and the classical forms. Although earlier attempts at preventing typhus by means of passive immunity were not satisfactory, Zinsser saw immunity as a viable solution to the problem of typhus. He determined that a large number of dead microorganisms was necessary to induce an immunity that would be effective. He and his colleagues set out to develop a method of growing organisms in large quantities by using tissue culture. The method started by infecting chick embryo yolk sac tissue with rickettsia. The infected tissue was used to inoculate large quantities of normal chick tissue. The infected tissue was then grown on the surface of agar in flasks. This provided Zinsser and his team with the quantities of microorganisms needed to produce the desired vaccine. The type of immunization Zinsser was proposing is known as passive immunity. The infecting organisms have markers on their cell surfaces known as antigens. The antigens are capable of eliciting an immune reaction regardless of whether the cell is living, weakened, or dead. The reaction involves recognition of the antigen by cells called macrophages and cells called "B" cells. The B cells produce antibodies that are capable of destroying the invading organism directly or attracting more macrophages to the area so that they can destroy the organism. B cells also produce "memory cells," which remain in the blood in order to trigger a rapid second response if there is a subsequent infection. Since the vaccine contains weakened or dead organisms, the person experiences a mild reaction to the vaccine but is not at risk of contracting the disease.

Impact of Event

Typhus is still prevalent in many areas of the world. Where it does persist, the disease is nurtured by poverty and overcrowded, unsanitary living conditions. Many countries that have experienced severe drought report high incidences of typhus. Epidemic typhus has not been reported in many countries for some time. The last report of the epidemic in the United States was in 1921. Endemic or murine typhus occurs more frequently. The incidence in the United States is low, with about fifty cases per year being reported. Since the organism is susceptible to antibiotics, such as tetracycline and chloramphenicol, reported cases can be treated; therefore, the mortality rate is low.

Zinsser's contribution to the treatment and prevention of the disease had a significant impact. By creating an orderly classification of the typhus diseases and identifying causative agents and vectors, Zinsser and his coworkers contributed significantly to the understanding of the disease which, in turn, allowed for attempts to discover a cure and establish preventive measures. Louse and rodent control and improved sanitation help to prevent the spread of the disease.

Zinsser's idea to grow large quantities of the rickettsia to make a vaccine led him to investigate tissue culture as a quick and reliable method of securing a good yield of the desired microorganism. The attention focused on the tissue-culture method and inspired researchers to modify and improve the technique so that now the use of tissue culture is a standard effective laboratory procedure.

Zinsser's greatest contribution to medicine was the development of a vaccine for typhus. This disease has a place not only in the history of medicine but also in the history of the world. Battles and wars were lost because louse-infected armies fell victim to typhus. Invading armies carried the disease across national boundaries; Europe witnessed a noninterrupted series of epidemics throughout the eighteenth and nineteenth centuries. The vaccine that Zinsser and his team developed ensured that even if wars continued and armies were subjected to living in undesirable conditions, the possibility of contracting typhus would be greatly reduced. The vaccine also provided a safeguard for the poor in crowded cities. People who were forced by financial circumstances to live in densely packed housing, where they might easily become infected with lice or rat fleas, gained protection against typhus once the vaccine became available.

Since Zinsser looked to immunology for a protection against typhus, he also had an impact on the growing science of immunology and its application to medicine. Vaccines have been developed against many pathogenic organisms, and their use has obliterated many diseases that were once commonplace. Zinsser was one of the pioneers in applying the principles of immunity to healthcare.

Unfortunately, Zinsser died before he could realize all benefits accrued from the production of a vaccine against typhus. He was an inspiring teacher whose students and associates appreciated his approach to science and his concern for the human condition which his work helped to alleviate.

Bibliography

Duma, Richard J., et al. "Epidemic Typhus in the United States Associated with Flying Squirrels." *JAMA* 245 (June 12, 1981): 2318. Flying squirrels have been added to the list of rickettsia vectors. Most cases of typhus in the United States involve contact with squirrels, as this article suggests.

Joklik, Wolfgang K., Hilda P. Willet, and D. Bernard Amos, eds. *Zinsser Microbiology*. 18th ed. East Norwalk, Conn.: Appleton & Lange, 1984. Excellent description of the rickettsia organism and typhus disease. Zinsser's contributions to the immunology of the disease are highlighted.

Olitsky, Peter K. "Hans Zinsser and His Studies on Typhus Fever." *Journal of the American Medical Association* 116 (January 8, 1941): 907-912. This article, written one year after the death of Hans Zinsser, presents a comprehensive recitation of the highlights of Zinsser's life and career. Olitsky describes Zinsser as a humanist and philosopher as well as a scientist. The article contains a summary of the typhus research available when Zinsser began his work in 1930. A detailed account of work carried out by Zinsser and his team makes up the bulk of the article.

Strong, Richard P. "Obituary—Hans Zinsser." *Science* 92 (September 27, 1940): 276-279. Richard Strong was obviously a great admirer of Zinsser; he makes a great effort to laud the nonscientist side of Zinsser's life. He writes about the poems and other literary works published by Zinsser under the pseudonym of

R. S. He also reveals the deep feelings of admiration many of Zinsser's students and colleagues had for him. Also included are the highlights of Zinsser's scientific work.

Zinsser, Hans. *Rats, Lice, and History.* Boston: Little, Brown, 1935. This is a classic. Zinsser presents what he calls a biography of a disease. Begins by presenting his views on science and its relationship with art; he then gives a rather detailed account of epidemics and their influence on history. The last five chapters of the book deal with the history of typhus. This book is readable, enjoyable, and a must for anyone who enjoys history as well as science.

Zinsser, Hans, and Philip H. Hiss. *Textbook of Bacteriology.* New York: Appleton-Century, 1929. Any one of the eight editions of this textbook can be read to understand the type of information available to the research immunologist when the typhus work was being done. Can be understood by readers with a minimum of science background.

Zinsser, Hans, Harry Plotz, and John F. Emders. "Scientific Apparatus and Laboratory Methods: Mass Production of Vaccine Against Typhus Fever of the European Type." *Science* 91 (January 12, 1940): 51-52. A firsthand account of the problems encountered and the modifications made in the development of a method to grow organisms in large quantities. The writing is clear and understandable to the nonscientist.

Rosemary Scheirer

Cross-References

Ehrlich and Metchnikoff Conduct Pioneering Research in Immunology (1908), p. 422; Theiler Introduces a Vaccine Against Yellow Fever (1937), p. 1091; Salk Develops a Polio Vaccine (1952), p. 1444; Sabin Develops an Oral Polio Vaccine (1957), p. 1522; A Vaccine Is Developed for German Measles (1960), p. 1655; A Genetically Engineered Vaccine for Hepatitis B Is Approved for Use (1986), p. 2326.

PAULING DEVELOPS HIS THEORY
OF THE CHEMICAL BOND

Categories of event: Chemistry and physics
Time: 1930-1931
Locale: Pasadena, California

By his ingenious use of quantum mechanics, Pauling developed a theory of the chemical bond that strongly influenced chemists, physicists, biologists, and mineralogists

Principal personages:

LINUS PAULING (1901-   ), an American physical chemist of broad scientific interests and a political activist for peace who won the 1954 Nobel Prize in Chemistry and the 1962 Nobel Peace Prize

GILBERT NEWTON LEWIS (1875-1946), an American chemist whose idea of a shared electron-pair bond had an influence on Pauling

JOHN C. SLATER (1900-1976), an American physicist whose research on the quantum theory of atoms, molecules, and crystals paralleled Pauling's

WALTER HEINRICH HEITLER (1904-1981), a German theoretical physicist whose application of quantum mechanics to the chemical bond influenced Pauling

FRITZ LONDON (1900-1954), a German physicist who developed important theories of the chemical bond, superconductivity, and superfluidity

Summary of Event

Whenever interviewers asked Pauling for his choice of his most important discovery, he often responded that he was extremely pleased by his work on the nature of the chemical bond. His series of papers on this topic in the early 1930's and his book *The Nature of the Chemical Bond and the Structure of Molecules and Crystals* (1939) clarified large areas of chemistry and contributed to important advances in such fields as biochemistry, mineralogy, and medicine. His work grew out of the contributions of his predecessors, and in several ways he was able to recapitulate the thinking of scientists who had lived many years before him. The idea of an atom's definite combining power had been developed in the nineteenth century, and it formed the theoretical backbone of a dynamic structural theory that was able, under the insightful tutelage of the Dutch physical chemist Jacobus Henricus van't Hoff, to reveal how the four valence bonds of certain carbon compounds are directed toward the corners of a regular tetrahedron, thus accounting for the right- and left-handed forms of particular organic molecules.

With the discovery of the electron by Sir Joseph John Thomson in 1897 and the discovery of the nucleus by Ernest Rutherford in 1911, theories about how atoms were linked together in compounds became more dependent on a physical model of the atom, especially how electrons are arranged around the nucleus. Pauling became fascinated by the ideas of Gilbert Newton Lewis, who had proposed a theory of the inner structure of the atom. In Lewis' model, electrons occupy the space around the nucleus in certain patterns that are responsible for an element's specific properties, including its bonding properties. Lewis pictured the atom as a series of concentric cubes whose corners could be occupied by electrons. He used this "cubical atom" to explain the formation of chemical bonds by the transfer of electrons from one atom to another. Lewis proposed that electrons could be shared between atoms in forming a covalent bond. This covalent (or shared electron-pair) bond had a great impact on Pauling.

As a graduate student at the California Institute of Technology, Pauling made use of Niels Bohr's quantum theory of the atom in his own theoretical speculations. Bohr had been successful in applying the quantum idea to the hydrogen atom, showing how its lone electron could exist solely in specific orbits (or quantized states) around its nuclear proton. Bohr's theory, however, was not very successful in accounting for the electronic structures of complex atoms or for the combinations of atoms in molecules. Pauling tried to use Arnold Sommerfeld's version (with elliptical rather than circular orbits) of Bohr's atomic model to explain the structure and properties of benzene, a ring compound of six carbon atoms, but the old quantum theory was simply too weak to enable Pauling or any other scientist to develop a satisfactory theory of chemical structures.

With the development of quantum mechanics in the mid-1920's, a tool was now available to resolve many of the deficiencies of the old theory. Pauling was influenced principally by Erwin Schrödinger's formulation of wave mechanics and was able to use the new quantum mechanics to predict the properties of various ions and to develop a perspicacious picture of the ionic bond (an interatomic link in which one of the atoms has a disproportionate share of the electronic charge). One of the ideas on which wave mechanics was built is the wave nature of the electron. Using his wave equation, Schrödinger was able to reveal many advantages in treating the electron as a wave rather than as a particle in a strictly defined orbit. In one interpretation of Schrödinger's equation, electrons occupy orbitals, often represented by such shaded geometric figures as spheres or somewhat distorted dumbbells, the intensity of the shading corresponding to the relative probability of finding an electron in this particular region. Although Schrödinger's treatment made it difficult to speak of atoms as rigid mechanical structures, it permitted a new view of chemical bonding, particularly in the hands of Walter Heinrich Heitler and Fritz London.

While in Munich, Pauling met Heitler, who was working toward his doctoral degree. In the summer of 1927, Pauling discussed quantum mechanics with Heitler and met London, who had a Rockefeller Foundation grant to work with Schrödinger. After Pauling returned to the United States, Heitler and London published a paper on the quantum mechanics of the chemical bond (which Pauling once called "the greatest single contribution to the clarification of the chemist's concept of valence"). In their paper, Heitler and London made use of the idea of resonance, which had been introduced by Werner Heisenberg in 1926, to explain how two hydrogen atoms could bond together when brought near to each other. In the resonance phenomenon, an interchange in position of the two electrons reduces the system's energy and causes the formation of a bond. Heitler and London supplied a quantum mechanical justification for Lewis' electron-pair idea. Their quantum mechanical method allowed them to calculate approximate values for various properties of the hydrogen molecule, for example, how much energy it would take to split the molecule into its component atoms.

In the fall of 1927, Pauling began a period of intense scientific creativity. He developed a theory for predicting the structures of crystals. He refined his wave mechanical treatment of the hydrogen molecule-ion (a hydrogen molecule with one rather than two electrons). Most important, he enunciated for the first time what later came to be called the hybridization of atomic orbitals. The idea of hybrid orbitals grew out of his chemical intuition. To physicists, it seemed strange that carbon, with two different types of orbitals (the spherical $2s$ and the dumbbell-shaped $2p$), should generate, in its chemical compounds, four identical bonds that were directed to the corners of a tetrahedron. To Pauling, it seemed strange that such tetrahedral compounds of carbon as methane (CH_4) could not be explained by atomic orbitals. A physicist would regard it as a very serious error to mix s and p orbitals, but Pauling recognized that the energy separation between the two orbital states was small, compared with the energy of the bond formed. For him, the ability to make the best possible bond was the most important consideration. In 1928, he published a short paper in which he reported that he had used quantum mechanical resonance to derive the four equivalent orbitals used in bonding by the carbon atom. Furthermore, these orbitals, which he also referred to as hybrid orbitals, are directed toward the corners of a regular tetrahedron.

Pauling had difficulties in translating his insight into a mathematical treatment that would be convincing to most scientists. When he was unable to solve the complex mathematical expressions, he set the matter aside. Meanwhile, in 1929, John C. Slater became interested in the quantum mechanics of the chemical bond. He had developed a method for interpreting the complex spectra of certain atoms, and when he applied his methods to molecules, he derived information about the valence and directional properties of these molecules. He first described his results in an informal talk at the Washington meeting of the American Physical Society in April, 1930. He published a paper in 1931 in the *Physical Review*, suggesting that the dumbbell-shaped charge clouds of certain orbitals were responsible for the directional properties of many chemical compounds. He also introduced the criterion of maximum overlapping of orbitals for bond strength, and he made extensive use of resonance. Further, he discussed the directional bonds formed in molecules with many atoms, and he even attempted to explain why the four valences of carbon have tetrahedral symmetry.

Slater's work stimulated Pauling to return to the problem he had set aside in 1928. In December, 1930, while he was doing some calculations, he had an idea about making an assumption to simplify the quantum mechanical equations describing the bonding orbitals of carbon so that they could be solved in an approximate way. The quantum mechanical equations describing the orbitals with which he was concerned have radial and angular parts, and since the radial part of the 2*s* wave function of the carbon atom (from which the orbital can be readily derived) is not very different from the radial part of the three 2*p* functions, Pauling concluded that little error would be introduced if he ignored the radial factor in the *p* function. This facilitated his calculations of various hybrid orbitals, for example, the tetrahedral hybrids, called *sp*³ because they involve a combination of the 2*s* and the three 2*p* orbitals. His semi-quantitative approach to the chemical bond proved so successful that he went on to develop the implications of his ideas. He was able to give explanations from the kinked structure of the water molecule to the transition from covalent to ionic bonding.

In January and February, 1931, he continued to make refinements and extend their application. His paper entitled "The Nature of the Chemical Bond: Applications of Results Obtained from the Quantum Mechanics and from a Theory of Paramagnetic Susceptibility to the Structure of Molecules," appeared in the *Journal of the American Chemical Society* on April 6, 1931. It is his most famous paper, and it established a framework for understanding the electronic and geometric structures of molecules and ions in terms of hybrid bond orbitals. Also, it permitted him to use the magnetic properties of molecules to distinguish between ionic and covalent bonding. Pauling explained how the energy barrier between *s* and *p* orbitals can be broken when strong bonds are formed. Since a large orbital overlap is associated with the formation of a strong bond, he was able to relate bond strength to the nature of the orbitals from which the bond is formed. He used the ideas of resonance and hybridization to explain the tetrahedral, square, and octahedral configurations of certain molecules.

From 1931 to 1933, Pauling published a series of papers on the nature of the chemical bond, in which he used the concepts of hybridization of bond orbitals and the resonance of molecules among two or more alternative structures to elucidate many basic chemical phenomena. For example, he was able to use hybrid orbitals and resonance to explain the properties of the benzene molecule, whose carbon-to-carbon bond lengths, planar structure, hexagonal symmetry, and great stability had puzzled chemists for generations. He was able to formulate an electronegativity scale of the elements, which proved to be extremely useful to chemists. Electronegativity is the tendency of an element in a compound to attract electrons to itself, and Pauling found a way to assign numbers to the elements to represent this power of attracting electrons.

Pauling's papers were so successful that, by 1935, he believed that he had a complete understanding of the nature of the chemical bond. He was able to give form to this understanding in the late 1930's, when he served as a professor of chemistry at

Cornell University. Out of his lectures came a book, *The Nature of the Chemical Bond and the Structure of Molecules and Crystals,* whose first edition was published in 1939. The book was received enthusiastically, one reviewer calling it "epoch-making." It was an excellent summation of his decade-long studies on the nature of the chemical bond.

Impact of Event

Pauling's theory of the chemical bond was a milestone in the development of modern chemistry. Chemists were deeply impressed by the power of his methods to unify a vast amount of previously unintegrated data. They were also impressed by the large amount of experimental data Pauling had collected, tabulated, and rationalized. Pauling's papers and book on the chemical bond accumulated thousands of citations in the 1930's and 1940's. Physicists, biochemists, molecular biologists, and mineralogists used his data and ideas to solve many problems in their disciplines. It is interesting that, while James D. Watson and Francis Crick were trying to figure out the structure of deoxyribonucleic acid (DNA), they made extensive use of Pauling's book.

Despite the great success of Pauling's work on the chemical bond, it shared the contingencies of all scientific achievement. Because of the many approximations involved in his approach, it had a number of limitations, which critics soon pointed out. Charles A. Coulson, for example, believed that while Pauling's comparison of bond length and orbital overlap is very useful in a qualitative sense, it is not adequate for the quantitative determination of bond energies for certain hybrid orbitals. Nevil Sidgwick also believed that Pauling's theory of the chemical bond should be "received with a certain reserve," because of its lack of mathematical rigor. Other scientists developed a theory—often called the molecular orbital (MO) method— that rivaled Pauling's. Pauling and Slater's method was a natural outgrowth of the work of Heitler and London; therefore, this approach, which viewed the chemical bond from the perspective of two separate atoms coming together, was sometimes called the Heitler-London-Slater-Pauling (HLSP) method, but it is known most often as the valence bond (VB) method. Other names given to the theory, "the method of localized pairs" or "the method of the directed valence bond," are not used often.

In the molecular orbital method, the problem of the chemical bond is attacked from the viewpoint of the single molecule produced by the coalescence of the atoms. During the late 1940's and through the 1950's, the MO method began to find favor with a number of chemists, and Pauling's valence-bond theory came increasingly under attack. Some European and American scientists pointed out that the VB theory was encountering difficulties in explaining the excited states of molecules, whereas the MO method was successful in its quantitative discussions of these excited states. During this same period, Pauling's theory came under attack on ideological grounds. Certain Soviet critics found Pauling's notion of resonance irrational, since it went against some of the basic tenets of dialectical materialism. Essentially, certain Soviet chemists criticized Pauling, whom they called a "decadent bourgeois scientist," for his attributing reality to his formal equations and models (for these Soviet critics, resonance structures were human-made, not real). In place of Pauling's theory, the Soviet chemists preferred to turn to the Soviet chemist Alexander M. Butlerov, whose theory of the mutual influence of atoms in molecules they found both scientifically and ideologically acceptable. It is ironic that Pauling, who shared the deterministic and realistic interpretation of quantum mechanics with many Soviet philosophers and scientists, should have encountered such animosity toward his theory of resonance, especially since he admitted that his resonance descriptions bore a close resemblance to the actual molecular structures. A further irony is that, while Soviet chemists were attacking him for his resonance theory, American politicians were criticizing him for his attitude toward the Soviet Union.

Despite these criticisms from the East and the West, Pauling's theory of the chemical bond proved to be useful for scientists for three decades. When the VB theory began to be replaced by the MO theory in the 1960's, Pauling continued to retain a deep loyalty to his views of the chemical bond. This is characteristic of his approach to science. When he is convinced of the value of a scientific idea, he clings to it tenaciously and uses it boldly. Resonance was such an idea. Early in his career, Pauling became convinced of its power and efficacy. Continued success in applying this idea to a great variety of chemical problems confirmed this attitude. Because of the strength of the resonance concept, he was less attracted to the new ideas about chemical bonding that came on the scene. Confronted with new problems, he tended to solve them in terms that he understood. This tenacity, which has a negative side, is also a part of his genius. Without his championing of the VB theory, modern structural chemistry's great successes, such as the determinations of the structures of DNA and proteins, would have been significantly delayed. Thus, it is impossible to understand the evolution of modern structural chemistry without Pauling's theories.

Bibliography

Coulson, Charles A. *Valence*. 2d ed. London: Oxford University Press, 1961. Coulson, an Oxford professor of mathematics who became a distinguished theoretical chemist, discusses how wave mechanics transformed valence theory. Although he makes use of mathematical formulas, his treatment is mostly qualitative. His basic purpose is to reveal, in a general way, why molecules are the way they are. His intended audience is, as he puts it, "the novice chemist with few mathematical attainments." The book has author, substance, and subject indexes.

Lagowski, J. J. *The Chemical Bond*. Boston: Houghton Mifflin, 1966. This book, part of the Classic Researches in General Chemistry series, uses the words of scientists to re-create for students the exciting process of discovery. Lagowski's approach is historical and accessible to both science and nonscience majors taking chemistry for the first time. Contains several helpful tables and diagrams, and includes lists of suggested readings at the ends of chapters.

Lewis, Gilbert Newton. *Valence and the Structure of Atoms and Molecules*. New

York: Dover, 1966. This edition, an unabridged reprint of a work originally published by the Chemical Catalog Company in 1923, contains an introduction by Kenneth Pitzer. Although Lewis wrote this interesting account of chemical bonding before the development of quantum mechanics, it is still valuable for the light he sheds both on his own ideas and on those of other scientists. Illustrated with figures; also has references and an index.

Palmer, William G. *A History of the Concept of Valency to 1930.* Cambridge, England: Cambridge University Press, 1965. Palmer, a lecturer in chemistry at the University of Cambridge, uses the theme of the increasingly fertile cooperation between physics and chemistry to explain how the idea of chemical valence was established and how the modern theory of the chemical bond evolved from it. A valuable source both on the early history of valence theories and on the later development of electronic theories.

Pauling, Linus. *The Nature of the Chemical Bond and the Structure of Molecules and Crystals: An Introduction to Modern Structural Chemistry.* 3d ed. Ithaca, N.Y.: Cornell University Press, 1960. Pauling's magnum opus. His approach is structural rather than mathematical, and therefore the book is accessible to those with modest backgrounds in chemistry, physics, and mathematics. He shunts off difficult material into twelve appendices. Contains an author and a subject index.

Pauling, Linus, and Roger Hayward. *The Architecture of Molecules.* San Francisco: W. H. Freeman, 1964. Pauling has an excellent ability to communicate clearly his understanding of molecules, and an artist captures Pauling's structural imagination in beautifully drawn and colored plates. Intended for young people who are beginning to develop an interest in science, but it can be appreciated by anyone with a curiosity about the natural world. Includes a periodic table of the elements and some tables of atomic radii.

Russell, C. A. *The History of Valency.* Leicester, England: Leicester University Press, 1971. A detailed study of the history of physical and chemical bonding ideas. The author has studied much primary and secondary material and organized it coherently. He treats controversial material in a balanced and insightful way. Well-prepared indexes allow ready access to the ideas and persons discussed.

Servos, John W. *Physical Chemistry from Ostwald to Pauling: The Making of a Science in America.* Princeton, N.J.: Princeton University Press, 1990. Servos, a historian of science, explores the evolution of physical chemistry in the United States by analyzing the key institutions and scientists who made this discipline into a fertile source of innovative ideas. The notes to the chapters at the book's end have extensive references to the primary and secondary literature. Detailed index.

Robert J. Paradowski

Cross-References

Thomson Wins the Nobel Prize for the Discovery of the Electron (1906), p. 356;

Bohr Writes a Trilogy on Atomic and Molecular Structure (1912), p. 507; Rutherford Presents His Theory of the Atom (1912), p. 527; Watson and Crick Develop the Double-Helix Model for DNA (1951), p. 1406; Sanger Wins the Nobel Prize for the Discovery of the Structure of Insulin (1958), p. 1567.

JANSKY'S EXPERIMENTS LEAD TO
THE FOUNDING OF RADIO ASTRONOMY

Category of event: Astronomy
Time: 1930-1932
Locale: Cliffwood, New Jersey

An antenna set up to detect the causes of interference with radio transmission detected the first-recognized signals from outside the solar system

Principal personages:
    KARL JANSKY (1905-1950), an American radio engineer whose investigations of radio static led to the discovery of radio astronomy
    ALBERT MELVIN SKELLETT (1901-   ), an American radio technician and astronomer who assisted Karl Jansky in the astronomical interpretation of his data
    GROTE REBER (1912-   ), an American radio engineer who became the first radio astronomer and who built the first true radio telescope

Summary of Event

Almost as soon as radio waves were discovered in 1888, scientists suspected that radio emissions from the sun might be detectable. Several investigators tried to detect such emissions, but all early attempts failed. In many cases, the detecting devices were too insensitive, but equally important was the then-unknown effect of the earth's atmosphere on radio signals. The atmosphere is opaque to many portions of the radio spectrum, and other radio wavelengths are scattered or reflected by the atmosphere during periods of high solar activity.

In 1928, Karl Jansky was hired by Bell Telephone Laboratories as a radio engineer. His first assignment was to investigate the causes of interference with transatlantic radio-telephone transmissions. The so-called short-wave band of radio frequencies (wavelengths of 1.5 to 15 meters) was just then beginning to be used, and little was known about natural radio sources in this wavelength range. To investigate these natural signals required a sensitive antenna whose frequency response and sensitivity were very stable. These characteristics are also ideal characteristics of any radio telescope.

The device Jansky built, a so-called Bruce array, detected signals at a wavelength of 14.6 meters (a frequency of 20.5 megahertz). The antenna consisted of two parallel frameworks of brass tubing; one frame was connected to a receiver, and the other acted as a signal reflector. The antenna detected signals only in a narrow sector at right angles to the length of the antenna and was similar to antennas then in use for transatlantic broadcasting except for one feature: It was mounted on four Model-T Ford wheels and rotated every twenty minutes on a circular track. The antenna, about 30 meters long and 4 meters in width and height, was nicknamed "the merry-go-round."

Jansky discovered there were three kinds of signal detectable with his instrument, which he first described in an article in 1932. Nearby thunderstorms created rare but powerful radio bursts. Distant thunderstorms created a weak steady signal as their radio signals were reflected off the ionosphere, an electrically-conducting layer in the upper atmosphere. The third signal, which created a steady hiss in receivers, was at first a mystery. Even though this signal was not a serious problem for radio reception, Jansky continued his efforts to identify the source. The signal varied in intensity in a daily cycle, and Jansky initially suspected it might originate with the sun. By unfortunate coincidence, the sun happened to be in line with the center of the galaxy when Jansky began collecting his data. After some months of additional data collection, it became clear that the sun was not the source of the signals.

The key observation that revealed the true source of the signals was the fact that they peaked a few minutes earlier each day. Jansky, who was unfamiliar with astronomy, did not appreciate the significance of that observation, but a friend, Albert Melvin Skellett, did. The earth takes 23 hours and 56 minutes to rotate with respect to the stars. Because the earth moves in its orbit by about a degree per day, it takes an extra four minutes to complete a rotation with respect to the sun. The signals were following sidereal (star) time; that is, they came from a source that was fixed with respect to the stars. In 1933, after a full year of observations, Jansky published his estimate of the source's location: in the southern Milky Way in the direction of Sagittarius. In 1935, after additional data analysis, Jansky reported that signals originated from all along the Milky Way.

Once Jansky understood the nature of the cosmic signals, he found that he was completely unable to detect the sun at all, a discovery he found quite puzzling. Jansky happened to be observing at a time of minimum sunspot activity. If he had observed at sunspot maximum, his equipment should have detected solar radio emissions. On the other hand, had he observed at sunspot maximum, the upper atmosphere would have been nearly opaque at the wavelengths he studied, and he would probably not have detected emissions from the Milky Way. Jansky realized that if he could not detect the sun, the signals from the Milky Way were not likely to originate in stars. He suggested that the radio signals originated from interstellar dust and gas instead, a supposition that proved to be correct.

Jansky's observations attracted much public notice. They were described in a front-page article in *The New York Times* on May 5, 1933, and a national radio program broadcast a few seconds of cosmic radio noise. Nevertheless, the discovery had little importance to practical communications. Jansky proposed construction of a 30-meter dish antenna to study the cosmic signals in greater detail, but his employers believed that such investigations were more appropriate for academic researchers, and turned down the proposal. Jansky went on to other areas of communications research, and received a commendation for his work on radio direction finders during World War II. He had always been in poor health and died in 1950 at the age of forty-four, just as radio astronomy was beginning to flourish.

The modern style of portraying cosmic radio emissions is on a celestial map.

Because most radio emissions come from the Milky Way, the map is usually drawn in galactic coordinates. That is, the equator of the map is the galactic equator or plane of the Milky Way, and zero longitude on the map is the center of the galaxy. The concept of mapping cosmic radio sources did not exist in Jansky's time, nor did it occur to him. Instead, Jansky calculated the signal traces that would be expected for different arrangements of radio sources and compared them to the actual signal traces recorded by his apparatus.

Unfortunately, Jansky's original data recordings were discarded in the late 1950's before anyone appreciated their historical significance. Nevertheless, enough has been preserved to allow reexamination of his data by more modern methods. Because the antenna rotated about a vertical axis, while the heavens appear to rotate around a tilted axis, the antenna swept over a large area of the sky every day, and in fact, except for temporary radio disturbances, recorded the same data every day. Thus, the single day's recording published in a 1932 article is representative of his entire data. The antenna was sensitive to signals in a roughly conical sector about 30 degrees across. Between the rotations of the antenna and the earth, the antenna mapped the whole sky visible from New Jersey except a small patch near the north celestial pole. The portion of sky within 40 degrees of the south celestial pole was always below the horizon at Jansky's latitude. Altogether, about 80 percent of the sky was scanned by Jansky's antenna. Maps of the radio sky prepared from Jansky's data by astronomer Woodruff Sullivan clearly show the plane of the Milky Way, as well as hints of other radio features not recognized until long after Jansky's discoveries.

Impact of Event

The immediate effect of Jansky's work was small. Few people had the necessary knowledge of both astronomy and radio to undertake radio observations. One who did was Grote Reber, who realized that investigating celestial radio sources would require completely different equipment from that Jansky had used. In 1937, Reber built a parabolic reflecting antenna with a diameter of 10 meters. For simplicity, the reflector was aimed at the meridian and could rotate only vertically. Maps of the sky were made by aiming the parabolic dish at different elevations and letting the earth's rotation carry radio sources across the field of view. This instrument was the first true radio telescope. After a series of initial failures, Reber was mapping celestial radio signals by 1939.

World War II provided a great stimulus for radio astronomy by stimulating the birth of radar and by the discovery of other sources of cosmic radio interference, for example, radar echoes from meteorite vapor trails and solar interference with radio and radar signals. After the war, radio astronomy began on a modest scale, but rapidly expanded. As astronomers explored ever fainter objects, radio telescopes became larger to collect the faint radio signals efficiently. The total radio energy from signals outside our galaxy ever collected by all the radio telescopes on Earth would light a flashlight bulb for only a fraction of a second.

The discovery of radio astronomy marked the first time astronomers used any part of the electromagnetic spectrum other than visible and infrared light. One of the greatest surprises of radio astronomy was that many of the most powerful radio sources were invisible or extremely faint in visible light, and that most bright stars were invisible at radio wavelengths. Astronomers were wholly unprepared for the discovery that the universe could look so different at optical and radio wavelengths or that objects could emit powerful radio signals yet be optically invisible. Many radio sources were detected optically only after very intensive searches. Also, many of the physical mechanisms that produce cosmic radio waves were unknown at the time radio astronomy began. The greatest effect of radio astronomy was to teach astronomers that every part of the electromagnetic spectrum conveys unique information and reveals new phenomena and new types of celestial objects. Astronomers now eagerly seek out and exploit new technologies to explore different wavelength bands of the electromagnetic spectrum.

The specific discoveries of radio astronomy are all but innumerable. Radio waves penetrate cosmic dust and gas clouds that block visible light, making it possible to map the structure of our galaxy. Radio astronomy has discovered great explosive bursts in other galaxies, some of which emit so much energy that their cause is a major scientific mystery. Radio astronomy also discovered pulsars, the first concrete evidence for neutron stars. Finally, radio astronomy has detected faint background radiation that most astronomers consider to be the echo of the big bang, the formation of the universe.

Bibliography

Hey, J. S. *The Evolution of Radio Astronomy.* New York: Science History, 1973. A history of radio astronomy that concentrates mostly on the period after World War II, but also provides some details of Karl Jansky's work.

Reber, Grote. "Radio Astronomy." *Scientific American* 181 (September, 1949): 34-41. Written by the first radio astronomer at the dawn of radio astronomy, this article shows some of the first published radio maps of the heavens and makes a number of conjectures (later proven correct) about the causes of some cosmic radio signals.

Spradley, Joseph L. "The First True Radio Telescope." *Sky and Telescope* 76 (July, 1988): 28-30. An account of the telescope of Grote Reber, who for over a decade was the only scientist to pursue Jansky's discoveries. Reber's construction and early attempts to detect cosmic radio signals are clearly described, and some of his first radio maps of the heavens are reproduced.

Sullivan, Woodruff T., III. "A New Look at Karl Jansky's Original Data." *Sky and Telescope* 56 (August, 1978): 101-105. A summary of the events that led to Jansky's discovery of extraterrestrial radio sources. Contains a reproduction of Jansky's original chart data and a reexamination of his data in the light of modern discoveries. The language is moderately technical, appropriate to an introductory college science course.

_____. "Radio Astronomy's Golden Anniversary." *Sky and Telescope* 64

(December, 1982): 544-550. A pictorial review of early radio astronomy from Jansky's initial discovery through 1967. Illustrations include major historical figures, equipment, and significant data recordings. The dramatic growth in equipment sophistication is well depicted.

Verschuur, Gerrit L. *The Invisible Universe Revealed: The Story of Radio Astronomy.* New York: Springer-Verlag, 1987. Written by a leading radio astronomer, this book surveys the major types of celestial radio phenomena and also summarizes the history of radio astronomy.

Steven I. Dutch

Cross-References

Transatlantic Radiotelephony Is First Demonstrated (1915), p. 615; The Principles of Shortwave Radio Communication Are Discovered (1919), p. 669; Watson-Watt and Associates Develop the First Radar (1935), p. 1040; Reber Builds the First Intentional Radio Telescope (1937), p. 1113; Reber Makes the First Radio Maps of the Universe (1942), p. 1193; Ryle's Radio Telescope Locates the First Known Radio Galaxy (1946), p. 1271; Franklin and Burke Discover Radio Emissions from Jupiter (1955), p. 1492; Ryle Constructs the First Radio Interferometer (1955), p. 1496; Schmidt Makes What Constitutes the First Recognition of a Quasar (1963), p. 1757; Penzias and Wilson Discover Cosmic Microwave Background Radiation (1963), p. 1762; Bell Discovers Pulsars, the Key to Neutron Stars (1967), p. 1862.

ARMSTRONG PERFECTS FM RADIO

Category of event: Applied science
Time: 1930-1935
Locale: New York City

During the early 1930's, Armstrong invented frequency modulated radio broadcasting, but would neither receive credit nor see it innovated in his lifetime

Principal personages:
EDWIN H. ARMSTRONG (1890-1954), the inventor of frequency modulated radio broadcasting, who spent the final two decades of his life unsuccessfully trying to bring his creation to the marketplace
DAVID SARNOFF (1891-1971), the founder and primary corporate creator of the Radio Corporation of America

Summary of Event

Because the original radio broadcasts used amplitude modulation (AM) to transmit their sounds, they were subject to a sizable amount of interference and static. Since amplitude modulation relies on the amount of energy transmitted, energy sources in the atmosphere between the station and the receiver can distort or weaken the original signal. This is particularly irritating for the transmission of music.

Edwin H. Armstrong provided a solution to this technological constraint. A graduate of Columbia University, Armstrong made a significant contribution to the development of radio with his basic inventions for circuits for amplitude modulated receivers. (Indeed, the monies Armstrong received from his earlier inventions financed the development of the frequency modulation—FM—system.) Armstrong was one among many contributors to amplitude modulation radio. For frequency modulation broadcasting, however, Armstrong must be ranked as the most important inventor.

During the 1920's, Armstrong established his own research laboratory in Alpine, New Jersey, across the Hudson River from New York City. With a small staff of dedicated assistants, he carried out research on radio circuitry and systems for nearly three decades. At that time, Armstrong also began to teach electrical engineering at Columbia University.

From 1928 to 1933, Armstrong worked diligently at his private laboratory at Columbia University to construct a working model of a frequency modulated radio broadcasting system. With the primitive limitations then imposed by the state of vacuum tube technology, a number of Armstrong's experimental circuits required as many as one hundred tubes. Between July, 1930, and January, 1933, Armstrong filed four basic frequency modulated patent applications; all were granted simultaneously on December 26, 1933.

Armstrong sought to perfect frequency modulated radio broadcasting, not to offer radio listeners better musical reception but to create an entirely new radio broadcasting system. On November 5, 1935, Armstrong made his first public demonstration of frequency modulated radio broadcasting in New York City to an audience of radio engineers. An amateur station owned by Armstrong's friend, Randolph Runyon, based in suburban Yonkers, New York, transmitted these first signals. The scientific world began to consider the advantages and disadvantages of frequency modulated radio broadcasting. Other laboratories began to craft their own versions of frequency modulated radio broadcasting. At the then-dominant Radio Corporation of America (RCA), scientists began to experiment with FM radio broadcasting.

Because Armstrong had no desire to become a manufacturer or broadcaster, he approached David Sarnoff, head of RCA. As owner of the top manufacturer of radio sets and the top radio broadcasting network, Sarnoff was interested in all advances of radio technology. Armstrong first demonstrated FM radio broadcasting for Sarnoff in December, 1933. This was followed by visits from RCA engineers, who were sufficiently impressed to recommend to Sarnoff that the company conduct field tests of the Armstrong system.

In 1934, Armstrong, with the cooperation of RCA, set up a test transmitter at the top of the Empire State Building, sharing facilities with the then experimental RCA television transmitter. From 1934 through 1935, tests were conducted using the Empire State facility, to mixed reactions of RCA's best engineers. AM radio broadcasting already had a performance record of nearly two decades. The engineers wondered if this new technology could replace something that had worked so well. This less than enthusiastic evaluation fueled the skepticism of RCA lawyers and salespeople. RCA had too much invested in the AM system, both as the leading manufacturer and as the dominant owner of the major radio network of the time, the National Broadcasting Company (NBC). Sarnoff was in no rush to adopt frequency modulation. To change systems would risk the millions of dollars RCA was making as America emerged from the Great Depression. Sarnoff believed it was too much of a risk.

In 1935, Sarnoff advised Armstrong that RCA would cease any further research and development activity in FM radio broadcasting. (Still, engineers at RCA laboratories continued to work on frequency modulation to protect the corporate patent position.) Sarnoff declared to the press that his company would push the frontiers of broadcasting by concentrating on research and development of radio with pictures, that is, television. As a tangible sign, Sarnoff ordered that Armstrong's FM radio broadcasting tower be removed from the top of the Empire State Building. Armstrong was outraged. By the mid-1930's, the development of FM radio broadcasting had grown into a mission for Armstrong. For the remainder of his life, Armstrong devoted his considerable talents to the promotion of FM radio broadcasting. Armstrong was certain that Sarnoff was simply trying to suppress FM radio broadcasting to preserve RCA's profits.

After the break with Sarnoff, Armstrong proceeded with plans to develop his own FM operation. Allied with two of RCA's biggest manufacturing competitors— Zenith and General Electric—Armstrong pressed ahead. In June of 1936, at a Federal Communications Commission (FCC) hearing, Armstrong proclaimed that FM broadcasting was the only static-free, noise-free, and uniform system—both day and night—available. He argued, correctly, that AM radio broadcasting had none of these qualities.

A frequency modulation radio broadcasting transmission tower was built in Alpine, New Jersey. In 1938, station W2XMN became the first FM station. Armstrong gained backing from the regional radio network and, in cooperation, a transmitter tower was built atop Mount Asnebumskit in Massachusetts. The radio network would invest a quarter of a million dollars in FM radio stations. The central question turned from the technological to the legal: What part of the spectrum should be allocated for frequency modulation? Space on the very high frequency band was set aside, and, in the days before World War II, preliminary licenses were granted for more than fifty stations. In 1941, the FCC decreed that sound for the new television system it had approved should be telecast by FM principles. (It remains so to the present.)

In December, 1941, World War II began. Innovation of frequency modulation was halted; the infant industry was maintained at an arrested stage of development. Armstrong gave the military permission to use frequency modulation with no compensation. That patriotic gesture cost Armstrong millions when the military soon became all frequency modulation. It did, however, expand interest in FM radio broadcasting. World War II had provided a field test of equipment and use.

Armstrong's final battle to institute frequency modulated radio broadcasting began in 1948 when he filed a lawsuit charging infringement of patents by RCA. This was a struggle for the claim of invention rather than the possible development of an industry. Armstrong would not live to see his invention of FM radio broadcasting come to mainstream use; on January 31, 1954, he committed suicide. The case was settled shortly thereafter. The court sidestepped the basic question of who had invented FM radio broadcasting but ordered RCA to pay the Armstrong estate $1 million for infringement of patents.

Impact of Event

It would take three decades before Armstrong's legacy of frequency modulated broadcasting made its full impact. When FM radio broadcasting licenses were granted by the FCC after World War II, most went to successful AM stations. The AM radio stations acquired the FM licenses to ensure that no serious competitor would threaten their market share.

During the 1950's, a handful of independent FM stations labored at the margins of the radio industry, playing ethnic, classical, jazz, and folk musical programming to small audiences. At that time, a radio receiver that could pick up FM radio broadcasts cost much more than a radio that could pick up the far more popular AM radio broadcasting signals. A particular impediment came with the lack of radios in automobiles that could pick up FM signals. As late as 1966, only one car radio in twenty-five was equipped to receive FM radio broadcasting.

The FCC initiated a change in 1966. To encourage greater diversity in programming, the FCC dictated that FM broadcasting licensees needed to provide at least 50 percent original programming on FM stations. That meant that those who owned an AM and FM station in the same market could no longer simulcast their signals. That is, they could no longer transmit the same signal on both outlets simultaneously. Although this meant hiring more staff and thus less profits in the short run, the disgruntled owners complied rather than lose their FM licenses. At first, there was abuse of the regulation. For example, a number of station owners simply ordered that staff members replay earlier tapes of the AM programming on the FM station. The signals were the same, but not simultaneous. Gradually, risk-taking station owners sought to differentiate their products to see if they could see greater profits in the long run. The first change came with alternative rock; then came all-jazz, all-talk, and all-sports FM stations. Listeners loved the fact that radio sounded as good as their stereo record players.

The result in the 1970's was tremendous growth in FM radio broadcasting. By 1972, one in three radio listeners tuned in an FM station some time during the day. Advertisers began to use FM radio stations to reach the young and affluent audiences that were turning to FM stations in greater numbers. The advertisers were attracted also by the low rates. Gross revenues soared from about $10 million for 1962 to nearly $85 million a decade later.

By the late 1970's, FM stations were surging past AM radio broadcasts. In 1976, the average FM station began to show a profit. By 1980, nearly half of radio listeners tuned in to FM stations on a regular basis. A decade later, FM radio listening accounted for more than two-thirds of audience time, and regulators and station owners were seeking ways to boost the fortunes of AM radio broadcasting. Armstrong's predictions that listeners would prefer the clear, static-free sounds offered by FM radio broadcasting had come to pass by the mid-1980's, nearly fifty years after Armstrong had commenced his struggle to make FM radio broadcasting a part of commercial radio.

Bibliography

Barnouw, Erik. *A History of Broadcasting in the United States.* 3 vols. New York: Oxford University Press, 1966-1970. The standard history of broadcasting in the United States. The coming of frequency modulation radio broadcasting is covered in the first two of the three volumes.

Bilby, Kenneth. *The General David Sarnoff and the Rise of the Communications Industry.* New York: Harper & Row, 1986. One of the two major works on the activities of RCA and its founder, David Sarnoff. Presents a detailed history of the activities of RCA in the invention and innovation of frequency modulation radio.

Dreher, Carl. *Sarnoff: An American Success.* New York: Quadrangle, 1977. Discusses the activities of RCA and its founder, David Sarnoff. Presents a detailed history of RCA's activities in the invention and innovation of FM radio. Less objective than Bilby's account (cited above).

Erickson, Don V. *Armstrong's Fight for FM Broadcasting: One Man Versus Big*

Business and Bureaucracy. Tuscaloosa: University of Alabama Press, 1973. Attempts to reclaim Armstrong's role in the history of broadcasting by exposing the
collaboration between the FCC and the entrenched broadcasting lobby to protect
then-dominant AM radio.

Head, Sydney W., and Christopher H. Sterling. *Broadcasting in America.* 5th ed.
Boston: Houghton Mifflin, 1987. The standard introduction to radio and television in the United States. Begins with an analysis of the invention of FM radio
broadcasting and Armstrong's role.

Inglis, Andrew F. *Behind the Tube: A History of Broadcasting Technology and Business.* Boston: Focal Press, 1990. Offers a contemporary examination of the technological history of the mass media. Chapter 3 provides a fine overview of the
history of frequency modulation radio, including Armstrong's contributions.

Lessing, Lawrence. *Man of High Fidelity: Edwin Howard Armstrong.* New York:
J. B. Lippincott, 1956. Seeks to paint a portrait of Armstrong as a great man
who, against the odds, was able to convince a nation to adopt frequency modulation radio broadcasting.

Lichty, Lawrence W., and Malachi C. Topping. *American Broadcasting: A Source
Book on the History of Radio and Television.* New York: Hastings House, 1975.
Contains articles and documents concerning the history of radio and television.
Treats invention and innovation of frequency modulation radio transmission in
some detail.

Sterling, Christopher H., and John M. Kittross. *Stay Tuned: A Concise History of
American Broadcasting.* Belmont, Calif.: Wadsworth, 1978. The standard, one-
volume history of radio and television in the United States. The best place to start
reading about the history of frequency modulation radio broadcasting, a particularly strong part of this fine introductory book.

Whetmore, Edward Jay. *The Magic Medium: An Introduction to Radio in America.*
Belmont, Calif.: Wadsworth, 1981. A fine textbook that covers all phases of radio,
including Armstrong's invention and attempted innovation of FM radio. A useful
way to position Armstrong's role in the history without the rhetoric of a wronged
man.

Douglas Gomery

Cross-References

Marconi Receives the First Transatlantic Telegraphic Radio Transmission (1901),
p. 128; Fessenden Perfects Radio by Transmitting Music and Voice (1906), p. 361;
Transatlantic Radiotelephony Is First Demonstrated (1915), p. 615; The Principles
of Shortwave Radio Communication Are Discovered (1919), p. 669; The First
Color Television Broadcast Takes Place (1940), p. 1166; Shockley, Bardeen, and
Brattain Discover the Transistor (1947), p. 1304; Sony Develops the Pocket-Sized
Transistor Radio (1957), p. 1528.

TOMBAUGH DISCOVERS PLUTO

Category of event: Astronomy
Time: February 18, 1930
Locale: Lowell Observatory, Flagstaff, Arizona

Tombaugh, a self-educated astronomer, culminated 150 years of astronomical work with his discovery of Pluto, the most distant planet in earth's solar system

Principal personages:
PERCIVAL LOWELL (1855-1916), an astronomer who founded the Lowell Observatory in Flagstaff, Arizona, with the primary mission of studying the planet Mars
CLYDE WILLIAM TOMBAUGH (1906-   ), an amateur astronomer who confirmed the existence of Pluto in 1930

Summary of Event

In 1920, Clyde William Tombaugh purchased a 5.7-centimeter telescope through the mail from the Sears-Roebuck Company and taught himself astronomy by reading everything he could obtain on the subject. In 1924, he was impressed with Latimer Wilson's article "The Drift of Jupiter's Markings" in *Popular Astronomy*. Wilson's drawings were made from observing the planet with a homemade telescope. Tombaugh learned how to make telescopes through correspondence with Wilson. When Tombaugh built his telescope, he observed Jupiter and Mars and in 1928 recorded these observations in drawings. Fascinated with drawings of Mars published in *Popular Astronomy* (1924) from the Lowell Observatory in Flagstaff, Arizona, Tombaugh sent his 1928 drawings to its director, Vesto Melvin Slipher, for critique. This began a correspondence that triggered the turning point in his life.

The Lowell Observatory was founded by Percival Lowell in Flagstaff in 1894. The observatory's primary mission was to study the planet Mars. Lowell was fascinated with the maps of the "canals" of Mars made popular by the Italian astronomer Giovanni Schiaparelli in 1877 to 1888. Lowell's observations extended the few dozen canals mapped by Schiaparelli to several hundred of his own description. Lowell later popularized his speculations of Mars and alien civilizations in *Mars* (1895), *Mars and Its Canals* (1906), *The Evolution of Worlds* (1909), and *Mars as the Abode of Life* (1908). Although Lowell's theories excited the public and inspired science fiction writers, astronomers were not convinced. The gulf between Lowell and the astronomical community grew. In an attempt to improve his credibility, Lowell initiated the search for a ninth planet, following the example of the discovery of Neptune, a triumph for theoretical astronomy.

Neptune's discovery in 1846 was based on its gravitational disturbance of the orbit of its neighbor, Uranus. In a similar fashion, the orbit of Neptune was not as predicted, and this led astronomers Lowell and William Pickering to hypothesize the gravitational influence of a yet more distant planet. Lowell called his hypothetical object Planet X; Pickering, Planet O. Lowell reasoned that if he could predict the orbit of a ninth planet beyond Neptune and then find it, the discovery would enhance his professional status and support for the Martian canals theory.

Lowell began searching with an astronomical camera in 1905 along the orbital plane of the other planets. (It is currently understood that Pluto's eccentric orbit placed it beyond the viewing area targeted by Lowell.) He was confident of its location in the constellation Gemini and that it should have a magnitude (brightness) of 13. Additionally, in 1911, Lowell obtained a new research tool, a blink-microscope comparator, from Carl Zeiss to examine the photographic plates. With this apparatus, the same star field of two photographic plates taken at different times are alternately seen or "blinked" in the viewer. Stellar objects, at their great distances, do not appear to move in the time between exposures and therefore appear stationary. Closer objects, such as planets or asteroids, shift on the photographic plate and appear to "blink." After ten years of negative research, Lowell became discouraged. His last area of exploration was the eastern area of Taurus, close to Gemini, where Pluto was later discovered, but his obsession with Planet X exhausted him. His Martian theories were ridiculed, his observatory ostracized by the professional community, and his Planet X undiscovered. The search for Planet X died with him. It is ironic that Planet X appeared on photographic plates taken on March 19, 1915, and again on April 7, 1915. The Milky Way background between Taurus and Gemini camouflaged the planet. In 1919, Pickering published his calculations of Planet O (Lowell's Planet X) predicting its position. The Mount Wilson Observatory photographed the region and (in hindsight) captured the planet on four different photographic plates, yet did not identify it. Failure to find it discouraged Pickering, though he recalculated the orbit in 1928.

In 1925, the Lowell Observatory resumed the quest for Planet X with the construction of a 33-centimeter telescope-camera. Insufficient funding and optical problems delayed its completion until February, 1929. Tombaugh's letter and drawings of 1928 could not have arrived at a better time. His observations and drawings of Jupiter and Mars caught the attention of Slipher, who was looking for a talented amateur to operate the new photographic telescope. Their correspondence culminated in a job offer, which Tombaugh accepted.

When Tombaugh arrived in Flagstaff, he found the construction of the telescope behind schedule. In April of 1929, the search for Planet X continued. Initially, Slipher directed Tombaugh's search to the Gemini region, Lowell's preferred region for the planet. It took about a week for Slipher and his brother, Edward, to blink the Gemini plates. (The camera recorded Pluto, but the Sliphers had missed it among the some 300,000 stars on the plate.) Disappointed, Slipher directed the research eastward through the zodiac and in June of 1929 asked Tombaugh to take over the task of plate blinking. Tombaugh found plate blinking tedious and was often distracted by the discovery of variable stars and asteroids. Frustrated with this Herculean task, he then devised a technique that would distinguish the rogue "planets" and spurious objects. His solution was to photograph the zodiac when the region of examination was at opposition, or the opposite side of the earth from the sun. It is at this position that the outer planets exhibit their maximum retrograde, or "backward," motion.

Tombaugh noticed that at opposition, asteroids shifted about 7 millimeters per day on the plates, whereas a planet should shift about 0.5 millimeter per day. He reasoned that if an object shifted less than Neptune, or approximately 2 millimeters per day, it would truly be a trans-Neptunian body, or Planet X. Unfortunately for Tombaugh, most of his previous work, about one hundred plates, were taken too far from opposition and had to be shot again.

In early 1930, Tombaugh resumed plate blinking, but the proximity to the Milky Way slowed his progress. It was then that Tombaugh realized that the Sliphers had blinked through the 1929 Gemini plates in only about a week. Tombaugh, utilizing the more discriminatory "opposition technique," needed about three to four weeks to cover the same area. Suspecting that the Sliphers had rushed through the 1929 plates, he decided to rephotograph the region, this time near opposition. The first exposure of the Gemini region on January 21, 1930, was disturbed by wind gusts, which buffeted the observatory, shaking the telescope and blurring the image. (Later, Tombaugh realized this blurry image contained his first record of Pluto.) He rephotographed this region on January 23 and 29 and began the tedious blink procedure.

Tombaugh retrieved the poor January 21 plate, compared it with the January 23 plate, and found Planet X exactly where it should be. Now sure of his finding, but in the methodology of good science, he compared the plates with a smaller backup camera with a hand magnifier. The object was in the same corresponding position on all three plates. Tombaugh then called C. O. Lampland and Slipher to the blink-comparator to confirm his find. Both agreed that the object could be Planet X, and Slipher asked Tombaugh to rephotograph the region as soon as possible. The sky was heavily overcast on February 18, so the opportunity of confirmation exposures did not seem promising. Clouds persisted until after 2:00 A.M. The Gemini region was setting and the Moon was rising. Tombaugh went to bed without the confirmation plate, but there would never be another day like February 18, 1930. Two days later, Lampland, Slipher, and Tombaugh looked farther into the solar system than anyone had looked before to confirm the unimpressive fifteenth-magnitude point of light, Planet X.

Impact of Event

Slipher was aware of the impact of the discovery and carefully prepared for the public announcement and the questions that would result. The observatory's reputation was in question over the Martian canal research, and they had to be very sure of not only their data but also of the protocol involved in the announcement. The observatory's trustee, Roger L. Puttnam, was anxious that a name for the planet come from the Lowell Staff or another party might claim priority. The politics of naming the planet were sensitive. Other observatories reviewed their photographic plates to both confirm the Tombaugh discovery and claim a share of the discovery. Indeed, some observatories found the planet on photographic plates as far back as 1908; Lowell's own in 1915, the Mount Wilson Observatory on a December, 1919, plate; Williams Bay in January, 1927; and Uccle Observatory on a January, 1927 plate. These confirmations gave a better fix on the orbit of the planet and a stake in naming the planet. Thousands of letters arrived suggesting names for the planet. In the convention that planets be named after mythological deities, however, three names headed the list: Minerva, Pluto, and Cronus. The first person to propose the name Pluto outside of the Lowell group seems to have been Miss Venetia Burney, eleven years old, of Oxford, England. Pickering, who had predicted a trans-Neptunian planet in 1908, also suggested Pluto after the Greek god of darkness, who was able at times to render himself invisible. Without doubt, all involved in the search would agree this quality of invisibility was appropriate for the new planet.

The Lowell group proposed the name Pluto to the American Astronomical Society and The Royal Society. It was accepted unanimously by both societies in 1930. In 1931, the Associated Press voted the discovery of the planet Pluto one of the top news stories in the world for 1930.

Bibliography

Hoyt, William G. *Planet X and Pluto.* Tucson: University of Arizona Press, 1980. The transition between Lowell's work and Tombaugh's is well documented in this book. This work is comprehensive and a good source for the interested reader.

Tombaugh, Clyde W. "The Discovery of Pluto: Some Generally Unknown Aspects of the Story." *Mercury* 15, no. 3 (1986): 66-72; and in 15, no. 4 (1986): 98-102. Tombaugh describes his experiences on becoming an astronomer and the events leading to the discovery. This is also available on audiotape from the Astronomical Society of the Pacific, 390 Ashton Avenue, San Francisco, CA 94112.

_____. "Reminiscences of the Discovery of Pluto." *Sky and Telescope* 19 (1960): 264-270. A summary of the people and events surrounding the discovery from the principal investigator.

Tombaugh, Clyde, and Patrick Moore. *Out of Darkness: The Planet Pluto.* Harrisburg, Pa.: Stackpole Books, 1980. A very readable work for the general reader. A good review of all the aspects of the search for planets and the personalities surrounding the events.

Whyte, A. J. *The Planet Pluto.* New York: Pergamon Press, 1980. This is a more advanced work for those who wish to dig into the details of the event. The content is appropriate for the general reader and provides an objective view of the process. A historical review is included.

Richard C. Jones

Cross-References

Hale Establishes Mount Wilson Observatory (1903), p. 194; Lowell Predicts the Existence of Pluto (1905), p. 291; Slipher Obtains the Spectrum of a Distant Galaxy (1912), p. 502; Pluto Is Found to Possess a Thin Atmosphere (1980), p. 2141.

CHANDRASEKHAR CALCULATES THE UPPER LIMIT OF A WHITE DWARF STAR'S MASS

Category of event: Astronomy
Time: 1931-1935
Locale: India and England

Chandrasekhar developed a mathematically rigorous theory of the structure of white dwarf stars, which indicated that their maximum mass is 1.4 solar masses

Principal personages:

SUBRAHMANYAN CHANDRASEKHAR (1910-   ), an Indian-born and British-trained theoretical astrophysicist, cowinner of the 1983 Nobel Prize in Physics

SIR ARTHUR STANLEY EDDINGTON (1882-1944), the most prominent astrophysicist of his time and a staunch opponent of Chandrasekhar's theory

RALPH HOWARD FOWLER (1899-1944), a respected astrophysicist and mentor to Chandrasekhar during his studies at Trinity College, Cambridge

WALTER SYDNEY ADAMS (1876-1956), an American astronomer specializing in examining the spectrum of stars, who demonstrated that the spectrum of Sirius B indicated that the star had unexpected properties

Summary of Event

White dwarf stars have challenged and perplexed astronomers since their accidental discovery in the mid-nineteenth century. The German astronomer Friedrich Bessel noted a wobble in the path of the star Sirius as it moved across the sky. After eliminating recognizable sources of error, in 1844, he concluded that there must be a small companion star which affected the motion of the larger, brighter Sirius. From the wobble in the motion of the larger star, the mass of the smaller star was calculated to be that of the sun.

In 1915, Walter Sydney Adams managed to channel the light from the companion star into a spectrograph. The light from the star, now called Sirius B, indicated that the surface of the star was almost as hot as Sirius. From the temperature and the brightness of Sirius B, astronomers calculated that Sirius B had a radius of about 24,000 kilometers (about twice that of Earth). Packing a mass nearly that of the sun into a volume fifty thousand times smaller yielded densities that were much larger than astronomers had ever known: One cubic centimeter of the star would weigh 100 kilograms.

Sir Arthur Stanley Eddington, the foremost astrophysicist of his time, was not completely convinced that these very small but bright stars, later called white dwarfs, were indeed very dense. Yet, many other skeptics were convinced by the 1925 measurement of the "redshift" of Sirius B. Light trying to escape from a white dwarf is strongly affected by the extreme gravitational force arising from the large mass of the white dwarf. The photons of light lose energy as they struggle against the intense gravity. The frequency of the light is "shifted" toward the red end of the spectrum (reflecting the loss of energy) as the light struggles to escape. Albert Einstein's general theory of relativity predicts that light will be affected in this manner by gravity. The amount of "shift" was equal to that predicted by Einstein's theory.

Eddington's influential *The Internal Constitution of the Stars* (1926) attempted to bring together fifty years of work involving the mechanical and physical conditions of the interior of stars. When it came to white dwarfs, his theory ran into problems. In his theory, most of a star's lifetime was spent balancing the outward pressure of the escaping heat of nuclear reactions with the inward pressure of gravity. Eventually, the store of nuclear fuel would be depleted and the star would collapse into a white dwarf. The nuclei and electrons, which make up the mass of the white dwarf, would then keep cooling down and the electrons that had been ripped from the nuclei would be able to reattach themselves to the nuclei in the star. The problem is that the amount of energy required to re-form the atoms of the star would be more than that available in the star. In effect, the star would not have enough energy to cool down. This paradox puzzled Eddington.

Eddington believed that the pace of work in the field was quickening and that the newly developed quantum mechanics might have a great impact on the theory of stellar interiors. He was correct on both counts. The paradox introduced by Eddington was resolved shortly after it was stated. Ralph Howard Fowler resolved the paradox using the recently developed quantum mechanics, but he showed that white dwarf stars were stranger. The pressure that kept the star from contracting indefinitely was not the result of the temperature of the star but that of "electron degeneracy." In the intense heat and pressure of the interior of stars, electrons are torn away from nuclei and move about freely. In the classical theory, the electrons can move about as they wish. According to quantum theory, however, the electrons are restricted to a discrete set of energies. In a normal star, electrons typically occupy many of the higher allowed energy levels.

In the interior of white dwarf stars, the electrons enter a special energy state. Electrons occupy all the lower energy levels. In this special case, the pressure exerted by the electrons becomes independent of the temperature. The star, according to Fowler, cannot contract anymore. The electrons cannot be forced into lower energy levels. The electrons are said to be "degenerate" because the electrons have become "neutralized"—they are no longer a factor in determining the resistance to gravitational collapse. Fowler resolved Eddington's paradox by showing that a white dwarf can resist the force of gravity through electron degeneracy. The temperature of the star no longer matters. White dwarfs can live out their lives slowly cooling off.

Subrahmanyan Chandrasekhar followed the latest developments in astrophysics during his studies in theoretical physics in India. Upon graduation in 1930, he went to Trinity College, Cambridge, on a scholarship. He won a copy of Eddington's *The Internal Constitution of the Stars* in a physics contest. He began to question Eddington's conclusions concerning white dwarfs and Fowler's calculations concerning electron degeneracy. He calculated that electrons in the dense core of a white dwarf would be moving at a velocity nearly that of light, so corrections must be made to the classical formulas describing the behavior of matter. Chandrasekhar made the necessary corrections and realized that the effect was dramatic. For stars with a mass greater than about 1.4 times that of the sun, the "pressure" exerted by electron degeneracy would not be enough to overcome the force of gravity. Instead of a long, slow cooling off, such stars would continue to contract, apparently indefinitely. Chandrasekhar did not speculate on the ultimate fate of stars more than 1.4 solar masses. Calculations done years later by others showed that those stars form either neutron stars or black holes.

From 1931 to 1935, Chandrasekhar published a series of papers of his findings. During this time, he worked with Fowler and Eddington. By 1935, Chandrasekhar had developed a detailed, quantitative, mathematically rigorous theory of white dwarf stars, and he fully expected Eddington to accept his theory. Eddington gave no indication to Chandrasekhar that he had any doubts about the surprising results Chandrasekhar's theory predicted. In 1935, Chandrasekhar was scheduled to present his results to the Royal Astronomical Society. One day before the meeting, Chandrasekhar received a program, and he noticed that Eddington was also giving a paper. At the meeting, Chandrasekhar discussed his results which indicated that the lifetime of a star of small mass must be essentially different from that of a star of large mass. Edward Arthur Milne, also attending the meeting, said that he had achieved similar results using a cruder method. Eddington then launched into a personal attack on Chandrasekhar and his theory.

Eddington was convinced that Chandrasekhar's method was faulty because it was based on a combination of relativistic mechanics and nonrelativistic quantum theory. He argued that his own result could still be obtained after suitable modifications of Chandrasekhar's theory. While Eddington admitted that he could find no fault with the technical details of Chandrasekhar's approach, he was compelled to challenge the results because of the unexpected result that large stars will continue to contract. The depth of Eddington's objections and the way in which they were made surprised and upset Chandrasekhar. He said that "Eddington effectively made a fool of me" at that meeting.

Impact of Event

As is well known, Eddington did not accept the most dramatic result of Chandrasekhar's theory: the calculation of the upper limit of a white dwarf's mass. The dispute with Eddington lasted years, yet the two remained friends. Chandrasekhar left England in 1937 for Chicago. In 1939, he summed up his work on stellar structure. In 1974, Chandrasekhar accounted for the delay in the acceptance of his theory: "[my conclusions] did not meet with the approval of the stalwarts of the day."

He noted the irony of Eddington's position: Eddington argued against the continual collapse of stars with a mass over the Chandrasekhar limit because such stars would "go on radiating and radiating and contracting and contracting until, I suppose, it gets down to a few km. radius when gravity becomes strong enough to hold the radiation and the star can at last find peace." These "black holes" that Eddington concluded were an absurdity, were accepted years later as the final fate of stars which were so massive that their gravity even prevented light from escaping.

Chandrasekhar's theory introduced the notion that not all stars behave as benignly in their old age as white dwarfs. He did not speculate what would happen to a star with a mass above the limit. For stars with masses below the limit, he devised a complete theory to account for their properties. Work on white dwarfs continued, and further evidence was presented in support for his calculations. Chandrasekhar's ideas gained gradual acceptance in the 1940's and 1950's as more white dwarfs were discovered and as spectrographic evidence mounted. He won the Nobel Prize in 1983 for his theoretical studies on the structure and evolution of stars.

Chandrasekhar's limit is the dividing line between the strange but benign white dwarfs, and the truly exotic black holes, pulsars, and neutron stars. It established the possibility that the strange behavior of stars nearing the end of their lives as white dwarfs could get stranger. Chandrasekhar's legacy is the mathmatical order that he brought to the theory of white dwarfs. He continued to bring mathematical order to other areas of astrophysics, including black holes.

Bibliography

Asimov, Isaac. *The Collapsing Universe.* New York: Walker and Co., 1977. Written in typical Asimov style, this book is intended for a wide audience. Taking particular care to make the reader aware of the immense range of stellar phenomena, this book succeeds in introducing astrophysics to the lay reader. No illustrations.

Chandrasekhar, Subrahmanyan. *Eddington: The Most Distinguished Astrophysicist of His Time.* Cambridge, England: Cambridge University Press, 1983. Presenting two Sir Arthur Stanley Eddington Centenary Lectures, this slim book encapsulates both Chandrasekhar's personality and his relationship with Eddington. With grace and style, Chandrasekhar reviews Eddington's contributions to astrophysics and politely points out where Eddington was incorrect. Moderately technical.

Cooke, Donald A. *The Life and Death of Stars.* New York: Crown, 1985. Profusely illustrated with both color and black-and-white photographs, charts, and diagrams, this book discusses the life history of stars. Clearly written and using minimal technical language (carefully introduced in the early chapters), this book is highly recommended as a general introduction to stellar astronomy.

Jastrow, Robert. *Red Giants and White Dwarfs.* New ed. New York: W. W. Norton, 1979. Widely available, but mistitled, the new edition of this book has been significantly revised and updated. The first ninety pages deal with stellar evolution, while the remaining two hundred pages deal with the solar system, UFOs, and the appearance and evolution of humans. Well illustrated and nontechnical.

Shipman, Harry L. *Black Holes, Quasars, and the Universe.* Boston: Houghton Mifflin, 1976. Written for interested nonastronomers and for use as a supplemental text in university courses for nonscientists, the first part of this book deals with black holes and white dwarfs. While not as elegantly written as other books in the field, this book delves into scientific methodology more than other books do. Provides summaries throughout.

Tierney, John. "Subrahmanyan Chandrasekhar: Quest for Order." In *A Passion to Know*, edited by Allen L. Hammond. New York: Charles Scribner's Sons, 1984. This chapter is an interview with Chandrasekhar with some additional biographical information. It deals more with Chandrasekhar's personality and work habits than with the technical details of his theories. Recommended for its informal style.

Roger Sensenbaugh

Cross-References

Hertzsprung Notes the Relationship Between Color and Luminosity of Stars (1905), p. 265; Hertzsprung Describes Giant and Dwarf Stellar Divisions (1907), p. 370; Russell Announces His Theory of Stellar Evolution (1913), p. 585; Eddington Formulates the Mass-Luminosity Law for Stars (1924), p. 785; Eddington Publishes *The Internal Constitution of the Stars* (1926), p. 815; Oppenheimer Calculates the Nature of Black Holes (1939), p. 1150; Wheeler Names the Phenomenon "Black Holes" (1968), p. 1881.

GREAT EVENTS
FROM
HISTORY II

CHRONOLOGICAL LIST OF EVENTS

VOLUME I

VOLUME II

VOLUME III

VOLUME IV

CHRONOLOGICAL LIST OF EVENTS

WITHDRAWN